CU01021101

M

PEERLESS
POWELL DUFFRYN
of the
South Wales Coalfield

In memory of
Rees Shore (1860-1912),
Aldridge Guy Shore (1888-1958)
and William Iorwerth Shore (1917-1977)

Like other Powell Duffryn mechanics, they
dedicated their lives to maintaining colliery
plant and equipment conceived of and
designed by engineers so that miners and
coal were raised safely

© Leslie M. Shore and Lightmoor Press 2012
Designed by Ian Pope
British Library Cataloguing-in-Publication Data. A catalogue record for this
book is available from the British Library
ISBN 13: 978 1899889 67 9

Lightmoor Press

Lightmoor Press is an imprint of Black Dwarf Lightmoor Publications Limited
144b Lydney Industrial Estate, Harbour Road
Lydney, Gloucestershire, GL15 4EJ
Printed and bound by Berforts Information Press, Eynsham, Oxfordshire

PEERLESS

POWELL DUFFRYN

of the

South Wales Coalfield

Leslie M. Shore

Powell Duffryn's Bargoed Colliery, in the first decade of the twentieth century, was a model colliery for the British coal industry to imitate. The colliery's engineering represented the work of Edmund Mills Hann, one of the South Wales Coalfield's greatest engineers. Coal from the colliery was exported to the world via the docks of Cardiff and Newport. The Brecon & Merthyr Railway, in the foreground, was used to haul coal to Newport, and the Rhymney Railway, on which a train can be seen at the left, took coal traffic to Cardiff. In 1965, L. S. Lowry painted 'Bargoed', which shows the colliery from the north. The painting is in the keeping of The Lowry, Salford Quays.

CONTENTS

GWAELODYWAUN FARM BARGOED.

Pope/Parkhouse Archive

Wagons had a brief stay in the sidings situated south of Bargoed Colliery during the boom years for steam coal. Separate branch lines linked the sidings to both the Rhymney Railway and the Brecon & Merthyr Railway. Aberbargoed junction on the Brecon & Merthyr Railway lay in the vicinity of the bridge to the left of the sidings and below Gwaelod-y-waun farm. One Brecon & Merthyr Railway line proceeded up the valley to the left from the junction to end at the company's Rhymney station, and the other line connected with the Rhymney Railway at Bargoed South Junction.

PREFACE

This work offers the first complete history about how Powell Duffryn earned wealth from mining and selling coal, and became Britain's greatest coal company of the twentieth century. An account is given of the company's expansion in terms of coal property and colliery investment, use of engineering technology, and its responses to the coal trade cycle. The history has meaning for people who belong to, or have ancestral links with communities in the South Wales Coalfield made vibrant by the company's operation. The citizens of Cardiff and Newport might be pleased to find that Powell Duffryn played a notable role in winning fame for their cities in the world due to the shipment of colossal tonnages of coal. County Durham people might appreciate knowing that at least two of its sons played key roles in the development of the South Wales Coalfield. Previous employees of the defunct industrial conglomerate that Powell Duffryn became after its coal interests were nationalized might find a story about the company's origins worthwhile to read. Powell Duffryn's story is an essential part of Britain's coal mining heritage.

My research into the company re-connected me with a heritage that I had earlier failed to appreciate. In the mid-1990s, Jack Edwards and I made a fruitless search for the remains of a water balance pithead winding gear at Cwmbyrgym, north of Pontypool. My fellow searcher, my father-in law, had enjoyed a long career in coal mining. He began his working life in the Sirhowy Valley at Tredegar Iron and Coal Company's Wylie Colliery. A professional engineer, he retired from British Coal, South Wales Area, as a senior project manager. After our search we proceeded up Mynydd Llanhilleth. Many years before, Jack had been responsible for re-engineering the railway line that served Blaenserchan Colliery. He was surprised to see from a viewpoint on Mynydd Llanhilleth the colliery's site being landscaped for a return to nature. He remarked that it was evidence of the rapid speed at which the South Wales coal industry was vanishing. Having that day failed to find an artefact that had once been vital to coal mining in that district, he wondered if the history of the South Wales Coalfield would also soon be forgotten. His thoughts though did not captivate me possibly due to an impediment: the nature of my familiarity with the industry.

Coal mining thrived in my native town, New Tredegar, until my late teens. We, the boys, used the town's Elliot Colliery as a playground. Ken Morgan, an Elliot School classmate, was the promoter of dares, some of which I pursued like taking rides on coal trams, or drams as we called them. My father, William Shore, learnt his trade as a mechanic at Powell Duffryn's Elliot Colliery. During his life he supervised craftsmen at two other collieries founded by the company, Ogilvie and Britannia. When I was about eight years of age, he took me and Alan, my younger brother, to inspect McLaren Colliery, Abertysswg. I remember both the colliery's spotlessly clean winding house, and a groomed pit pony that had been shown at the Bedwellty Show. A family shopping trip to Bargoed, involved a walk from a bus stop known as 'top-of-the-pit' through a colliery founded by Powell Duffryn. My father identified features of the colliery as we walked. Yet, I did not value what was commonplace. However, through researching this history I realised that Powell Duffryn's collieries in my home valley, the Rhymney, were not only a vital part of Welsh industrial history, but their successful operation shaped a future in coal mining of major British importance.

Powell Duffryn ranked as the pre-eminent private sector coal company of Great Britain at the time the coal industry was nationalized in 1947. The Powell Duffryn Steam Coal Company was founded in 1864 due to the acquisition by investors of a number of steam coal collieries sunk, or purchased, by Thomas Powell of The Gaer, Newport. Since the origins of the history of the company are due to Thomas Powell's explorations for coal in Glamorgan and Monmouthshire, this aspect begins the history. Although only a sketch is given about one of the pioneers of deep-mining in the South Wales Coalfield, it hopefully conveys an idea of the gambles, and troubles faced by a driven entrepreneur whose luck was to find, mine, and sell coal, particularly steam coal. Thomas Powell's period as a coalowner saw a rapid change in valley communications. The work relates how he made use of, first, canals served by tramways, and then railways to move coal. A description of the 1854 disaster at Powell's Middle Duffryn Colliery recalls the dangers and horrors that miners could face underground. He, like many other coalowners, frustrated miners' struggles for better pay. Coalfield-wide trade union activity later became organised partly as a result. The Chartist movement awakened in Valley people a need for political change, which when achieved in the form of the 1945 Labour Government proved fatal for coal companies. Indeed, the well of grudges Thomas Powell left among miners in the parts of the South Wales Coalfield he operated as a coalowner was less than a favourable gift of his to the founder of Powell Duffryn.

Revealing the portfolio of interests of, and the course of the life of the company's founder, George Elliot, who was later made a baronet, is presented as an essential theme of the work. He prospered first in the Durham Coalfield. He led Powell Duffryn's initial phase of thrusting expansion. Although the focus of his expansion work was in the Cynon Valley, in 1883 he initiated Elliot Colliery. The only major colliery disaster in the company's history, at New Tredegar Colliery in 1875, occurred when he was in charge, and an account of it is presented. During the 1870s disaffection with Sir George Elliot's 'practical direction' of the company arose among shareholders. The company slid towards bankruptcy. His desire to act as a benevolent employer faded with his demise as a force in the company. Yet, the memorials he left, although a display of vanity, recollect a notable industrialist of Victorian times. His quest for wealth involved imaginative schemes that created employment for people.

The body of this history covers the growth of Powell Duffryn from 1883 up until the start of the second decade of the twentieth century. The overall trend in demand for the steam coal the company mined rose during this period to reach a peak in 1913. Steam coal from the South Wales Coalfield was ranked as the world's superior fuel for powering naval and merchant ships. Featured for this period is a study of notable engineering as the company's new Rhymney Valley collieries, redevelopment of old collieries, and electrical and chemical engineering assets. The company's colliery sinkings were part of a boom in the South

Wales Coalfield. The boom lured many migrants from other parts of Wales, England and Ireland to the valleys of South Wales in search of work. As a result of Powell Duffryn's growth, new communities were created. Homes and buildings were built to house not only the families of miners, mechanics, blacksmiths electricians, engineers, and colliery officials, but also members of the professions and trades people.

Powell Duffryn's pivotal figure corresponding to the period identified above was Edmund Mills Hann. He was a Durham Coalfield trained mining engineer who served the company as its general manager of collieries from 1883 to 1921. Joseph Shaw KC, served as the company's chairman for most of Hann's period of service to the company. Hann was ranked by his peers in the South Wales Coalfield as a great engineer. Such a rank can be appreciated through reading about the company's colliery developments under his charge, and valuing the company's leap in progress made as a result. His works of engineering realised for the company low cost colliery operations, which distinguished the company from most of its rivals, and enabled it to prosper as a business. He was also to the fore in trying to make the dangerous job of a miner's as safe as was technically possible. The leadership he gave establishing in the Cynon and Rhymney Valleys pioneering colliery rescue stations in the South Wales Coalfield, and cottage hospitals, portrayed his humanity. Documented are instances of his clashes with miners, some sudden and violent. The work notes the effect that the First World War had upon the company whereas the peace after war heralded the start to the company's final chapters.

The grip that some of Edmund Mill Hann's sons took of the management of Powell Duffryn proved key to sustaining the company's progress. In 1921, due to his father's retirement from the company, Edmund Lawrence Hann became the company's general manager of collieries, and later, in 1933, succeeded Joseph Shaw as the company's chairman. The coverage of his period in charge of the company has as its backdrop the decline of King Coal in South Wales. The marketing and distribution of coal took on greater importance. The unique attractiveness of Powell Duffryn for capital investors helped the company grow whilst many of its rivals contemplated liquidation. The company sank new collieries, two on the 'South Crop' of the South Wales Coalfield. Powell Duffryn's purchase of the Rhymney Iron Company in 1921 was a precedent set by Edmund Mills Hann

that his son followed. In addition, in 1925, Edmund Lawrence Hann negotiated a joint mining venture with the Ocean Coal Company to open Taff-Merthyr Colliery. In 1928, the Rhondda Valley based Lewis Merthyr Consolidated and Great Western Colliery companies were taken over by the company.

The company's responses to dire economic times of the late 1920s and 1930s bred scorn and hostility within its workforce. The company's fight to supply coal at competitive prices to retain markets involved wage cuts. Falls in demand for coal saw periods of workforce layoffs. An unbridgeable divide between the wants of the South Wales Miners' Federation and the needs of the South Wales Coalfield's coalowners manifested itself as the catastrophic 1926 strike. An inter-union battle at Taff-Merthyr Colliery in 1934 was one sequel of the 1926 strike. The trauma and humiliation South Wales Coalfield valley communities suffered as a consequence of the strike and the Depression survived as deep-seated, vivid memories.

Yet, in spite of the slump in the world's economy, the astute management of Powell Duffryn saw an awesome achievement. In 1935, Edmund Lawrence Hann finalised negotiations for Powell Duffryn to achieve possibly the greatest coup in not only Welsh industrial history, but also in the British private sector coal industry. The company, as an annual producer of 5 million tonnes of coal acquired through merger a struggling coal company, Welsh Associated Collieries, which mined yearly 10 million tons of coal. The result was that Powell Duffryn Associated Collieries became the largest private sector coal company in the history of British coal industry. In 1945, Powell Duffryn employed a total of 35,000 men assigned to work at nearly sixty collieries that raised around forty per cent of the South Wales Coalfield's output. In 1947, the state took over the assets of coal companies to form the National Coal Board to give the industry's miners a means to control their destinies in the world energy market.

Last, a number of coincidences became apparent to me when producing this history. My first job was as a technical apprentice with Rhymney Engineering Company Limited, a part of Powell Duffryn, which became Hy-Mac, a pioneer of the hydraulic excavator in Europe. My father, grandfather, and great-grandfather all worked for Powell Duffryn. Where Jack Edwards and I stood on Llanhilleth Mountain, to view the site of Blaenserchan Colliery, was close to where Thomas Powell is considered to have begun his vocation as a coalowner.

Imperial and metric units
Length
1 inch (in.) = 25.400 millimetres (mm)
12 inches = 1 foot (ft) = .305 metre (m)
3 feet = 1 yard = 0.914 metre
1,760 yards = 1 mile = 1.609 kilometre (km)
Liquid
1 gallon = 4.546 litre
Weight
1 ton = 20 hundred weight (cwt.) = 2,240 pounds (lb.) = 1,016 kilogram
1 Tonne (metric) = 2,205 pounds = 1,000 kilograms
Pressure
1 pound per square inch = 0.07 bar
Currency
1 Pound (£) = 20 shillings (s) = 240 pennies (d)
1 shilling = 5 new pence (post 1971)

ACKNOWLEDGEMENTS

The opening of the Elliot Colliery Winding House Museum, in May, 2002, was the spur for me to start research that grew into this history about Powell Duffryn as a coal company. The plaudits that the Caerphilly County Borough Council won for creating the museum were deserved.

I have many people to thank for keenly supporting the exciting labour of research. I begin with the support obtained from representatives of the Caerphilly County Borough Council's Museums/Heritage service such as Heather Perry, Chris Morgan and Gillian Levy; and the volunteers of the Museum's Friends especially Larry Ferris, Clive Fussel, Gareth Salway, and Colin White. Other invaluable input from New Tredegar came from Joyce and Ken Jones, Idris Williams, and David Williams.

Research work made me a great admirer of the trouble that librarians will go to so as to provide a vital British information service. I am indebted to: Emyr Evans, National Library of Wales; Anne Edwards and Alan Prescott, Newport City Council Central Library; Nick Kelland, Richard Reed, and John White, Aberdare Library, Hywel Matthews, Pontypridd Library, and Anthony Pritchard, Treorchy Library, all part of Rhondda Cynon Taf Libraries; Alison Jones, Bargoed Library, Caerphilly Borough Council; the staff of Glamorgan Records Office; Houghton Library, County Durham; Anne Cowie, Lloyd's Register of Ships; Margaret McCollum, Durham University; and Linda McCormick of Ulverston Library in Cumbria. People associated with the engineering institutions and history societies also made invaluable contributions like Cherry Cronly of the South Wales Institute of Engineers, that survives as an educational trust; Keith Moore, once librarian at the Institution of Mechanical Engineers; Carol Morgan, Institution of Civil Engineers; Frances Perry, mining archives, the Institute of Materials; members of the Cynon Valley History Society especially Douglas Williams and Geoffrey Evans; Simon Chapman, Teeside Industrial Archaeology Society; Marie Dudgeon and Jennifer Kelly, North of England Institute of Mining and Engineers Archives; Laura Gardner of the then IEE [Institution of Electrical Engineers] Archives; and Chris Holdrien and Brian Hillsdon members of the Newcomen Society.

Regarding the history's cast of principal characters my knowledge of them was enriched due to contributions. I was given vital facts by John Evans about Thomas Powell. Hopefully my attempt to revive interest in the notable life of Sir George Elliot will meet the approval of givers of associated information like Paul Lanagan, Friends of Houghton Hillside Cemetery; Revd Peter Hood, All Saints' Church, Penshaw; Father David Way, St Margaret's Church, Aberaman; and Revd D. M. L. Beck, St Mary's, West Rainton. I gained particular pleasure from researching the life of Edmund Mills Hann. An aid to this aspect of my research was information from: David Leslie Davies, and Miss Mary Greening who gave me permission to make use of the papers written by Edwin Greening, her father; and also the Glamorgan Family History Society. For finding rare biographical details about Joseph Shaw KC, I thank Dr Claire Rider, Middle Temple, London, and Marcus Buffey, Herefordshire Archives Service.

My knowledge of colliery engineering developed as a result of guidance I received from a special set of engineers, men who were once employed as such in the coal industry. In this regard, Jack Edwards and John Boucher were my main teachers. Regarding information about the South Wales Coalfield and Britain's coal industry in general I thank: Rhian Hicks and Tom Sharpe, Geologist's Association South Wales Group; Carolyn Charles, curator, The Collections Centre, Nantgarw, National Museum of Wales; Lucy Jaques, National Coal Mining Museum of England; George Gardner of the University of Glasgow's archives; and Dr Bill Jones, Cardiff University.

Regarding other contributions and help I thank: Steve Riley; Raymond Lawrence; Ceri Thomson, Big Pit, National Mining Museum of Wales; Menna James, Colleen Phillips and Carol Thomas, Gwent Healthcare NHS Trust; Professor John Caldwell; Terry McCarthy, Gelligaer Historical Society; FETL's Kate Gibbons, Carole Morby, and Gary Pilkington; and Derek Bigland.

For sourcing of some of the illustrations I am grateful to: Cwmbach's David Llewellyn; Debbie Wildgust, curator, Pontypool Museum Trust; Pontypool photographer Brian Griffiths; Mark Smith of the National Mining Memorabilia Association; Lyn Gladwyn; Lyndon Rees; Kay Kays, National Museums & Galleries of Wales; Brian Liddy, National Media Museum; Lettica Ferrer, the Science Museum; and Lucinda Walker, English Heritage.

I direct though my greatest thanks to five supreme supporters. First, without Ian Pope of Black Dwarf Lightmoor there would be no book. The publisher's commitment to industrial history defies what I see as a trend towards the erasure from the British memory of the crucial role that industry and engineering can play in creating a nation's wealth. Ian Pope also gave me access to a vast library of relevant illustrations, especially from the collection of Paul Jackson. Second, my wife, Pamela, showed much consideration, support, and toleration of my solitary pursuits of research and writing. Third, Ken Weaver rigorously read the final drafts of my work, and due to his findings, queries, and our many discussions, I corrected errors, and clarified my thoughts with regard to dozens of aspects. Fourth, Brian Davies, curator, Pontypridd Museum, gave crucial lively support and pertinent inputs. In October, 2005, he showed me the precious, preserved, Hetty steam winding engine. Afterwards, at our tea break at the Rhondda Heritage Centre, formerly Lewis Merthyr Collieries, I set my goal to produce a history of Powell Duffryn. Last, I extend my greatest thanks to Professor Trevor Boyns, Cardiff Business School. He was generous in sharing with me his research into the company's business history, answered my many queries with amazing promptness, somehow found time to read drafts of my work, and returned them to me with constructive comments usually supported with copious new information.

One thing that I learnt in writing this history was that the developing text had to be viewed as a provisional statement. I hope that the care taken by the people to supply me with authentic information has been accurately represented in my work. Nevertheless, I accept responsibility for both factual errors and mistakes.

Leslie Shore, Ulverston, March 2012

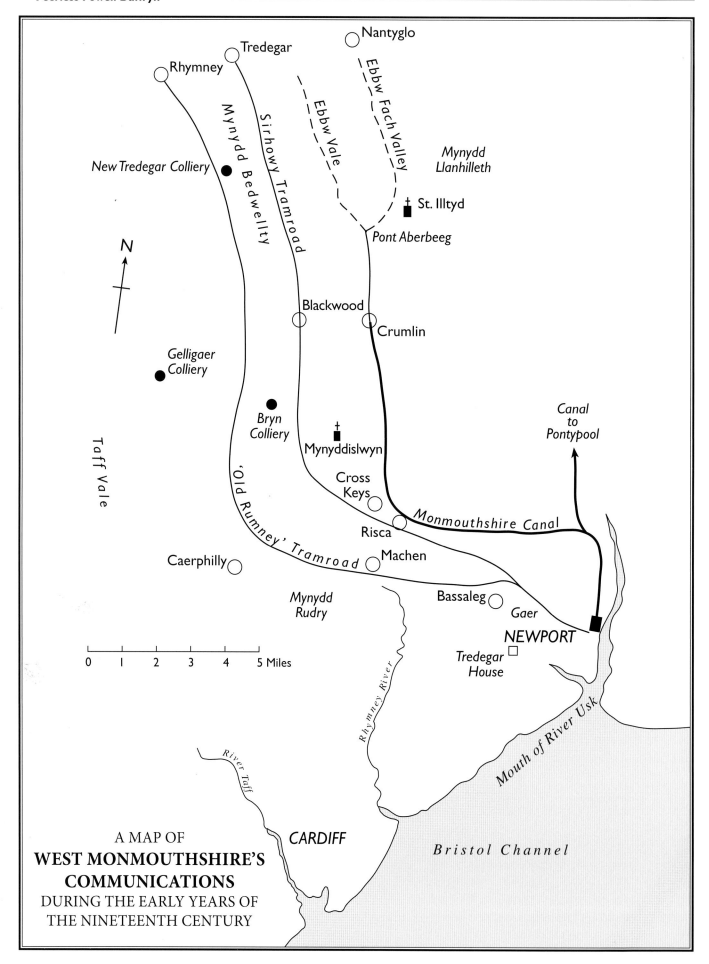

N

Nantyglo

Tredegar

Rhymney

Ebbw Fach Valley

Ebbw Vale

Mynydd Llanhilleth

Mynydd Bedwellty

Sirhowy Tramroad

New Tredegar Colliery

† St. Illtyd

Pont Aberbeeg

Blackwood

Crumlin

Gelligaer Colliery

Canal to Pontypool

Bryn Colliery

†
Mynyddislwyn

Taff Vale

Cross Keys

Monmouthshire Canal

Risca

'Old Rumney' Tramroad

Caerphilly

Machen

Bassaleg

Gaer

Mynydd Rudry

Rhymney River

Tredegar House

NEWPORT

0   1   2   3   4   5 Miles

River Taff

A MAP OF
WEST MONMOUTHSHIRE'S COMMUNICATIONS
DURING THE EARLY YEARS OF
THE NINETEENTH CENTURY

CARDIFF

Bristol Channel

Mouth of River Usk

Chapter One
HOLLOWING OUT MOUNTAINS

Powell Duffryn was Britain's superior private sector coal company before the coal industry was nationalized in 1947. In the second decade of the twentieth century, the company bragged that its abbreviated name, PD, was a byword for Welsh steam coal around the world. Such a rank as a coal company, and boasting about success in selling coal, seemed to be an absurd possibility during periods of gloom and doom in the company's history. Powell Duffryn's survival and expansion, though, was determined by the way it managed its part of a labour intensive industry to deal with the peaks and troughs of the coal market.

The Powell Duffryn Steam Coal Company was formed in 1864 to buy from the sons of Thomas Powell a number of South Wales collieries, and one coal level, today described as a drift mine. George Elliot, later made a baronet, an experienced Durham Coalfield coalowner with ambitions as an industrialist, conceived the collieries'

Thomas Powell (1779-1863)
of the Gaer, Newport – a pioneer of deep mining in the South Wales Coalfield.

purchase idea. The capital needed to fund the acquisition of collieries, and the coal level, was raised from investors who became the company's shareholders. Most of the purchased collieries lay in the upper reaches of the Cynon Valley in the region of the town of Aberdare, in the county of Glamorgan. Powell Duffryn used the term Aberdare Valley to identify where these Glamorgan collieries stood. At the northern end of the Rhymney Valley, in the old county of Monmouthshire, lay two further purchases: New Tredegar Colliery, and to the south of it the coal level, known as White Rose.

An early task for George Elliot was to identify the legacy and snags left due to the way in which the colliery assets had previously been managed. The County Durham man, initially a stranger in the South Wales Coalfield, might have thought it wise to learn about an aspect of the coalfield's development by acquiring information about Thomas Powell, the man who had created the colliery assets that Powell Duffryn came to own.

Thomas Powell, one of the first coal magnates of the South Wales Coalfield, ran the acquired collieries, including the coal level, up until his death in the spring of 1863. His fortune as a coalowner was made whilst settled at Newport, Monmouthshire. Monmouth, the county town, has been judged to be his birthplace, and similarly the year of his birth, 1779.[1] The southern flowing Usk bisected Monmouthshire, and, as John Wood's 1836 map shows, Newport occupied this tidal river's western bank. The ships that put to sea from Newport's wharfs piloted the River Severn that fanned out to the west as the Bristol Channel, a seaway to the ports of the world. Yet, around the start to the nineteenth century, Bristol Channel seafarers' interest in Newport was due mainly to its aspect,

which they called the 'creek of Cardiff'. Some nine miles west of Newport, in the neighbouring county of Glamorgan, lay the town of Cardiff. Sea trade at Cardiff was greater than Newport's. The rivalry between Cardiff and Newport was set for growth due to the mineral resources under the hills and valleys of their northern hinterlands.

On the 3rd June, 1792, an Act of Parliament was passed to enable the Monmouthshire Canal Company to build a canal network, and to construct railways within a distance of eight miles from their canal.[2] Newport was the southern terminus of this canal network, and so its people, in 1801, estimated to number 1,087, were placed at a hub of intelligence about the mineral potential of the valleys to the north. Writing in 1866, about the development of the Newport docks, Bassett reflected: '*About 1790, an impression was fast gaining grounds to the effect that existed in the district to the north of the limestone, which is to be seen at Risca, lying at a severe inclination, large and valuable seams of Coal and Limestone*'.[3] The outcrop of limestone at Risca, six miles north-west of Newport, can be used to pinpoint a section of the south-eastern arc of the South Wales Coalfield's boundary. The northern ends of the Monmouthshire and Glamorgan Valleys can also serve to mark the northern arc of the boundary of the South Wales Coalfield.

Clay-band ironstone, as well as coal, was a constituent element of the South Wales Coalfield. In the eighteenth and nineteenth centuries, the clay-band ironstone found in the sweep of the Coalfield's northern borderland, from Pontypool, in the east, to Merthyr Tydfil in the west, was 'extensively worked as an ore of iron'.[4] Bassett observed regarding the formation of the Monmouthshire Canal Company that the '*shipment of coal was not contemplated, but only the transit of iron*' from the ironmaking districts of Pontypool and Blaenavon, to Newport.[5] A branch of this canal was constructed up the Ebbw Vale to Crumlin. Moreover, the 1802 Act of Parliament that enabled the Monmouthshire Canal Company to operate led to the opening of a tramroad from Newport to Nine Mile Point, in the Sirhowy Valley.[6] The Sirhowy Tramroad Company, which was also created due to the Act, extended the tramroad from Nine Mile Point to Tredegar at the head of the Sirhowy Valley. Such a transport infrastructure spawned commercial opportunities.

From modest beginnings, Powell grew a timber merchant business in Newport.[7] An obituary about Thomas Powell indicates that he resided in Newport in 1813.[8] 'Timbering', according to Charles Wilkins was an '*essential feature of coal working, and in several ways the necessities for pitwood would bring coalowner and timber merchant into contact*'. No evidence was found to prove that such dealings instigated Powell's interest in coal mining. Nonetheless, Thomas Powell, at some unknown moment, made a decision to explore what the trading prospects were for Monmouthshire household coal.

The parish of Llanhilleth has become the favoured site for Powell's first coal venture.[9] For example, Howard Meyrick proposed that Powell commenced coal mining in 1810 by purchasing a level at Llanhilleth, which makes it probable that Powell arrived in Newport to start a business earlier than 1810.[10] A geographical reference for locating a place in the Llanhilleth Parish is Pont Aberbeeg, where the Ebbw Fach River joins the Ebbw River. The Ebbw River flows southward down the Ebbw Vale to join the Usk south of Newport.

Tithe maps and plans for the parish give clues that point to places east-south-east of St. Illtyd, the old parish church, where Thomas Powell mined for coal. The church stands to the east of Pont Aberbeeg on the western edge of Llanhilleth Mountain at 1,200ft. The mountain continues to rise in a northern-easterly direction from the church to plateau near 1,500ft. Under the upper reaches of the mountain lay resources of what was termed as Mynyddislwyn coal, which was ideal for household purposes. The term for the coal had its origin in mining the mountain atop of which stands the hamlet of Mynyddislwyn. The hamlet's church of St. Tudur's stands about five miles southward from St. Iltyd church. The 'celebrated Red Ash Mynyddislwyn Seam', before the introduction of canals and railways, was the chief source of Monmouthshire coal shipped out of Newport.[11] Early in the nineteenth century coal was moved from the parish of Llanhilleth by tramroad, south to Crumlin, for forwarding by barge on the Monmouthshire Canal to Newport.

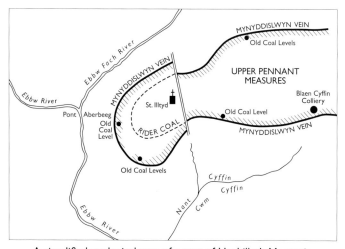

A simplified geological map of a part of Llanhilleth Mountain.

W. W. Price proposed that Thomas Powell joined three other men to set up a Llanhilleth coal venture.[12] The proposal appears sound since forming such a partnership was the means by which new businesses were formed at the outset of the Industrial Revolution. More than likely at least one of the partners in the Llanhilleth venture had mining knowledge and experience. The recruitment and supervision of miners might have been handled by the same man, or another of the partners who previously managed miners. Since the Ebbw Vale to the west of St. Illtyd church was occupied by a sparse population, the recruitment and retention of miners to work at a remote spot was not an easy task to manage.

Nonetheless, the availability of an engineered transport route to Newport and the reputation of Mynyddislwyn coal made investing in a Llanhilleth parish level an attractive proposition for a man with surplus capital, or having access to clients who could be persuaded to provide capital. In this respect, one candidate can be suggested: Thomas Prothero, a Newport solicitor. A lawyer, as a partner, was suited both for the wheeler-dealing of conveyancing, and likely to be approved of by the landowner as a fitting owner occupier. Indeed, Prothero once owned a level one mile east-south-east of St. Illtyd church at the head of Nant Cynw. The opening of this level, if set up as a partnership, might have given Thomas Powell's his introduction to mining. The future would see Prothero and Powell not only as partners in a number of coal mining ventures, but of significance for Llanhilleth mining, as barge operators on the Monmouthshire Canal

Thomas Powell brought to a partnership, in addition to a share of the funding, commercial knowledge and experience. He had a record as a salesman, was practiced in the craft of negotiation, knew something about the maritime trade, and had access to market intelligence. As a trader in timber his business compass brought him into contact with the commercial world that lay beyond the shore's of Monmouthshire. He also seemed qualified to take a grip of running the commercial side of a mining business. Initially, though, a junior role in a partnership might have suited him. As a hedge against failure in a coal mining venture it would have been wise for Powell to have maintained his Newport timber business. Indeed, a directory of 1839 showed that he still held 'possession' of a timber business.[13]

John Wood's 1836 map of Newport can prompt speculation about where Thomas Powell's timber business once stood. A building, its owner marked as 'T. Powel (sic) Esq.', stands on a plot of land on the west bank of the Usk. Jack's Pill, an inlet, serves as the plot's southern boundary. The pill could have been used to soak imported logs as part of a timber seasoning process. South of the pill operated a likely customer for Powell's timber, Mr Perkin's shipyard for building, or repairing, wooden ships.

Nonetheless, Wood's map of Newport contains rich clues about where Thomas Powell managed trading in at least Llanhilleth coal. 'Thomas Powell Esquire' occupied a prime commercial site close to the terminus of the Monmouthshire Canal. A tram road, which was linked to the Sirhowy tram road, ran parallel to the northern boundary of the site. Nearby, to the west of the site, a branch line of the local tram road layout served the Tredegar Iron Company's Wharf. Powell's site also stood on the edge of Dock Parade, which gave immediate access to Newport's dock opened in 1812. In 1820, he was chartering Bristol Channel vessels although the cargo moved was not detailed.[14] A plot of ground with buildings and jetties for Usk shipping, standing between the iron company's wharf and the Powell operation, is identified with 'T. Protheroe (sic) Esquire'. Perhaps Powell-Prothero partnership working was encouraged due to them operating as near neighbours.

Yet, regarding Powell's mining activities in the parish of Llanhilleth, they proved difficult to locate, or date. On the whole, conveyancing records, do not disclose members of a mining partnership, only its representative. Nevertheless, although for the parish of Llanhilleth there is a general absence of Thomas Powell's name as an owner occupier, compared with Thomas Prothero's for example, such a situation does not rule out the idea that he began mining here as a junior partner. In the Llanhilleth parish, though,

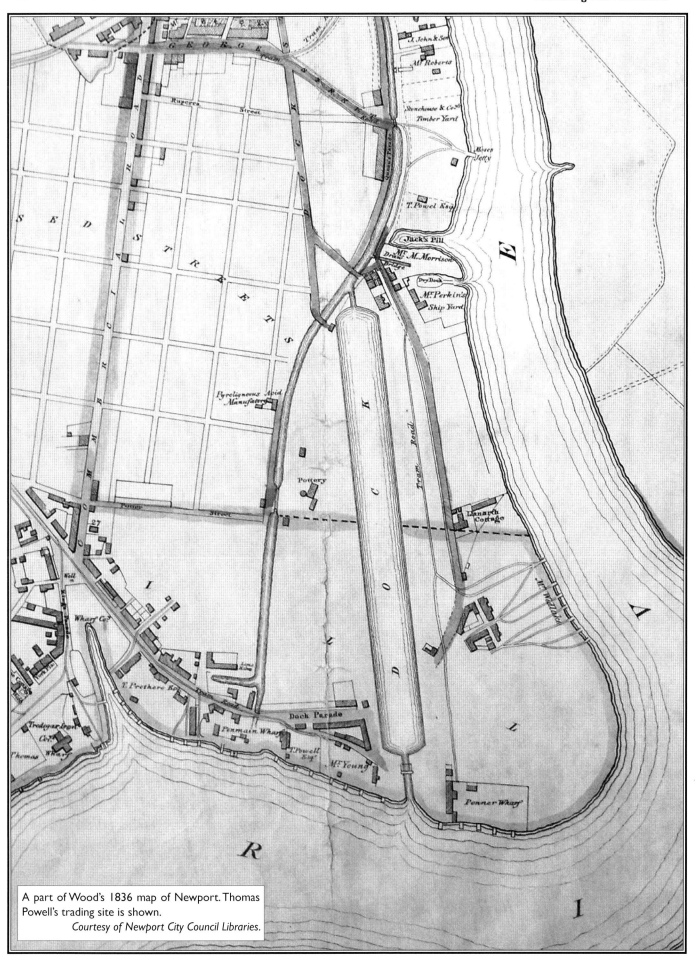

A part of Wood's 1836 map of Newport. Thomas Powell's trading site is shown.

Courtesy of Newport City Council Libraries.

Powell can be linked with the early days of Blaen-Cyffin Colliery that once operated half-a-mile east-south-east of St. Illtyd Church.[15]

Regardless of whether, or not, the Llanhilleth parish was where Powell began in coal mining, a part of his route across south Wales to open collieries in the Aberdare Valley can be traced. His ventures, that exploited the Mynyddislwyn Seam that spreads westwards from the Llanhilleth parish, serve to plot this route. The laying of tramroads also aided his transition from coal trader to the manager of an integrated mining and coal trading business.

The Ebbw Vale's western neighbour is the Sirhowy Valley where, at its northern end, the Tredegar Iron Works began to operate in 1801 on land owned by a notable family of Wales, the Morgans. In 1402, Llewelyn ap Morgan became the owner of Tredegar House sited near where the Ebbw River begins its final run eastwards to join the Usk just south of Newport. Tredegar House became 'one of the architectural wonders of Wales and one of the most significant late seventeenth century houses in the whole of the British Isles'.[16] The community that came to huddle around the iron works was called Tredegar. The Sirhowy Valley surrenders its independence to the Ebbw Vale at a town now called Cross Keys. Situated half way along the Sirhowy Valley stands today's town of Blackwood.

In the Blackwood district, Thomas Powell was owner occupier of land for a period before 1839, upon which he operated at least two collieries that worked the Mynyddislwyn seam.[17] His Bryn Colliery, located south-west of Pontllanfraith, could have been opened before the mid-1820s.[18] He also operated a level at Gelligroes just about half a mile to the south-east of Bryn Colliery. East of nearby Pontllanfraith, dated to 1827, was another venture of Powell's, Llyspentwyn (Cwm Philkins). Mined coal of the district was moved by tram-roads to the Sirhowy Tram Road, which was opened for traffic in August, 1811.[19] The colliery operations were supervised for him by a 'steward', or agent. Circa 1840s, he put in charge of the underground workings at Bryn Colliery the illiterate Rees Price who was assisted by a clerk.[20] Thomas Powell set some rules, and issued demands for coal. So, it can be imagined that whispers among the miners employed at Powell's collieries in the Blackwood district were overheard by his agents to learn about a pending local campaign for political change.

In 1839, an army of Monmouthshire Valleys' Chartists marched on Newport. The county's iron workers and miners believed the Chartist movement offered a way towards resolving grievances they held like those against their employers.[21] The plan for the march on Newport was conceived in Blackwood at the 'Coach and Horse Inn'. On the 4th November, 1839, bystanders on the streets of Newport saw miners and iron workers confront infantry armed with muskets. A riot was put down, and around twenty Chartists were killed. Valley people did not accept that the Newport debacle halted their quest for political change.

Regarding Thomas Powell's march westwards as a coalowner, he had crossed the Rhymney Valley into the county of Glamorgan by 1829. The Rhymney River drains the valley that has the Sirhowy Valley as its eastern neighbour. The Rhymney River enters the sea just east of Cardiff, and generally marked the boundary between Monmouthshire and Glamorgan.

Gelligaer Colliery

The coal venture Powell operated in Glamorgan by 1829 lay in the parish of Gelligaer. The parish church of St. Catwg stands on the western side of the Rhymney Valley at the centre

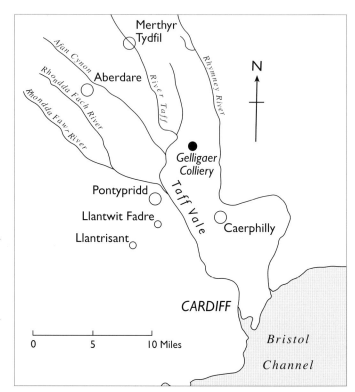

A simplified map of eastern Glamorgan.

of the hamlet of Gelligaer. Gelligaer with Neath, west Glamorgan, have been considered the earliest sites for coal mining in South Wales. Charles Wilkins, with regard to mining at Gelligaer, referred to G. T. Clark, described as a 'scholar ironmaster in the Victorian age'.[22] Clark's study of *Compotus*, or Minister's Accounts for Glamorgan, for the ninth year of the reign of Edward I, 1281, identified a statement in Latin that in translation said: '*From the mill of Llandivedon (Llanvabon) nothing because it was destroyed by fire in the war. From the farming of the coal mine there nothing through lack of workmen on account of the war*'.[23]

Wilkins proposed that the thirteenth century mine was '*very likely that of Velin Fach, Llanvabon, which old men*, [had] *stated to have been of very early date*', which he reasoned was an '*outcrop of the Mynyddislwyn* [coal seam]'.[24] The whereabouts of this mine can be suggested as south-west from Gelligaer near the village of Nelson. Nelson's Norman style church is dedicated to St. Mabon (Llanfabon). Thomas Powell's Gelligaer Colliery lay about half a mile east of Nelson, in an east-west valley that connects the valleys of the Rhymney and the Taff.[25]

Thomas Powell's Gelligaer Colliery worked, maybe, both the 'Old Colliery' and the 'New Colliery' east of Nelson. A part of an early nineteenth century geological map.

Courtesy of David Llewellyn's map collection

Powell's Gelligaer colliery venture was riskier than a Llanhilleth coal level since a shaft was sunk in the hope of finding the Mynyddislwyn seam. W. W. Price wrote: '*As far back as the 17th November, 1829, he* [Powell] *had sunk two shafts of 112 yards each to reach coal at Gelligaer, and discovered there a vein of coal nearly six feet thick, which created great excitement in the neighbourhood. He connected the colliery by tram-road with the canal* [in the Taff Valley to the west] *so as to ship out of Cardiff*.[26]

The Glamorganshire Canal linked Cardiff with Merthyr Tydfil, at the head of the Taff Valley, for ironmasters to transport goods. Opened in 1794, the canal soon became crowded with barges due to the colossal output of iron made at Merthyr Tydfil. A tramroad was then constructed between Merthyr and Cardiff. That rival means were available for moving coal to Cardiff no doubt featured in Thomas Powell's thoughts as he made his decision to open Gelligaer Colliery. Moreover, shipping out from Cardiff gave him a lever to haggle in both Newport and Cardiff for reduced shipping rates. Thomas Powell's expanding breadth of commercial responsibilities, say from the late 1820s, became burdensome, but the way in which he managed his affairs achieved success.

W. W. Price noted, from *The Cambrian*, 21st November, 1829, admiration for the risk Powell took opening the colliery. '*Undaunted by difficulties, unappalled by the enormous expense – and by the representations of people who wished to dissuade him from prosecuting what they deemed an unprofitable undertaking, he fearlessly persevered and complete success has been the well-earned recompense of energetic perseverance*'. Thomas Powell also gained a name for charity. W. W. Price found from *The Cambrian*, 13th February, 1830, that the Newport man 'distributed 50 tons of coal from his colliery at Gelligaer amongst the labouring poor of Cardiff'.[27]

More notably, perhaps, the efforts of Gelligaer Colliery's miners achieved especial fame for Thomas Powell in the South Wales Coalfield. In 1985, D. L. Davies observed: '*If, as seems certain from this precise reference, Powell was involved in pit sinking from 1829 onwards, then he is one of the earliest developers of deep mine in South Wales*.'[28]

Powell's Gelligaer Colliery miners were not in awe of their pioneering coalowner. In 1840, the colliery's miners went on strike for better wages.[29] The ten week strike was settled with a sliding scale payment scheme based upon the selling price of coal. Thomas Powell had linked the wages of his miners to the price that coal could fetch in the market.

The work practices regime at Gelligaer Colliery earned Powell a less than favourable reputation. In 1841, the Commissioners for the Employment of Children in Coal Mines visited the colliery and found employed at 'dooring' [open and closing underground doors to regulate ventilation] boys of seven years of age earning 6d. per day.[30] The boys were given a free ration of candles, but if they had needed more they bought them from their 'meagre earnings, but more often than not they went without'. Wilkins noted that Powell 'had one explosion at Gellygaer (sic), but no one was killed. The men "dusted" the gas out with their jackets when it became troublesome'. The colliery's manager, perhaps the 'clerk and under-agent' William Jenkins, maybe oversaw such practices.[31]

Thomas Powell's family's life at Newport was isolated from his confrontations with miners over demands for wage increases, or calls from them for improvements in their conditions of work. By 1841, Thomas Powell resided at The Gaer.[32] His home lay

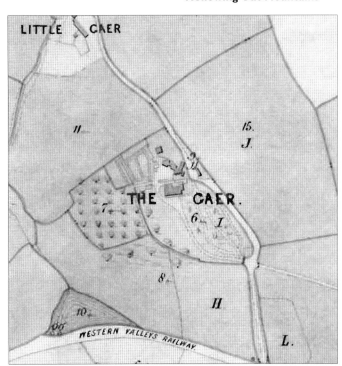

Plan of Thomas Powell's residence – 'The Gaer'.
Courtesy of Newport City Council Libraries

on the outskirts of Newport whose population had grown ten fold since 1801, the census of 1841 showing a town of 10,492 people. Moreover, the town remained his base for the pursuit of commercial priorities. The day-to-day management of collieries rested with his agents or managers. His drive was to expand his coal mining interests.

Gelligaer Colliery sat on the threshold of the eastern valleys of Glamorgan that converged upon Cardiff. In Cardiff, John Crichton Stuart Bute, 2nd Marquis (1793-1848), had staked his family's wealth on opening West Bute Dock in 1839 in anticipation of trade based upon ironmaking, mainly at Merthyr Tydfil. However, ambitious coalowners like Powell were to gift the Marquis of Bute a rich bonus for his dock investment, coal exports.

Thomas Powell heard news about the mining success of the Waynes in the Cynon Valley, locally called the Aberdare Valley, due to the main town in the district being Aberdare. In 1837, the Waynes' Abernant y Groes Colliery became the first deep pit sunk 'to the lower coal measures for sale purposes' as household coal.[33] The Waynes' action represented business diversification since they owned the nearby Gadlys Ironworks.

Coincidentally, another ironmaster, Crawshay Bailey, a scion of a notable family of Merthyr Tydfil ironmasters, took ownership, on the 17th February, 1837, of the Aberaman Estate, that lay to the south of Aberdare.[34] W. W. Price identified that the Aberaman Estate was once 'self supporting'. The estate '*had its fields of corn, its meadows for hay and pastures for beasts, and the adjoining mountains for the sheep, while the rivers around teemed with salmon, trout, and sewin* [sea-trout]'.[35] Aberaman Estate's rural charm was put in peril of being lost due to the business ambitions of Crawshay Bailey, and coalowners like Thomas Powell. The sinking of Waynes' Abernant y Groes Colliery was the bellwether that Thomas immediately followed. Powell afterwards established his name as a coalowner well beyond the shores of South Wales due to mining in the Aberdare district.

Powell's Aberdare Valley Collieries

The chronology of Thomas Powell's Aberdare Valley colliery sinkings were:[36]

Tir Ffounder [later known as Old Duffryn]	February 1840 to June 1842
Upper Duffryn	1844
Middle Duffryn	1850
Cwm Pennar [Lower Duffryn, Upper & Lower Pits]	March 1850 to 1854
Cwmdare	1852-1854
Abergwawr [Plough Pit]	circa 1855

In general, the area of territory leased to Thomas Powell for mining per colliery was not found. However, on the 1st January, 1854, Crawshay Bailey leased to him the Four Foot seam under 65 acres of the Aberaman Estate.[37] Although the lease acreage may have been his first workings at Abergwawr, perhaps much more usefully it gives a rough idea of the scale of areas Thomas Powell leased for mining in at least the Aberdare Valley.

Evidently Powell considered the transportation of coal, initially by canal, to Cardiff when choosing a site for an Aberdare Valley colliery. Tir-Ffounder Colliery stood near to where the village of Cwmbach grew.[38] Upper Duffryn Colliery lay immediately westward of Tir-Ffounder Colliery. Middle Duffryn Colliery lay at a distance of about half a mile eastwards from Tir-Ffounder Colliery, and both collieries stood adjacent to the Aberdare Canal.[39]

Cwm Pennar Colliery, with its Upper and Lower Pits, later known as Lower Duffryn Colliery, was sited just north of today's town of Mountain Ash.[40]

Cwmdare Colliery was sited north-west of Aberdare.[41] The colliery was known as Powell's Pit (No. 3) among some people of the Aberdare district maybe to distinguish it from at least

one other colliery called Cwmdare Colliery. In contrast with the chronological list of Powell's collieries given above, John F. Mare noted that Thomas Powell took some form of ownership of the colliery in 1846, and began operation in 1850.[42]

Abergwawr, otherwise known as Plough Pit, was located at Aberaman.[43] Plough Pit has been identified as a Powell & Prothero venture.[44] However, W. W. Price presented the Pit as if it was part of Crawshay Bailey's plan to open an ironworks, and collieries, at Aberaman.[45] Certainly Crawshay Bailey's and Powell's interests coincided at Plough Pit in part due to the opening in 1846 of the Aberdare Railway, which served the Aberaman ironworks. This railway linked Aberdare with the Taff Vale Railway at Navigation House, Abercynon, for connections with Cardiff.

The Taff Vale Railway had been formed a number of years earlier, in October, 1835, with Josiah John Guest, later knighted, as chairman.[46] By October 1840, the Brunel engineered railway ran from Cardiff to Navigation House, Abercynon, and it was extended to Merthyr Tydfil by 1841. The Newport coalowner seized an opportunity to invest £20,000 in the Taff Vale Railway, and became a company director.[47]

Canal and railway connections with Cardiff were vital for Powell's development of Aberdare Valley collieries, but how useful geological maps were for guiding his mining adventures is not known. By the end of the eighteenth century, William Smith had mapped, in South Wales, the outcrop of the Red Sandstone of Brecon, the 'Derbyshire Limestone' and the Millstone Grit and Coal measures. Smith's work was followed by a rapid advance in the early decades of the 19th century: Greenough prepared a map of Glamorgan that was astonishingly detailed and accurate for the time of its production; Conybeare described the multiple folding to be seen in the South

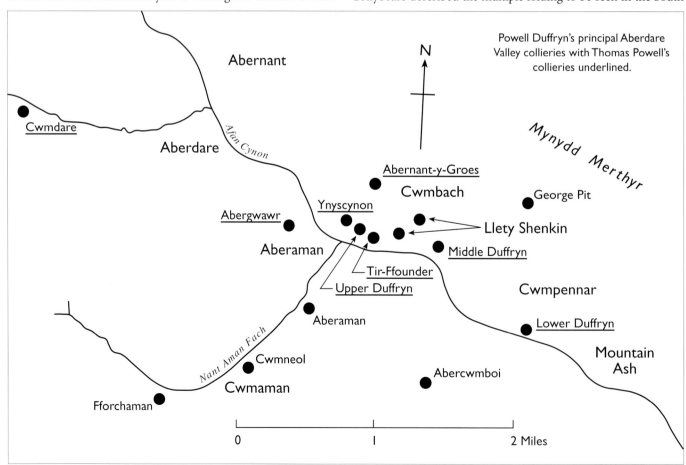

Powell Duffryn's principal Aberdare Valley collieries with Thomas Powell's collieries underlined.

Lower Duffryn Colliery. Sunk 1850-1854 at Cwm Pennar, near Mountain Ash. In 1875, the colliery's workforce comprised 893 men and boys.
John Ryan Collection

Wales coalfield and De la Beche began his systematic study of the regional geology of South Wales. Thus, 'in a few years after 1830 the major features of the stratigraphy and structure in the geological frame of South Wales were established'.[48] So, the oval shaped boundary of the Coalfield, as viewed by a bird in flight, and its saucer like rock structure, became known. However, the 1833 geological map showed only the outcrops of coal seams on the valleys' hillsides. What coal lay under the floor of the valleys was a matter for speculation.

That the Waynes proved coal under the Aberdare Valley was probably more important than a geological map's information for encouraging Powell to sink Tir-Ffounder in 1840. However, a question arises: was Powell attracted to the Aberdare District due to the Waynes' decision to diversify into selling household coal? If Powell's aim in sinking Tir-Ffounder had been to raise household coal then the market that developed for the coal found was not only a surprise for him, but brought him even richer rewards than he might have expected.

Steam Coal

In 1842, Powell struck at Tir-Ffounder what would become the 'famous Four Foot Seam' at a depth of 247ft 4in.[49] The depth of the Four Feet seam at Lower Duffryn Colliery was found at 264 yards.[50] Coal from the Four Foot seam won fame as a fuel of great importance. 'The 1820s saw rapid growth in the application of steam to ship propulsion although vessels so powered were generally confined to rivers and coastal waters'.[51] Engineers who designed the propulsion systems of steamships took notice of the properties of coal. Of interest to a merchant steamship owner was maximising a ship's weight of cargo, which bunkers of coal hindered. A coal that possessed the most energy, or best steam raising properties per unit weight of coal burnt, helped achieve that aim. A notable example of the pioneering stage of ocean going steamships was Brunel's paddle propelled *Great*

Western. Coal burnt in a flue-type steam raising boiler powered the *Great Western*, which completed her maiden voyage in 1838. Nonetheless, from 1840 to 1843, John Nixon (1815-1899) acted as Thomas Powell's sales agent in France.[52] The sale of Powell's Tir-Ffounder coal to France, after Nixon convinced French river shippers about the coal's superiority for marine steam power, was an historical step towards winning international recognition among marine engineers for South Wales coal.[53]

The Powell-Nixon relationship soured. According to John Nixon, the Newport coalowner refused to pay him the commission he was due in accordance with an agreement they had reached before he embarked upon his French sales mission.[54] Thomas Powell's refusal was on the 'grounds that Nixon was making more out of the transaction than himself'. At a meeting, Powell scorned John Nixon's threat of legal action by telling him that he had won a lawsuit involving Lord Bute. Nixon did not pursue the matter in the courts. Instead, as becomes apparent later, used his abilities as an engineer to become a coalowner, and of great importance, pioneered the sale of Aberdare Valley coal to a nation's navy, the French.[55] Powell retained a coal trade with France.

The 1840s saw marked growth in the number of steamboats making voyages across the world's oceans. In 1845, the sale of Tir-Ffounder Colliery's coal to power Brunel's pioneering screwship, The *Great Britain*, was notable, and reveals that Powell was supplying the merchant steam ship market.[56] However, much more significantly, 'the expansion of the British steam-powered fleet took place during the 1840s'.[57] At sometime between the years 1844 and 1845, the Admiralty invited tenders for the supply of coal from 'Powell's Duffryn' and others like 'Tredegar'.[58]

The first report on Admiralty tests, or trials of coal as they were also called, was published in 1848 with the second, and final report in 1851.[59] Five Welsh coals, which included those of the Cynon Valley, Aberaman Merthyr, Duffryn, Nixon's Merthyr, were ranked as the highest in terms of their 'evaporative power' – the energy per unit weight of coal fired to heat water to make steam. Moreover, what also marked them out as suitable for naval marine power was that 'the best Welsh coals lit easily, blew up steam rapidly, produced a fine clear fire with little clinker, and gave off very little smoke. The best Newcastle coals, on the other hand, all caked excessively choking the draught and demanding constant attention, and gave off dense black smoke'.[60]

Thomas Powell and his former French sales agent, John Nixon, established by 1851 in the Aberdare Valley as a coalowner, were to the fore in defending the merits of Welsh coal against a challenge by northern coalowners for a share of Admiralty coal orders.[61] Left smarting by the results of the Admiralty's first trials, the northern coalowners lobbied Government to get their coal approved for British naval use. Powell and Nixon objected in a letter to *The Times* in 1851 to an apparatus, invented as a result of a competition sponsored by northern coalowners' used in a marine boiler to prevent smoke emissions. The two South Wales coalowners contended that the apparatus was 'of a construction not similar to any now in use in the Royal or mercantile steam navies'. The Admiralty held new trials, and the conclusions from the results, published in 1859, gave 'no verdict … in favour of either side'. The battle between the owners of the two coalfields for British naval coal orders continued, but ultimately the Admiralty favoured South Wales Coalfield steam coal.[62] And 'Admiralty Lists' of coal 'proved of inestimable value in extending [a listed coal's] sales'. The Admiralty's stamp of approval was also a fillip for marketing coal to steam shipping companies. The reputation of Welsh steam coal was undoubtedly a factor in making George Elliot's case for forming Powell Duffryn.

Sometime later, the South Wales Coalfield was differentiated as zones according to types of coal. The zones were given appellations equivalent to the practice used in France today to discriminate the quality of winemaking districts such as in Burgundy as *Grand Cru*, and *Premier Cru*. To the north of Aberaman coal was classed as 'Dry Steam', and to its south, 'Smokeless Steam'.[63] The border line, between two classes of coal, was perhaps more arbitrarily drawn than that accepted by the wine producers of Burgundy. The exact date when the term 'steam coal' was introduced is not known. Moreover, finding a definitive meaning for 'dry steam coal' was also found to be illusive. However, to market a product based upon some idea of quality differentiation was an attractive practice for both coalowner and coal factors to adopt. Two French coal classifications, published in 1870s, can be credited for 'the start of detailed coal classification tables'.[64]

Subsequently many attempts were made in Britain to devise a comprehensive classification of coals in order that the properties, such as carbon content, volatiles, calorific value, and moisture content could be accurately and consistently measured.[65] The application of coals could then be better predicted. Nevertheless, the later advertisements of coalowners show they exploited what ever classification suited their purpose with alacrity. However, coalowners in the South Wales Coalfield like Thomas Powell appeared in no hurry to advance the use of engineering in their collieries.

Colliery Ventilation and Deaths

Regarding Thomas Powell's investment in colliery engineering in the Aberdare Valley it was typically meagre compared with five decades later. Water-balance winders were used at his Aberdare Valley collieries to raise coal from the Four Feet seam.[66] Furnace ventilation removed foul air from his collieries' underground workings.[67] In the early 1800s, though, mechanical ventilation systems were not available.

Powell's first decade of mining in the Aberdare Valley saw a pattern of explosions that gave rise to doubts about colliery ventilation. In 1844, there was an underground explosion at Upper Duffryn Colliery. In July 1845, at this furnace ventilated colliery,

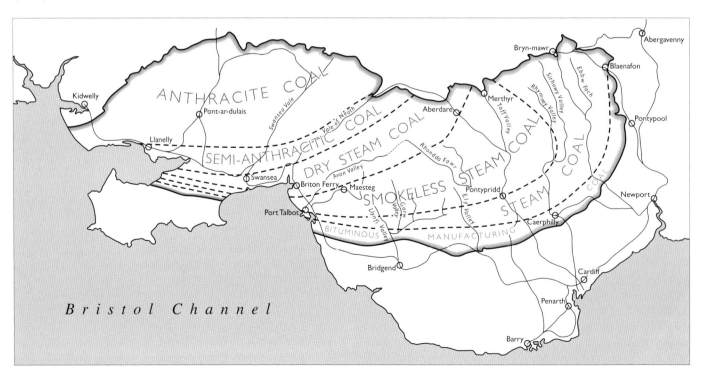

South Wales Coalfield and its varieties of coal. Used by the coal industry of South Wales at the start of the twentieth century.
South Wales Institute of Engineers (SWIE) Proceedings, Plate II, Vol. XXXVI, (1920)

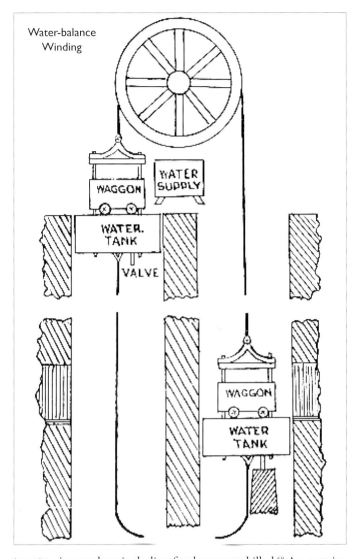

Water-balance
Winding

WATER
SUPPLY

WAGGON

WATER.
TANK

VALVE

WAGGON

WATER
TANK

The 1852 Middle Duffryn Colliery disaster

Then, in May 1852, Middle Duffryn Colliery was the scene of the Cynon Valley's worst mining disaster, which saw the deaths of forty-seven men and eighteen boys.[73] Immediately prior to the 1852 Middle Duffryn disaster, 200 men and boys worked about the pit.[74] During the three months preceding the 1852 disaster, 140 miners had worked by day and the remainder at night, to produce 340 tons of coal per 24 hours of working at Middle Duffryn. The colliery's engineering featured two shafts – one for winding coal, and the other for pumping. The pumping shaft was 'furnished with ladders and stages, by which the men could ascend from the bottom of the pit to the surface'.[75] Twelve miners were killed when the ladders 'gave way' as they attempted to escape from an underground explosion. The bodies of forty-six miners, some 'burnt, but nearly the whole were suffocated', were found huddled together at one underground location.

The 1852 Middle Duffryn disaster caused *The Times* to write a 'powerful leading article' demanding that 'a rigid scrutiny' occur. The *London Gazette* also produced illustrations of the colliery after the disaster. One illustration shows that a horse-gin was operated there, and another one shows a chain being wrapped around a winding drum to raise a cage in which miners stand, but the drum does not appear to be powered by the horse-gin. For those that investigated the disaster this technical detail was of minor interest. The disaster was raised in the House of Commons and the Government gave instructions for a 'strict investigation'.

Herbert Mackworth, according to the *Cardiff & Merthyr Guardian* '*a gentleman of great scientific attainments*', was the Government Inspector assigned to examine the disaster. He was assisted by J. K. Blackwell, 'late government inspector', Mr Llewellin, 'the eminent mineral surveyor of Pontypool', and Mr Dobson, a 'mineral surgeon'. The previous government inspector's report was read out at the 1852 inquiry and so it heard Blackwell's opinion that '*coal in the Middle Duffryn pit was highly charged with gas and recommended the use of the Davy lamp, while the "brattice" system existed* [for ventilation]'.[76]

During the coroner's inquest, Mackworth questioned Mr Shipley, Middle Duffryn's colliery manager, or colliery agent as reported. Shipley, with 'great experience of the collieries of the north', had taken up the post as the colliery's manager after the

twenty-nine workers including five boys were killed.[68] An enquiry into the disaster judged that it was due to inadequate ventilation.[69] In circa 1846, between thirty and forty lives were lost at Powell's Tir-Ffounder due to an explosion.[70]

Lower Duffryn's sinking was overshadowed by a mining disaster at Middle Duffryn Colliery in December 1850, which took the lives of nine miners.[71] Party to an inquest into this disaster was a Government inspector, J. K. Blackwell. He berated the miners' use of naked candlelight underground, and the colliery's ventilation. A feature of the colliery's ventilating system was the dual use of the colliery's shaft as a 'downcast' and 'upcast'. This was achieved using a vertical partition structure, known as a brattice, installed in the shaft.

The inquest into the 1850 Middle Duffryn disaster prompted the *Cardiff & Merthyr Guardian* to praise Thomas Powell for being '*one of the most extensive, public spirited colliery proprietors in this or the adjoining counties*'. If this praise was true, he would have acted to prevent a repeat of such a disaster. For example, he could have instructed his colliery managers to equip the miners with safety lamps that had been made available to their counterparts in the North of England Coalfield since the 1820s. He was undoubtedly aware of their availability. He was sufficiently informed about that Coalfield's activities to quote, in a quarrel over charges with the Taff Vale Railway (TVR), that the Stockton & Darlington's railway 'charges were a trifle more than half that of the TVR'.[72]

Middle Duffryn Colliery. Sunk by Thomas Powell in 1850. In May 1852, an explosion at the colliery killed sixty-five men and boys.

London Illustrated News

previous explosion at Middle Duffryn. The colliery's manager confirmed he had some knowledge about the previous explosion. However, asked about Blackwell's report, in particular about its advice regarding Davy lamps, Shipley admitted that he had never 'heard of' the report.[77] He added: '*I have been in charge of collieries for thirty years, and have never lost a man before. If all the Davy lamps in the world were in the pit, the explosion would not have been avoided*'. Shipley's dismissal of the virtues of the Davy lamp for underground safety seemed ill judged since the inquiry recognised that the coal of Middle Duffryn Colliery 'was highly charged with gas'.[78] However, in Britain, the prevailing scientific explanation for the underground explosion process would later be shown to be primitive.

The Government Inspector also questioned the colliery manager about the use of brattice structures at the colliery and tested him to see if he had ideas for altering the underground ventilating furnace. Shipley's replies were less than clear, as were his plans for colliery improvement. However, challenged by the coroner, George Overton, if he could 'devise no mode of preventing deaths from fire damp?' Shipley said: '*I have directed my attention to it. The chief object is to send in air as soon as possible. I do all I can at the colliery; and Mr Powell directs me to spare no expense in that respect*'.

However, Mackworth's report criticized the colliery's ventilation system for its use of a brattice structure. Notably he was '*compelled emphatically to condemn the entire neglect of the safeguards insisted on at the former inquest*' contained in J. K. Blackwell's report. He recommended, for the colliery, the 'entire exclusion of naked lights, and a larger ventilation'.

John Lewis, as its foreman, announced the jury's verdict about the Middle Duffryn Colliery disaster. '*The deaths had certainly resulted from the explosion – that was the preliminary cause, the stepping [a door used to guide the flow of air underground] blown down, and the motion of the fresh air prevented thereby*'.[79]

The *Cardiff & Merthyr Guardian* reckoned that the inquest contained unfair criticism of the coalowner. The explosion, the newspaper claimed, '*tends to show the hopelessness of ensuring the non-recurrence of similar accidents, for it is affirmed that measures had been taken, in the ventilation of the works, to make the air course, and the condition of the workmen as perfect as human ingenuity and skill could render them*'.[80] Regarding colliery ventilation, the newspaper's appraisal of the state of colliery engineering was partly fair. Indeed, the government inspector, Herbert Mackworth, did not request that furnace ventilation be abandoned at Middle Duffryn Colliery in favour of say a mechanical system.

The inquiry called Swansea's William Price Struvé, and he spoke against furnace ventilation and advocated his reciprocating air pump.[81] 'The first Struvé ventilator was installed at Eaglebush Colliery, South Wales, and began to work in February 1849; the upcast shaft was 60 yards deep and the quantity of the air circulated was 56,000 cubic feet per minute'.[82] Also noteworthy is the fact that, in 1849, Thomas Powell's Gelligaer Colliery featured a centrifugal fan designed by William Brunton (1777-1851) for ventilation. Brunton's design featured an 'open running radial-bladed centrifugal type [fan], with its plane horizontal', and 'although satisfactory, was handicapped by much too narrow return airways and the inevitable explosion [no details given] happened'.[83] Indeed, an 1852 Government Select Committee report implied support for furnace ventilation since it advised against the use of 'complicated machinery'.[84]

Nonetheless, what seems surprising about the inquiry into the 1852 Middle Duffryn disaster was its failure not to probe why Shipley did not know about the report on the colliery's 1850 disaster. Maybe if he had read the report he would have given more thought to planning measures so as to try and reduce the risk of an underground explosion at the colliery in his charge. Thomas Powell might then have been called to explain what he saw was his duty of care towards miners.

One response of the coalowner to the disaster was to pay around £600 into a fund set up to give aid to the widows and orphans. The *Monmouthshire Merlin* praised the 'generosity' of his act, which was 'quite characteristic' of him.[85] Yet, miners of the Aberdare Valley would have been less inclined to flatter the Newport coalowner, or any of his rivals regarding colliery explosions. Moreover, the Coal Mines Act of 1850 did not appear to check the danger to life working at a Powell colliery, and a year after the Middle Duffryn disaster an agent for Thomas Powell had to recruit miners to man a new colliery of his in the Rhymney Valley.

New Tredegar Colliery

Possibly around 1853, Thomas Powell opened New Tredegar Colliery in the Rhymney Valley.[86] The colliery stood on the valley's Monmouthshire side, and some two miles, south-east of Rhymney Ironworks. The three decades, starting with the 1830s, according to Carr and Taplin, were 'the heyday of Welsh iron rail'.[87] Indeed, the busy ironmasters of Rhymney may have treated Thomas Powell's arrival nearby with some disinterest.

Crawshay Bailey, as one of the investors in the Rhymney Tramroad Company, welcomed Powell's New Tredegar Colliery. The Rhymney tramroad ran from the Rhymney ironworks down the eastern side of the valley, and gained the name 'Old Rumney'. Opened in 1826 for horse-drawn wagons, the tramroad's 'significance lay in its connection below Bassaleg with the Sirhowy and Park Mile tramroads', so enabling a through route to Newport'.[88] Steam locomotives began running on the tramroad between 1840 and 1845.[89] Powell's colliery stood near to this tramroad, which in 1861 became a railway owned by the Brecon & Merthyr Railway Company.

Compared with other 'great' ironworks of the Heads of the Valleys, industrial scale ironmaking came later to Rhymney. It began modestly, with the Old Upper Furnace of 1801. Between 1825 and 1834, an ironworks grew on Marquis of Bute land north of Pontlottyn, a village to the south of the town of Rhymney.[90] The delay in such development was not due to the vicinity lacking coal or clay-band ironstone.

In the broad vale, which cradles the town of Rhymney, the location of the northern rim of the South Wales Coalfield can be easily plotted. David Emlyn Evans (1915–1997), a geologist, revealed an empathy with the activities of the early prospectors for coal in his tour of this district's geology.[91] He pointed, for example, to where prospectors would have searched for coal. He described that: '*Between Pontlottyn and Rhymney Bridge the [Rhymney] river flows southwards over the gently and southerly inclined mudstones, sandstones, coal seams and seatearths of the Lower and Middle Coal measures in a valley which becomes increasingly deeper*'.[92] He further drew people's attention to a Rhymney location where: '*immediately below the bridge on the east side of the stream there is a good exposure of the "Lower Four Foot" or the "Old" coal*.[93] *It consists here of the "Lower Four Foot Yard" and the lower as the*

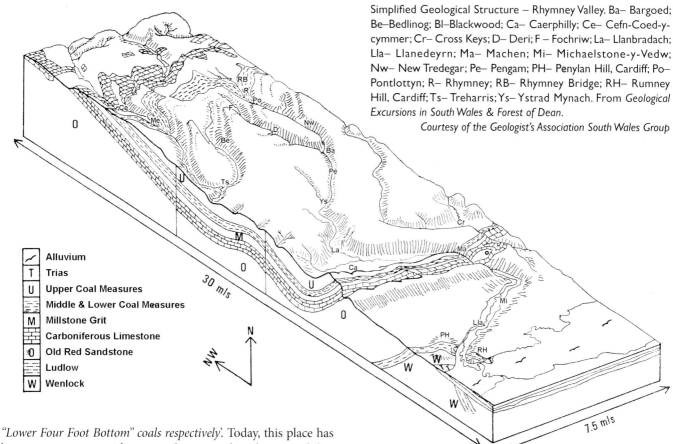

Simplified Geological Structure – Rhymney Valley. Ba– Bargoed; Be–Bedlinog; Bl–Blackwood; Ca– Caerphilly; Ce– Cefn-Coed-y-cymmer; Cr– Cross Keys; D– Deri; F – Fochriw; La– Llanbradach; Lla– Llanedeyrn; Ma– Machen; Mi– Michaelstone-y-Vedw; Nw– New Tredegar; Pe– Pengam; PH– Penylan Hill, Cardiff; Po–Pontlottyn; R– Rhymney; RB– Rhymney Bridge; RH– Rumney Hill, Cardiff; Ts– Treharris; Ys– Ystrad Mynach. From *Geological Excursions in South Wales & Forest of Dean*.

Courtesy of the Geologist's Association South Wales Group

Alluvium	
T	Trias
U	Upper Coal Measures
	Middle & Lower Coal Measures
M	Millstone Grit
	Carboniferous Limestone
0	Old Red Sandstone
	Ludlow
W	Wenlock

"*Lower Four Foot Bottom*" coals respectively'. Today, this place has become overgrown with trees and grass, and so the accessibility of such potential stocks of coal might not be so easily, or safely, appreciated.

In the Rhymney district, like elsewhere along the Heads of the Valleys, coal and clay-band ironstone was raised from pits with modest investment, in both shaft excavation, and winding machines. Many of the pits sunk around Rhymney were named after people associated with them for example Pwll (Welsh for pit) Elias, and Pwll William Jones.[94]

Brynpwllog, otherwise known as Roger's Pit, Blaen Carno, Rhymney, accessed the Upper Four Foot and Big Vein seams in its early days, circa 1830.[95] In around 1850, Brynpwllog was sunk further to 57 yards. To enable the pit's water-balance winder to operate, a miner's shout from underground, might have been heard at the surface by a rain soaked worker as an order to fill a cage's tank with water. The despised rainfall of the locality was an asset. However, water-balance winding was vulnerable to the whims of the weather. George Watkins observed in 1978: 'a natural water supply was desirable, but during the severe droughts of the 1860s Crawshays [ironmasters of Merthyr Tydfil] decided that if they continued, steam winding must be adopted'.[96] The time of the demise of water-balance winders had neared. Fortunately, the National Museum of Wales salvaged the one used at Brynpwllog Pit.[97] Preserved, it stands at the Big Pit: National Museum of Wales, Blaenavon. New Tredegar Colliery was probably the first colliery in the Rhymney Valley to use steam winding engines, though records to definitely confirm this claim no longer exist.

New Tredegar Colliery's coal property appears to have been leased, on the whole, from the Morgan family of Tredegar House. Perhaps the origin of the name, for both the colliery and the attendant village that grew to its south, was due to the

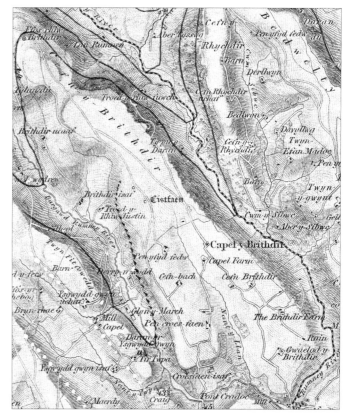

This section of an early nineteenth century geological map predates Thomas Powell's New Tredegar Colliery, which was sited, approximately, to the west of Cefn y Rychdir farm and adjacent to the eastern bank of the Rhymney River. *Courtesy of David Llewellyn's map collection*

lease. As the development of New Tredegar Colliery progressed, Sir Charles Morgan's personal concern was for the well-being of his son, Godfrey Charles Morgan. Sir Charles Morgan, who succeeded his deceased father of the same name in 1846, was in 1859 made the first Baron Tredegar. In 1854, his son, as a captain in the 17th Lancers, participated in the Charge of the Light Brigade at Balaclava.

The colliery was another gamble for Powell since the ground under the floor of the Rhymney Valley, south of Rhymney, was largely unexplored for coal. Moreover, Powell's commercial ambitions, to export New Tredegar coal via Newport depended on a problem being solved: its dock was a bottleneck to further growth in maritime trade.

In 1852, as a shareholder of the Monmouthshire Railway & Canal Company, Thomas Powell possessed knowledge that enabled him to foresee Newport docks' future. That year the railway company awaited the successful passage of a bill in Parliament so that it could complete the Newport & Pontypool Railway, which was later achieved.[98] The logic of such railway expansion added to the case for extending Newport docks. Consequently, in 1854, an Act of Parliament enabled dock extensions, which were opened in March 1858.[99] Coal was then shipped without any worry about dock limitations for sometime into the future.

New Tredegar Colliery appears to have been ready for operation in 1853, since an inscribed tablet on one of its building announced that it was: 'Erected in 1853, by Thomas Powell, Esq., Gaer, Newport, Mon'.[100] The colliery's shaft called the 'old side' may

have earned its name due to being sunk as a sole one to raise coal from the No. 2 Rhondda Seam at around 85 yards. The seam might have proved less than attractive to mine, but Powell persisted in a search for good coal. The first coal seam of value to him appears to have been the 'Big Vein', also called the Four-Feet, which lay at an estimated depth of 275 yards. Although it was not until an Act of Parliament in 1862 made it illegal for any colliery employing more than twenty people to operate using just one shaft, it seems likely that New Tredegar operated from an early stage in its life with two shafts. Tredegar Estate coal was mined from the 'Old Side' and Bute coal from the second shaft, the 'River-side'. Powell Duffryn acquired the colliery as a steam coal pit, which suggests that steam coal at 345 yards was already being worked.[101] In 1858, New Tredegar colliery's manager was James Naysmith who reported to Thomas Powell via a position called colliery 'viewer', who was possibly Samuel Dobson.[102]

Regarding underground ventilation, notably in December 1875, a Struvé ventilator was in use at the colliery circulating 20,000ft³ of air per minute per shaft. The choice of a Struvé air pump might suggest that Thomas Powell heeded the comments made by its inventor at the 1852 Middle Duffryn Colliery inquiry.[104] Records giving the number of men and boys employed at New Tredegar Colliery during its first decade of operation have not been found. By 1875, the colliery employed over 1,000 miners, and produced 3,500 tons of coal per week.[103]

The octogenarian Newport coalowner's quest for coal continued. The Aberdare, Rhondda and Merthyr Valleys transfixed most

New Tredegar Colliery circa 1902. Thomas Powell opened the colliery possibly in 1853. 600 miners were employed at this Powell Duffryn colliery in 1875. The sinking of No. 3 Pit is shown on the right.

Paul Jackson Collection

of his coalowner rivals. Geological maps marked the southern boundary of the South Wales Coalfield and the Glamorgan town of Llantrisant served as one of its markers, north-east of which lay Llanwit Fadre. Possibly in the late 1850s, he sank for coal at Llanwit Fadre. This colliery, near the 'South Crop', a term commonly used for the southern boundary of the coalfield, probably helped establish him as the coalowner with the greatest geographical coverage in the South Wales Coalfield for the period.

In February 1858, at Lower Duffryn Colliery, nineteen miners were killed in an explosion.[105] Thomas Powell rushed from Cardiff to Mountain Ash to take charge of the rescue operations which included arranging a special train to fetch his chief agent and engineer to the colliery.[106] Powell reached a state of collapse by the end of the rescue. The inquest into the explosion, led by coroner George Overton, 'concluded that the mine was insufficiently ventilated and he recommended that an additional furnace should be placed at the bottom of the upcast shaft'. The 1858 Lower Duffryn tragedy 'touched' Powell. 'He would allow no public subscription but supported the widows and orphans out of his own pocket, granting each widow a house and coal and a pension of 9s. 0d. a week'.[107]

In 1863, he bought T. & M. Wayne's Abernant-y-Groes Colliery from the Aberdare Coal Company.[108] Thus, he bought the colliery that may have inspired his interest in the Aberdare Valley. Moreover, sometime earlier he had purchased a level called the White Rose Coal Colliery at New Tredegar. The level, for which a Mr Merryweather has been identified as a previous owner, burrowed into the valley's west facing, oak tree covered, steep hillside to access the Brithdir seam.[109] Nevertheless, Thomas Powell's management of his coal business ended in 1863.[110]

Death and Legacy

Thomas Powell died on Tuesday, 24th March, 1863, aged eighty-three according to his obituary in *The Star of Gwent*.[111] The newspaper gave two days notice of Thomas Powell's funeral at St Basil's Church, Bassaleg. This notice does not accord with Howard Meyrick's later description of an almost secretive cortège on the 31st March, 1863 which brought the late coalowner's coffin to the church for a burial service before his interment in a family vault.[112]

Thomas Powell's will 'was stolen but recovered by a policeman disguised in woman's clothing'.[113] The crime may have involved a member, or members of Powell's surviving families. He was married three times. He had a daughter, Mary Anne, from his first marriage to Mary Pearce who died in 1812. The issues of his second wife, Anne Hardwick of Westbury, Somerset, were: Sarah Emily, who predeceased him; and Francis Elizabeth who married Augustus Gore of London. His sons Thomas Jnr, Walter, and Henry were from his third marriage to Anne Williams of Bristol. W. W. Price identified that 'before his death he had taken his two eldest sons into partnership under the style of Thomas Powell and Sons' but his will, dated 20th February, 1863, 'bequeathed all his collieries to his sons in equal shares'.[114]

Thomas Powell's reputation also lived on. The mean way in which he dealt with strikes was remembered. For example, a 'great strike paralysed the industry [of South Wales] in 1858 when the masters, led by Powell, enforced a 15% reduction in wages which led to a complete turn-out of the colliers'.[115] The strike continued for many weeks, and after it ended the 'masters' imposed 'a further 5% wage reduction in order to recoup the losses they had suffered'.

By 1860, the death toll due to disasters at Powell's Aberdare Valley collieries was nearly two hundred people. He ranked first in an Aberdare Valley coalowners' death toll league table tallied over the same period. Second in this disreputable league table was William Thomas (Waunwyllt) due to nearly sixty deaths at his Llety Shenkin Colliery. Powell's acts of charity after colliery disasters appear not to have won him any regard.

The tales of the miners who experienced his authoritarian master and servant style of management at the hands of his colliery managers were passed on to succeeding generations of miners. Foul talk among miners about events experienced under his charge, not least deaths due to underground explosions, and frustrated quests for better wages, promoted myths about him. A century after his death, Howard Meyrick wrote that Powell 'earned little esteem but much public vilification and had caused anguish and suffering to many in his relentless pursuit of wealth. He was to coal as the ruthless Crawshay Bailey was to iron and he, alike, became legendary in his lifetime'.[116] Arguably the stigma of poverty and death linked to Powell Duffryn's abbreviation, PD, originated as a reflection of Thomas Powell's period of ownership.

Regardless, a valuing of Powell's success as a business man lay beyond the orbit of his miners. Dock and railway operators of the South Wales Coalfield were among many stung by Powell's belligerence.[117] Such conduct by a business magnate is not unusual, but an acid test of it arises in negotiations. On balance, Thomas Powell's belligerence proved gainful to himself. As he aged, Powell also became deaf and loud in speech, and some of his listeners may have reacted with anger due to being bawled at. So, rows ensued with a man obsessed with the coal trade. The enmity he created among a section of the commercial men of South Wales did not stop some of this group of men entering into alliances with him. For instance, it seems, he was the founder of the first 'coal ring' in South Wales, the Newport Coal Association. A belief has prevailed that he tried to create a personal monopoly of Aberdare Valley steam coal.[118]

Attempts at profiteering might have been a natural action for the first coalowners to take as a means for balancing the risks they took in their favour. W. W. Price astutely observed: 'These early pioneering coalowners deserve credit for what they accomplished in their time. They had scarcely any capital. Very little was known of geology, and faults in the local mines had not been mapped out'.[119] He also perceived that 'Thomas Powell was a keen salesman and an able accountant with it is said, a flair for collecting outstanding debts'.[120] The Newport coalowner did not need to be a first class salesman since the Carboniferous Age's gift to him was Welsh steam coal. Yet, Howard Meyrick's reckoning that Powell used 'aggressive selling methods' adds bite to W. W. Price's perception.[121]

Thomas Powell's dedication to his work up until his death at a remarkable age suggests he thrived bearing considerable business risk. Charles Wilkins noted: 'In his speculative ventures at the outset he [Powell] was necessarily at times driven to get advances from bankers, and it is said that his overdraft was so great that the banker called his attention to it and wished him to put it right. "I cannot do it yet", was his reply, "but if you pull me down I will pull you with me!" All he wanted was time. He had confidence in the great mines of wealth that he was engaged in, and the banker, inspired by his hope and energy, waited patiently until the corner was turned and he was above the need of help'.[122]

The foregoing quote hints that Thomas Powell faced the brink of going-to-the-wall as he grew his coal business. In this respect, Wilkins could have reconciled the rewards that his subject earned: '*He was the amasser of wealth, and doing so, in growing up from small beginnings, was like men of his class, frugal and careful of small things*'. Indeed, The Gaer was never noted as a monument to wealth like Tredegar House. He appeared to reinvest most of the profits his business earned to expand such interests across South Wales.

Days after his death *The Star of Gwent* assessed Thomas Powell. The newspaper praised him for being '*far-sighted and enterprising, he had built the fabric of his own fortune with wonderful rapidity, and on a colossal scale and his career is a striking instance of what industry combined with a clear head and sound judgment will accomplish*'. As '*the owner of from sixteen to twenty collieries in full work … [he] was the largest employer of labour in the South Wales district, and in these capacities his name became "a household name". Wheresoever the march of civilization has brought in its train the wonders of steam power, there the name of Powell is known. The shipments of coal last year amounted to 700,000 tons, probably the largest quantity exported by any single firm in the world*'.[123]

Following their father's death the Powells, Thomas Jnr, Walter, and Henry, invited a trio of leading mining engineers from the county of Durham, George Elliot, Thomas Emerson Forster, and William Armstrong, to assess their coal business. Perhaps Elliot heard an anecdote that Charles Wilkins later related. Thomas Powell boasted to a friend that in his possession was sufficient acreage of coal to last a thousand years. Mocked by his listener, that he was unlikely to live that long, his retort was, '*There's the rub; but I am very careful of myself, and can see my way to last a hundred years*.' He was also chided by another friend that he was 'hollowing out the mountains' at such a rate that there would be no legacy for other generations to enjoy. Thomas Powell replied: '*That the future must look after itself, and that the man would be a fool who would not drive out and sell as much coal as possible*'.

The trio of mining engineers produced a report in April, 1864, about the coal business Thomas Powell had left to his sons. George Elliot's imagination was excited by the report's findings. He led an acquisition of the Powells' steam coal interests through the founding of Powell Duffryn Steam Coal Company. So, what talents, knowledge, experience, contacts, and resources did George Elliot possess that enabled him to lead the acquisition

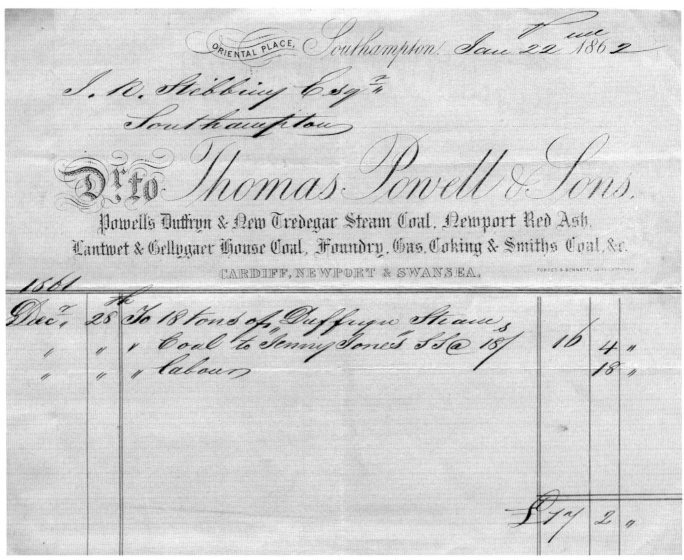

This invoice reveals that Thomas Powell had a sales office in Southampton, which indicates that his sales organisation spread beyond South Wales.
Ian Pope Collection

NOTES

1   According to Bradney [*History of Monmouthshire: Volume III* (1923) his date of birth was 6 January, 1779, but other evidence suggests a later date; his christening is recorded as 10 February, 1781'. G. W. J. Lowering, 'Thomas Powell of The Gaer, Newport (1780? – 1863). *Gwent Local History*, No. 84 (Spring 1998), p.4.

2   C. J. O. Evans, *Monmouthshire*. (Cardiff-William Lewis, 1952), p.37.

3   A. Bassett, 'The Port of Newport and the Coal Field', *Proceedings, South Wales Institute of Engineers*, Vol. V, (1866), p.139. Proceedings, South Wales Institute of Engineers hereafter SWIE.

4   F. J. North, *Coal, and the Coalfields in Wales*. (National Museum of Wales, 1931), pp.198-199.

5   A. Bassett, *op. cit.*, p.140.

6   A. Bassett, *op. cit.*, p.145.

7   Thomas Powell's father, John Powell, died when he was a boy, 'probably in 1788'. His mother, Elizabeth Powell, 'died four years later'; see G. W. J. Lovering, *op. cit.*, p.4. Thomas Powell's trade as a timber merchant is attributed to Charles Wilkins, *The South Wales Coalfield Coal Trade and its Allied Industries*. (Daniel Owen, 1888), pp.90-4.

8   'He had resided in Newport for fifty years' according to 'Death of Thomas Powell, Esq.', *The Star of Gwent*, 28 March 1863, p.5.

9   Elizabeth Phillips wrote: 'He [Thomas Powell] took it into his head to buy a small colliery between Llanhilleth and Aberbeeg, and he and two or three other men went from Newport with picks and shovels on their backs to start the place'. Elizabeth Phillips, *A History of the Welsh Coalfield*. (*Western Mail*, 1925), p.127.

10 Howard G. Meyrick, 'Thomas Powell: Coal Owner', *op. cit.*, p.45.

11 A. Bassett, 'The Port of Newport and the Coal Field', *SWIE*, Vol. VII, No. 3, (Dec 1866), p.158. The Mynyddislwyn seam was a general term. It was found in some locations as four separate seams of coal, the Lower and Upper Mynyddislwyn, the Small Rider and the Big Rider.

12 W. W. Price submitted that Powell 'at the age of sixty, had started from Newport, with three other men, to open a level at Llanhilleth'. He dated the Llanhilleth venture to be around 1839. W. W. Price, 'The History of Powell Duffryn in the Aberdare Valley', *Old Aberdare* (Vol. IV). (Cynon Valley History Society, 1985), p.8. The article was compiled generally 'intact' by D. L. Davies from W. W. Price's articles published in a series of *Powell Duffryn Review* issues: No. 50 (April, 1942); No. 51 (July, 1942); No. 53 (January, 1943); and No. 54 (April, 1943).

13 Howard G. Meyrick, 'Thomas Powell: Coal Owner', *op. cit.*, p.45. G. W. J. Lowering identified that at a site in Newport, between the canal and the Usk, Thomas Powell 'leased wharf ground from John Jones of Llanarth' in 1822. G. W. J. Lovering, *op. cit.*, p.4.

14 *The Bristol Mercury*, 13 March 1820, p.1.

15 The Llanhilleth parish tithe map and plans, 26 Feb. 1840, indicates that Thomas Powell used a small plot of land at Blaen Cyffin for a coal tip. G. W. J. Lovering, *op. cit.*, p.7, noted that Powell 'secured a lease here in 1832, although two years later he had departed'.

16 David Freeman, *Tredegar House*, (Newport Borough Council), p.1.

17 Bedwellty parish tithe map and plans, 31 July 1839, identify mining at Gelligroes and the Bryn as does John Prujean's 1843 map, Ironworks and Collieries of Monmouthshire.

18 One list of collieries and levels in the Sirhowy Valley dated Bryn Colliery to circa 1820-1850 see Rayne Rosser, *Collieries of the Sirhowy Valley*. (Old Bakehouse, 1996), p.117.

19 G. W. J. Lovering, *op. cit.*, p.4.

20 R. H. Walters, *The Economic and Business History of the South Wales Steam Coal Industry, 1840-1914*, (PhD thesis, Oxford University, 1975), p.153.

21 The Chartist movement's quest was for annual parliaments, vote by ballot, universal suffrage, electoral districts with equal representation, abolition of property qualifications, and the payment of representatives.

22 Brian Ll. James, 'The Making of a Scholar Ironmaster: An Introduction to the Life of G. T. Clark', *G. T. Clark*. (University of Wales Press, 1998), p.1.

23 The Latin statement was *De molendino de Landivedon nichil quia combustum et destructum fuit in guerre. De firma mine carbonum ibidem nichil pro defectu operariorum causa guerra. Sum: vy s. viij d.* Charles Wilkins, *op. cit.*, p.13. The mention of war probably refers to a guerrilla war pursued by the Welsh against the Plantagenets.

24 Charles Wilkins, *op. cit.*, p.14.

25 OS Reference ST123959. At the lower, western end of a reclaimed field, the line of a possible tram-road to the Taff Valley can be imagined.

26 W. W. Price, *op. cit.*, p.10.

27 In general the ton used in this work is the imperial unit that equates to 2,240 lb. The Mines Regulations Act of 1872 required 'returns to be made' in Imperial tons. Before 1872 parish and colliery data generally referred to the long ton or collier's ton 'that varied from one iron works to the next'. In 1873, instituted 'to allow for breakages over and above Imperial measure' was a Welsh ton for steam coal collieries of 2,520 lbs. R. H. Walters, *op. cit.*, p.xv.

28 W. W. Price, *op. cit.*, p.35.

29 *The Gelligaer Story*, (Gelligaer Urban District Council, 1959), p.90.

30 *The Gelligaer Story*, *op. cit.*, p.89.

31 R. H. Walters, *op. cit.*, p.153.

32 The 1841 tithe map and apportionments for St. Woolos Parish, Newport, reveals that Thomas Powell owned farmland of around 103 acres in the vicinity of The Gaer.

33 W. W. Price, *op. cit.*, p.3.

34 W. W. Price, *op. cit.*, p.35.

35 W. W. Price, *op. cit.*, p.4.

36 R. H. Walters, *op. cit.*, p.22: except Upper Duffryn Colliery, *q.v. Cynon Coal, op. cit.*, below

37 W. W. Price, *op. cit.*, p.9.

38 OS Reference S0 025012.

39 OS Reference S0 031003.

40 OS Reference S0 041002.

41 Cynon Valley History Society, *Cynon Coal*. (Cynon Valley History Society, 2001), p.233. The colliery once stood at a site within Aberdare's County Park Centre. The colliery also appears to be known as Bwllfa No. 3. W. W. Price, *op. cit.*, p.9.

42 Cynon Valley History Society, *op. cit.*, p.233. John F. Mear, *The Story of Cwmdare*. (Further details unknown).

43 OS Reference S0 014014.

44 Cynon Valley History Society, *Cynon Coal, op. cit.*, p.202. As a Powell & Prothero venture it would have been arranged before April 1853 when Thomas Prothero died. Prothero, born October 1780, was buried at the parish church of St. Mary, Malpas. His home was at Malpas Court that overlooked the vale carrying the Monmouthshire & Brecon Canal.

45 W. W. Price, *op. cit.*, pp.6-7.

46 Edgar Jones, *A History of GKN, Volume 1: Innovation and Enterprise, 1759–1918*. (Macmillan, 1987), p.99.

47 Howard G. Meyrick, *Thomas Powell: Coal Owner, op cit.*, p.46.

48 T. Neville George, *British Regional Geology – South Wales*. (HMSO, 1970), p.8.

49 A. W. Woodland & W. B. Evans, *Geology of the South Wales Coalfield Part IV: The country around Pontypridd and Macsteg. Explanation of One-inch Geological Sheet 248.* (HMSO, 1964), xiv, p.91. In general, the mining engineers of the South Wales Coalfield used yards.

50 A. W. Woodland & W. B. Evans, *Geology of the South Wales Coalfield Part IV: The country around Pontypridd and Maesteg. Explanation of One-inch Geological Sheet 248, op. cit..*

51 Denis Griffiths, *Steam at Sea*. (Conway Maritime, 1997), p.10.

52 R. H. Walters, *op. cit.*, pp.54-5. John Nixon began his career as a mining engineer in the Durham Coalfield. He worked as an assistant to the Marquis of Bute's mineral agent before working for a period in French coal mining.

53 J. H. Morris and L. J. Williams, *The South Wales Coal Industry 1841-1875*. (University of Wales Press, 1958), pp.31-2.

54 Elizabeth Phillips, *op. cit.*, p.128-9

55 J. H. Morris and L. J. Williams, *op. cit.*, p.32.

56 Cynon Valley History Society, *Cynon Coal*. (Cynon Valley History Society, 2001), p.230.

57 Denis Griffiths, *op. cit.*, p.71.

58 J. H. Morris and L. J. Williams, *op. cit.*, p.29.

59 *Reports on the Coals suited for the Steam Navy*, (1847- 8), xxviii; 1849 (1086), xxxii; 1851 (1345), xxxiii. J. H. Morris and L. J. Williams, *op. cit.*, p.34-35.

60 J. H. Morris and L. J. Williams, *op. cit.*, p.35.

61 J. H. Morris and L. J. Williams, *op. cit.*, pp.36-7.

62 In 1869, the northern English coalowners persuaded the Admiralty to mix northern coal with Welsh coal and complete trials 'under terms of reference which largely prejudged in favour of mixed coals'. Senior naval officers were 'forceful' in favour of Welsh coal. Coal mixtures were adopted but restricted in use. H. Morris and L. J. Williams, *op. cit.*, pp.39-40.

63 This classification of coal, into such subdivisions, seemed to be accepted by the 1910s in the South Wales Coalfield. In general, the use of the term steam coal in this work is based upon this classification but it was 'out of necessity arbitrary'.

64 Email, Robert Protheroe Jones to Writer, 10 Apr 2007. Grunner's, published in the French governmental school of mines journal (*Annales des Mines*, series 3, Vol. 4, p.4, (1873), p. 182), and Regnault journal (*Annales des Mines*, series 3, Vol. 12, p.205.

65 In 1942, the South Wales Fuel Efficiency Committee coal used a classification that called coal under the Aberdare district, from south of Mountain Ash to the northern boundary of the South Wales Coalfield 'sub-bituminous' and categorised as two (Dry Steams) groups: A & B; see *South Wales Coalfield (Including Pembrokeshire) Regional Survey Report*, (HMSO, 194.6), pp.20-21 The volatile matter [that is the constituent that is easily evaporated, does not include the moisture in the coal, and is defined as the percentage loss in weight when coal is heated under carefully controlled conditions] was 9-12% and 12-14 % for Group A and Group B respectively. The respective ranges of volatile matter suggest that group A was previously known as 'dry steam coal', and group B 'smokeless steam coal'. The calorific value of a sub-bituminous coal ranged from 15,600 to 15,760 Btu/lb. However, since a coal's characteristics are site specific range values of properties serve only as a rough guide.

66 Cynon Valley History Society, *Cynon Coal*, op. cit., p.230.
67 Cynon Valley History Society, *Cynon Coal*, op. cit., *passim*.
68 Cynon Valley History Society, op. cit., p.241.
69 Cynon Valley History Society, op. cit., p.148.
70 *The Monmouthshire Merlin & South Wales Advertiser*, 21 May 1852, p.8.
71 Cynon Valley History Society, op. cit., p.148.
72 Howard G. Meyrick 'Thomas Powell: Coal Owner', p.49.
73 Cynon Valley History Society, op. cit., p.149.
74 *The Monmouthshire Merlin & South Wales Advertiser*, 28 May 1852, p.2.
75 *The Monmouthshire Merlin & South Wales Advertiser*, 21 May 1852, p.8.
76 *The Monmouthshire Merlin & South Wales Advertiser*, 21 May 1852, p.8.
77 *The Monmouthshire Merlin & South Wales Advertiser*, 28 May 1852, p.2.
78 *The Monmouthshire Merlin & South Wales Advertiser*, 21 May 1852, p.8.
79 *The Monmouthshire Merlin & South Wales Advertiser*, 28 May 1852, p.3.
80 Cynon Valley History Society, op. cit., p.149.
81 *The Monmouthshire Merlin & South Wales Advertiser*, 28 May 1852, p.3.
82 The pump acted to discharge air from the mine into the atmosphere. Prof. F. B. Hinsley, 'The Development of Coal Mine Ventilation in Great Britain up to the end of the Nineteenth Century', *Transactions, Newcomen Society*, Vol. 42 (1969-70), p.31.
83 Howard G. Meyrick 'Thomas Powell: Coal Owner', p.50. Howard G. Meyrick, 'The Powell's Works Pump', Gelligaer, *Gelligaer Historical Society*, Vol. 8, (1971), pp.32-34.
84 Prof. F. B. Hinsley, op. cit., p.30.
85 *The Monmouthshire Merlin & South Wales Advertiser*, 28 July 1852, p.5.
86 OS grid reference SO 136046.
87 J. C. Carr and W. Taplin, *History of the British Steel Industry*. (Basil Blackwell, 1962), p.7.
88 D. S. Barrie, *The Brecon & Merthyr Railway*. (Oakwood Press, 1957), p.111.
89 E. E. Edwards, *Echoes of Rhymney*. (The Starling Press, 1974). pp.44-5.
90 D. S. Jones, 'Hanes Rhymney a Pontlottyn', (Translation from Welsh by G. M. Harries), Gelligaer, *Gelligaer Historical Society*, Vol. 9 (1972), pp.19-20.

91 Dr Douglas Basset, Keeper, Department of Geology, National Museum of Wales, judged Emlyn Evans to be a 'father figure (a 'guru') among the many teachers of geography' during the 1960s and 1970s. The writer, as a school boy, was captivated by a talk given by David Emlyn Evans, Assistant Keeper, Department of Geology, National Museum of Wales.
92 D. Emlyn Evans, 'A Traverse Across the Eastern Part of the South Wales Coalfield via the Rhymney Valley' in *Geological Excursions in South Wales & The Forest of Dean*, ed. Douglas A. Bassett & Michael G. Bassett. (Geological Association of South Wales Group, 1971), pp.68-69.
93 OS Ref SO 1270 0482
94 D. S. Jones, 'Hanes Rhymney a Pontlottyn', op. cit., p.19.
95 E. E. Edwards, *Echoes of Rhymney*, (Starling Press, 1974), p.50.
96 G. M. Watkins, 'The Development of the Steam Winding Engine', *Transactions, Newcomen Society*, Vol. 50 (1979), p.11.
97 *Amgueddfa* – Bulletin of the National Museum of Wales, 'Preservation of Industrial Relics', Spring 1972, p.2.
98 *The Monmouthshire Merlin & South Wales Advertiser*, 28 April 1852, p.4.
99 Douglas A. Basset *et al.*, op. cit., p.150.
100 *The Western Mail*, 'Colliery Explosion at New Tredegar', 6 Dec. 1875, p.3, col.3.
101 *The Monmouthshire Merlin & South Wales Advertiser*, 10 Dec. 1875, p.3.
102 R. H. Walters, op. cit., p.153.
103 *The Monmouthshire Merlin & South Wales Advertiser*, 'Terrible Colliery Accident at New Tredegar', 10 Dec. 1875, p.3, col. 1.
104 *Western Mail*, op. cit., 21 Dec 1875, p.6, col.3.
105 Cynon Valley History Society, op. cit., p.226.
106 Howard G. Meyrick 'Thomas Powell: Coal Owner', p.51.
107 Howard G. Meyrick 'Thomas Powell: Coal Owner', p.51.
108 Cynon Valley History Society, op. cit., p.202.
109 Tony Fisher, *A Few Steps Away – Coal Mining in the Rhymney Valley: 1816-190*. (Rhymney Valley Urban District Council, 1991), p.7.
110 Hilda M. Evans, *New Tredegar in Focus*, (Starling Press, 1977), p.53.
111 *The Star of Gwent*, 'Death of Thos. Powell, Esq', 28 March 1863, p.5.
112 Howard G. Meyrick 'Thomas Powell: Coal Owner', p.44.
113 J. H. Morris and L. J. Williams, op. cit., pp.159-60.
114 W. W. Price, op. cit., pp.10-11.
115 Howard G. Meyrick 'Thomas Powell: Coal Owner', pp.50-51.
116 Howard G. Meyrick 'Thomas Powell: Coal Owner', p.44.
117 See for example G. Meyrick, 'Thomas Powell: Coal Owner', passim, and Powell's plundering of 'Place Bedwellty' coal in the 1830s, see Letters, Frederick Justice to Sir Charles Morgan, 25 July 1840, Tredegar Papers, Part 3 of Schedule, No. 57/139, National Library of Wales, and 'The dispute between Sir Charles Morgan, Bart., and Thomas Powell', date and publisher of paper unknown.
118 See Cynon Valley History Society, op. cit., p.267.
119 W. W. Price, op. cit., p.10.
120 W. W. Price, op. cit., p.8.
121 Howard G. Meyrick 'Thomas Powell: Coal Owner', p.46.
122 Charles Wilkins, op. cit., p.91.
123 *The Star of Gwent*, 'Death of Thos. Powell, Esq', 28 March 1863, p.5.

Chapter 2
FOUNDER'S INTERESTS

George Elliot, the son of a coal miner, was born on the 18th March, 1815, at Gateshead-on-Tyne in County Durham. His childhood was spent five miles south of Gateshead, at Chandler's Row, Shiney Row, which was located west of the village of Penshaw (spelt as 'Painsher' during his youth). He began work at nine years of age at a coal pit known as Whitfield Colliery, which lay near to Penshaw.[1]

Robert Patterson, a 'brakesman' at the Whitfield Pit, Elliot recalled, had lowered him as a boy down Whitfield's shaft. This *'was in 1825 or 1826, and the boys then … worked fourteen hours a day down the pit'.* The effect: *'for many years he never saw the light of the sun from Sunday until the Saturday, and in the winter months they never saw the light of the sun on a week day'.* However, due to the *'great strike* [of 1831 and 1832] *– which was perhaps, the greatest strike ever known in the North of England',* his day's shift underground was reduced from fourteen hours a day to twelve.

The period associated with George Elliot's early years of work saw change at the Londonderry family owned Penshaw colliery. 'During the first half of the nineteenth century, central Durham provided some of the best available household quality, or "Wallsend", coal from the Hutton seam, which attained high prices on the London market'.[2] In August 1822, Charles Stewart (1778–1854), as the 3rd Marquess of Londonderry, took on the task of managing his inherited coal mining interests, and found that 'the collieries at Rainton and Penshaw comprising seven pits and providing all the family's coal sales in 1819 were rather run down'. So, he appointed John Buddle (1778-1843) as his agent and colliery manager with the task of improving the mining assets.

According to an obituary, George Elliot progressed from being a miner due to his own efforts and through taking fullest advantage of career opportunities:

'Until about twenty years old he worked underground as a collier. During his youth, however, he applied his leisure to the study of mathematics and so successful was his self-tuition that he left the pit to be received into a surveyor's office in Newcastle-on-Tyne. This engagement proved the first step to fortune. Close application to business as a draughtsman enabled him in six months to return to the colliery as overseer. He passed successively through all the stages of mining employment until he became head viewer at Monkwearmouth and when only twenty-four years of age was placed in charge of the largest and deepest pits in England.

George Elliot's position now brought him into contact with capitalists and engineers. In 1840 he advised the purchase of

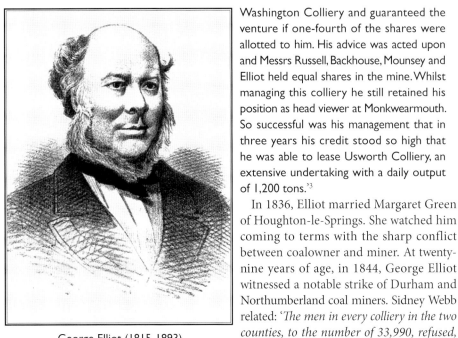

George Elliot (1815-1893)
The founder of the Powell Duffryn Steam Coal Company. He rose from a Durham Coalfield pit boy to become a coal owner and industrialist. He also served as a Member of Parliament, and became a baronet.

Washington Colliery and guaranteed the venture if one-fourth of the shares were allotted to him. His advice was acted upon and Messrs Russell, Backhouse, Mounsey and Elliot held equal shares in the mine. Whilst managing this colliery he still retained his position as head viewer at Monkwearmouth. So successful was his management that in three years his credit stood so high that he was able to lease Usworth Colliery, an extensive undertaking with a daily output of 1,200 tons.'[3]

In 1836, Elliot married Margaret Green of Houghton-le-Springs. She watched him coming to terms with the sharp conflict between coalowner and miner. At twenty-nine years of age, in 1844, George Elliot witnessed a notable strike of Durham and Northumberland coal miners. Sidney Webb related: *'The men in every colliery in the two counties, to the number of 33,990, refused, on 5th April 1844, to renew the* [Yearly] *Bond, unless the harsh penal conditions were relaxed, and an advance of wages was conceded'.*[4] In August 1844, the men returned to work 'completely beaten by long-continued privation'. The Yearly Bond was eventually superseded by an arrangement for a shorter period of service in a colliery. Elliot, though, in addition to managing the consequences of the effects of this strike upon Durham miners, took on a new kind of business challenge in London.

In 1849, Lawson noted: 'The business of Messrs Kuper & Co., wire-rope manufacturers, was in a process of liquidation, and Mr Elliot was appointed to act in the capacity of agent. In the course of two years he succeeded in reducing the debts considerably, and resolved on purchasing the business in its entirety'.[5] However, in 1851, George Elliot resigned his post at Monkwearmouth and took the position of Londonderry Company's manager of collieries, or as its 'Viewer'.[6]

The Londonderry's Collieries Viewer

As the Londonderry Viewer, Elliot held a post that ranked him among the leading managers of collieries in the Durham Coalfield. On the 9th June, 1852, he participated in an inquest into a disaster at Setton Colliery.[7] An explosion at the colliery killed six men and a boy. The inquest led to a meeting of mining experts at the Mill Inn, Seaham, on the 23rd June, to discuss how pit explosions could be prevented.[8] Present among others with Elliot was Thomas Emerson Forster, who over a decade later joined Elliot to assess the coal interests of the sons of Thomas Powell. At the Seaham meeting, Forster proposed, seconded by Elliot, the formation of a society, 'The North of England Society for the Prevention of Accidents'.[9] There was an immediate sequel: on the 3rd July, 1852,

Elliot joined ten men at a meeting and it agreed to found the North of England Institute of Mining Engineers, which later became the North England Institute of Mining and Mechanical Engineers.

A remit of the Londonderry position included responsibilities for civil engineering projects. On the 8th February, 1853, George Elliot presented a silver spade to Marquess Londonderry to begin the ceremony of 'cutting the turf' for the new Seaham and Sunderland railway.[10] A commissioned painting of the occasion captures Londonderry, with the spade in his right hand, and making a gesture with his other hand, delivering a speech that was possibly his final public address.

On the 17th January, 1854, George Elliot reported to the family that the railway was opened for coals, merchandize and passengers as far as Ryhope. *'The locomotive had gone three trips to and fro over the entire length with coals and passengers'*, and that *'the viaducts and formations have all proved substantial, without a shake'*.[11] His report was a prelude to a sad one: the Marquess of Londonderry died on the 6th March, 1854.

Frances Anne became sole executrix of the Lord Londonderry's will. She was 'left complete control of the collieries, which again became her own property, and of the Garron Tower which she had built on her Antrim estate'.[12] Lord Londonderry had purchased the Seaham pits, which in addition to those she had inherited from her father, made her the owner of 'the largest colliery property in England in the hands of a single individual, covering an area of 12,000 acres between Sunderland and Seaham on the coast extending as far inland as the city of Durham; at this date [1856] the production of the collieries amounted to not less than one million tons annually'.[13]

During the 1850s, George Elliot continued to manage Kuper & Company, at Camberwell, London. Around 1852, Elliot invited (later Sir) N. A. Glass to become a partner in the wire rope company. Glass had developed a wire covering method useful for laying telegraphy cables on the ocean's floor.

According to Edith, Marchioness of Londonderry, writing a century later, George Elliot's stewardship of the Londonderry collieries, during the 1850s, coincided with a period when 'so far as can be ascertained there were no fatal accidents'. She conceded: 'No doubt to some extent that this was due to chance as well as good management on the part of Mr Elliot and his assistants'. She also appraised that 'Mr Elliot, the colliery manager, who seems to have been a fairly long-suffering individual, was frequently sent for [by Frances Anne], especially when things went wrong'.[14] Despite dealing with a tyrant in someways, George Elliot's career flourished under the 'Industrial Queen', McCutcheon's term for Lady Londonderry. The Londonderry family had earlier authorised the construction of Carnlough Harbour to improve access to their Irish retreat, Garron Tower. Frances Anne Vane's first landing on its quayside took place on the 20th August, 1855.[15] Elliot, as the family's 'Sole Engineer' for the construction of the harbour, was enabled to further expand his engineering and business knowledge.

In 1856, when George Elliot was forty-one years of age, the Marchioness of Londonderry was the host for a great dinner at Chilton Moor, County Durham. Her guests numbered between three and four thousand made up of people employed in a range of Londonderry businesses. At a point in her speech, she addressed principally the 'pitmen' and stated *'without, vanity or presumption that no collieries are more carefully looked after'*. Adding: *'We need not travel beyond the precincts of this building for instances of persons*

who have been the architects of their own fortune. It is the pride and boast of your head viewer [Elliot] *that he was reared and nursed a boy in these pits and it must be encouraging to look around this great mining county and see many instances of men who won their way to wealth and fame by labour and perseverance.'*[16] However, George Elliot's service to the Londonderry family had entered its closing phase, but when his service ended has not been identified.

In 1858, Kuper & Company was party to an attempt to lay the first telegraphic connection between Great Britain and the United States of America.[17] However, the cable failed in service. Undaunted, Elliot and Glass searched for more capital finance so he became a face among the Capital City's business community. By 1863 George Elliot's business ambitions included coal mining in South Wales.

Powell Duffryn Steam Coal Company's Logo in 1914.

Powell Duffryn Steam Coal Company Limited

According to Powell Duffryn's fifty year history of the company: *'In 1863 Thomas Powell junior instructed Thomas Emerson Forster, William Armstrong, and George Elliot to value his steam coal collieries'* as a step before offering them for sale.[18] Their findings encouraged Elliot to lead a group of investors to purchase a part of Powell's collieries and to form, in 1864, the Powell Duffryn Steam Coal Company Limited, under the 1862 Companies Act.[19] Coining the name of the company fell to someone. The name chosen could have been due to uniting the perceived origin, represented by 'Powell', and its noted product, 'Steam Coal'. The introduction of 'Duffryn' may have been a benign acknowledgement of the value, in the acquisition, of the Lower Duffryn and Middle Duffryn collieries.[20] However, it seems that during the 1840s, as noted earlier, the term Powell's Duffryn had been adopted within at least Admiralty circles to speak about a preferred coal for marine steam power. So, it was possible that someone saw the possibility that by merely erasing the apostrophe 's' the company's title served also as a marketing brand.

The Powell Duffryn Steam Coal Company took ownership of the following collieries: Cwmdare, Abernant-y-Groes, Abergwawr, Tir-Ffounder, Middle Duffryn, and Cwm Pennar in the Aberdare Valley and New Tredegar in the Rhymney Valley, and also the House Coal Level called 'White Rose' at New Tredegar.[21] The collieries total output at the time was about 400,000 tons of coal per annum, which represented nearly a 4% share of the total output of the South Wales Coalfield.

The company was founded with a nominal Capital of £500,000. The company's first shareholders became its directors who, in addition to Elliot were: Thomas Brassey, Alexander Ogilvie, J. Swift, W. Wagstaff, J. R. McClean, S. E. Bolden (Chairman),

R. Potter and P. G. Heyworth.[22] The nominal capital was divided into £5,000 shares, which the shareholders were allotted.[23] R. H. Walters later revealed that to meet the cost of the purchase price of £365,000, £100,000 was paid in cash by the shareholders, led by George Elliot, drawn from the London railway and engineering contracting fraternity. 'The initial cost was met by a call in 1865 and the remainder by a succession of calls instalments to 1871'.[24]

Brassey, McLean, and Ogilvie

Elliot's quest to find investors, to back his prospective South Wales coal venture, could have begun with Brassey. Thomas Brassey (1805-1870) had strong ties with railway construction engineers. Foremost among them was Alexander Ogilvie (1812-1886), born at Clocksbrigg, Forfar, Scotland, and a graduate of Edinburgh University. Ogilvie learnt his practical engineering in Cheshire where Brassey was born, and where the two first met. Brassey tended to take the initiative in the pursuit of business. Before 1844, they were independent bidders for a contract to build the Colchester & Ipswich Railway but an initiative of Brassey's saw them progress the contract as partners.[25] And so 'during the life of Mr Brassey, Mr Ogilvie had him as partner in all the works engaged in'.[26]

Thomas Brassey also knew John Robinson McClean MP, FRS (1813-73). The Belfast born civil engineer was employed first by Brassey as Engineer for the construction of the South Staffordshire Railway, in 1861.[27] During his distinguished career as a civil engineer, McClean took a leading part in many major civil engineering projects including, in South Wales, some Cardiff dock developments.[28] He was elected president of the Institution of Civil Engineers for the years 1864 and 1865.

In the case of Richard Potter, he had a reason to be grateful to Brassey for his advice about doing business in France. According to his daughter, Beatrice Webb (née Potter), her father 'developed a taste for adventurous enterprise and a talent for industrial diplomacy'. She noted that her father had 'graduated in the New London University .... He was called to the Bar, without intending to practice', and was prompted, due to the financial crisis of 1847-8, to take up an offer of 'partnership in an old-established timber merchant's business in Gloucester. From this position of vantage my father became a capitalist at large'.[29] She judged that her father was 'a honourable and loyal colleague; he retained throughout his life the close friendship of his partners; his co-operation was always being sought for by capitalists; he never left a colleague in a tight place; he was generous in giving credit to subordinates; he was forgiving to an old enemy who had fallen on evil times. But he thought, and acted in terms of personal relationship; he had no clear vision of the public good'. Beatrice Webb also highlighted a contrast between her father's 'rooted distaste for the work of inspection and control [of business]', and thought his success 'as a money-maker arose from his talent for negotiating new agreements; his genius was, in fact for planning, and not executing'.

Nevertheless, a web of contacts, spun for the sake of transacting business, made 'gentlemanly capitalism' of Victorian times possible. Over a period of time, men who pursued business together acquired trust in one another. An individual's integrity was exposed during the trials of enterprise. Brassey was 'straightforward, prompt, and honourable'.[30] Ogilvie was 'a man of cautious temperament, with excellent judgment', and 'was trusted with the management of the largest and most intricate works, and very rarely, if ever, was he known to fail'.[31] McClean displayed 'uniformly, upright,

conscientious conduct'.[32] Sharing the business risk within such a group of shareholders had merit.

Of course the risk taken by Powell Duffryn's shareholders was predicated upon hope of gaining financial returns from the company's future profits. Earning such returns had the potential to create at least envy. As Sir Arthur Helps wrote regarding Thomas Brassey: 'The acquisition of a great fortune by any man is not a thing which is intrinsically pleasing to the rest of mankind'.[33] Nonetheless, the assembled shareholders gambled in part upon the uncertainties of the market for coal, and the skill and judgment of a mining engineer. George Elliot predicted that Powell's steam coal collieries 'would be a paying proposition'. And so an Article of Agreement was signed with the Powells on the 18th July, 1864.[34] The Powell Duffryn Steam Coal Company was registered on the the 28th July, 1864.[35]

Under another agreement Elliot took charge of the 'general supervision of the company's business as long as he held shares of value more than £50,000. In addition to a salary of £1,000 per annum he was to receive 15% of the net profit, though this might cease altogether if the company made less than £50,000 profit for two consecutive years. If the enterprise was sold for more than cost price he was to receive 10% of the excess'.[36] His skill and experience in business was subsequently tested. Perhaps intentionally, Thomas Powell's sons had underestimated the cost of working the steam coal pits.

The Powells' cost of working the steam coal pits was disputed by George Elliot. He identified the issue after the Article of Agreement was signed. He placed the matter in the hands of lawyers, and a tussle began in Chancery between the company and the Powell brothers. Nevertheless, one thing did not alter: Thomas Powell of The Gaer's former coal mining business was divided into two parts. The Powell brothers retained an interest in collieries at Llanwit Fadre and the eastern part of the South Wales Coalfield. Powell Duffryn took control of the other part, the steam coal collieries, and White Rose Level.

The successful career that George Elliot had enjoyed up until the founding of Powell Duffryn, suggested that he was capable of performing the company role he had entered into an agreement to deliver. Of course, time would tell if George Elliot could manage his portfolio of business interests, and satisfy, in particular, Powell Duffryn's shareholders hopes for financial returns for their investment. In the year that Powell Duffryn was founded, he extended his interests in the Durham Coalfield. 'One of the proudest moments of his life, however, may be said to have been that when in 1864 he was able to purchase the Whitfield Colliery in the county of Durham, where years before he had worked as a doorboy'.[37]

Maybe it was for leisure that George Elliot took an interest in Whitby, an ancient seaside town of the North Riding of Yorkshire. He took a house there in the 1860s, and it was said to have been the 'last' house on the 'Crescent'. Nikolaus Pevsner described the house as 'curious at least, Baroque affair with bay and pediments and out of the way decoration'.[38] The design of this house suggests that its first owner was a person with an urge to be noticed.

However, the year after Powell Duffryn was founded an Atlantic Ocean project gripped Elliot's attention.[39] Glass and Elliot succeeded in raising capital to further their business in submarine cables that was later 'converted' into the Telegraph Construction & Maintenance Company.[40] Fortunately, for Glass and Elliot, in 1866, after a number of setbacks they achieved telegraph communication between Europe to America.[41]

More Aberdare Valley Collieries

In addition to the submarine cable-laying project, in 1866, George Elliot prepared Powell Duffryn ready to acquire collieries in the Aberdare Valley. He directed the company to increase its capital through an issue of preference shares in that year, and so raised its total to £600,000.[42] The issue would be cancelled decades later, in 1898.

Elliot, undaunted by any doubts concerning Powell Duffryn's ongoing legal issue with the Powells, also made a notable acquisition in the Aberdare Valley. On the 2nd February, 1867, the Aberaman Estate was purchased for the company from Crawshay Bailey. W. W. Price found that: '*The total price was £123,500 of which £95,950 was for the freehold estate, messuages, cottages ground-*

rents, ironworks, collieries [which included Aberaman Colliery], *brickworks, and a two-third share of the underlying mineral estate which Crawshay Bailey had been able to purchase from the descendants of Hugh Lord and William Curre*'.[43]

The North East of England man's local kudos was most certainly enhanced when it became known that the surveyors for Powell Duffryn enabled Elliot to contest Crawshay Bailey's measurement of the estate's area. Price noted that '*the estate was found to be 1,075 acres of statute measure – which meant that Crawshay Bailey, the hard-headed Yorkshire man, had apparently been deprived of 453 acres. It arose so we are told, because of a local customary measure according to which one acre of such measure is equal to about two-thirds of an acre of statute*

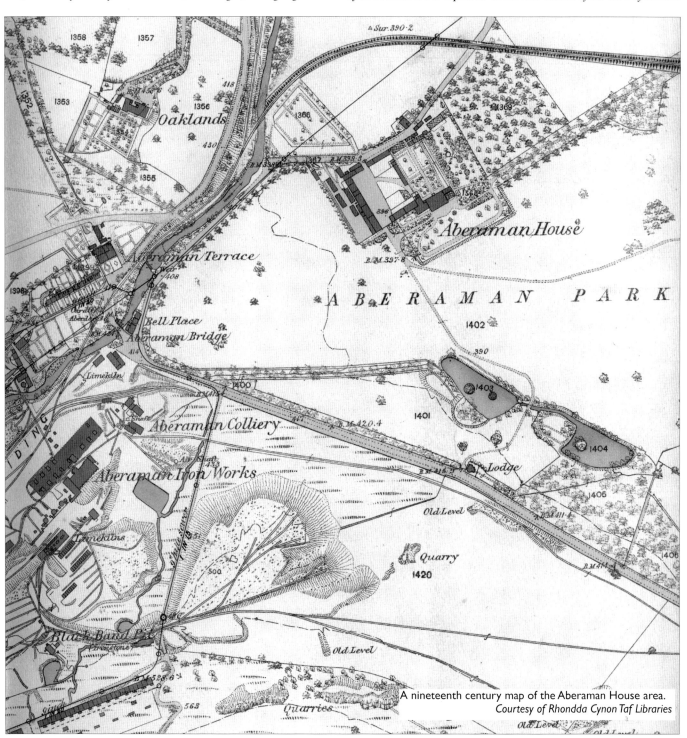

A nineteenth century map of the Aberaman House area.
Courtesy of Rhondda Cynon Taf Libraries

Powell Duffryn took ownership of Aberaman Colliery in 1867 as a result of purchasing the Aberaman Estate from Crawshay Bailey. Aberaman became the company's headquarters for the management of the collieries. *Pope/Parkhouse Archive*
Inset : Miner's Lamp Check. A miner's lamp check was exchanged for a miner's lamp for going underground, and, in the event of a disaster made a count of missing people possible. *Courtesy of Lyndon Rees*

measure.[44] If Crawshay Bailey felt chagrin, Powell Duffryn enjoyed the consequences. In 1909, Edmund Mills Hann reflected: '*This was undoubtedly a good purchase, and must have been of material assistance to the concern, ...; in most recent times nothing has contributed more to the success than the working of the lower seams in the Aberaman property*'. Hann later noted: '*Following on from this* [the acquisition of the Aberaman Estate], *Aberaman was made the headquarters of the Company, so far as its practical operations and working staff were concerned*'.

The company's ownership of the Aberaman Estate included Aberaman House. Wilkins likened it to a Welsh homestead, which was a modest description for a mansion. The County Durham man and his family, with a household of servants, used Aberaman House for sojourns. The nearby railway also enabled him, his family and household, to move at short notice to other destinations, whether they be in the North of England, or London, or abroad. Charles Wilkins's observation that Elliot was a 'far-travelled man' had validity.

Aberaman House. Purchased by Powell Duffryn as part of the Aberaman Estate and adopted by Sir George Elliot as his South Wales home for the practical direction of the company.
Courtesy of Rhondda Cynon Taf Libraries

Further Aberdare Valley colliery purchases took place in 1867. These collieries were Treaman and Ynyscynon for £8,750, a 'small' price'. Ynyscynon was also known as, or gained the name High Duffryn, and was situated near the town of Aberdare.[45] The colliery's sale to Powell Duffryn was due to the death in 1863 of its founder, David Williams, who was 'known throughout Wales as Alaw Goch the Bard, and as a promoter of the National Eisteddfod of Wales'.[46] According to Hann, Treaman and Ynyscynon were 'a wise' buy since they proved 'advantageous' to the company.[47]

Treaman Colliery stood nearly midway between Aberaman Colliery, and Powell's Abergwawr Colliery [Plough Pit]. The three collieries as a set created contiguous underground property. Treaman Colliery was called the 'Nici-Naci' Pit, but was also known either as Williams' Pit, or Pwll Bara Menyn. It appears that it was not unusual in the Aberdare Valley for a colliery to have been known by a number of names, some with variations in their spellings. This no doubt caused bewilderment for at least strangers visiting the area, but they would have been able to find their way to Treaman Colliery. It acquired its nickname, Nici-Naci, due to the noise that emanated from the rattle of the pit's rope, more than likely an iron chain, running over the headgear's sheave.[48]

Also in 1867, George Elliot accompanied Thomas Brassey on a business trip to Europe. Brassey was worldwide traveller due to railway construction. In October, Brassey's trip took in France and Italy, and Elliot met him in Turin. However Brassey fell ill, and Elliot telegraphed his family about his condition. Elliot's telegram was an early warning of the decline in health of this eminent railway constructor. Brassey died at Hastings in 1870, and so his son, Thomas Brassey Jnr, replaced him on the board of Powell Duffryn.

Elliot began 1868 by buying for Powell Duffryn, on the 6th February, Cwmneol and Fforchaman collieries from United Merthyr Collieries Co. Ltd for £80,000.[49] Both these collieries stood in a small cwm, or cirque, west of Aberaman. According to W. W. Price 'Cwm-neol' meant 'the valley of the brook called Neol', and 'Fforch-aman' the 'fork by of the River Aman'. Aman, according to D. L. Davies, was derived from the archaic noun 'banw', meaning young pig.[50]

Cwmneol Colliery was sunk in the 1850s by Messrs John Carr of Roseworth, near Newcastle upon Tyne, Charles Carr of Seghill House in the county of Northumberland, and Martin Morrison of Newport, Monmouthshire.[51] Cwmneol was also known as Morris's Pit. In 1859, Crawshay Bailey became party to a lease involving these three men in order that another shaft could be sunk there so as to work: the 'Two Foot Nine inches' seam; the Upper Four Feet; the 'Fros-y-Fran' or Lower Four Feet; and the 'Ras Las' or Nine Feet vein. The colliery experienced numerous difficulties, and was assigned to the Aman (Aberdare) Colliery Co. Ltd. Again, things did not proceed easily, and on the 20th May, 1864, Aman (Aberdare) Colliery Co. assigned the colliery to the United Merthyr Collieries Co. Ltd. After Powell Duffryn purchased the colliery it was 'discovered that the workings of Cwmneol had made a trespass into the Abergwawr property, and a sum, apparently by consent, [was] deducted from the purchase price' offered to United Merthyr Collieries Co. Ltd.[52]

Cwmneol Colliery. Bought by Powell Duffryn in 1868 from United Merthyr Collieries. Sunk in the 1850s, and was also known as Morris's Pit. The colliery's workforce was 400 in 1870.
Courtesy of Rhondda Cynon Taf Libraries
Inset : A Cwmneol Colliery lamp check.
Courtesy of Mark Smith

A group of Cwmneol Colliery miners in 1905.
Courtesy of Rhondda Cynon Taf Libraries

Fforchaman Colliery was also known as 'Brown's Pit'. James Brown, of Bryn Glas in the County of Monmouth, was one of seven partners that invested in its sinking which took place on the Fforchaman farm. Four of the partners were relations of Thomas Prothero, senior. The same people who had leased mineral property for Cwmneol Colliery owned the coal under the farm. The owner of Fforchaman farm, Mrs Mary Kingsbury, judged that she was entitled to royalties and wayleaves from the mining venture.[53] She fought an expensive lawsuit about the matter, and lost. On the 23rd May, 1856, the owners of the Upper Four seam; the Lower Four Foot seam; and the Nine Feet seam granted a mining lease to the Fforchaman partners. The land lease agreement, essential for the erection of surface colliery buildings, was signed by Mrs Kingsbury on the 26th March, 1858, which suggests that the colliery was sunk after this date. On the 16th June, 1864, this Colliery also was assigned to the United Merthyr Collieries Ltd, who finally sold Cwmneol and Fforchaman to Powell Duffryn.

In 1868, George Elliot was present in Newport when Lady Tredegar cut the first sod in a ceremony that marked the start to constructing Alexandra Docks.[54] John Robinson McClean, a Powell Duffryn director, might have introduced him to the Tredegar family. If Powell Duffryn affairs took more of his time during the 1860s, then absence in London and South Wales did not erode his reputation in the north-east of England.

President and Member of Parliament

On the 7th November, 1868, George Elliot delivered, as a duty of being the President of the North of England Institute of Mining Engineers, an address in Newcastle upon Tyne. His address revealed both his liking for innovation in colliery engineering, and his gift of foresight. He thought that scarcely one per cent of coal had been removed from South Wales. He called for improvement in the ventilation of mines. He chided his colleagues in the Northern English Coalfield for running 'in the old groove' regarding mining systems.[55]

Fforchaman Colliery. The colliery was sunk in circa 1858, and was also known as Brown's Pit. The company purchased the colliery in 1868 from United Merthyr Collieries. In 1870, a workforce of 410 won coal at the colliery. The colliery's coal output, with that of Aberaman Colliery's, would decades later help secure a future for Powell Duffryn.
Inset : A Fforchaman lamp check.
Courtesy of Rhondda Cynon Taf Libraries
Courtesy of Lyndon Rees

Sir George Elliot stands in the doorway of Aberaman House surrounded by members of his family. The photograph was saved from destruction by the Cynon Valley History Society and placed in the keeping of Rhondda Cynon Taf Libraries and is used with courtesy of both bodies.

The mining changes he recommended included 'long wall' (that involved removing coal along a continuous face, or 'wall', that afterwards saw the overlying strata settling into the vacuity: known as a 'goaf' or 'gob'), since elsewhere the method was proving to be less wasteful at coal recovery. He questioned the integrity of safety lamps. He appealed for the use of gunpowder in mines to be abolished, and revealed that he had seen a possible way that this could be achieved, namely the introduction of mechanical machines (hydraulic wedging machines), as had been done in 'my collieries in South Wales'.

His address featured a campaign of his: to elevate the status of mining engineer to one recognised as a profession. He had been 'in communication with the Senate of Durham [University]' with the aim of bringing both university and professional honours closer to the mining engineer. He further issued another challenge: that the North of England Institute of Mining Engineers should co-operate more with the Institution of Civil Engineers so as to gain professional recognition. He proposed that the Institute should take a national not provincial form, and no doubt amazed some of its members when he suggested that the Institute substitute 'Great Britain and Northern Ireland' for 'North of England'.

Advocating harmless recreation for the working miner, such as cricket, was a further aspect of his address. Some of his audience no doubt felt that he had bowled them too many googlies. Maybe those troubled by what he had said in his address were glad that he did not hold office for long. Elliot's stay as the Institute's president lasted just nine months.[56]

Business in Egypt had become an additional interest of George Elliot's and may have been part of the reason that caused him to resign from the presidency of the Institute. In August 1869, the year the Suez Canal was officially opened, he met in Paris Nuba Pasha who was involved with the affairs of the Suez Canal Company.[57] The Paris meeting might have been arranged due to him having made contact with Ismail Pasha, the Khedive, or viceroy of Egypt under Turkish rule, during, or earlier than 1867.[58]

Another factor that may have had a bearing upon George Elliot's decision to resign from the presidency of the North of England Institute of Mining Engineers was his entry into national politics. On the 23rd November, 1868, he was adopted as a Conservative Party candidate for the parliamentary constituency of North Durham.[59] It was not a good year to stand as a Conservative candidate at the General Election of November 1868 since the party lost to the Liberals. However, Elliot was elected as a Member of Parliament.

Houghton Hall, Houghton-le-Springs, was then, and would remain, his County Durham address. This large house stands at a junction between the town's Church Street and Hall Lane, with St Michael's Church nearby. The 'hospitality' of Houghton Hall was noted as 'very kind'. He dispensed 'generous charity' to 'the many needy' of the locality.[60]

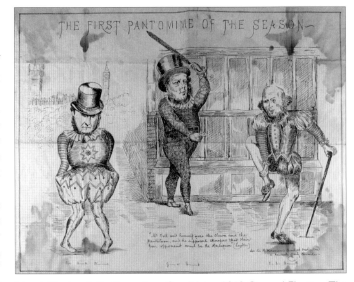

North Durham's Parliamentary Candidates 1868 General Election. The candidates (L to R) were Sir Hugh Williamson, George Elliot, and Isaac Lothian Bell. *Baker Baker Prints courtesy of Durham University Library*

A Hectic Life

George Elliot's start as a parliamentarian coincided with the effect of constitutional change, and also a period 'very fertile in industrial and social legislation'.[61] Due, maybe, to enlightened self-interest, he became a member of Royal Commissions about Coal Supply, and on Accidents in Coal Mines. George Elliot met men in the House of Commons having strong associations with the South Wales Coalfield. Walter Powell, son of Thomas Powell, had been elected as a Conservative MP, for Malmesbury.

However, one of the most notable contacts he made was Henry Austin Bruce (1815-95), who was destined to become the 1st Lord Aberdare. Bruce had chaired a meeting at Aberdare, in 1852, that led to a fund being set up to give aid to the widows and orphans of the Middle Duffryn Colliery disaster. A barrister, he was a month younger than Elliot, but had already acquired nearly two decades of parliamentary experience. He first entered the House of Commons in 1852 as MP for Merthyr. In 1863, he was made Home Secretary in a Gladstone Liberal government, and later became the Lord President of the Council, in 1873, the year that saw him made a baron. Historian Gwyn A. Williams described him as '*a man of political presence, member of a legal dynasty, enmeshed with the works masters who had towered politically for sixteen years over the valleys as any landlord in the west, but who had to walk a sight more carefully, indeed often he had to tread as delicately as Agag*'.[62]

Yet, Elliot knew that Bruce had suffered a political setback. Bruce lost his Merthyr Tydfil seat at the 1868 election due to his unpopularity among at least the constituency's miners. A long bitter strike of 1857 was a factor. The miners thought that Bruce had not fairly put the colliers case during [earlier] debates on the Mine Inspection Act, but had rather supported the objections of the masters to the colliers' demands, and, in addition they 'had evidence – or believed they had evidence, that Bruce supported the coalowners in their attempt to impose a Double Shift system in their collieries'.[63] Although rejected by the voters of Merthyr Tydfil, he was returned as the Member of Parliament for Renfrewshire, serving from 1869 to 1873.

Upon his return to the House of Commons, in 1869, Henry Austin Bruce took a prominent role in the development of the Mines Regulation Act. It would seem that George Elliot's apparent paternalistic, or pragmatic, attitude helped shape the Act: 'For years [Elliot] used his utmost endeavours to ameliorate the conditions of the miner, and it was his boast that he had preserved a table on which Lord Aberdare and he had drawn up an agreement that led to the introduction of the Mines Regulation Act [1872], by which the hours of labour were reduced from fourteen to nine.'[64]

Charles Wilkins gained access to both men and recorded Lord Aberdare's comments about his relationship with Elliot.[65] Lord Aberdare said, '*Not only did I receive from Sir George invaluable advice, with reference to the more technical parts of the Bill, but that he also displayed the warmest sympathy with the interests of the mining population.*' Aberdare elaborated that Elliot was '*full of humane consideration*' for the welfare of the miners. He also gave a hint that suggested that there were moments of tension between them, '*I can remember,*' announced Lord Aberdare, '*that on more than one occasion I felt it my duty to resist the insertion of provisions devised by Sir George in the interest of the workmen, but which appeared to me to be beyond the due province of the Legislature.*'

By the end of the 1860s, shareholders of Powell Duffryn could look forward to reaping benefits from Elliot's work on their account. In the Aberdare Valley, the company operated ten collieries compared with Thomas Powell's six collieries. This augured well for future business rewards for the company. However, Powell Duffryn's earnings were hit by the South Wales Colliers' strike of 1871.

The Member of Parliament for North Durham emerged as a conciliator during the strike. In March 1871, the ironmasters of the colliery proprietors of Monmouth and Glamorgan gave notice to 'colliers, workmen, and others', of a reduction in wages.[66] Coal and iron markets had slumped and were depressed. On the 31st May, 14,698 men and boys, employed in the coalowners' pits, went on strike having essentially rejected the notice. Powell Duffryn's employees formed the largest share of this total of men and boys on strike. The Amalgamated Association of Miners, which was then seen as being 'new in South Wales' led the strike. There was strike breaking, and shilly-shallying by both sides as the dispute's duration dragged out.

At Westminster, early in August 1871, 'Lord Elcho and G. Elliot, MP, had several discussions as to the best mode of terminating this serious conflict, and agreed to consult Messrs Macdonald and Halliday (the representatives of the workmen), who were in London watching the progress of the Mines Regulation Bill'.[67] This led to a Bristol meeting between both sides of the dispute. However, 'misapprehension on the part of the coalowners', led to Elliot being the only 'master' present. Dalziel wrote afterwards that 'the slight difference of opinion between Mr Elliot and the other coalowners as to this meeting was easily explained and adjusted. The men were much pleased with Mr Elliot for meeting them, and they were just as much displeased with the other masters for not doing so'. The absent coalowners later claimed they knew nothing about the Bristol meeting.

At the Royal Hotel, Cardiff, on the 15th August George Elliot chaired a meeting that involved miners from sixteen collieries, and 'masters'.[68] The miners' delegates spoke first at the meeting. Then, he put the masters' point of view. The meeting ended with both sides agreeing to arbitration, although its first sitting did not occur until months later, on the 29th January, 1872. Agreement was signed on the 13th February, 1872, and saw the granting of small concessions to the miners. The agreed wage principle was that miners' wages would rise and fall 'guided by the general rise and fall of wages at the ironmasters' pits in Monmouthshire and South Wales'.[69]

In April 1872, the price of coal increased. The miners called for an advance in wages.[70] So a meeting was held, 25th April, 1872, between both parties to the agreement.[71] During the meeting its chairman, the coalowner John Nixon – in the early 1840s Thomas Powell's French agent – read out a letter from Elliot that challenged the delegates to remain bound to the arrangements of the agreement. John Nixon appealed to the delegates to listen to 'Mr Elliot ... one of the greatest employers of labour in this district', who he further claimed, generally held the views of 'the colliery proprietors'. On the 9th May, 1872, the South Wales Steam Coal Collieries' Association conceded an advance of wages.

According to Alexander Dalziel, a '*pleasing feature of the arbitration*', was the establishment of an insurance fund for '*the relief and support of those who might be left hapless and penniless by fatal accidents to the workmen*'. The proposed fund was to be based upon subscriptions from both the employees and employers. Powell Duffryn subscribed a thirty-five per cent share of the total amount pooled by the 'masters'. The rival company Nixon, Taylor, and Cory, gave roughly a quarter of the amount.[72] Nevertheless, the insurance fund failed. Dalziel reflected: '*The masters offered to give from their abundance, the men by reason of their poverty refused to give anything. In justice it must be said that the positions were not parallel*'.[73] The colliers, and other workmen, were deeply in debt due to the strike.

The 1871 strike provided a test for Elliot as a negotiator. Maybe his presidential address to the North of England Institute of Mining Engineers gave an insight into his approach to industrial relations. In the address he said: 'It is a grave error to suppose that coarse language or a rough demeanour is effective or necessary in dealing with our pitman; firmness and discretion, accompanied by urbanity and knowledge, have, on the contrary, infinitely more effect than the most violent arguments or the roughest mien. I have seen mild, soft-mannered men carry their point with miners by sheer tact, when other and rougher means had brought matters to a standstill'.[74] However, other South Wales Coalfield owners did not necessarily approve of George Elliot's attitude towards colliery workers. Nevertheless, more relevant to Powell Duffryn, what was the effect of George Elliot's management upon the company in at least the Aberdare Valley?

In 1872, Alexander Dalziel presented a report that gave a picture of the changes the coal mining industry had undergone in the Aberdare Valley since the days of Thomas Powell and his coalowner contemporaries.[75] He wrote:

> At the time whence we date public recognition of the hitherto unknown excellencies of the Welsh Smokeless Steam Coal, now some forty years ago, the entire population of the Aberdare Valley including the town of Aberdare, did not exceed 6,000, the most of whom obtained their livelihood by agriculture and iron making. At the present time the population is probably over 40,000, all the more or less dependent upon the production of coal and manufacture of iron.
>
> This great increase is attributable solely to the development of mines. Taking as our authority the parish returns for assessment of the poor's rate in Aberdare and Llanwonno, the production of coal was during the years:

1844	71,031 tons
1856	1,173,459 tons
1870	2,342,792 tons

These figures reveal sustained growth during Thomas Powell's era, and after the founding of Powell Duffryn such growth continued. However, during the late 1860s 'the coal trade passed through severe and continuous depression'.[76] For 1870, the employment and output statistics per Powell Duffryn colliery in the Aberdare Valley were as follows:[77]

Colliery	Employed Men & Boys	Output Tons
Lower Duffryn (2 pits)	893	191,694
Middle Duffryn	575	126,058
High Duffryn	218	47,976
Old Duffryn	71	27,498
Abergwawr	332	90,497
Fforchaman	410	94,252
Cwmdare	222	41,926
Cwmneol	400	62,954
Aberaman	522	58,171
Total	**3,643**	**741,026**

Useful for comparison, Dalziel's account identified that Powell Duffryn's nearest rival in the Aberdare Valley was Nixon, Taylor & Cory whose two collieries, Navigation and Deep Duffryn, employed a total of 1,112 men and boys, and produced 278,546 tons in 1870. So, this concern was roughly one-third the size of Powell Duffryn. A general reckoning of the ton per 'man and boy' produced by Nixon, Taylor & Cory collieries, might suggest that they out produced Powell Duffryn counterparts by twenty-five per cent. Assuming common underground circumstances, and that the number of men employed at the collieries were calculated upon the same basis, John Nixon's management appeared to be have been superior to George Elliot's leadership.

Nonetheless, Elliot's reflections about the state of the coal mining industry in 1872 revealed his knowledge of the coal business. Church documented that Elliot stated: '*If there is a scarcity of coal you are on a beam ends; you know not what to do; you must have it at any price. And the very apprehension of such a possibility was ... one of the great reasons for the rise*.' Elliot pointed to two 'real' factors the coincidence of which upset the coal markets: the thirteen-week strike by miners in South Wales and the expansion in demand for coal in the burgeoning iron industry of Middlesbrough. But Elliot suggested that of possibly even greater significance in precipitating the unprecedented rise in prices was the 'panic' which the public got into that there was going to be this scarcity, and the 'persons who had their large fleet of ships, others who had large companies and large businesses altogether depending upon the supply of coal took alarm.'[78]

However, the business, and political duties, which George Elliot committed himself to from the late 1860s onwards, involved a peripatetic lifestyle. This had an effect upon the running of the companies under his control. In 1873, regarding Powell Duffryn, he was freed from involvement in a lengthy case in Chancery between the company and the Powell brothers. On the 23rd July, 1873, a decree was issued by Sir James Bacon. The decree directed that Licences, Titles, Deeds, Documents be handed over to the Powell Duffryn Company, with the money owed, and the Powell's incurring the legal charges. Powell Duffryn Steam Coal Company 'secured an abatement of £72,564 4s. 9d. in the purchase price'.[79] The assignment was not completed until the 10th November, 1873: 'that is, nine years after the Company had commenced operations'.[80] The process of law was not alone in taking time to conduct its business.

The administration of Powell Duffryn, under Elliot, 'could be frustratingly slow and unresponsive'.[81] R. H. Walters's quoted an extract from an 1873 letter of John Nixon to the Monmouthshire and South Wales Steam Collieries Association as evidence: '*It has taken three years to get Elliot to sign the present deed and if any alteration be made he will require to have a meeting of his partners. It will then be studied by Swift, a lawyer, a counsel's opinion will be taken, alterations made and afterwards sent down to Phillipson in Newcastle for his approval, and, if any suggestions are made by the latter – another meeting of the Powell Duffryn Company – Swift again to peruse, counsel's opinion and so on endlessly.*'[82]

George Elliot had an inclination for legal recourse. Yet, his portfolio of business matters, political duties, and travel itinerary did not make for quick and efficient administration of his affairs. Moreover, as the 1870s aged, the need for him to give more attention to Powell Duffryn's affairs grew. However, in 1874, George Elliot's priority was to secure his seat as a Member of Parliament.

Voted Out and In

George Elliot stood again as a Conservative candidate in a General Election for the North Durham seat. One satirical cartoon of him, as a pit pony, was displayed during the election campaign. Any slur intended by the cartoon possibly had a minor effect upon Elliot's rejection by the voters in the election held in February 1874.[83] The February election campaign featured 'fierce electioneering' and was 'a contest of unparalleled excitement.'[84] Some riotous acts occurred during the campaign. 'Echoes of it reached the High Court' to hear a petition for a fresh election on account of 'intimidation' that was alleged to have taken place. The court judged that the election was 'null and void'.

At the subsequent election on the 8th June, 1874, George Elliot retained the North Durham constituency for the Conservatives. The nation's general election vote returned a Conservative Government, led by Disraeli. The year also saw George Elliot awarded a baronet for his public services.

Such a highlight in Sir George Elliot's life coincided with troubled times at Powell Duffryn. In 1874, there was a slump in trade, and coal prices tumbled. Powell Duffryn's reaction, although savage, appeared to be slow in taking form. In 1875, the Aberaman ironworks was closed, and five collieries: Cwmdare, High Duffryn, Upper Duffryn, Abergwawr, and the Upper Pit, Lower Duffryn. High Duffryn, Upper Duffryn, and Abergwawr, 'were never again worked'.[85] The closure of the ironworks was possibly inevitable since in Hann's opinion it 'never possessed any advantage'. The output was further 'curtailed at some other pits, such as Lower Duffryn where inferior and costly seams were being worked'.

However, Powell Duffryn's shareholders had yet to muster a force of objection about the way that Sir George Elliot ran the company's affairs. Another South Wales business had also won his attention.

Alexandra Dock at Newport

Sometime before 1874, Sir George Elliot weighed in to help with the completion of the Alexandra Dock, in Newport. He attributed his involvement in the project to the vision of John Robinson McLean who died in 1873.[86] The dock was constructed lower down the River Usk from the Town Dock of Thomas Powell's days, which was known thereafter as the Old Docks. Sir George Elliot's son-in-law, J. C. Parkinson, became the managing director of the new dock's construction. In a report dated the 1st September, 1874, to the Board of Directors of the company set up to build the dock, Parkinson announced that the resident engineer, James Abernethy Jnr, was set to exceed the project's budget.[87] Elliot got involved to deal with the forecasted financial loss so as to avert an even greater embarrassment, an incomplete project.

An 1874 Act of Parliament enabled a new company to be formed with 'fresh powers to raise money for completing the work'.[88] The company was restructured as a leasing company. The new company's 'directorate' comprised eight men. The Elliot influence in this body was significant since in addition to Sir George Elliot as a director there was his son, George W. Elliot MP, and J. C. Parkinson. A Conservative and a Disraeli loyalist, the first Lord Tredegar, the local benefactor of the dock project, was also a member of the directorate.

The Alexandra Dock was opened on Tuesday, 10th April 1875. *The Monmouthshire Merlin & South Wales Advertiser* extolled the opening of the dock as 'a red letter day', and recorded that Newport 'outshone itself'.[89] The absence of Lord Tredegar, due to a serious illness that may have preceded his death later that year, saw the County Durham baronet take a leading role at the dock's opening. Bands paraded through Newport to herald the start to the dock opening proceedings. An 'imposing and animated' scene

Alexandra Dock, Newport, with South Dock notable in the foreground. The North Dock, top left, opened in 1875, was the first phase of the dock's development. Sir George Elliot claimed he had 'pulled the stroke oar' that realized the dock's opening. *Pope/Parkhouse Archive*

of 40,000 people collected at the docks though this estimate was reported as being a 'slightly exaggerated one'.

The dock opening gave Sir George Elliot a stage for self-promotion. He delivered some five speeches during the day. He spoke for the dock company's directors, proposed toasts and offered thanks. In a speech of the town's mayor, Benjamin Evans, Elliot was praised for the 'prominent part' he had played in making the dock a 'successful issue'.

The Mayoress of Newport, Mrs Evans, opened the dock. To the noise of cannon salutes, cheers, and singing of Rule Britannia, the first ship that glided across the water of the dock was a cargo steamer, the *George Elliot*.[90] The steamer took a mooring near a 'coal tip' – a hill of coal weighing four hundred tons [406 tonne]. Called 'Griffin' coal, the stock had been hauled to the dock from the Nantyglo and Blaina Works of G. W. Jones, Heard, & Company. Griffin coal was touted at the time as having 'superior qualities for steam purpose'. The coal was shipped to Southampton for the Royal Mail Steamboat Company.

Newport's day of celebrations continued at Victoria Hall. The audience at the hall heard a reading of a telegram from the Prince of Wales congratulating the 'inhabitants of Wales on the success of this undertaking'. The Alexandra Docks had been named after Her Royal Highness Princess of Wales. Afterwards, Sir George Elliot stood to a hurricane of applause and spoke. Regarding Alexandra Dock, he stated, without '*any feeling of vanity or egotism, because the fact was well known,*' that he was only one of three people to '*have taken upon themselves the great responsibility*' for carrying out the work. Lord Tredegar, and John Robertson McLean were, he said, 'much more instrumental in bringing about' the dock than himself. He then preached about his belief in cooperation for the pursuit of business.

In early 1875, there was another prolonged colliers' strike in the South Wales Coalfield. Sir George Elliot mentioned that there had been no strike action in the Durham Coalfield since 1844. He continued: '*I have no doubt that I am speaking for myself – that if the owners of this district, with whom I am associated (and I surrendered my opinion to theirs, not because I am of their opinion, but because I am amongst them)*' before calling for arbitration, or conciliation, so as to end the 'unfortunate' strike. Arbitration, or conciliation he thought, were better than 'playing the game' of "beggar my neighbour". The end of this part of his speech received a burst of loud applause. He then added, 'I shall no doubt be rebuked by some of my friends, for what I have said, and shall also be very much found fault with by the workman'. Some colliery owners of the South Wales Coalfield no doubt saw him as a maverick, and hoped that his time in charge of Powell Duffryn could be ended.

Sir George Elliot's favourite simile for indicating what he had done in the matter of dock accommodation at Newport used to be that he had pulled the stroke oar.[91] Yet, the dock's position had been hopeless before Elliot's intervention. After the opening of Alexandra Docks, with Newport's praise still ringing in his ears, the County Durham baronet may have journeyed to give some attention to Powell Duffryn's affairs. He had at least to face the chore of helping to find closure to the twelve week strike that began around January 1875. However, any lingering strike issues abruptly ceased to have any topical importance in communities around New Tredegar Colliery.

A 'Calamitous Accident'

For Saturday, 4th December, 1875, New Tredegar Colliery was described as 'situated in a peaceful valley, a fair representative of the dips between the hills which form a characteristic feature of the Southern part of the Principality'.[92] Moreover, the above ground workings 'hardly give an idea of the treasure of lives and wealth which from day to day are hidden below'. Such a picture contrasted with an underground tragedy.

A prelude to the tragedy occurred during the colliery's Friday night shift on the 3rd December. John Williams was the night shift's fireman for an underground district served by a main roadway known as the 'Main Deep'.[93] The district was located west of the colliery's 'river-side' shaft. Williams's main duty was to ensure that air circulated through the workings. His other duties included testing for gas, and carrying out the firing of a shot, a small explosive, so as to break up a coal seam.

Sometime around 11 o'clock in the evening, near a site in the district called 'Sprangley's stall', John Williams tested for gas, and 'could not find any', but 'could not be answerable for what was in the ground'. He then fired a shot using a small wire fuse so as to loosen coal in the Rhas Las seam. He later described its effect as a 'dead fire'. He watched it flash and sparkle. '*The current of wind* [due to the underground ventilation] *bore it right away from the rib*' of the exposed strata. Then a 'little' explosion took place in a part of the district called Owen Davies's Level (or Slant). Scorched by the heat of the explosion were two colliers, Aaron Williams and William Batten. Aaron Williams was badly burnt whereas only one of Batten's hands was so harmed.[94] John Williams advised his overman, Joseph Hancock, that the explosion 'occurred from the fuse'. The seriousness of the event called for the attention of the colliery manager, Robert Lonie, a man of 'urbane' character according to a reporter for the *Western Mail*.

On being told about the event, the manager visited the pit. There he met Joseph Hancock and so heard John William's report.[95] Lonie, with Hancock, then descended underground where they met the fireman. Lonie first cross-examined Williams about the gas checks he had conducted. Then, using a miner's safety lamp, he also completed one in 'Joel Hancock's stall'. No traces of gas were found. He then instructed the two officials to erect a sheet, a partition given the term of brattice in coal mining, below this stall.

Any gas seeping from the stratum underground was mainly methane, which being lighter than air, collected at high points. The positioning of brattice sheets, in combination with door boys following a routine of opening and closing wooden doors, enabled the flow of air to disperse gas. The brattice sheets' positioning allowed air to go over the top of them to clear the gas. If a door, or brattice, was left open for a period then gas pockets could be swept away by moving air. However, if gas collected at a location and so formed a reservoir, it was ripe for ignition as an explosion of some magnitude.

The colliery manager judged that it was good practice to '*turn the full body of wind into the stall*'. He then went '*down into George Richard's stall, and went around the back of Hancock's stall up the face, and could not find any traces of gas there*'. William Evans, the day overman joined them. The quartet then proceeded down the Main Deep and witnessed another test for gas. Not a trace of gas was found.

Robert Lonie then told William Evans, in front of Joseph Hancock and John Williams, '*not to allow a man to go down on that day, and*

In 1875, New Tredegar Colliery was the scene of an underground explosion that killed twenty-three miners comprising men and boys. The Number 3 pit headgear shown in the photograph was one result of the colliery's 1905-1906 redevelopment. *Pope/Parkhouse Archive*

not for 24 hours'. Evans, though, pleaded with him to allow the men to go down arguing that '*we should lose a great quantity of coal*'. This appeal was spurned. The manager said that '*it did not matter to him if we lost 200 tons of coal per day*'. He further instructed that '*in any place where he found a capful of gas he was to stop it and not to allow a man to work it*'. '*Very well*', replied the overman.

Miners at the colliery were wary of working the 3ft 8in. thick Rhas Las seam of coal in the vicinity of the Main Deep. The seam was '*accompanied by a good deal of gas*', which made it notorious as '*a fair sample of the 'Fiery Vein'*.[96] William Evans had been employed at New Tredegar Colliery for several years. Although he had only been a day shift overman for a week, he had been a night shift overman for an undisclosed period previously.[97] Besides being responsible for coal production, he had a duty for the safety of the men and boys under his charge. So although it appeared wise for Evans to heed the instructions of a manager showing care for miners' safety, there existed a selfish reason to obey the instruction. An official could be dismissed for flouting a manager's instruction.

The colliery manager and the other officials then separated. Robert Lonie came up the pit at three o'clock Saturday morning. Joseph Hancock proceeded to do a round of the colliery's workings before he also returned to the surface, at about half-past four o'clock in the morning. John Williams received the manager's last instruction underground: to check again for gas, and to report his findings on the following morning. The fireman did as he was told, and proved that the workings were free of gas. He retreated from underground sometime between five and six o'clock in the morning after having finished his shift. Williams Evans was left in charge of the River-side workings.

William Strong, the day shift's fireman, spoke with William Evans at an underground cabin sometime after seven o'clock that morning.[98] There he learnt of the manager's instruction. He then realised, that contrary to it, men and boys were at work in the district. So he quizzed Evans about the matter, who in reply merely said, '*but*', and then fell silent. Working on the colliery's River-side were an estimated 150 men and boys, whereas some 250 men and boys worked on its east side.[99] Strong later made an explicit statement that it was Evans that had allowed them to work in '*opposition to Mr Lonie's orders*'.

The day shift's fireman left Evans, and walked to Clarke's level. William Strong arrived at the level just before nine o'clock, and was greeted by door boys anxious to tell him that '*something was the matter*' in Main Deep. He proceeded to the district and upon approaching it saw dust flying, and guessed that an explosion of gas had occurred. Nevertheless, he continued further, and met a group of miners rooted to a spot. He appealed to them to follow him '*down to Owen Davies's level to see if the doors were all right*'. Escorted with some of these miners, they reached the site of the first door, but found it had been blown away. Improvising, using a brattice sheet, he repaired the door. Then, with his escorts, he advanced to James James's deep, and found gas just below Joel Hancock's stall. Bravery, caution, and humane concerns tussled for supremacy in their minds.

When asked weeks later about the nature of the gas, William Strong described that '*it was browncap mixed with an afterdamp. It was very brown*'. The explosion's residual atmosphere was called 'afterdamp'. It comprised a mixture of carbon dioxide, water-vapour, and nitrogen, and so could suffocate a human being. Nevertheless, he choose to go on to Owen Davies's level to 'double the door', but was forced back due to strong afterdamp. He then proceeded, with his escorts, to other doors, and brattice sheet locations, in order that underground air ventilation could be regulated.

News of the explosion travelled with some speed. Robert Lonie received a message that something had happened in the pit at about five minutes to nine on the Saturday morning. He rushed to the pit head, and with a party of men, descended a shaft. He first satisfied himself that the ventilation at the foot of the shaft was acceptable. Then he and his party walked to Owen Davies's level. Charging towards them, at one stage, was an injured John Pegley, 'with a coat over his head, and his arm hanging down', and screaming for help, which he received. Then an encounter with afterdamp caused the party to make a brief retreat. Maybe there was some confusion caused by the retreat since it was when the manager sent William Strong to check the doors at John Jones's level. Strong failed to remember been given this instruction when later he was called upon to recollect events.

Robert Lonie then led a party, carrying brattice sheets, further forwards. He first found William Evans and Stephen Sellick. They were badly injured, but alive. On reaching Sprangley's stall they found four dead men: John Davies, Ethel Edwards,[100] John Jones, and Moses Sprangley.[101] The manager judged that the rest of the men further down the slant were also dead. He decided that his priority was to examine other doors, and finding them in order, he went up the pit to set the ventilator on as fast as possible.

The colliery manager afterwards descended underground once again where he saw trams conveying bodies to the pit bottom. The living, but injured colliery workers, had been given precedence over the dead. The explorers had by then 'seen one body "burnt to coke"; there was another lying in his heading as he had lain while at work; beyond a third lifeless, without a mark upon his body'.[102]

An unnamed survivor recounted his experiences later that day.[103] He had been working with his son, a youth of fourteen, or fifteen years of age, called Thomas, within two hundred yards of where lives were lost. He heard the *breaking of the "blower"* [a mining term for a gas outbreak], *and smelt the gas*'. He screamed at his son to lie down, but witnessed Thomas being blown two to three yards due to the strength of a wind of sulphur and dust. In an instant, after it had passed, he clasped his son in his arms, and ran for his life in the dark. A 'rather weakly' Thomas gave an account about the shouting and screaming of other men and boys attempting to escape. It had been awful, with two horses barring their exit, they had to run over them; and get past the other two that were not hurt. On the surface they, and other injured survivors, were administered to by Dr Evans, called from Tirphil, a hamlet to the south-west of the colliery, on the Glamorgan side of the valley.

Six men of the colliery were critically ill, with some of them close to death. In twenty minutes the dead, the count then was twenty, mainly men, but also boys, were wound up to the valley's surface.

Bystanders surrounded the pit bank 'in a marvellously short space of time'. A crowd of wives and mothers were 'anxiously desirous of hearing if they were bereaved, or if a father, or son, or brother was injured'. However, on the whole there was 'an absence of that excitement which generally surrounds such scenes'.

Indeed, the presence of Police Constable Young was sufficient to keep order among the crowd. He was joined later by Police Superintendent Fowler who had journeyed from Tredegar in the Sirhowy Valley. The policemen were lonely sentries at the colliery

by one o'clock in the afternoon since the crowd had dispersed. The 'ghastly' personal 'burdens' of the day moved into homes at Pontlottyn, a village that lay a mile and a half mile to the north-west of the colliery, to the village's southern satellite, a small collection of houses called Troedrhiwfuch, Craig Rhymney, situated north of Pontlottyn, New Tredegar, and Tirphil. New Tredegar Colliery's tragic news spread across South Wales.

The two policemen were among the first people to see the arrival at the colliery of both George Wilkinson, head manager under the Powell Duffryn Steam Coal Company, and Mr Snape, the company's mechanical engineer at around two in the afternoon.[104] George Wilkinson had taken up this position in the company when it was owned by the Powells due to a recommendation of Sir George Elliot's.[105] Wilkinson had made his mining reputation running collieries in the Northumberland and Durham Coalfields.[106] The disaster risked harming his career since it was the first of moment that had happened in South Wales Coalfield since a new Mines Regulation Act had come into operation regulating the ventilation of mines.

Wilkinson expressed deep regret for the bereaved families and spoke of the support they had been given by the company's secretary, Mr Dallas (sic).[107] An immediate action taken by the company was to expedite the making of coffins in Cardiff for delivery by way of the Rhymney Railway. In the dark of the day's evening, Wilkinson and Snape returned to the Aberdare Valley possibly having been informed that two further men, brought alive to the pit head, had died. They were Stephen Sellick and Samuel Jenkins.

The Sunday in New Tredegar was one of contrasts.[108] It was seen as being 'picturesque', due to snow and furze covered mountains. Yet, 'Parties of people were to be seen walking in Indian file along narrow winding paths, while each train which stopped at Tyrphil (sic) Railway Station brought loads of passengers who were impatient to learn the worst or the best news, as the case may' have been. The miners' agent, Henry Mitchard of Blackwood, arrived and was busy all day. This 'lively' scene did not contrive to hide the truth of a locality in mourning. Blinds were tightly drawn on household windows, either at homes of the bereaved, or neighbours demonstrating sympathy. Black flags hung out of windows of the village's Tredegar Arms to signify that as a club house of a local benefit society had lost a number of its members. Similar scenes prevailed at Tirphil, Troedrhiwfuch, and Pontlottyn.

Two coroner inquests took place on the Monday. Coroner W. H. Brewer, of Newport, opened one at the Tredegar Arms, New Tredegar, so as to find an explanation for the cause of death of the miners whose former home addresses lay in Monmouthshire. Early that morning news came that the total fatalities had reached its final count of twenty-three with the death of the overman, William Evans. The General Picton Hotel, Pontlottyn, was the venue for the other inquest, before the coroner for Merthyr Tydfil district, George Overton, which concerned men and boys that had formerly lived in Glamorgan. Juries were sworn in both places, and their members were directed to visit the homes of the dead so as to view the bodies. County jurisdictions created difficulties for the two coroners, which gave rise to complications for their respective inquiries. Nevertheless, the local population were probably more concerned with, and affected by, other sequels

An estimated 5,000 people attended a funeral held at Pontlottyn, on Thursday the 9th December.[109] 'The crowd witnessed a 'sad' procession involving fifteen coffins containing men and boys who had once lived at Pontlottyn, Tirphil, and Troedrhiwfuch. A burial service took place at Pontlottyn church's graveyard. It was read, one portion in Welsh, and another in English, by the Reverends W. Evans, Vicar of Rhymney, and T. Theophilus, Vicar of Pontlottyn. Present were three hundred voices of the Rhymney United Choir. John Williams, killed in the explosion, had been one of their fellow choristers. At the conclusion of the last rites they 'most solemnly and effectively sang "Over There" from the hymns of Mr Sankey'.

Reported also that day was a company announcement.[110] The *Western Mail* noted that: '*A principal member of which is Sir George Elliot, have promised to provide for the helpless women and children. Such noble conduct as this is above praise and recommends itself to the appreciation of everyone. As a matter of dry fact it does not appear, at any rate as yet, that the future recipients of this well-timed bounty have any legal claim on the beneficence of the firm*'. The newspaper added praise about the baronet: '*But no one need be surprised at any act of benevolence on the part of a commercial concern whose chief partner could set an example to his fellow Colliery Owners' Association with the workmen, by sitting in private consultation with his workmen, and sapping the very root of a trade difficulty of many months of standing by an act of personal condescension, and an exhibition of kindly and reasonable feeling before unparalleled*'. The people of the communities of the northern part of the Rhymney Valley may not have been interested in endorsing such praise. Their thoughts, and prayers, contemplated only the consequences of the disaster.

The Adjourned Inquest

The Adjourned Inquest into the calamitous accident re-opened on the 15th December.[111] Held at the Tredegar Arms, New Tredegar, Coroner Brewer led the inquest. Present, in addition to invited witnesses, were: Lionel Brough, Her Majesty's Inspector of Mines; Mr Cadman, assistant-inspector of mines for the district; representing the company were George Wilkinson, his assistant, Llewellyn Llewellyn, Robert Lonie, Mr Daleze (sic) [Dalziel?], secretary, and J. Snape; Mr York, who watched on behalf of the National Union of Miners; Henry Mitchard, the miner's agent for Monmouthshire; and Police Superintendent Fowler.

Laid out on a table at the start of the inquest was the plan of New Tredegar Colliery's workings. Brewer acknowledged that this had been done at the suggestion of the coroner of an inquest into an explosion at Llan Colliery. This explosion occurred two days after the New Tredegar tragedy, on Monday the 7th December, and saw twelve men killed. This colliery was found some five miles north-west from the centre of Cardiff, in the vicinity of Pentyrch. William Galloway was the assistant mines inspector at this inquest.

William Strong was the first person called for questioning at the New Tredegar Colliery inquest. Some aspects of his answers to questions were used in the earlier description of the disaster. However, two notable items were omitted. He was asked about the finding of a miner's lamp that had been holed by a mandrel (a miner's pick). He was also quizzed about a suspicion that a collier had a pipe on his person. His reply to the first question caused the Inspector of Mines, Lionel Brough, to observe, '*I do not believe in the mandril* (sic) *hole myself not till I have better evidence; but if man did hit the lamp with the mandril* (sic) … [then] … *he was a dead man*'. The, presumed deceased, user of the lamp was a John Jones. Killed were two miners of this name, each from different villages, but they were not distinguished. Further, Brough thought that the matter of the pipe was a rumour with no substance. The

inquest was then adjourned until Monday, the 20th December.

At the session of the inquiry held on the 20th December, John Williams, Joseph Hancock, collier William Williams, and Robert Lonie appeared.[112] Again parts of their answers to questions helped sketch the earlier story of the disaster. However, fireman John Williams proposed at the inquest that someone had left underground doors open, and that the hole in the lamp caused the explosion. He also ventured to say that if no manager's directions had been given early on the Saturday morning of the explosion then, based upon the gas tests' findings, there was no reason to stop the men from working.

William Williams was called to verify the finding of the holed lamp. The lamp was found about forty yards from Sprangley's stall.

The colliery's manager was the final witness on that Monday's session. Asked by the coroner if his 'strict orders' to William Evans, not to work the district were conditional 'as to whether it [the gas] was clear or not', Robert Lonie replied '*No*'. The coroner then added, '*And he let them go down in spite of your orders?*' Lonie in reply said, '*I suppose so*'. The matter was not examined further.

A summary of the verdict of the inquest was published on the last day of 1875 in the *Western Mail*. '*The inquiry did not reveal negligence, and we can only hope that all parties will see that the utmost attention is paid to the known methods of safety, so as to ensure a maximum immunity from loss of life and destruction of property*'.[113]

The industrial correspondent of the newspaper thought that the '*chief cause of that catastrophe was an interruption to the system of ventilation adopted, or else the gas which exploded would have been swept, before the pure air, and found its way up the shaft*'. At the inquest on the 20th December, Robert Lonie reported that a fan was being erected at the colliery.[114]

If the inquest's result was inconclusive about who was negligent on the 4th December, 1875, the explosion at the colliery had killed twenty-three human beings. Compiled from reports of the *Western Mail*, the deceased were as follows. From New Tredegar: Thomas Evans, married, dependents a wife and four children; William Evans, married, wife and twelve children; Edward Hinder, boy; and Stephen Sellick, married, wife and several children. From Pontlottyn: Moses Prangley, married, wife and three children; Roger Williams, married, wife and one child; John Williams, single; William Williams, single; Thomas Price, married, wife and two children; James James, married, wife and five children; Samuel Jenkins, married, wife and four children; Arthur Thomas, single; John Thomas, single; John Jones, single; John Davies, boy; and Arthur Edwards, boy. From Craig Rhymney: John Jones, married, wife and several children; and John Thomas, married, wife and two children. From Tyr Phil: Llewellyn Jones, single. From Troedyrhiwfuch: Jonathan Richards, boy; Thomas John Williams, boy; George Williams, cited in one reference to be a boy, and in another as having a wife and five children; and George Saunders, single.[115] In addition, recorded as being injured were: George Batten, married, New Tredegar; John Pugless, married, of Craig Rhymney; and Aaron Williams, single of Pontlottyn.[116]

At the New Tredegar Colliery inquest on the 20th December, William Williams mentioned that he had found a watch in Sprangley's stall. The watch had stopped at seventeen minutes past nine in the morning, and he believed that this gave the time when the explosion had occurred. If the watch's time had been deliberately set nearly a half an hour earlier than the actual time, then it suggests that its unidentified owner was eager never to be late for work.

The living victims of the explosion were the mothers, who had lost their sons, eleven widows, and orphaned children, and the injured miners. The company 'granted' a weekly allowance of 5s. 0d. per widow, and 2s. 6d. per child, which was a reasonable income since the average weekly wage of a miner was around £1.[117] Moreover, the company's payment scheme was possibly 'unique' in the South Wales Coalfield.[118] The scheme continued with a gradually diminishing number of recipients until in 1909 when one person received the allowance.

But personal anxiety, and grief, cannot be valued in terms of either money, or goods. Households had lost a key figure of a family. An estimated forty-four children were left fatherless. Some mothers may have been traumatised for the rest of their lives through losing their sons. Some distraught people no doubt dreamed about a future when men and boys no longer had a need to work underground.

All those affected would have drawn little comfort in knowing that they were not alone that December in their suffering. However, concerning the Llan Colliery disaster, mentioned earlier, the junior Inspector of Mines at its inquiry, William Galloway, had begun to ponder if the blamed gas was the sole incendiary medium in a colliery's explosion. Nevertheless, as if defying tragedy, ignoring family misgivings, the character of a miner was such that he continued to pursue such a dangerous occupation.

Following the New Tredegar Colliery explosion, according to Powell Duffryn's history, negotiations concerning the 1875 strike ended with an agreement. Applied as a result of the agreement was a means for regulating colliery workers wages that used an 'automatic scale of wages, depending upon the price of Coal, and on December 11, 1875, the first sliding scale agreement was made'.[119] It operated in accord with the following principle: A standard wage was set as that paid at each colliery in 1869, plus 5 per cent, and the standard prices of coal 'free on board Cardiff, Newport, or Swansea' was set at, Steam Coal 12s., and Mynyddislwyn and No. 3 Rhondda 11s. The Sliding Scale served to pay an additional 7.5 percentage on the standard wage to the men when the coalowners obtained 1s. per ton in excess of a particular mined coal's standard price. A check was instituted every six months of the price of coal by taking an average price of all Large Coal during the preceding six months. The lowest range for wages was set at the standard wage, with its ceiling put at 67.5 per cent above the standard wage. A read of the agreement and its supporting tables today reveals a complex means for wage calculation.[120] If pessimistic colliery workers anticipated that they would become poorer as a result, the coalowners had grounds for expecting financial gains in the future from future customers of Welsh steam coal.

Foreign Lands

The reputation of Welsh Steam coal was flourishing. By 1875, Welsh steam coal was placed on the lists of the English, French, Spanish, and Italian Governments and the following awards were made: Diplôme d'Honneur, Exposition Maritime International, 1868; Diplôme d'Honneur, Exposition Internationale, Paris, 1875; and, a number of years later the Medaille d'Argent, (1er Prix), Exposition Universalle, Paris, 1878.[121] Of particular importance was that in the 'Blue Book Navy Admiralty Trial of Coal', 1876, Powell Duffryn's coal was given the highest place, and was destined to remain on the Admiralty

Lists into the future.[122] Such home and foreign recognition was an endorsement of the County Durham baronet's initiative to organise the purchase of Thomas Powell's steam coal collieries.

In Egypt, on the 12th January, 1876, Sir George Elliot met Ismail Pasha, the Khedive.[123] At the meeting Elliot presented a scheme for the consolidation of the Egyptian Debt and for its management.[124] The scheme was cabled to the British Foreign Secretary, the 14th Earl of Derby, but an intervention of the French Consul in Egypt, saw Elliot's plan rejected. However, maybe, the main reason that Elliot was in Egypt was as the contractor for the harbour-works of Alexandria.

Although the duties of business caused him to leave the warmth of the Middle East winter for Britain, Egypt had charmed him. As a visitor to Aberaman House, Charles Wilkins noted: '*Wall papers representing many interesting eastern scenes*', and '*if fancy persuades you that you are passing through the famous Canal of Suez, or actually amidst the very phases of Egyptian Life*'.[125] Although Elliot's tastes had been influenced by an ancient world, the troubles affecting Powell Duffryn were pressing, and current.

Retirement

Bad market conditions for coal that prevailed in 1875 continued until 1877. The gloom within the company was compounded in 1877 when the company took financial measures to stave off business failure. According to Edmund Hann, the measures took form as: '(a) 97 Ordinary Shares of £1,250 each of which, however, £550 per share was credited in respect of profits made in previous years but expended on Capital Account instead of being divided (three of these shares remained unissued until 1901); and (b) an issue of Ten per cent Cumulative Preference Shares to the extent of 297, redeemable at £110 each. These issues brought the Capital up to £750,950'.[126] One casualty of this period was the company's founder.

In 1877, the board of Powell Duffryn decided to retire Sir George Elliot from giving 'practical direction' to the company. The Durham baronet retained his seat on the company's board of directors. He was sixty-two years of age.

The congregation of West Rainton's St. Mary's church, north-east of the city of Durham, took a more kindly view of Elliot. He sponsored the building of a broach spire atop a new tower erected for the church. The deposed founder of Powell Duffryn undoubtedly attended some ceremony there, but his thoughts included a new business opportunity.

At an Alexandra Dock Board meeting, on the 16th July, 1877, an idea arose. The idea's aim was to attract coal traffic from the eastern Valleys of Glamorgan to the Newport dock.[127] The MP for North Durham was attracted to the railway idea. In 1878, an Act of Parliament was passed and so the Pontypridd, Caerphilly & Newport Railway Company was founded.[128] Proposed was a railway link from the south end of Pontypridd Station to another junction with the Rhymney Railway near Caerphilly together with running powers over the Caerphilly Branch of the Brecon & Merthyr through Machen to Bassaleg Junction. Sir George Elliot took on the challenge of realizing the idea by negotiating with at least four railway companies: Taff Vale, Rhymney Railway, Brecon & Merthyr, and the Great Western Railway (GWR). South Wales remained as part of Elliot's business itinerary. Circulation in South Wales gave him an opportunity to keep in touch with Powell Duffryn's operational activities.

NOTES

1   Charles Wilkins, *op. cit.*, pp.113-4.
2   Don Bowman, 'The Rainton to Seaham Railway, 1820-1840', *Transactions, Newcomen Society*, Vol. 69, No. 2 (1997-98), p.249.
3   Obituary, Sir George Elliot, Bart., *Institution of Civil Engineers Minutes of Proceedings*, Vol. 116, (1893-4) p.355.
4   Sidney Webb, *The Story of the Durham Miners* (1662-1921). (Fabian Society, 1921), pp.42-9. The Bond bound miners to fines and conditions and work at one colliery for a whole year, but the colliery owner gave no undertaking as to continuous employment.
5   William D. Lawson, *Lawson's Tyneside Celebrities*. (Lawson, 1873), pp.231-2.
6   Obituary, Sir George Elliot, Bart., *op. cit.*, p.355.
7   John E. McCutcheon, *Troubled Seams*, (County Durham Books, 1994), pp.34-5.
8   John E. McCutcheon, *op. cit.*, p.45.
9   George Elliot, Inaugural Address, *Transactions, North England Institute of Mining Engineers*, Vol. 18, (1868-1869), p.20.
10 Edith, Marchioness of Londonderry, *Francis Anne; the Life and Times of Frances Anne, Marchioness of Londonderry, and her husband Charles the Third Marquess of Londonderry*. (1958), p.251.
11 Edith, Marchioness of Londonderry, *op. cit.*, p.256.
12 Edith, Marchioness of Londonderry, *op. cit.*, p.259.
13 Edith, Marchioness of Londonderry, *op. cit.*, pp.276-7.
14 Edith, Marchioness of Londonderry, *op. cit.*, p.271.
15 Edith, Marchioness of Londonderry, *op. cit.*, pp.264-5.
16 Edith, Marchioness of Londonderry, *op. cit.*, pp.276-8.
17 *Western Mail*, 'Death of Sir George Elliot', 26 Dec 1893, p.5, col.5.
18 *The Powell Duffryn Steam Coal Company 1864-1914*. (Powell Duffryn, 1914), p.18.
19 W. W. Price, *op. cit.*, p.11.
20 W. W. Price, *op. cit.*, p.9.
21 Upper Duffryn Colliery is not mentioned in the company's list. However, the colliery's closure is noted by E. M. Hann, see text p.37. *The Powell Duffryn Steam Coal Company 1864-1914, op. cit.*, p.18.
22 *The Powell Duffryn Steam Coal Company 1864-1914, op. cit.*, p.18.
23 J. H. Morris and L. J. Williams, *op. cit.*, p.160.
24 R. H. Walters, *op. cit.*, p.104.
25 Arthur Helps, *Life & Labours of Mr Brassey*. (Reprint 1969, Evelyn, Adams & McKay) p.161.
26 Obituary, Alexander Ogilvie, *Institution of Civil Engineers Minutes of Proceedings*, Vol. 86, (1885-6), pp.373-374.
27 Sir Arthur Helps, *op. cit.*, p.165.
28 Obituary, Mr. John Robinson McClean MP FRS, *Institution of Civil Engineers Minutes of Proceedings*, Vol. 38, (1873-4) p.288.
29 Beatrice Webb, *My Apprenticeship*, (Longmans, 1926), pp.2-7.
30 Obituary, Mr. Thomas Brassey, *Institution of Civil Engineers Minutes of Proceedings*, Vol.33, (1872), p.250.
31 *Suffolk Chronicle*, 16 Feb. 1886, 'Death of Mr. Alexander Ogilvie', Institution of Civil Engineers Archives, Frank Smith Collection [ESAB 10].
32 Obituary, Mr. John Robinson McClean MP FRS, *op. cit.*, p.291.
33 Sir Arthur Helps, *op. cit.*, p.165.
34 W. W. Price, *op. cit.*, p.11.
35 W. W. Price, *op. cit.*, p.11.
36 R. H. Walters, *op. cit.*, pp.175-6.
37 Obituary, Sir George Elliot, Bart, *Institution of Civil Engineers Minutes of Proceedings, op. cit.*, p.355.
38 Nikolaus Pevsner, *The Buildings of England, Yorkshire: The North Riding*. (Penguin, 1966), p.399.
39 *Western Mail*, 'Death of Sir George Elliot', 26 Dec 1893, p.5, col.5.
40 Obituary, Sir George Elliot, Bart., *Institution of Civil Engineers Minutes of Proceedings, op. cit.*, p.356.
41 'Sir George Elliot', *The Engineer*, Vol. 76, 29 Dec. 1893, p.617.
42 E. M. Hann, *Brief History of The Powell Duffryn Steam Coal Company Limited 1864-1921*, p.5. This history evolved in three stages. The first part, pp.3 to 32, was 'written in 1909'. The second part, pp.34 to 46, covered the period 1910-1914. The final part dealt with the period 1914-1921.
43 W. W. Price, *op. cit.*, p.14.
44 W. W. Price, *op. cit.*, p.14.
45 W. W. Price, *op. cit.*, pp.15-16. *In The Powell Duffryn Steam Coal Company 1864-1914, op. cit.*, p.18 dates the purchase to 1866.
46 W. W. Price, *op. cit.*, p.15.
47 E. M. Hann, *op. cit.*, p.6.
48 Cynon Valley History Society, *Cynon Coal, op. cit.*, p.240.
49 In *The Powell Duffryn Steam Coal Company 1864-1914, op. cit.*, these collieries were recorded as being purchased in 1866. For Fforchaman and Cwmneol see p.37 and p.38 respectively. W. W. Price's research found information that showed that this date was inaccurate.
50 W. W. Price, *op. cit.*, p.36, footnote no. 108.
51 W. W. Price, *op. cit.*, pp.16-17.
52 E. M. Hann, *op. cit.* p.6.
53 A royalty is paid to a landlord proportionate to the amount of coal worked from a mine over a certain period, and the method of calculation can be peculiar to a mining district.
54 *The Monmouthshire Merlin & South Wales Advertiser*, 'Opening of the Alexandra Docks at Newport', 16 April 1875, p.2, col.6.
55 George Elliot, Inaugural Address, *Transactions, North England Institute of Mining Engineers*, Vol. 18, (1868-1869), pp.19-35.
56 Letter, Marie Dudgeon to Writer, Jan. 2004. Marie Dudgeon, Librarian of the North of England Institute of Mining. Elliot's resignation letter was read at a meeting of the Institute on the 31st July, 1869. A search did not find a record of the letter.
57 George Elliot, 'Inaugural Address', *Transactions, North England Institute of Mining Engineers, op. cit.*, p.155.
58 The plaque at West Rainton Church, county Durham, notes that Elliot obtained the plaque's material in 1867 with the permission of the Khedive.
59 William D. Lawson, *op. cit.*, pp.233-5.
60 William D. Lawson, *op. cit.*, p.233.
61 G. D. H. Cole and A. W. Filson, *British Working Class Movements, Select Documents 1789-1875*. (Macmillan, 1967), p.583.
62 Gwyn A. Williams, *When was Wales?* (Penguin, 1985), p.216.
63 Edited Brian Ll. James, *op. cit.*, p.67.
64 Obituary, Sir George Elliot, Bart., *Institution of Civil Engineers Minutes of Proceedings, op. cit.*, p.355.
65 Charles Wilkins, *op. cit.*, p.115.
66 Alexander Dalziel, *The Colliers' Strike in South Wales*. (1872), p.19.
67 Alexander Dalziel, *op. cit.*, pp.110-3.
68 Alexander Dalziel, *op. cit.*, pp.131-3.
69 Alexander Dalziel, *op. cit.*, pp.260.
70 Alexander Dalziel, *op. cit.*, pp.262.
71 Alexander Dalziel, *op. cit.*, pp.265-280.
72 Alexander Dalziel, *op. cit.*, pp.34 & p.281.
73 Alexander Dalziel, *op. cit.*, pp.286.
74 George Elliot, 'Inaugural Address', *Transactions, North England Institute of Mining Engineers, op. cit.*, p.34.
75 Alexander Dalziel, *op. cit.*, pp.14-15.
76 The *Powell Duffryn Steam Coal Company 1864-1914, op. cit.*, p.19.
77 Alexander Dalziel, *op. cit.*, p.34. Powell Duffryn bought Lower Duffryn as Cwm Pennar. High Duffryn was Ynyscynon, and Old Duffryn was preferred to its original name, Tir-Ffounder. Abernant-y-Groes was not mentioned in his listing of Powell Duffryn's Aberdare Valley collieries.
78 Roy Church, *The History of the British Coal Industry*, Vol. 3. (Clarendon, 1986), p.57.
79 J. H. Morris and L. J. Williams, *op. cit.*, pp.161-62.
80 W. W. Price, *op. cit.*, p.12.
81 R. H. Walters, *op. cit.*, p.175.
82 L. J. Williams, *The Monmouthshire and South Wales Coal Owners' Association: 1873-1914*, MA. Thesis, Aberystwyth; (1957), p.30. Letter of John Nixon's to the Monmouthshire and South Wales Steam Collieries Association, 13 August 1873.
83 John E. McCutcheon, *op. cit.*, p.74.
84 John E. McCutcheon, *op. cit.*, pp.73-8.
85 E. M. Hann, *op. cit.*, p.7.
86 *The Monmouthshire Merlin and South Wales Advertiser*, 'Opening of the Alexandra Docks at Newport', 16 April 1875, p.2, col.4
87 John Hutton, *The Newport Docks & Railway Company*. (Silver Link Publishing, 1996), p.9. Problems met excavating the dock, and building the dock's railway system caused costs to rise.
88 *The Monmouthshire Merlin & South Wales Advertiser, op. cit.*, p.2, col.3.
89 *The Monmouthshire Merlin & South Wales Advertiser, op. cit.*, p.2 and p.5. The source of the following description of the Dock's opening celebrations.
90 The 700 ton [711 tonne] gross weight *George Elliot* was an iron screw schooner built in 1872 by R. Thompson, Jnr, Sunderland. Source: *Lloyd's Register of Ships* 1874-75 edition.
91 *Western Mail*, 'Death of Sir George Elliot', 26 Dec 1893, p.5, col.5.
92 *Western Mail*, 'Colliery Explosion at New Tredegar', 6 Dec 1875, p.5, col.3. In E. M. Hann, *Brief History of the Powell Duffryn Steam Coal Company Ltd., op. cit.*, the event is dated as December 1876,

see p.7, and this error is repeated in *The Powell Duffryn Steam Coal Company 1864-1914, op. cit.*, see p.7 & p.20.

93 *Western Mail*, 'Colliery Explosion at New Tredegar', 21 Dec 1875, p.6, cols.1 & 2. The title fireman was years later changed to Deputy who reported to the Overman who reported, sometimes via an Assistant Manager, to the Colliery Manager.

94 *Western Mail*, 'Colliery Explosion at New Tredegar', 16 Dec 1875, p.6, col.4.

95 *Western Mail, op. cit.*, 21 Dec 1875, p.6, col.3.

96 *Western Mail, op. cit.*, 6 Dec 1875, p.5, col.3.

97 *Western Mail, op. cit.*, 16 Dec 1875, p.6, col.5.

98 *Western Mail, op. cit.*, 16 Dec 1875, p.6, col.5.

99 *Western Mail, op. cit.*, 6 Dec 1875, p.5, col.3.

100 According to the final death toll list, see later, his name was Arthur Edwards.

101 His correct name was Moses Prangley aged 30 years. 'Entry of Death' record of the General Register Office, Merthyr Tydfil District, and dated January, February & March 1876, Vol. 11a, p. 285. Sprangley's stall is repeated as spelt in subsequent *Western Mail* reports.

102 *Western Mail, op. cit.*, 6 Dec 1875, p.5, col.4.

103 *Western Mail, op. cit.*, 6 Dec 1875, p.5, col.4.

104 *Western Mail, op. cit.*, 7 Dec 1875, p.6, col.2.

105 E. M. Hann, *op. cit.*, p.4.

106 J. H. Morris and L. J. Williams, *op. cit.*, p.55.

107 *Western Mail, op. cit.*, 6 Dec 1875, p.5, col.4. 'Dallas' appears to be 'Dalziel', see later.

108 *Western Mail, op. cit.*, 6 Dec 1875, p.5, col.4.

109 *The Monmouthshire Merlin & South Wales Advertiser*, 'Terrible Colliery Accident at New Tredegar', 10 Dec 1875, p.3, col.2.

110 *Western Mail, op. cit.*, 10 Dec 1875, p.5, col.2.

111 *Western Mail, op. cit.*, 16 Dec 1875, p.6, cols.4 & 5.

112 *Western Mail, op. cit.*, 21 Dec 1875, p.6, cols.1 to 5.

113 *Western Mail, op. cit.*, 31 Dec 1875, p.6, col.6.

114 *Western Mail, op. cit.*, 21 Dec 1875, p.6, col.4.

115 Concerning the dependents details, *Western Mail, op. cit.*, 7 Dec 1875, p.5, col.1; otherwise *Western Mail, op. cit.*, 6 Dec 1875, p.5, col.4.

116 *The Monmouthshire Merlin & South Wales Advertiser*, 'Terrible Colliery Accident at New Tredegar', 10 Dec 1875, p.3, col.1. This reports these men as dead. Moreover, John Thomas's name was omitted from the deceased.

117 Estimated from a statement made by W. Gasgoyne Dalziel, a January copy of the *South Wales News*, in which the total wages lost by 10,000 men due to the 12 week strike in 1875 was put at £120,000. *Records of the several Coal Owners' Association of Monmouthshire and South Wales 1864 to 1895.* (Monmouthshire and South Wales Coal Owners' Association), p.176.

118 E. M. Hann, *op. cit.*, p.8.

119 *The Powell Duffryn Steam Coal Company 1864-1914, op. cit.*, pp.19-20.

120 See Records of the several Coal Owners' Association of Monmouthshire and South Wales 1864 to 1895. (Monmouthshire and South Wales Coal Owners' Association).

121 Charles Wilkins, *op. cit.*, p.84.

122 *The Powell Duffryn Steam Coal Company 1864-1914, op. cit.*, p.20.

123 D. A. Farne, *East and West of Suez.* (Clarendon, 1969), p.246.

124 D. A. Farne, *op. cit.*, p.247.

125 Charles Wilkins, *op. cit.*, p.112-3.

126 E. M. Hann, *op. cit.*, p.8.

127 John Hutton, *op. cit.*, p.64.

128 D. S. M. Barrie, *op. cit.*, pp.104 -6.

Chapter 3
ELLIOT COLLIERY

Following Sir George Elliot's retirement in 1877, Powell Duffryn appointed two men in his place. William Young Craig and Joseph Charles Parkinson were recruited, and called managing directors. Edmund Mills Hann described Craig as being '*an energetic and clever Colliery Manager, who had taken charge of collieries in South Staffordshire belonging to Sir George Elliot and others, and had also become an owner of Collieries there*'.[1] J. C. Parkinson, as mentioned earlier, was Sir George Elliot's son-in-law.

Craig and Parkinson set about reorganising the company. In 1878, the company's general manager of collieries, George Wilkinson, was pensioned off upon reaching his sixty-fifth birthday. Llewellyn Llewellyn, George Wilkinson's assistant and son-in-law, left the company for Risca Collieries.[2] Also in that year, Edmund Mills Hann applied for the vacant general manager of collieries' position. He became a candidate but Samuel Gilroy, who had been an Assistant Government Inspector of Mines for a few years, was chosen for the post.[3]

The year also saw the company action another notable management change. Bickerton Pratt was appointed general manager of 'the Commercial side'. He had served in the position of chief accountant from 1866 until 1873 when he was made joint general manager of the commercial side with David Griffiths, about whom nothing more was found.

Edmund Mills Hann

Regarding Edmund Mills Hann, though, early in 1879, Powell Duffryn offered him another position, which he accepted. The post, according to him, concerned supervising the opening out of the 'Ras Las' seam at the New Tredegar Colliery.[4] He started with the company in April 1879.

Edmund Mills Hann was born on the 22nd December, 1850, at Hetton-le-Hole, County Durham.[5] This mining community lay just south of Houghton-le-Spring where Sir George Elliot had his County Durham home. According to a dictionary of English surnames Hann, like Hancock, and Hankin, has 'usually' been 'regarded as a Flemish form of John, but they are probably English formations, sometimes from Johan, 'John'. Hanne was a very common Christian name in the thirteenth century Yorkshire'.[6] David Hann, writing in 1995, noted that Edmund Hann was the only child of William and Caroline née Hutchinson and was named after his maternal grandfather, a master mariner.[7] William Hann had been a colliery official before becoming a colliery agent. Tragedy struck this fledgling family. 'Within a year his mother had died, and he was brought up by his father helped by a disciplinarian servant, Margaret Hepple. He attended the

Edmund Mills Hann (1850-1931)
He joined Powell Duffryn in 1879 having been a Durham Coalfield mining engineer with Cleveland ironstone mining experience.   *Courtesy SWIE*

local school until he was fourteen years of age, when he left to begin work in coal mining at the Hetton collieries'.

A partner in Hetton Collieries was Nicholas Wood (1795-1865), the founding president of the North of England Institute of Mining Engineers, and known to Sir George Elliot. In 1925, Edmund Mills Hann recalled that Wood was endowed with a noble face and form, was frequently referred to as the Colliery Czar, and he saluted him as the '*prince of mining engineers*'.[8]

Edmund Mills Hann's link with Nicholas Wood may not have been personally close, but it was brief, lasting one year. Nicholas Wood died in 1865. Wood had been a promoter of education of knowledge for the mining industry, so it seems likely that technical study was encouraged at Hetton collieries. Indeed, Hann recalled that '*in my earlier days of mining the only facilities in the direction of technical education were a few evening classes, started by the Science of Arts Department, in which I was one of the earlier pupils*'.[9]

In 1868, Hann was elected to graduate membership of the North of England Institute of Mining Engineers.[10] This achievement, and a sense of duty to the Institute, was a reason for him to attend its presidential address that year, which was given by George Elliot. Being elected a full member of the North of England Institute of Mining Engineers was regarded among the coal mining fraternity of the counties of Durham and Northumberland as something prestigious. When the Mines Regulations Act of 1872 came into force, it required that a manager's certificate qualification, awarded through examinations, was needed for a colliery manager's post. Edmund Mills Hann classified himself throughout his career as a 'Mining Engineer', but the timing of his formation as an engineer suggests that he sat no examinations to obtain an associated qualification. However, he was elected a member of the North of England Institute of Mining in 1874, at twenty-four years of age, and this accolade possibly gave him the right to class himself as 'Mining Engineer'.

Edmund Mills Hann, after serving as Assistant Manager at Hetton Collieries, between the years 1865-72, joined Loftus Iron Company Limited. In 1873, he bid farewell to Glenside Cottage, his family's home at Hetton-le-Hole, and headed south to take a position either as the company's engineer, or manager.[11]

Cleveland Ironstone Mining

The Loftus Iron Company Limited was incorporated in June 1872. Its purpose was to mine ironstone on a part of an estate called South Loftus, which was located in countryside between the Cleveland Hills and the North Sea. Edmund Mills Hann lived at Brotton Hall, in the village of Brotton, situated ten miles east of Middlesbrough. After taking up his appointment he married Mary

Anne Brown of Shildon, County Durham. Their wedding took place at Shildon's parish church on the 11th August, 1874. Their first child, Florence Mable, was born in 1875, and their second, William Reginald, in 1876.

Test boring work, for the Loftus Iron Company, eventually yielded satisfactory results at South Loftus. Ironstone was found at 221 yards in one bore hole and at another, at 137 yards. Edmund Mills Hann reported that the analysis revealed excellent iron ore, but mining work was less than successful.

Around the time Hann joined Loftus Iron Company, his employer acquired mining interests on the South Crop of the South Wales Coalfield. In March 1873, the company purchased two collieries, Lanelay,[12] and Trecastle. At the time, the name of Thomas Powell Junior, as the seller of these collieries to Loftus Iron Company, had no meaning for Hann.[13]

Around the mid-1870s, the scope of Edmund Mills Hann's work in Cleveland grew. In June 1873, Loftus Iron Company took a lease for a pilot mine at a location close to South Loftus called Skinningrove Ridge. The mine's pilot shaft was later used as the downshaft for another acquisition, North Loftus, which became a success. In 1874, Edmund Mills Hann supervised the erection of two blast furnaces in the vicinity of the Cleveland mines. Subsequently, due to rivalry between the Whitby, Middlesbrough & Redcar Railway Company, and the North Eastern Railway, the blast furnaces became isolated from the railway system, and Loftus Iron Company's business suffered.

Edmund Mills Hann's career résumé for his application for membership of the Institution of Civil Engineers states: '*1872-77, in charge of opening ironstone mines in Cleveland, and collieries in South Wales, and in connection with blast furnaces*'.[14] So, Hann was gifted a forward position to obtain intelligence about managerial openings in South Wales. He fortunately moved to a new post in South Wales in 1877 since the Loftus Iron Company was wound up on the 2nd April, 1878.

Landore-Siemens Steel Company

Edmund Mills Hann became the Mining Engineer for the Landore-Siemens Steel Company, Swansea.[15] The sea town of Swansea was a venue for the meetings of the South Wales Institute of Engineers. He was elected a member of the Institute in 1878, and so came into contact with the leading engineers of the iron and steel, and coal mining industries of the South Wales Coalfield. Another engineer who had yet to make his mark in the South Wales Institute of Engineers was William Galloway.[16]

A Scot, Galloway, born in 1840, was the eldest son of William Galloway of Paisley, an owner of a shawl factory and a colliery. William Jnr studied at University of Giessen, the Blergakademie at Freiberg, Saxony and University College, London. After taking up the post of an assistant junior Inspector of Mines, he moved to the South Wales Coalfield, where in December 1875, he was party to investigating the Llan Colliery explosion mentioned earlier. This caused him to pursue research into the subject of coal dust in relation to colliery explosions.[17] In December 1911, Hann recalled: '*It was sometime in 1878 that Dr Galloway and I travelled together between Port Talbot and Swansea, and he related to me pretty fully the results of experiments that he had been making with coal dust, and his statement produced a great effect upon my mind at the time*'.[18] They were both destined to share at least one thing in common: sinking a colliery in the Rhymney Valley.

New Tredegar Colliery Assignment

The life of the Hann family experienced an unsettling period at the start of 1879. Edmund Hann's family relocated to Glanmore Crescent, Uplands, Swansea. In February 1879, his second son, George Gilroy, was born at Brotton, but his birth was registered in Swansea.[19] A short time afterwards, in April 1879, Edmund Mills Hann joined Powell Duffryn, and the family moved again, to Merthyr Tydfil, Glamorgan.[20]

Being based at Merthyr Tydfil indicated that Hann was recruited for company-wide assignments as a mining engineer. Geographically, Merthyr Tydfil lay roughly halfway between the company's Aberdare Valley collieries and the New Tredegar Colliery, the place for his first assignment. In supervising the opening out of the 'Ras Las' seam at the colliery, he undoubtedly heard accounts about the colliery's 1875 explosion.

Merthyr Tydfil, in addition to being a venue for meetings of the South Wales Institute of Engineers, was an international meeting centre for ironmakers and steelmakers. By mixing with engineers of this industry, as well as mining engineers, Hann stood to learn from their experiences, and ideas. For example, lessons learnt from the iron industry's coking processes could enable the likes of Powell Duffryn to improve its supply of coke for the blast furnace market. Nonetheless, Hann's stay in Merthyr Tydfil was short-lived.

In July 1880, Powell Duffryn saw a whirlwind of change in its board of directors.[21] First, due to the death of S. E. Bolden, Alexander Ogilvie became the company's chairman. Much more notably, perhaps, Sir George Elliot returned to run the company's operation. If he had regained the approval of the company's directors, the electorate of the North Durham Parliamentary constituency had rejected him at that year's General Election.

According to Edmund Mills Hann, Elliot's return was due to the results of William Young Craig and Joseph Charles Parkinson's management proving 'very unsatisfactory'. Craig and Parkinson's initial impact must have heartened the board since a loss of £43,000, in 1879, was followed by no further losses until about 1881. Yet, the company's intrinsic financial health was in a critical state.[22] The company was exposed to many liabilities such as: a £20,000 Lloyds Bond; a temporary loan of £60,000 from Rock Life Insurance; an excess of debits over credits of £80,000 to tradesmen, etc.; and a considerable overdraft at the bank. Edmund Mills Hann was to recall, in 1909, that '*it was generally considered both inside and outside the concern that the position was well nigh hopeless*'.

The baronet acted with decisiveness. William Craig was retired from his position as joint managing director, and Samuel Gilroy was dismissed as general manager of collieries. Since no details were found about what happened to Joseph Charles Parkinson during this cull of managers this might suggest that he left his position due to his own volition.

Sir George Elliot also recruited Henry W. Martin so that he could execute other management changes. Henry's father, George Martin (d. 1887), was a notable mining engineer of the South Wales Coalfield being the mining agent for the Dowlais Iron Company.[23] Henry Martin's early career involved assignments under Sir George Elliot in County Durham. In 1873, the Japanese Government commissioned Henry Martin to open collieries, and following this assignment he joined Powell Duffryn, and was put in charge of Lower and Middle Duffryn Collieries. Another management change saw John Noel made the manager of the Aberaman Works. Edmund Mills Hann was removed to Aberaman, and given charge of Fforchaman, Cwm Neol, Aberaman, and Old Duffryn Pits. Moreover, at the time, there was an intention to appoint a new colliery manager at New Tredegar Colliery, but since no promising person appeared, Hann retained the position.

Maybe for the first time in their lives, two County Durham men, Elliot and Hann, met. Hann was aware of Sir George Elliot's political activities since he recalled, in 1909, that 'about 1870 or a little later' an instance of 'Mr Elliot giving evidence before a Committee, or making a speech in Parliament' on the subject of the profitability of coal mining.[24] What opinion Elliot formed about Hann is unknown. Sir George Elliot was considered by Hann to be 'a man of very great mental abilities'.[25]

George Pit

Sir George Elliot return marked the start of another phase of colliery expansion by the company. He ignored the state of the company's finances, which was heading into the 'red'. In 1881, instructions were given to recommence the sinking of George Pit, high up on Mynydd Merthyr, north of Cwmpennar, Aberdare Valley. The sinking had begun in 1877, and proceeded into 1878. However, if naming George Pit represented a company's apology to its founder, for having retired him previously, it was gifted additional financial anxiety. No provision was made in the company's accounts for the £60,000 needed to fulfil his plans for George Pit. Nevertheless, two shafts were sunk, with its deepest, the Number 2, proving the Seven Foot seam at 486 yards.[26] Coal production began at George Pit in 1884.

Also, in 1881, Sir George Elliot directed the company to purchase Abercwmboi Colliery from Messrs D. Davis & Sons for £4,900. The colliery stood about one mile east of Aberaman. Hann later reflected that Abercwmboi Colliery's 'great service' to the company' was being used for 'pumping and ventilating, and in extending greatly the profitable life of Aberaman Pit'.[27] However, at least one event that year caused Elliot to suspend his renewed 'practical direction' of the company. Joicy, a newly elected Member of Parliament for the North Durham constituency, died, and a by-election, in September, 1881, saw Sir George Elliot returned to Westminster as a Member of Parliament.

Nonetheless, Edmund Hann had been told to sink a staple pit – an underground shaft connecting two seams – below the Nine Foot seam at Aberaman Colliery. The staple pit enabled the finding of the Yard and the Seven Foot seams, at 212 yards and 222 yards respectively.[28] However, there was a 'struggle to find a market for the coal'. Bickerton Pratt, the general manager of the commercial side of the company, was so disconsolate about the sales prospects for the Aberaman coal that he said to Hann: 'That will be your Lower Duffryn.' Lower Duffryn, according to Hann, had become a 'synonym in the company for everything that was bad, as he [Mr Pratt] had at that time computed a total loss at Lower Duffryn over a number of years at £200,000'.[29]

Fortunately, no doubt due partly to Bickerton Pratt's efforts, the warning he gave to Hann proved false. Edmund Mills Hann noted, decades later, that a market was eventually found for the Aberaman coal, and 'the low cost at which it could be produced assisted greatly,' and saliently added that it was 'from the working of these seams at the Aberaman Colliery that to a great extent provided the capital to sink new pits'.

If Powell Duffryn's esteem for Sir George Elliot had undergone a reappraisal, Durham University regarded him highly. On the 27th

June, 1882, the university awarded him an honorary Doctor of Civil Law. The Professor of Divinity, Reverend A. S. Farrar, praised him as a 'true son of the North', and noted that he was 'endowed with robustness of mind, fixedness of purpose, and untiring industry'.[30] Farrar also remarked upon Elliot's financial donations to public institutions 'such as our Newcastle Physical [Science] College, and has proved his ability and skill in the arts by encouraging the progress of the mechanical arts and directing public works'.

So what, ultimately, did Sir George Elliot's efforts and money help create? The North of England Institute of Mining Engineers' first president, Nicholas Wood, instigated an idea for a School of Mines, and also the study of 'geology … mineralogy, chemistry, mechanical philosophy, pneumatics, and mechanics' be part of the education of mining engineers'.[31] However, after Nicholas Wood's death, in December 1865, his wish went unfulfilled until George Elliot intervened, which 'was the start of a new initiative which was to be successfully developed'.[32] His initiative involved dealings with Durham University, which were eventually realised as Newcastle's College of Physical Science, which opened for its first academic year, which was 1871-72. The College was constituted under the auspices of Durham University. The college was a spur for further college developments, and so, in 1963, due to their higher education standing, the University of Newcastle upon Tyne was founded. Such an achievement lay in the future, but in the early 1880s Sir George Elliot's initiatives in the South Wales Coalfield were strategically important for Powell Duffryn.

General Manager of Collieries

In 1883, the founder of Powell Duffryn made a major appointment, the company's general manager of collieries. The minute books of the company's directors meetings also refer to this position as the Mineral Manager, which may explain why in later years it carried responsibility as the Company's Agent.[33]

Henry Martin was one Powell Duffryn manager who had a record of experience that made him a frontrunner for the position. However, Martin decided to leave the company in 1883 to take up the management of the Dowlais Iron Company's collieries. His departure may have helped Hann's promotion.

In 1883, at thirty-two years of age, Edmund Mills Hann became general manager of Powell Duffryn's collieries. He and his family took occupancy of the company's manager's house at Aberaman Terrace, Forge Row, Aberaman. He needed such a large home to accommodate his wife and, by the end of 1883, their five children. His third son, Edmund Lawrence, was born at Aberdare in 1881. Edmund Lawrence became the elder brother of Harold Browne who was born in 1883. The Hann's new home was a stroll away from the company's offices. He sat with his staff for a group photograph, perhaps taken circa 1888. It shows him wearing the badge of a manager of the period: a black bowler hat. He then had a wiry frame, and his full black beard framed a stern glare that casts an impression that he was less than comfortable with the occasion.

On the 29th September, 1883, he probably sat in the congregation of Aberaman's new Anglican Church. He and Bickerton Pratt reported to the sponsor of the building of the church, Sir George Elliot. The church was dedicated to St. Margaret of Antioch. That the diocesan powers of Llandaff approved the dedication suggests it was tolerant of some vanity. A wall mounted, brass plaque in the church was 'dedicated' to the memory of Sir George Elliot's wife, Margaret, and their daughter, Elizabeth'. His wife died in 1880,

Aberaman Offices Staff circa 1890. Standing (L to R): D. Edmunds - telephone clerk; W. B. Davies, works clerk; T. Thomas, correspondence clerk; Trevor Jones?, surveyor; R. W. Roberts, Accounts Department; D. M. Jones, assistant surface traffic; E. Hunt, traffic; T. Griffiths, colliery clerk. Seated: Mr Walker, chief surveyor; J. Lewis, draughtsman; J. M. Greenhow, engineer; E. M. Hann; Mr Harding, cashier; Mr Williams, surveyor; Rees Davies, traffic clerk; D. Jenkins, colliery clerk. Sitting on ground: D. M. Hughes, assistant colliery clerk; and Master Venables, messenger.

Courtesy of the late Edwin Greening Collection

and his daughter in 1861. Edmund Mills Hann became a devoted member of the church, and he had already begun to take an active part in the life of the community. In 1880, he became a member of the Aberdare Board of Health.[34]

When the County Durham mining engineer took up the post of general manager of collieries, he appraised the state of the company's colliery engineering. He was scolding of the Aberdare Valley colliery operation during the earlier Elliot era: '*Unfortunately, the working of the Powell Duffryn Collieries betwixt 1850 and 1875 was in careless hands*', which might explain the comparative low productivity of the company's collieries in 1870 versus Nixon, Taylor & Cory Co. Ltd.[35] The George Pit he reflected, '*was started as an air pit only, and the results have shewn that it would have been much better had it never been started*'. The expenditure in total '*was not only unremunerative, but blocked the way to far more important things, and prolonged very greatly, the duration of the Company's difficulties*'.[36] Indeed, '*in 1879 and 1880 the plant at the* [other] *pits was worn out and obsolete*'.[37]

Edmund Mills Hann was also put in an embarrassing position due the critical state of the company's finances. For the period, from around 1881 onwards up to about 1884 he wrote: '*I think – it was a very frequent occurrence for extreme difficulty in raising sufficient funds for the workmen's wages on pay day*'.[38] Although beset with financial woes, Powell Duffryn's general manager of collieries could only have been astounded to receive an instruction in 1883 to engineer a new colliery in the Rhymney Valley, Elliot Colliery.

Elliot Colliery

Sir George Elliot led the way to establish Elliot Colliery in the Rhymney Valley, at a location twenty miles north of Cardiff.[39] Sometime before 1883, in some secrecy, he speedily dealt with preliminary work aimed at establishing the colliery. R. H. Walters identified three actions pursued by Elliot.[40] The first action saw Elliot negotiate with Lord Tredegar's agent a mining lease.

R. H. Walters found that Elliot's role in securing the lease was vital since Lord Tredegar's agent disliked leasing property to limited companies, and Elliot became lessee on behalf of the company. Perhaps this was the reason why the colliery took his name. In 1895, The *Colliery Guardian* gave a description of the property leased:

'The Rumney (sic) River here forms the division between the counties of Monmouth and Glamorgan. Though Elliot pits are situated in Monmouthshire – about fifty yards east of the river – the entire property of 4,400 acres lies in almost equal portions under the two counties. The company's field of coal is not more than three and a-half miles east of Merthyr Vale, and their steam coal possess a near approach in point of quality to those of Merthyr and Aberdare valleys, the notable feature of the latter being the smokeless and high calorific properties.'[41]

Elliot's second action saw him take charge of negotiating railway rates, and supervising the construction of the company's private connecting railway. From an impartial point of view, Elliot was in a favourable position to negotiate railway rates in the company's favour. Two fierce rivals served the upper part of the Rhymney Valley: the Rhymney Railway Company, and the Brecon & Merthyr Railway Company.[42] The rails of the Rhymney Railway, which enabled coal to be transported to Cardiff, took the Rhymney Valley's western side. Formed in circa 1855, support for the Rhymney Railway Bill was gained in June 1854 from the First Lord of the Admiralty, Sir James Graham, who '*stated that the supply of Cardiff steam coal was unequal to the naval demand and any railway which could afford a new supply was an object of national importance*'.[43] The Brecon & Merthyr traced its way up the eastern side of the Rhymney Valley.[44] Sir George Elliot chose the Brecon & Merthyr so that the colliery's coal for export could be shipped out from Alexandra Dock, Newport.[45]

Nevertheless, what had spurred the baronet into action? The development of coal mining in the district surrounding New Tredegar appears to have regressed compared with coal mining's growth in other parts of the South Wales Coalfield. Nearly three decades had elapsed since Thomas Powell ventured into the Rhymney Valley, to sink New Tredegar Colliery. Even in 1871, many families left the district because they thought that the local levels and mines were soon to close.[46] Since 1864, Sir George Elliot's focus had been upon expanding Powell Duffryn's interests in the Aberdare Valley. The Rhymney Valley seemed to be far from his thoughts and, indeed, also those of other ambitious coalowners.

Charles Wilkins' 1888 survey of the 'Mineral Riches' of the South Wales Coalfield helpfully noted the districts in the van of winning steam coal:

'The Merthyr Four Feet steam coal, represented by the Four Feet from the Castle Pit, Cyfathfa, by Plymouth, Merthyr Vale, at Aberdare, and Rhondda, may be taken as the standard of excellence, and the closer approach to these nearer perfection of smokeless coal. From the original working of these coals at Merthyr and Aberdare, the best varieties of steam coal are called "Merthyr steam coal".

It is curious fact that the lower seams, Six and Nine Feet, that underlie the standard measure of Four Feet share in degree their superiority. We do not name this invidiously, and do not pretend to account for it, but the fact remains.'[47]

Nonetheless, of particular relevance to the northern end of the Rhymney Valley, Charles Wilkins gave a brief assessment. Regarding south of the town of Rhymney, he was speculative: '*From New Tredegar to Caerphilly a great field remains*' to be discovered. The coalowners had studied the structural geology of the Rhymney Valley. The geology forewarned them that desired coal seams lay at a greater depth under the valley's floor compared, for example, with the associated seams in the Aberdare and Rhondda Valleys.

Sir George Elliot's spur for action came from learning, 'about the year 1882', that the Rhymney Iron Company and the landowner, Lord Tredegar, were in an advanced state of negotiations regarding the land south of New Tredegar Colliery. He acted with bravado. According to Hann, he intervened under an old agreement betwixt Lord Tredegar and himself, and took lease of it, and so the Elliot Colliery site was secured.[48] The deal also involved further potential coal mining territory to the south of the site. The baronet's activities, and negotiations, took place without Hann's knowledge.

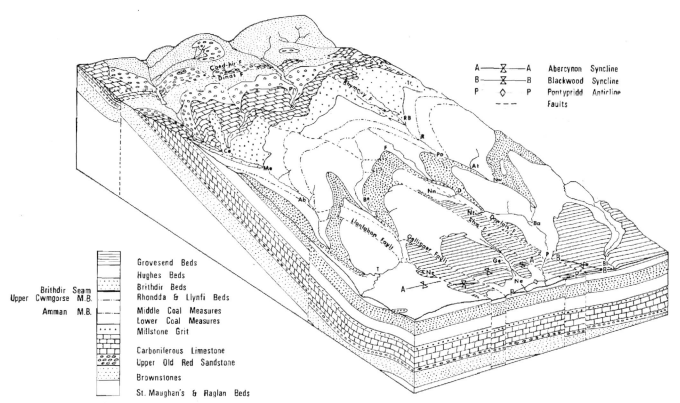

Geological Structure of the upper Rhymney Valley. Ab– Aberafan; At– Abertyssg; Ba– Bargoed*; Nant Cylla*; Be– Bedlinog; Bl– Blackwood; Ce– Cefn Coed-y-cymmer; D– Deri*; F– Fochriw; Ge– Gelligaer; Me– Merthyr Tydfil; Ne– Nelson; Nl– Nant Cylla*; Nn– Nant Ffynon; Nt– Nant Twpa; Nw– New Tredegar*; Pe– Pengam*; Po– Pontlottyn; R– Rhymney; RB– Rhymney Bridge; Tr–Trefil; Ts– Treharris.
NB: * indicates locations where Powell Duffryn sank collieries.
D. Emlyn Evans, 'A Traverse Across the Eastern Part of the South Wales Coalfield via the Rhymney Valley' in Geological Excursions in South Wales & Forest of Dean. *Courtesy of the Geologists' Association South Wales Group.*

Elliot Colliery. Elliot West, headgear left of picture, was sunk in 1883, and afterwards, in 1888, the sinking of Elliot East began, which is the headgear right of picture. These were Powell Duffryn's first sinkings in the Rhymney Valley, and the first new colliery engineered by Edmund Mills Hann, which he considered became operational in 1890.   *Pope/Parkhouse Archive*

Edmund Mills Hann wrote: '*Early in the year 1883, I received sudden instructions to commence the sinking of the West Elliot Shaft*'.[49] Hann's candour about the event prompts a notion that it was intended as a reproach of Sir George Elliot's way of doing business. Indeed, the sinking of new pits and allocation of contract work was the third and last of the actions that Elliot took charge of, so usurping a role of the general manager of collieries. Although faced with a *fait accompli* as regards the allocation of colliery plant contract work, Edmund Mills Hann's task involved engineering his first major colliery.

New Tredegar District's Mining

Elliot pit's site stood just southward of the narrowest part of the Rhymney Valley on roughly the 700 foot contour. The site lay not far from the right-hand bank of the Nant Syfiog [Strawberry Brook] before the brook joined the Rhymney River.

In the early 1880s, north-west of the village of New Tredegar on the Glamorgan side of the valley, were two coal levels north of the hamlet of Tirphil. Smoke from coke ovens adjacent to these levels hung around the basin of the valley's floor on the edge of New Tredegar. The basin was contemptuously referred to as Pantymyg (Smoky Hollow).[50]

In the district around New Tredegar, in addition to Powell Duffryn's colliery to its north and the White Rose Level, there were in the early 1880s four further collieries. Complete with an engine house was Tirphil Colliery, which stood south of the same-named hamlet. Westwards from the site of the Elliot pit, on the Glamorgan side of the Rhymney River, was the Brithdir Colliery,

a level, opened in 1875, and closed that year due to flooding – a warning for Powell Duffryn to heed.

Immediately south of the site of Elliot pit was Hope Colliery. A possible previous owner of the colliery was Thomas Powell since in 1875 the colliery's proprietors were Messr H. & W. Powell, his sons.[51] The Hope Colliery worked the Brithdir seam at roughly 30 yards below the surface. In 1861, there was an explosion at the colliery, but searches found no record of deaths.

However, finding a record about the demise of the Powell brothers compensated.[52] Thomas Powell, junior, who lived at Coldra Hall [now the Celtic Manor Hotel, Newport], was murdered with his wife and a child on a shooting expedition in Abyssinia (Ethiopia) on the 8th April, 1869.[53] His youngest brother, Walter Powell, was elected a Conservative M. P. for Malmesbury in 1868. A bachelor, he acquired a passion for ballooning. On the 10th December, 1881, then thirty-nine years of age, Powell flew in a government balloon with two other men. Spying the English Channel, during attempts to land the balloon, his fellow crewmen fell over board and were seriously injured. The balloon climbed rapidly skywards, and Walter Powell was never seen again. The surviving brother, Henry St. John Powell, lived to fifty-six years of age dying at Cirencester on the 13th December, 1894, suffering a 'sharp attack of gout, followed by a paralytic stroke'.[54] Hope Colliery, of course, also had a life span, and was abandoned in 1877, although the 1885 Ordnance Survey map shows it with coke ovens.[55]

About a half a mile south of Hope Colliery, on the Glamorgan side of the valley, was the Cefn y Brithdir Colliery. On a walk to a terrace of houses near the colliery was the George Inn that the Rhymney

Railway had used to name the adjacent station. The date when the colliery was sunk is not known, but it closed in 1908 having worked the Brithdir seam.[56] The colliery seems to have also been called George Colliery before it closed. Cefn y Brithdir Colliery was owned by the Rhymney Iron Company, and its main purpose was to supply the Rhymney Iron Company's blast furnaces with coke.

A steam coal venture of the Rhymney Iron Company, New Duffryn Colliery, occurred nearly two decades earlier, in 1867, and it mined for house coal at Mardy Colliery, which was opened in 1876.[57] The New Duffryn Colliery stood westward of the company's iron works. The Mardy Colliery was located on the outskirts of Pontlottyn. So, the iron making company appeared to be in no rush to diversify its business into the steam coal trade. However, the offer that the Rhymney Iron Company made to the Tredegar Estate for mining rights for what became the Elliot pit suggests that the company's aim was to grow its steam coal business.

Sir George Elliot had nurtured some personal relationship with Lord Tredegar. In 1875, following the opening of Newport's Alexandra Docks, Godfrey Morgan, who somehow had survived the 'Charge of the Light Brigade', became the 2nd Baron Tredegar following the death of his father. Nevertheless, Elliot entered into a competition to obtain a mining lease from the Tredegar Estate. Maybe Sir George Elliot's victory bid for the Tredegar Estate lease was due to him having a greater hunger for steam coal than the Rhymney Iron Company. Regardless, just as in business, there was also no sentiment among the parties to the lease negotiations for preserving the attractions of the natural features of the district.

Rising steeply eastwards from the site of Elliot pit was a flank of Mynydd Bedwellty [Mynydd, mountain; the meaning of Bedwellty has been proposed as being 'birch covered slopes']. The hillside of Mynydd Bedwellty held on to rural charm. The whale-back ridge of Mynydd Bedwellty separated the Rhymney Valley from its eastern neighbour, the Sirhowy Valley. Woods of oak trees clung to the hillside east of the Elliot pit. Acres of fern and gorse fought for ground in the woods. Carpets of bluebells flowered in late spring under the boughs of the trees. The red dots of foxgloves decorated the green of the fern in summer.

The Nant Syfiog rose in a subsidiary valley to the Rhymney Valley, known as Cwm Syfiog [strawberry valley]. In this valley, hill farms had fields set aside for arable farming, meadow, and pasture. A conflict between the district's rural aspect and Industrial Society began with the arrival of the sinking contractor for Elliot pit. Eventually the brook, that had taken centuries to etch its course into Pennant Sandstone, would be culverted under the Elliot pit's site. The engineer had an interest in the water of the Nant Syfiog as a resource for raising steam to power engines. The brook was dammed to serve as a reservoir.

Sir George Elliot's original intention was to ventilate the underground workings of Elliot Colliery from New Tredegar Colliery so deeming that only one pit needed to be sunk.[58] Edmund Mills Hann's problem was: could New Tredegar Colliery's ventilation system safely manage Elliot pit's workings located over a mile away underground?

In 1883 the sinking of Elliot's pit began. A shaft eighteen feet in diameter was excavated. Hann knew, as McCutcheon later recorded, that sinking to such depths in the North-East of England 'meant special hazards ... water-bearing strata and quicksands'. McCutcheon also wrote about a 'battle between sinkers and underground rivers' which he referred to as feeders of water.[59]

The actual method adopted by the contractors, to sink the Elliot Colliery shaft, is not known. Sinking a pit's shaft, though, was an adventure in engineering. The *Colliery Guardian* reported, in 1895, that during the sinking at Elliot Colliery '*considerable feeders of water were met with at various beds of sandstone*', and described how they were managed:

'Water was dealt with by placing "Cameron" pumps at various depths in the shaft up to 220 yards, where a lodge room was made at the side, and a Cameron pump with two inverted steam cylinders and two 6 in. single-acting rams, was fixed on buntons for a top lift. The sinking was continued further, Cameron pump of two 12-inch steam cylinders and two 4½-inch rams employed for draining other beds of sandstone below, until a depth of 392 yards was attained, where the Cameron pump last named was fixed on buntons. The sinking 48 yards further to the Red seam was not attended with any difficulties arising from water. The maximum feeder was given out from a bed of sandstone at 320 yards depth, with other feeders above, amounted to 600 gallons per minute for a short time.'[60]

The shaft was lined with 9-inch firebrick, set in Aberthaw lime. No action was taken to either install cast iron tubing, or watertight brick, to keep the water back.

The company's fifty years history can be interpreted to suggest that there was an air of conquest within it about the sinking of Elliot Colliery. The writer of the history appeared to brag that nature had submitted to man.[61] However, this might have been written due to sanguine reflection rather than smugness. The sinking work was attended with the greatest difficulties, owing to immense flow of water. Revealingly, the writer attributed the compliments for the great skill and perseverance that occurred during the pit's sinking to the management, Edmund Mills Hann.

The clangour of the activity associated with Elliot's pit's single shaft halted in April, 1885, when at a depth of 440 yards mining of the Red Vein commenced. The initial results were not satisfactory for a long time owing to a lack of ventilation, and a lot of barren ground.[62] Much more menacingly, during 1885, coal 'seams where were won were found to be too fiery to carry out the original intention'.[63] With the properties of the coal at the Elliot pit being more or less similar to that at New Tredegar Colliery, and its 1875 disaster being a comparatively recent event, this phenomenon of nature could have been foreseen. So, when Edmund Mills Hann was instructed by Sir George Elliot to begin sinking the Elliot pit, hope and haste triumphed at the expense of reason. Powell Duffryn, as explained more fully later, reacted to the unsatisfactory underground results, and decided to sink another pit, which became Elliot East and was designated as the 'downcast' shaft, so assigning as the 'upcast', the first pit, which became Elliot West.[64]

Elliot East

In 1888, the sinking of Elliot East began, and in fifteen months the Lower Four-Feet seam was reached at 530 yards.[65] Mrs E. M. Hann may have cut the first turf to mark the start of its sinking.[66] The shaft was 18ft in diameter, and located 43 yards distant from the first shaft, which thereafter was known as the West shaft, or pit. 'In sinking the East shaft the water was easily managed, draining to the west pit either naturally or through drifts made between the shafts. The Elliot East shaft was also lined with 9-inch firebrick set in Aberthaw lias lime'. A permanent pumping engine was afterwards placed at each shaft. The West shaft was also sunk a

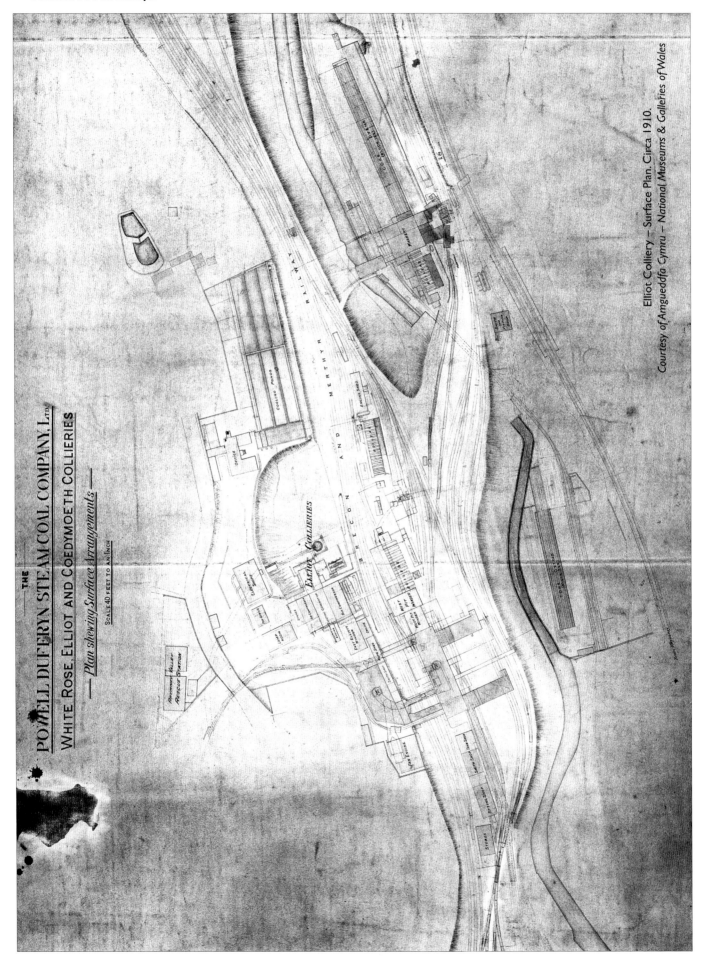

THE

POWELL DUFFRYN STEAM COAL COMPANY, L<small>TD.</small>

WHITE ROSE, ELLIOT AND COEDYMOETH COLLIERIES

— *Plan shewing Surface Arrangements* —

SCALE 40 FEET TO AN INCH

Elliot Colliery – Surface Plan. Circa 1910.
Courtesy of Amgueddfa Cymru – National Museums & Galleries of Wales

further 90 yards so as to make a connection with the Lower Four-Feet seam. The shafts bottomed out at nearly one thousand feet below sea level.

Hilda Evans proposed that some of the oldest families in New Tredegar were descendants of the original sinkers in the area. She named them as the Lee's, Gulliver's, Hayward's, Hayfield's, Perriman's, Russell's, Radford's, Stephen's, and Bellamy's.[67] Sinking a shaft was a filthy shift of toil. Oz Clarke once wrote: '*Thirsty work … demands quenching beer, not head banging stuff*'.[68] By 1867, the sinkers could drink beer supplied by Andrew Buchan & Company's brewery at Rhymney, which was 'considered the largest in South Wales'. 'In 1888 Buchan's Old Beer won a silver medal at the Brewers Exhibition in London, with the stout taking the bronze'.[69] The sinkers' talk might have included reports about the remains of the Earth nearly 280 million years ago. However, the coal seams they found were of greater interest to Powell Duffryn than their impressions about the Carboniferous system of the Mesozoic era.[70]

Coal Seam	Thickness in Feet	Depth from Surface in Yards
Upper Coal Measures:		
Brithdir or Tillery	3ft 5in.	30
Middle Coal Measures:		
Elled	1ft 3in.	385
Big Vein	6ft 9in.	405
Yard Vein	4ft 9in.	408
Red Vein	3ft 6in.	440
Ras Las	3ft 8in.	450
Little Vein	3ft 0in.	483
Lower Four	5ft 6in.	530
Sump of shaft – depth	18 yards	548

The bill for sinking Elliot Colliery was an acute concern of Powell Duffryn's. R. H. Walters found that the capital cost of sinking both the Elliot East and West shafts was £209,772.[71] Of the thirty-three collieries he studied, four were more expensive to sink than Elliot Colliery. The Harris Navigation Colliery, of the Harris Navigation Steam Coal Company, situated at Treharris, five miles north-north-east from Pontypridd in the Taff Vale, was the most expensive where circa £350,000 was spent sinking its shaft No. 2 to 760 yards, in 1878. This was then a record depth for a shaft in the South Wales Coalfield.

A Rhymney Valley contemporary of the sinking of Elliot Colliery was Cardiff Steam Coal Collieries Co. Ltd, Llanbradach Colliery, that cost £270,434 for two shafts, one being 572 yards, and the other 584 yards deep. The sinking of Llanbradach colliery began in 1887, under the direction of William Galloway, then a consulting engineer.[72]

Nonetheless, the decision to sink two shafts at Elliot Colliery caused a commitment to buy colliery plant and machinery. Powell Duffryn's capital outlay can be estimated to have been in the region of £183,000.[73] So, with the company in financial difficulty, where did the money come to pay for such investment? In the context of the continued survival of Powell Duffryn throughout the 1870s and 1880s it would appear, according to Trevor Boyns, '*to have been the very low costs of production at the Fforchaman and Aberaman collieries*' that was influential according to a statement of Edmund Mills Hann's: '*Nothing so much assisted the Company throughout the bad years of 1875 to 1882, as the cheap working*

of Fforchaman Colliery; and since those years too, it has been a great factor in providing sinking the Elliot Pits and making other extensions and improvements.'[74]

Trevor Boyns evaluated this statement: '*It would appear then that the factor enabling the company to sink new collieries after 1880 was the low cost of production at certain of the Aberdare collieries. How much of the cost of sinking Elliot pits of £209,772 was actually contributed by the Fforchaman colliery is uncertain, but it seems clear that, without this colliery the company would have been forced to raise far more capital in the form of loans, than the substantial amounts which were actually borrowed.*'[75]

Elliot Colliery was a gamble. For a company in a perilous financial state, the outcome could have been fatal. The risk could be made less severe if the operating costs of the colliery's coal production could be kept low. Key to achieving low operating costs was the design of the colliery's plant and equipment, and the performance of its workforce. So, on what plant and equipment was foraged funds spent to engineer the colliery?

Winding Wealth

A pit's wheel spinning atop a headgear structure, erected over a shaft, was a sign that either a cage carrying trams of coal was being wound, or one carrying miners was in transit. Colliery headgears also attract people's attention. The tallest of structures in a locality tend to draw the eye to them. As spires, and towers distinguish churches one from another, so collieries could be considered different from each other due to headgears. Headgears further caught the imagination of some people in the South Wales Coalfield as symbols of work, life, and death. Elliot Colliery's headgear utilised joists and lattice girders in its structural design.

The winding of miners and coal involved an integrated system of plant, machinery, and equipment. Steam energy from a boiler powered a winding engine that moved a crank mechanism to turn a drum, on which a rope coiled, or uncoiled. The moving rope ran up and over a headgear's sheaves [pulleys]. A rope's end was attached, via a rigging of chain, to a cage. In practice each drum accommodated two winding ropes, one for each of two cages, which were 'raised and lowered alternately and which at any instant' were 'moving at the same speed, though in opposite directions'.[76] Such an operation was the result of centuries of engineering development.[77] The engine and drum, were installed in a building known as a winding house.

At Elliot Colliery two winding houses were built. One served the West shaft, and the other the East, which has been preserved. The most important technical decision that Edmund Mills Hann made at this stage for Elliot Colliery concerned winding engines.

Winding Engines

The first steam engine erected at Elliot Colliery was supplied by Messrs Joicey & Co. The engine was assembled in what became the West's winding house. As a rough guide to the date of the introduction of steam winding into the South Wales Coalfield, the first one in the Rhondda Valley was erected at the Newbridge Pit, near Pontypridd, by John Calvert, in 1844.[78] Perhaps a useful general measure of the advance of steam technology in the South Wales Coalfield can be made by referring to Morris and Williams who judged that 'by 1874, when the Griffin pit, Nant-y-glo, changed over to steam winding', water-balance winding could be referred to as 'old fashioned'.[79]

Elliot Colliery circa 1903. In the foreground is a branch line of the Rhymney Railway, which was built immediately after parliamentary approval in 1900. Right of the foot of the chimney stack appears to be a Lancashire boiler, which might be a sign of changes to boiler plant so as to enable the introduction of compound steam winding at the colliery. *Pope/Parkhouse Archive*

ELLIOT COLLIERY, NEW TREDEGAR.

Durham Coalfield engineers had a fondness for Joicey steam winding engines. Watkins considered that the vertical type of engine appeared 'to have originated in the county of Durham with the patent of Phineas Crowther of Newcastle-on-Tyne in 1800', and 'since Crowther was a Newcastle man it is probable that this type of engine was used in the Durham pits soon after its inception'.[80] The company, Messrs J. & G. Joicey, was founded in 1855.[81] A merit of he Joicey design, it seems, was 'to dispense with the usual beam by placing the crankshaft above the cylinder and guiding the crosshead by a parallel motion similar to that included in James Watt's patent of 1784'. Watkins observed that: 'one of the distinctive features of the vertical winding engine was the tall ashlar engine-house, a feature of the Durham scene ... Their massive proportions and the horizontal rope leading to the headgear pulleys were characteristic of the type'.[82] And its vertical single-steam winding engine 'became a standard type' in the Durham Coalfield.

The Joicey engine supplied to Elliot Colliery did not conform in respect of the type of engine commonly used in the Durham Coalfield. Installed at Elliot West Colliery was a simple steam engine, which used Cornish valves, featured two horizontal cylinders 36-inch diameter having a 6ft stroke. The Joicey engine powered a drum, 20ft in diameter, 7ft 6in. wide.

Regarding the winding engine used for the 'East Elliot Pit', Edward Mills Hann gave prospective engine suppliers a demanding specification to meet. *Engineering*, in 1892, later noted the outcome: the 'Pit is expected to rank shortly as the most important in South Wales, and the engines have … been designed with a view

of raising 1,400 tons of coal per day'.[83] The cargo, which the East Elliot engine was designed to lift, was two trams, each weighing 9 cwt. and each carrying 27 cwt. of coal.[84] Thus making the total coal lifted per cage equal to 2 ton 14 cwt., and so demanding of the engine some 520 cage lifts of coal per day.

Engine Number 604

The Elliot East's engine was made in the workshops of Thornewill & Warham, Burton upon Trent, Staffordshire. Thornewill & Co., was created in the 1740s, and became Thornewill & Warham in 1849 due to the formation of a partnership between Robert Thornewill and John Robson Warham. By 1870, Thornewill & Warham had acquired a national reputation for steam engine manufacture.[85]

Powell Duffryn placed an order with Thornewill & Warham to supply a steam engine to Elliot Colliery around 1888. Thornewill & Warham's number for the Elliot East engine was 604, and this was dated to 1891. Today, Briggs of Burton PLC, who acquired Thornewill & Warham by 1930, no longer possess old records since they were destroyed in a fire.[86] Luckily, Dr C. C. Owen made a record of a sample of orders before this mishap.[87] He revealed that from circa 1855 to 1900, that the company supplied engines of various types to breweries, collieries, mines, a pottery works, a sanitary works, and a laundry. A Welsh gold mine was supplied a horizontal engine, number 227. Engines were exported to at least Argentina, British Guiana, Peru, Japan, and Australia. The Elliot Colliery engine found itself between a pumping and winding

Elliot East Colliery's Thornewill & Warham Winding Engine. Made in Burton upon Trent, the cylinders of the simple steam engine were 42-inch diameter x 6ft stroke. The engine drove a drum of 24ft diameter and winding raised 2 tons 14 cwt of coal per cage lifted.
Courtesy of the Institution of Mechanical Engineers

engine (numbers 597-8) for Taeping Colliery, China, and a winding engine (number 630) for Dundee Coal Company, Natal, South Africa.

The engine that Thornewill & Warham made, and erected inside the East Elliot winding house was a twin cylinder engine. In 1892, *Engineering* described that it had:

'Valves worked by a rocking lever, the cut-off being adjustable by the governor. The cylinders are 42in. in diameter and the stroke is 6ft; the metal is 1⅝in. thick. They are fixed to bedplates by eight 2in. bolts. The nozzle-boxes, at each end of the cylinders contain two valves each, both of the Cornish type. ..... The steam valve is 10½in. in diameter and the exhaust valve is made very deep to reduce clearance. The spindles of the steam valves are fitted with dashpots at their upper ends, and those of the exhaust valves with cylindrical weights. ..... The yoke of the steam valve is fitted with an adjustable spring-loaded tumbler having steel toes which engage with similar toes on the wiper. This tumbler is adjustable in position by the governor and regulates the cut-off. The reversing gear is of the Allan straight-link type, and the eccentrics are placed on the opposite side of the cylinders to the valves.'[88]

Engine number 604 was classed as a simple engine: a single cylinder with its piston double acting. That is its piston moved (expanded) by steam being admitted alternately to either side of it. In the 1880s, steam pressure at around 80 pound per square inch was commonly used to operate winding engines. An engine was dimensionally sized to meet its predicted duty with some contingency allowance.

The Thornewill & Warham winding operation commenced raising coal 'about the middle of August 1891'.[89] George Watkins, reflecting upon the engine in 1978, was of the opinion that it was 'typical of many hundreds of heavy duty winders that sustained the coal industry for nearly a century'.[90]

Boiler Plant

Like most collieries of its time, Elliot Colliery's steam raising boiler plant stood remote from the winding house. Steam was piped from the boilers to the winding engine. When Elliot Colliery opened, Lancashire boilers most likely supplied steam for the colliery.[91] However, records show that the colliery used both Lancashire and Babcock & Wilcox water-tube boilers by 1895. 'Bennis' mechanical stokers fed the furnace of these boilers.

The use of theses stokers seems to suggest an advance on the common practice of them being 'hand fired'. In this a fireman shovelled coal through furnace doors into the mouth of the flue. He heard the 'ring of the shovel and the clang of the iron door'. Probably coal was manually loaded into the feed hopper of the Bennis stoker.

Barnard wrote that the popularity of the Lancashire boiler was due to 'its simple construction, its ability to cope with sudden large demands for steam [essential when starting winding a cage from the foot of a shaft], and the fact that it can use inferior feed water with less trouble than the water-tube type'.[92] Although generally popular he advised that, 'it *takes at least six hours to get a Lancashire "up to steam", where a water-tube boiler can "have steam up" in two'.[93]

Babcock & Wilcox supplied the eight water-tube boilers erected at Elliot Colliery.[94] The boilers used waste gases piped from coke ovens, dealt with later, to heat water. The boiler making company was established in the United States of America in 1881 having evolved from an earlier partnership between two engineers, Stephen Wilcox, and George Herman Babcock. In 1856, Stephen Wilcox conceived a significant break-through for water tube boilers. The design he developed incorporated inclined water tubes connecting water spaces at the front and rear, allowing better water circulation and more heating surface. In 1881, the company set up a sales office in Glasgow, and ten years later a British company, Babcock & Wilcox Ltd, was formed. The first completely British-built Babcock boiler was made in 1885 at the Singer sewing machine company works, Clydebank, Glasgow. In 1895, the boiler making company opened its own manufacturing plant at Renfrew, near Glasgow.

So, the boilers made for Elliot Colliery were made at the Singer works. It was, perhaps, something of a coincidence that some part of the wages of workers at the colliery would later be spent on buying Singer sewing machines for their housewives to make, or repair clothes. Patched clothing was also sensible for men to wear if they had to crawl around the inside of a shut down water-tube boiler to inspect its condition. The boilers went back into service once any maintenance was completed. They were designed to work at 120 lb/in² pressure, but were operated at 80 lb/in². With steam raised, the winding engines were set in motion to drive the winding drum.

In 1895, the Thornewill and Warham engine drove a parallel drum of 24ft diameter around which rope was wound. The drum was an assembly of cast iron centres, and wrought iron arms, with the rim being a cylinder made of wrought iron plate.[95] For comparison, the West pit's winding drum was of identical form, but 20ft diameter. The wound ropes ran out through apertures in the wall of the winding house.

Wire Rope

Elliot Colliery's miners entrusted their lives, for just a brief moment, twice a work shift, to the integrity of a steel rope of just less than two-inches in diameter during their descent, or ascent of a pit's shaft. At the time when Elliot Colliery began production T. H. Deakin of Lydney, a colliery manager in the Forest of Dean Coalfield, wrote an historical account about the development of wire ropes.[96]

Of particular interest, Deakin mentioned rope recently made by Messrs G. Elliot & Company. The company's head office was at 23, Great George Street, Westminster, London, which also served as Powell Duffryn's Registered Office. The coincidence certainly made it easier for Sir George Elliot to fulfil at least two London business engagements. Messrs G. Elliot & Company had works at Cardiff, and near Newcastle upon Tyne.[97] At some stage the company hired the services of Arthur Latch (1847-1910), and subsequently he qualified for being in the good books of Sir George Elliot.[98] Latch was '*dissatisfied with the wire rope then being made*'. '*It was of left-handed lay referred to nowadays as ordinary or reverse lay*'. '*In this the amount of individual wire surface presented to wear was limited, consequently excessive abrasion and wear took place and the wires fractured prematurely*'.

Arthur Latch's concern about the lay of a wire rope moved him to raise it as a topic with his cousin, Telford Clarence Batchelor (1857-1947), who possessed a gift for invention. Batchelor was born on the 2nd August, 1857, at Christchurch, Newport, Monmouthshire.[99] Telford Batchelor's father, Henry, was a shipbuilder and is said to have built Wales' first iron ship, *Cinderella*, at a Newport yard.[100]

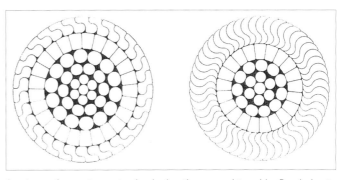

Sections of two pioneering Locked-coil ropes achieved by Batchelor in 1883-84.
T. H. Davies, Telford Clarence Batchelor (1857-1947); A Memoir.

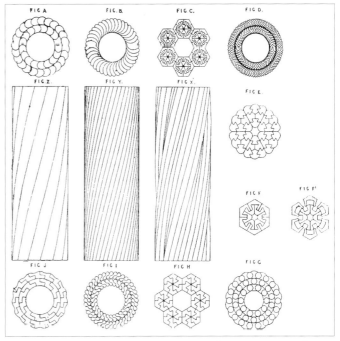

Telford Clarence Batchelor (1857-1947)
Born at Christchurch, Newport, Monmouthshire he invented locked-coil and flattened-strand wire ropes. Sir George Elliot sponsored the commercial development of these inventions.
T. H. Davies, Telford Clarence Batchelor (1857-1947); A Memoir

Diagrams accompanying the Locked-coil ropes master Patent Specification No. 5724 dated 1884.
T. H. Davies, Telford Clarence Batchelor (1857-1947); A Memoir.

Telford Batchelor served a mechanical engineering apprenticeship, and developed a skill for the draughtsmanship of complex mechanisms. His father relocated his financially troubled business to London around 1877, and, upon his death, in 1888, Telford Batchelor took over its running. Telford's speciality was in ship's machinery. He had no practical experience with ropes and had no knowledge of their manufacture prior to him listening to Arthur Latch express his hope for improvements in wire making. The sequel was, according to Dr H. W. Dickinson, 'a great step in advance'.[101] Telford Batchelor invented locked-coil and flattened-strand wire ropes. Arthur Latch then confided in Sir George Elliot about the technical achievement. Elliot was so enthusiastic about the invention that he furnished facilities for making the rope in his company's works at Cardiff's Bute Docks and at Newcastle.

T. H. Davies judged that without powerful support it was '*highly doubtful whether the invention [locked-coil rope] would have been persisted in*'. He added an inventor's refrain: '*Such are the trials and difficulties that, contrary to popular belief, occur in bringing master inventions to fruition*'.[102] Elliot's support of Batchelor's inventiveness was as much a gamble as it was a pursuit of self-interest.[103] Messrs G. Elliot & Company stood to lose money if the invention failed commercially, but the reward for a viable locked-coil rope could be a rich return for the risk. On the 2nd July 1886, a locked-coil

rope licence was granted to Elliot's wire rope company.[104] The first recorded customer for a locked-coil rope was the Old Delabole slate quarry, Cornwall, in July 1886.[105] Latch and Batchelor's locked-coil wire ropes, as they were first branded, was pilot marketed by Elliot's company at The International Inventions Exhibition of 1885. Later it was shown at an exhibition held at Newcastle in 1887.[106] Powell Duffryn collieries were supplied with ropes made by Messrs G. Elliot & Company. Locked-coil ropes became the standard used in Britain for winding applications.

The descent underground affected colliery workers in different ways. Some men would exchange scraps of news about the town's political, sporting, and social life. Other men preferred their own privacy, and may have meditated upon how their life depended upon the strength of steel wire. Miners might have drawn comfort from the later findings of a Government Inspector of Mines, A. E. Crook. In 1946, he reported that '*the number of people who are transported each day, it is very gratifying to know that the accident-rate is comparatively low*'. Significantly, for the late 1940s, the scale of human movement was exceedingly large: '*More than 500,000 persons are lowered and raised in shafts every day [in the British coal industry], and the number of persons who can be in shaft at one time*

A wire rope making machine having a link with 'Sir George Elliot & Co.'. Displayed at Royal Mining, Engineering and Industrial Exhibition at Newcastle upon Tyne, 1887.

varies from 4 at small collieries to more than 100 at large collieries'.[107] Good engineering practice, policed due to Government regulation, made such an outcome possible.

Indeed, colliery engineers, and mechanics, shouldered a considerable responsibility when installing a new winding rope. The handover after this work, by the colliery engineer to production, resulted in the responsibility for winding passing to an engineman.

The Colliery's Steersman

Enginemen controlled the operation of the winding engines at Elliot Colliery.[108] The rarity of winding accidents was a 'tribute to the skill and care of engineers and engineman alike'. Their eyes and ears at the pit bottom, and pit top, were respectively known as an 'Onsetter', and 'Banksman'. A signal system enabled them to communicate.

The engineman needed some special personal capabilities, regardless of engineered safeguards, to deal with winding mistakes. He needed to be ever alert, quick to react when there was a mishap, and remain calm when taking corrective action. He had also to be at home with solitude since his was generally a lonely occupation. His technical knowledge had to be adequate for helping the diagnosis of winding problems.

Trevor Boyns noted that the winding-engineman garnered praise: '*Numerous technological developments led to greater safety in this respect* [protection against over-winding], *and with the increase skill of the winding-engineman, deaths from this cause was almost totally eliminated. Indeed towards the end of the nineteenth century the inspectors often remark upon the skill and efficiency of this group of workers'.*[109] With the exception of the colliery manager, the enginemen were the best paid men at the colliery.

A visit to the engine houses at Elliot Colliery would have left an impression about the pride, and sense of ownership, that these men had in their place of work. They dressed as if they were office staff, and displayed a gold watch and chain. Permission to enter a winding house was granted by an engineman as if it was a regal favour. The inside walls of each winding house were painted green up to the window sills, and white above to the ceilings. Engine bedplates, cranks and drums were painted black. The steel cladding covering the steam cylinders had a blue finish. Guide bars and associated components featured a dual green colour scheme. Selected youths kept the place and the equipment spotlessly clean. The engines and equipment looked in pristine condition. Moving parts of the engine were burnished steel and regularly polished with tallow. The brass and copper scantlings, like oil pots and gauges, were polished to a mirror-like finish. When the sun shone on Elliot Colliery the polished items sparkled with the reflected beams of light entering through dormer-like windows set into the winding houses' roofs. Moreover, the atmosphere inside both engine houses contained in the air a mixture of steam and oil, which had a pleasant fragrance that was never forgotten.[110]

The engineman sat in a key communication's command post regarding the operation of Elliot Colliery. At his command, Powell Duffryn's investment in plant and equipment, engineered as a system on the colliery's surface, combined to wind coal, or miners.

Longwall Coal Mining

In general, British mining engineers applied either one of two methods for coal working: Bord-and-Pillar, and Longwall to win coal.[111] The term Bord-and-Pillar was also known as Bord-and-Wall, or Pillar-and-Stall, or Post-and-Stall, or Stoop-and-Room. Bord-and-Wall involved first removing coal from two sets of working places, called bords, and headways driven at right angles to each other, and forming between them rectangular pillars of coal sufficiently large to support the roof. This method was practised in the Northumberland and Durham Coalfields. In 1895, Longwall was applied at Elliot Colliery.[112]

Longwall saw coal removed along a continuous face or 'wall' with the overlying strata allowed to settle into the mined hollow (called a 'goaf', or 'gob'). There were two methods: 'Longwall Advancing' – working away from a shaft and towards the boundaries of a coal seam leased to the company; and 'Longwall Retreating' – working back from the boundaries towards the shaft. John Nixon, the owner of Navigation and Deep Duffryn collieries, Aberdare Valley, pioneered the introduction of Longwall in the South Wales Coalfield.[113]

Longwall's use at Elliot Colliery in the 1890s was not followed as a rule at the colliery. Perhaps earlier than the 1920s, the Rhas Las seam was worked using Pillar and Stall.[114]

Nevertheless, winning coal at the colliery, in the 1890s, saw the coal hewers, also known as colliers, winning coal at the face using a mandrel. The pieces of coal they removed were required to be as large as was possible, and also 'round'. The colliery's blacksmiths regularly sharpened the colliers' mandrels. The collier had particular attributes. A description of the ideal collier given in 1875 was relevant twenty years later:

'From the peculiarity of his occupation, it has long been known as a saying among underground workers that "the least man makes the best collier," and the reasons for this is obvious for work has to be done in positions and under circumstances where as a rule, big brawny artisans would find it a positive hardship to exist. In such cramped spaces, with but one means of ingress for themselves and for the means of sustaining life, thousands of men work away together, and but the slightest hitch is necessary to send them to eternity.'[115]

The collier's work initiated the activities of other miners. Probably a youth carefully manhandled coal pieces into a curling box, and carried, or dragged it, for careful loading into a tram, otherwise known as a dram. The use of a shovel was frowned upon since it gave rise to small coal that had no value to the company. Miners known as hauliers and riders then took charge of moving the coal to the pit bottom by means of a journey of trams [a number of trams coupled together] pulled by horses, or using a mechanised system. A roadheadman was tasked with erecting pit props in the roadways, supplied to him by a timberman. A packer ensured that 'the gob' created by the efforts of the collier, working Longwall, was filled with rubble, and stone, so as to form an earthen prop thereby easing the ground's loading on the coal face.

Underground Haulage

The transfer of the coal from the face to the pit bottom used either trams hauled by horses, and also, in the case of Elliot Colliery, by a mechanical haulage system. In the case of the Red seam, in 1895, there were four haulage engines, and they were powered by compressed air.[116] The air compressor, located on the colliery's surface, was driven by a compound engine made by Messrs Walker, of Wigan.

Assembled underground was a network of mechanically powered rope systems arranged as coal haulage stages. A haulage engine was saliently placed to operate its allotted stage. The network's layout was aimed at optimising the flow of coal with attention also given to minimising the impact of equipment breakdowns. Yet, a breakdown of the haulage stage feeding the Elliot Colliery's upshaft halted the movement of coal from at least three coal face areas. So, quality ropes, and sheaves were selected to help reduce the risk of breakdowns. Ropes used were sized to satisfy factors of safety of up to six or seven times that needed to haul normal loads. The mechanic responsible for installing the ropes had to be diligent in the practice of rope work, and ever watchful about the state of the rope. Haulage equipment maintenance work was potentially dangerous.

Trevor Boyns found that haulage deaths were far more prevalent in South Wales than in any district.[117] He added that many of the deaths were due to 'illegal riding on journey of trams', and that, in 1911, '31 persons [were] run over by trams on mechanical haulage-ways'. The matter came to the attention of those drafting the 1911 Coal Mines Regulations Act that made it illegal for riders to travel on journies travelling at three miles per hour; the death toll was reduced in consequence. He also identified a possible human cause of haulage tragedies:

'hauliers were subjected to pressure by the hewers and colliery officials for an adequate supply of trams and materials to be maintained at the face. With hewers paid at piece rate and hauliers by the shift, tensions could obviously develop between the two groups. The pressure exerted on the hauliers, together with the poor conditions under which they had to work, often led them to undertake tasks singly, such as putting trams back on to the rails after a derailment in order to minimise any delay that may occur, when the task could have been carried out more safely with the aid of others'.[118]

Another possible cause of death was a lapse of concentration, or slowness to react to moving tram traffic, by the casualty. Indeed, a haulier's mistake could cause the death of an unaware party, such

Miners waiting to descend Elliot West Colliery. The tram appears to contain mandrels for cutting coal. The colliery's blacksmiths would have sharpened the mandrels.
John Ryan Collection

as a foreman mechanic, or even a colliery manager. 'Cwmtwch' Rees Rees, the colliery manager of Cwmneol Colliery, was killed in such a way in late March 1893. Arthur Graeme Ogilvie witnessed Rees Rees's death.[119] Arthur Graeme Ogilvie, the son of Alexander Ogilvie, a founding shareholder and chairman of Powell Duffryn between 1880 and 1886, suffered bruising. So, not only miners died underground in the quest to win coal. Colliery officials and mechanics, like the miners, needed to breathe air to survive.

Mechanical Ventilation

Sir George Elliot was an early advocate for mechanical ventilation of colliery workings. His opponents, adherents of furnace ventilation, would have probably worshipped the goddess *Scaptensula* in Roman times. She was the goddess of mine ventilation, according to Lucretius.[120] 'The efficiency of furnaces to generate air flow was found to increase with depth and they were less effective in shallow mines. The coal mines sunk during the mid-1800s in South Wales were relatively shallow and so 'mechanical ventilation was first developed there to much greater extent than in any other coalfields of Great Britain'.[121]

The pioneering of mechanical ventilation in South Wales Coalfield was partly identified earlier in terms of the state of colliery engineering existing at the time of Thomas Powell. The innovations of both Swansea's William Price Struvé and William Brunton were particularly identified. At Abercarn Colliery, at the southern end of the Ebbw Vale, James Nasmyth's design of 'double inlet open running centrifugal fan' was put into use in 1854.[122] The fan was fixed above the upcast division of a shaft in which a brattice structure was fitted that made the other division of the shaft the downcast. The Nasmyth fan rotated at sixty revolutions per minute, and extracted 45,000ft³ per minute of air from underground. John Nixon developed a large reciprocating air pump in 1859 at Deep Duffryn Colliery, Mountain Ash, and it moved 93,000ft³ per minute of air.[123]

Technical innovation yielded further mechanical ventilation systems. Christian Schiele of Manchester patented a design in 1863. It was 'the first British fan to be enclosed in an iron volute casing, which collected the air discharged from the fan wheel and guided it into the atmosphere'.[124] Yet, 'one of the most successful centrifugal fans developed during the middle of the nineteenth century', was invented by Theophile Guibal (1814-88).[125]

In 1868, George Elliot, seemingly alert to the advance of mechanical ventilating systems in the South Wales Coalfield, appeared to attack the reluctance among north-east of England colliery owners to take up such systems:

'The ventilation of our mines, the advantages and drawbacks attending the old and yet common method of producing rarefaction by furnaces, as compared to newer systems of ventilation by the aid of machinery, is a subject claiming our earnest attention. The great depths at which many of our pits are worked, and the vast extent of their lateral ramifications, make it more than ever necessary that we should secure the best mode of rendering the supply of air certain, regular, and safe. It is maintained that ventilating by machinery insures these desiderata; that the nicety with which mechanical appliances may be regulated, the delicate adjustment of power of which they are capable, and the complete safety with which they may be worked, place them far before the system they are intended to supersede.'[126]

Yet, the state of Powell Duffryn's ventilation systems in the late 1860s under George Elliot made his advocacy of mechanical

ventilation seem somewhat absurd. In 1879 and 1880, regarding the company's Aberdare collieries, Edmund Mills Hann judged that '*the ventilation, generally speaking, and with slight exceptions* [was], *in a positively dangerous condition*'.[127]

Waddle of Llanelli

The ventilating machine Edmund Mills Hann chose for Elliot Colliery was designed and made by Waddle. Maybe he was told of a remark made by Lionel Brough, Her Majesty's Inspector of Mines, at the New Tredegar Colliery explosion inquiry: 'I have sometime ago, agitated for a fan at this colliery, but Mr Waddle has much to do'.[128]

John Roberts Waddle (1817-1888?) of Llanelli was both an inventor and an industrialist. In 1844, at twenty-seven years of age, he joined his father, Hugh Waddle, to found the Llanmore Iron Company in Llanelli, which in addition to operating a foundry made engineering products like steam engines. About 1864, John Waddle supervised at Bonville's Court Colliery, Saundersfoot, Pembrokeshire the installation of the first of his fan design.[129]

The Waddle fan has been described as follows: 'The runner of this fan is composed of two circular iron discs which shroud the blades which are bent backwards from the direction of rotation. One of the discs is convex on the outside and the inlet opening is made in the middle of this disc. The Waddle fan was not cased and the air was expelled all round the periphery of the runner directly into the atmosphere'.[130] In operation, a rotating fan displaced air from its axis outwards towards its periphery. Thus a low-pressure zone was created around the fan's axis. With the axis zone open to the upcast shaft, and the periphery to the Valley's atmosphere, a continuous flow of air was established. Stale air was sucked up the West shaft, so drawing an influx of fresh air down the East shaft.

In 1867, John Roberts Waddle's fan design was the subject of critical scrutiny.[131] Waddle heard Mr Brough, who might have been the Her Majesty's Inspector of Mines previously mentioned, criticise the Guibal fan. He regarded the Guibal shutter feature as an 'awkward thing'. Mr Brough, though, seemed to be in favour of the Waddle fan since it was made in Wales, and that it did not carry the extra expense of shutters. But he advocated furnace ventilation.[132] Dowlais Iron Company's William Menelaus spoke for the Guibal fan. The design of the Guibal fan, he judged, enabled air to be exhausted at a low velocity, and so it used less power than other designs. Waddle agreed with Menelaus's point, but argued that his fan should not be compared with an open one. '*An open fan*', he said, '*simply revolved between two walls in an open space; his fan was encased at the sides*'.

The success of Waddle fans won for its inventor's company further sales growth. Recreation as a country gentleman was a fair reward for John Roberts Waddle's enterprise. In later life he was described as 'being of exceedingly good dress and charm of manner, a skilful judge of horse-flesh who could handle ribbons in style'.

Elliot Colliery's Waddle fan was 45ft diameter.[133] The fan was located on the colliery's surface 37 yards from the upcast shaft, the West pit. The fan was driven by a compound condensing steam engine. A further engine was provided as a stand-by. The fan produced a circulation of air at the intakes of 190,000ft³ per minute at a water gauge of 3.4 inch.

Some years before the First World War, Cantrill described what the atmosphere was like underground: the breathing of men and horses, the burning of lights, and coal-dust diffused in the

Waddle Fan – Nixon's Navigation North Pit, Mountain Ash.
Courtesy of Brian Davies

air, made 'it essential that this foul air should be continuously and steadily swept out of the mine and replaced by fresh'.[134] According to Cantrill's guidelines, the Elliot Colliery Waddle fan could satisfy the breathing needs of up to 1,900 men working underground. However, air provision for pit ponies, and for the combustion of coal used in any underground steam engines, had also to be made.

From 1860 onwards 'the centrifugal fan began to displace the furnace on the score of safety, economy and efficiency. The main types of fans installed [in Britain] were the large Guibals and Waddles, with some smaller fans of the Schiele type'.[135] Nevertheless, it was a Waddle fan that once created Zephyrs above Elliot Town and made redundant a need to offer a prayer to *Scaptensula* before going underground. Neither was there a need to offer a plea to Apollo, the Roman god of light.

Electric Lighting

Elliot Colliery featured up-to-date use of electrical lighting. I. C. R. Byatt found that 'as early as 1879, exhibitions of arc lighting were held in Britain', and 'the municipalities became very keen to try out electric lighting in the years 1880-2'.[136] Indeed, in 1879 electric lights were in use at the Alexandra Docks, Newport.[137] But most of the first electrical light installations did not shine beyond 1882. Byatt observed that '*the attempt to establish electricity supply for lighting failed*'.

Electrical lighting was more expensive than its competitor, gas lighting. However, 'by the late 1870s dynamos … were able to generate electricity cheaply enough for the commercial use of electric lighting and power to become possible'.[138] Messrs Crompton & Company supplied the dynamo that was installed at Elliot Colliery to power the electrical lights. R. E. B. Crompton manufactured the appropriate dynamo to enable Swan's incandescent lamp to become a commercial lighting system in 1882.[139] The driver of the dynamo at Elliot Colliery was a 'quick-speed' engine made by Messrs Marshall of Gainsborough, Lincolnshire. The associated electrical specification was 380 Amperes and 110 Volts.

'Beginning in the 1880s electric light began to supersede gas-light installations underground at pit bottom and main gate roads, though diffusion was relatively slow until after 1900'.[140] Cannock Chase Colliery was where the first electric lighting system was installed underground, in 1883. The actual sites illuminated at Elliot Colliery by 1895 are not known. The engine houses and the pit banks were most likely lit. It was considered hazardous to place electric lights in underground passages, and at the coalface, due to the risks of gas, roof falls, and squeezes. Only the dim light from a safety lamp's flickering flame was used at the coalface.

The Safety Lamp

The invention of the safety lamp had its origins in the Coalfield of Northern England. So, both Sir George Elliot and Edmund Mills Hann would have been intimate with the associated story. 'The Davy lamp seems to have quickly penetrated into the collieries'.[141] However, a Royal Commission report, around 1888, reached a damming conclusion about the early safety lamps: 'in the present improved ventilation of collieries, ordinary Davy and Clanny lamps have ceased to afford protection from explosion, and that the Stephenson lamp, though more secure than the two former, cannot be relied upon'.[142] The Commission ruled that these lamps should be prohibited, unless they were enclosed in cases capable of effectually preventing the gauze from being exposed to the full forces of the current of air. It recognised though that there were many makes of lamps that were able to cope with such conditions. Such lamps offered ample time through a 'shut off' appliance, to extinguish the flame 'produced by the illuminant and by ignited gas within the lamp'.

Four types of lamps, though, were granted 'special attention', combining a high degree of security with fair illuminating power and simplicity of construction': Gray's Lamp, Marsault's lamp, the bonneted Muesler lamp, and Evan Thomas's modification of the bonneted Clanny lamp. In 1860, Evan Thomas formed Evan Thomas & Company to make mining lamps, and made Aberdare the base for his business.

Concerning George Elliot, in February 1853, he spoke for the Clanny lamp, claiming he 'employed several hundreds of them'.[143] Adding, there was no case, that he had been acquainted with, of 'a single instance where the safety of miners had 'been imperilled by any accident of the glass'. A faulty assembly of the glass into the metal structure of the lamp's seatings was considered to be a lamp's Achilles' heel. A bang on such a lamp could cause the glass to shatter. He was aware that the Stephenson's Lamp was used to very great extent, and was 'found to answer every purpose required'. But, 'it goes out at a certain point, when sufficient air cannot get through the apertures so as to support the flame'.[144]

Bonneted Clanny Lamp. Dated to circa 1890, and although it bears no maker's stamp, the maker is believed to be Thomas & Williams of Aberdare. *Courtesy of Mark Smith*

An early Elliot Colliery lamp check.
Courtesy of Lyndon Rees

Regarding the possible flaw in Clanny lamp assembly, he had for some years cured this by using vulcanised India rubber rings in the seatings with satisfactory results.[145] Elliot's support was explicit: '*You may take a Clanny lamp and sit with it until doomsday, and it will not become heated, unless there is a very large quantity of gas*'.[146]

The lamp chosen for use at Elliot Colliery in 1895 was a bonneted Clanny, and nine hundred were purchased.[147] Charles Wilkins wrote: '*perhaps the "Clanny" is the greatest favourite, the*

Muesler & Thomas' of Aberdare coming next. The latest addition [to the Clanny] *has been to affix a partial or complete shield so as to prevent a strong draught upon the flame*'.[148] When, Edmund Mills Hann presented his first paper to the South Wales Institute of Engineers, in 1886, it concerned an innovation for safety lamps. He described how a platinum wire, situated close to a safety lamp's wick, energised with a small electrical current to a sufficient temperature, could ignite an extinguished oil fuelled flame.[149] The innovation was successfully tested using a Clanny lamp, and judged acceptable.[150]

The maintenance of an oil-fuelled safety lamp saw lamp room men scrupulous examining a returned lamp for component flaws, fastidious when cleaning it, trimming it with care and precision, and completing a full test of its operation before racking for its next tour underground. Each lamp was lit and locked on the surface to prevent them from being opened underground so exposing a naked flame to the atmosphere. In the case of Powell Duffryn, a lamp could only be unlocked with a strong electro-magnet kept in the lamp room. A miner exchanged a lamp check for a lit lamp. Early in the 1900s, if the lamp's light went out underground, the lamps issued were fitted with an apparatus by means of which, taking energy from an electric battery, a spark was produced that ignited a wick without the lamp having to be opened.[151] The company had put into effect Edmund Mills Hann's invention.

The miners at Elliot Colliery could only hope that the company's general manager of collieries had made the correct decision regarding the type of lamp that they were given to use. After a miner handed in his lamp after a shift of work underground he went home. The won coal proceeded to screening.

Screening

On the colliery's surface an arrangement of mechanical screens, like sieves, sorted various sized coals from each other. The prized 'round' coal, the term for large coal, was sorted first. Hand-pickers, standing or sitting aside a travelling-belt, seized any good coal that passed through mechanical screening. The din from the plant's machinery caused deafness among its attendant workers. Disabled miners and women were often employed on screen work. Later in the process, the following types of coals were separated: cobbles – sized between one and four inches; nuts – between $^3/_4$ inch to $2^1/_2$ inch; beans – between $^5/_8$ inch to $1^1/_4$ inch; and peas – pieces of coal $^3/_8$ inch to $^3/_4$ inch in size. Fine coal dust, called duff, was inevitable. Hann, though, viewed duff as having commercial potential, and he was keen to find a means to this end. Rubbish, such as bad coal, shale, and rock, remained for disposal.

Aerial Ropeways & Rubbish Tips

With coal at Elliot Colliery sorted into marketable form, rubbish was moved in buckets from the colliery's surface by a high wire system to a tipping site. Locked-coil ropes moved the buckets. Information for Elliot Colliery, about 'the buckets', as the system was called in New Tredegar, was not found. However, Fforchaman Colliery's buckets, also known as cars, had a capacity of 13 cubic feet, and handled 60 ton per hour. The rope had a speed of 300ft per minute. The cars emptied automatically at the rubbish tip.[152] At Elliot Colliery, over a period of decades, rubbish massed at two sites.

Elliot Colliery's first tip bestrode Cwm Syfiog with its base to the east of the colliery, at about 800ft above sea level. Ultimately the summit of the tip grew to around 1,150ft in height by the end of the 1960s, and was a playground for boys. The colliery's other rubbish tip collected at the 1,110 foot contour of Cefn y Brithdir, to the west of the colliery. Spion Kop, as it was known locally, lay immediately above the village of Brithdir, and its presence greatly troubled its people after the 21st October, 1966. On that day an avalanche of coal waste from the Merthyr Vale Colliery swept down a hillside above the village of Aberfan, situated four miles south of Merthyr Tydfil. One hundred and forty-four people, that included one hundred and sixteen children, entrapped in a school, were killed. Subsequent government inquiries changed coal waste tipping practices, and ultimately the removal of many tips like Spion Kop. The Aberfan tragedy confirmed a belief that coal tips in addition to marring the landscape were a latent evil.

Idris Davies (1905-1953), the Rhymney born poet, also portrayed other effects that coal mining had upon the environment. As a young man he worked as a collier at a Rhymney Valley colliery owned by Powell Duffryn, before becoming a teacher, taking an appointment, in 1947, at Cwmsyfiog's Junior School. He wrote:

Cwmsyfiog
How long ago, no one can tell,
Some Welshman named you Strawberry Dell,
But now, by your polluted stream,
I see no strawberries nor cream.[153]

Colliery headgear, he saw as a symbol of human exploitation:

When greed was born
In Monmouthshire
The hills were torn
For Mammon's fire,
And wheels went round
And skulls were cracked,
And limbs were ground
And nerves were wracked.[154]

The work of the mining engineer appears not to have attracted poetic praise. Yet, Charles Wilkins gave an elegiac description of one, Sir William Thomas Lewis:

'The poet, we are told is born not made. The mining engineer, the geologist, the mathematician, are the results of patient industry. The poet flashes his inspiration out upon us with the same spontaneity as nature does in her pictures of the beautiful and the terrible. Not so with our mining engineers and others we link with them. Their own plastic mind becomes the subject matter of laborious study, of treatment, and discipline, and the results are in the degree such as the sculptor produces from his lump of clay, only that in the case of our men we have active agency produced for doing a manhood's work in the world; in the other, only an ornament to delight the eye.'[155]

Elliot Colliery was the tangible result of Sir George Elliot's imagination.

Elliot Colliery's Cwm Syfiog coal tip in 1971 as it was after the colliery's closure. The tip was earlier used as a source for foundation material for a steelworks at Llanwern, Newport. Stone from the quarry was used during a local building boom. The scene has now been landscaped.   *Author*

NOTES

1 E. M. Hann, *Brief History of the Powell Duffryn Steam Coal Company Ltd*, p.8.

2 Llewellyn Llewellyn joined the Risca Colliery group (London & South Wales Colliery Co. Ltd). He joined the company the year that Risca Colliery, where sinking began in 1875, began to produce coal. He lived at Risca House until, in the mid-1880s, he became mining adviser to the Chilean Government. Between 1901 and 1911, he resided at Abersychan House, Abersychan, near Pontypool. By 1911, he had retired. Preliminary research by John Venn shared with writer early 2012. See also endnote 125 Chapter 5.

3 E. M. Hann, *op. cit.*, p.9.

4 E. M. Hann, *op. cit.*, p.9.

5 Candidate Circular – for Election as Member, (Institution of Civil Engineers, circa. 1 Dec. 1885), p.10.

6 P. H. Reaney & R. M. Wilson, *A Dictionary of British Surnames*. (Routledge & Kegan Paul, revised 1976), p.165.

7 David Hann, 'The Hann Family – A Mining Dynasty of South Wales part 1', *Glamorgan Family History Society, Journal No.38*, (June, 1995) p.38.

8 E. M. Hann, Special General Meeting   New Honorary Members, *SWIE*, Vol. XXLI, No.3, (Sept., 1925), p.222.

9 E. M. Hann, Special General Meeting–New Honorary Members, *op. cit.*, p.223.

10 General Index to Transactions, *Transactions, North of England Institute of Mining Engineers*, Vol's I to XV, p.73. Elected: graduate member 5 Sept. 1868; and member 1872.

11 Simon Chapman, *Wheels Turning and Smoke Rising*. (Peter Tuffs, 1997), pp.69-73. Hann's Cleveland years are drawn from this source, unless otherwise stated.

12 This colliery was later known as Cardiff Navigation Colliery.

13 Hann Research Notes, Edwin Greening, undated, p.53. Retained in the keeping of D. L. Davies, Cwmaman, Aberdare, Dec 2005.

14 Candidate Circular – for 'Election as Member', (Institution of Civil Engineers, circa 1 Dec. 1885), p.10.

15 For a brief account about the formation of the landore Siemens Steel Company see pp.34-5 J. C. Carr and W. Taplin, *History of the British Steel Industry*. (Basil Blackwell, 1962).

16 *Oxford Dictionary of National Biography*, Vol. 21. (Oxford University Press, 2004), pp.399-400.

17 'Dr Galloway's Response', *SWIE*, Vol. XXX (1914), p.555.

18 'Presentation of Portrait', *SWIE*, Vol. XXX (1914), pp.548-50.

19 Hann Research Notes, Edwin Greening, p.53.

20 David Hann, *op. cit.*, p.39.

21 E. M. Hann, *Brief History of the Powell Duffryn Steam Coal Company Ltd*, *op. cit.*, p.9.

22 E. M. Hann, *op. cit.*, p.10.

23 C. Wilkins, *op. cit.*, pp.240-2.

24 E. M. Hann, *op. cit.*, p.6.

25 E. M. Hann, Special General Meeting – New Honorary Members, *SWIE*, Vol. XXLI, No.3, (Sept., 1925), p.233.

26 Cynon Valley Historical Society, *Cynon Coal, op. cit.*, p.200.

27 E. M. Hann, *Brief History of the Powell Duffryn Steam Coal Company Ltd*, p.11.

28 A. W. Woodland & W. B. Evans, *Geology of the South Wales Coalfield Part IV: The county around Pontypridd and Maesteg. Explanation of One-inch Geological Sheet 248, op. cit.*. The noted depths in imperial measurements were: the Yard seam at 634ft 11 inches, and the Seven Feet at 665ft 9 inches respectively.

29 E. M. Hann, *op. cit.*, p.12.

30 Email, Margaret Collum to writer, 13 Oct 2006. Michael Stansfield, Durham University, had sourced the information from the *Durham Advertiser*, 30 June 1882.

31 *Transactions*, North England Institute of Mining Engineers, Vol. 1, (1852-1853), pp.13-32.

32 Public Lecture, Professor F. B. Hinsley, 'The North of England Institute of Mining Engineers and the Establishment of Physical Sciences at Newcastle Upon Tyne', 9 July 1971, p.10. Archives of the North England Institute of Mining Engineers.

33 For Example, see Minute Book of Directors' Meetings, Powell Steam Coal Company Limited, Book No. 3, D/D PD1, Glamorgan Record Office. Hereafter GR PDMBDM No. 3. Between pp.19-20 is inserted a report dated May 1888 of a shareholders' committee, on the report's p. 1 Hann is referred to as Mineral Manager.

34 W. W. Price, Card Records, Hann 2, item 5. National Library of Wales.

35 E. M. Hann, *op. cit.*, p.28.

36 E. M. Hann, *op. cit.*, pp.10-11.

37 E. M. Hann, *op. cit.*, p.11.

38 E. M. Hann, *op. cit.*, p.10.

39 OS grid reference SO 153998.

40 R. H. Walters, *op. cit.*, p.175.

41 'The Monmouthshire Coalfield, VIII–The Elliot Pits, New Tredegar Collieries', *The Colliery Guardian*, 23 Aug 1895, p.362. Its coals were classified in 1942 as follows: the upper seams bituminous I : volatiles 17-23%, carbon ranged from 90-92%, hydrogen 4.3–5%, and calorific value 15,650 to 15,800 Btu/lb; and its lower seams semi-bituminous, and granted the distinction of being 'caking steam': volatiles 13-18%, carbon ranged from 90.5-92.5%, hydrogen 4.0–5%, and calorific value 15,600 to 15,800 Btu/lb. *South Wales Coalfield (Including Pembrokeshire) Regional Survey Report, op. cit.*, pp.20-21.

42 Founded in 1859. D. S. Barrie, *The Brecon & Merthyr Railway, op. cit.*, p.96.

43 J. H. Morris and L. J. Williams, *op. cit.*, p.36.

44 D. S. Barrie, *The Brecon & Merthyr Railway, op. cit.*, p.98-99.

45 D. S. Barrie, *A Regional History of the Railways of Great Britain*, Vol. XII South Wales. (Thomas & Lochar, 1994), p.27 & p.148.

46 G. M. Harries, A Short History of New Tredegar. (1972), p.3. The document was prepared for a lecture given to the Bargoed Historical Society. Joyce Jones Collection

47 Charles Wilkins, *op. cit.*, pp.225-6.

48 E. M. Hann, *Brief History of The Powell Duffryn Steam Coal Company Ltd.*, p.11.

49 E. M. Hann, *op. cit.*, p.12.

50 G. M. Harries, *op. cit.*, pp.1-2.

51 *Western Mail*, 2 Jan 1875, p.5. The colliery's miners did not appear to join the South Wales Coalfield strike of that year, and produced 300 tons of coal per day.

52 W. W. Price, *op. cit.*, p.10.

53 W. W. Price, *op. cit.*, p.10.

54 W. W. Price, *op. cit.*, p.10.

55 *Catalogue of Abandoned Mines, Monmouthshire*. (HMSO, 1930), p.34.

56 R. H. Walters, *op. cit.*, p.17.

57 R. H. Walters, *op. cit.*, p.17. There was the explosion at New Duffryn Colliery in 1882, Marion Evans, *A Portrait of Rhymney*, (Old Bakehouse, 1994), p.29.

58 *The Powell Duffryn Steam Coal Company 1864-1914, op. cit.*, p.21.

59 John E. McCutcheon, *op. cit.*, pp.34-8.

60 *The Colliery Guardian, op. cit.*, p.362.

61 *The Powell Duffryn Steam Coal Company 1864-1914, op. cit.*, p.22.

62 E. M. Hann, *op. cit.*, p.12.

63 *The Powell Duffryn Steam Coal Company 1864-1914, op. cit.*, p.21.

64 *The Powell Duffryn Steam Coal Company 1864-1914, op. cit.*, p.21.

65 'The Monmouthshire Coalfield, VIII–The Elliot Pits, New Tredegar Collieries'. *The Colliery Guardian, op. cit.*, p. 362. E. M. Hann dates the sinking to 1889 to 1890; see E. M. Hann, *Brief History of The Powell Duffryn Steam Coal Company Ltd*, p.13.

66 Hilda M. Evans, *New Tredegar Again, op. cit.*, p.12. One of the sinkers, George Stephens, was reputed to have made the spade for the ceremony.

67 Hilda M. Evans, *New Tredegar Again, op. cit.*, p.12.

68 *The Daily Telegraph*, 29 Jan. 1994.

69 Brian Glover, *Prince of Ales*. (Alan Sutton, 1993), p.57.

70 The worked seams, in 1914, were the Yard Vein and those below. Big Vein comprised two seams: one 2ft 9in. thick and the other 4ft; the Yard Vein comprised two seams: 1ft 7in. and 3ft 2in. 'The Monmouthshire Coalfield, VII–The Elliot Pits, New Tredegar Collieries'. *The Colliery Guardian, op. cit.*, p.362.

71 R. H. Walters, *op. cit.*, p.90.

72 See William Galloway, 'Sinking Appliances at Llanbradach', *SWIE*, Vol. XVI (1888 & 1899).

73 Roy Church, *op. cit.*, p.112.

74 E. M. Hann, *op. cit.*, p.6.

75 Trevor Boyns, 'Growth in the Coal Industry: the Cases of Powell Duffryn and the Ocean Coal Company', ed. Colin Baber and L. J. Williams, *Modern South Wales: Essays in Economic History*. (University of Wales Press, 1986), p.162.

76 T. R. Barnard, *Mechanical Engineering*, (Virtue, 1954), p.302.

77 A list giving examples concerning 'the rise and decline in the use of various appliances and arrangements' for winding was presented by Hugh Bramwell, of the Great Western Colliery Company near Pontypridd. 'President's Inaugural Address', 'The Raising of Coal from Vertical Shafts', *SWIE*, Vol. XXX (1917), pp.5-15.

78 Major E. Ivor David, 'The History of Winding Engines', *Iron & Coal Trades Review*, Diamond Jubilee Issue, (December, 1927), pp.22-3.

79   J. H. Morris and L. J. Williams, *op. cit.*, p.71.
80   G. M. Watkins, 'The Vertical Winding Engines of Durham', *Transactions, Newcomen Society*, Vol. 29 (1953-55), p.205.
81   G. M. Watkins, *op. cit.*, p.205.
82   G. M. Watkins, *op. cit.*, p.206.
83   'Winding Engines for the East Elliot Pit of the Powell-Duffryn Colliery Company', *Engineering*, Vol. 54 (1892), p.478.
84   The Colliery Guardian, *op. cit.*, p.362.
85   C. C. Owen, *The Development of Industry in Burton upon Trent*, (Unwin Brothers, 1978). pp.110-120.
86   Letter, John Andrews, chairman, Briggs of Burton PLC, to Writer, 3 Dec. 2002.
87   C. C. Owen, *op. cit.*, pp.240-241.
88   'Winding Engines for the East Elliot Pit of the Powell-Duffryn Colliery Company', *Engineering*, Vol. 54 (1892), p.478.
89   E. M. Hann, 'An Outburst of Water, and the Means of Dealing With It', *SWIE*, Vol. XIX (1894-1895), p.143.
90   G. M. Watkins, *op. cit.*, p.15.
91   'Lancashire' was a name acquired by a design of boiler based upon an 1844 patent whose inventors were William Fairbairn and John Hetherington of Manchester. Twelve Lancashire boilers were installed at Elliot Colliery.
92   T. R. Barnard, *op. cit.*, p.149.
93   T. R. Barnard, *op. cit.*, p.149.
94   When the writer joined Babcock Power as a graduate trainee in 1972, his father, William Shore, referred to Babcock's association with Elliot Colliery. However, his son did not fully value the significance at the time.
95   'Winding Engines for the East Elliot Pit of the Powell Duffryn Colliery Company', *Engineering*, Vol. 54 (1892), p.478.
96   T. H. Deakin, 'On Wire Ropes', *SWIE*, Vol. XVI (1888 & 1889), pp.305-334.
97   *Western Mail*, 'Death of Sir George Elliot', 26 Dec 1893, p.5, col.5.
98   T. H. Davies, *Telford Clarence Batchelor (1857-1947); A Memoir describing the Invention and Development of Locked-Coil and Flattened-Strand Wire Ropes.* (Courier Press, 1951), pp.1-11.
99   T. H. Davies, *op. cit.*, pp.1-9.
100 A cousin of Henry Batchelor's was John Batchelor, a member of the Liberal Party, Mayor of Cardiff (1854-4), and a statue of him stands at The Hayes, Cardiff. T. H. Davies. *op. cit.*, p.2.
101 T. H. Davies, *op. cit.*, p.iii.
102 T. H. Davies, *op. cit.*, p.34.
103 Telford Batchelor acted as a consultant to Messrs Elliot's from 1884 to 1891. See T. H. Davies, *op. cit.*, p.44.
104 T. H. Davies, *op. cit.*, p.31.
105 The Durham Coalfield's North Biddick Colliery, which Sir George Elliot was reputed to have owned, was also an early customer for the rope. An 1888 inquiry into the death of five men sinking Douglas Hall Colliery, Lancashire, noted 'the great excellency of the winding ropes, which is what is known as Sir George Elliot's'. Furthermore, H. Hall, Her Majesty's Inspector of Mines stated that 'he found the rope to run more steadily than he had ever remembered any rope to do in a sinking pit before.' See A T. H. Davies. *op. cit.*, pp.31-32.
106 T. H. Davies, *op. cit.*, p.19.
107 A. E. Crook, 'Precautions Against Overwindings, *Transactions of the Institution of Mining Engineers*, Vol. 105, 1945-46, p.597.
108 T. R. Barnard, *op. cit.*, p.345.
109 T. Boyns, 'Work and Death in the South Wales Coalfield, 1874-1914', *The Welsh History Review: Cylchgrawn Hanes Cymru*, Vol.12, No.4, (1985), p.250.
110 An interview of Writer, on 22nd October, 2006, with both Ken Jones, clerk to the manager of Elliot Colliery in the early 1950s, and Idris Williams, a collier at the colliery for over twenty years. During Idris William's time at the colliery, he worked the Lower Four Foot (Scammel), Upper Four Foot (P), and the Meadow Vein. He ended his career as an instructor at the Britannia School of Mines.
111 T. C. Cantrill, *Coal Mining.* (Cambridge University Press, 1914), pp.95-106.
112 'The Monmouthshire Coalfield, VIII–The Elliot Pits, New Tredegar Collieries', *The Colliery Guardian*, 23 Aug 1895, p.362.
113 Charles Wilkins, *op. cit.*, p.94-8.
114 Interview. Writer with Ken Jones, 22 Oct. 2006.
115 *Western Mail*, *op. cit.*, 31 Dec 1875, p.6, col.2.
116 'The Monmouthshire Coalfield, VIII–The Elliot Pits, New Tredegar Collieries', *The Colliery Guardian*, 23 Aug 1895, p.362.
117 T. Boyns, 'Work and Death in the South Wales Coalfield, 1874-1914', *The Welsh History Review: Cylchgrawn Hanes Cymru*, Vol. 12, No. 4. p.526.
118 T. Boyns, *op. cit.*, p.528.
119 E. M. Hann, *Brief History of The Powell Duffryn Steam Coal Company Ltd*, p.16.
120 Prof. F. B. Hinsley, 'The Development of Coal Mine Ventilation in Great Britain up to the end of the Nineteenth Century', *Transactions*, Newcomen Society, Vol. 42 (1969-70), p.38.
121 Prof. F. B. Hinsley, *op. cit.*, p.31.
122 E. Rogers, 'Description of the ventilating fan at Abercarn Collieries', *Proceedings Institution of Mechanical Engineers*. (1856), pp.251-59.
123 Report of Committee on Mechanical Ventilators, *Transactions*, North England Institute of Mining Engineers, Vol. 30, (1880-81), pp.273-287.
124 Prof. F. B. Hinsley, *op. cit.*, p.33.
125 Prof. F. B. Hinsley, *op. cit.*, p.34. Guibal, born at Toulouse, educated in Paris, became Professor of Exploitation of Mines at the University of Mons.
126 George Elliot, Inaugural Address, *Transactions*, North England Institute of Mining Engineers, Vol. 18, (1868-1869), p.22.
127 Hann also remarked that 'the plant at the pits was worn out and obsolete'. E. M. Hann, *Brief History of Powell Duffryn Steam Coal Company*, p.11.
128 *Western Mail*, 21 Dec 1875, p.6, col.4.
129 CD, '*Llanelli, A Birth of a Town*', (Meiros Publications, 2003) various pages. Also G. Pearce, 'On Mechanical Ventilation', discussion, *SWIE*, Vol. V, (1866-67), p.202.
130 Prof. F. B. Hinsley, *op. cit.*, p.34.
131 G. C. Pearce, 'On Mechanical Ventilation', *SWIE*, Vol. V (1866), pp.116-127.
132 'On Mechanical Ventilation - Discussion', *SWIE*, Vol. V (1867), p.200-9.
133 'The Monmouthshire Coalfield, VIII–The Elliot Pits, New Tredegar Collieries', *The Colliery Guardian*, 23 Aug 1895, p.362.
134 T. C. Cantrill, *Coal Mining.* (Cambridge University Press, 1914), pp.109-110.
135 Prof. F. B. Hinsley, *op. cit.*, p.35.
136 I. C. R. Byatt, *The British Electrical Industry 1875-1914.* (Clarendon, 1979), pp.16-23.
137 *Western Mail*, 'Centenary Review', 1 May 1969, p.12.
138 I. C. R. Byatt, *op. cit.*, p.1.
139 I. C. R. Byatt, *op. cit.*, p.16.
140 Roy Church, *op. cit.*, p.328.
141 Frank A. J. L. James, *op. cit.*, p.212.
142 Charles Wilkins, *op. cit.*, p.270.
143 'General Meeting', *Transactions*, North England Institute of Mining Engineers, Vol. I, (1853), pp.190-1.
144 'General Meeting', *Transactions*, North England Institute of Mining Engineers, *op. cit.*, p.256.
145 'General Meeting', *Transactions*, North England Institute of Mining Engineers, *op. cit.*, p.270.
146 'General Meeting', *Transactions*, North England Institute of Mining Engineers, *op. cit.*, p.191.
147 'The Monmouthshire Coalfield, VIII–The Elliot Pits, New Tredegar Collieries', *The Colliery Guardian*, 23 Aug 1895, p.362.
148 Charles Wilkins, *The South Wales Coalfield Coal Trade and its Allied Industries.* (Daniel Owen, 1888), pp.368-9.
149 E. M. Hann, 'Lighting Safety Lamps when Locked', *SWIE*, Vol. XV, (1886-1887), pp.74-5.
150 'Lighting Safety Lamps when Locked', *op. cit.*, Vol. XV (1886-1887), pp.107-112.
151 From a remnant of a Powell Duffryn advertising leaflet, title unknown, (undated but clues suggest it was issued before 1905), p.7.
152 *The Powell Duffryn Steam Coal Company 1864-1914*, *op. cit.*, pp.36-7.
153 *Border Voices*, ed. Geraint Eirug Davies, (Gomer, 1999). p.25.
154 *Collected Poems of Idris Davies*, ed. Islwyn Jenkins, (Gomerian Press, 1972).
155 Charles Wilkins, *op. cit.*, p.253.

A Pontypridd, Caerphilly & Newport Railway train. Alexandra & Newport Docks Railway No. 14, an ex GWR '517' Class 0-4-2 tank engine, is seen with one of the ex Barnum & Bailey's circus train carriages purchased by the A&NDR on approach to Pontypridd station sometime prior to 1923.
Courtesy Pontypridd Museum

Chapter 4
NEMESIS & CHANGE

Sir George Elliot took some interest in the engineering of his eponymous Rhymney Valley colliery, but he probably gave greater attention to other schemes. In 1883, the sixty-eight year old baronet joined a short-lived executive committee of the Association of Steamship Owners Trading with the East.[1] During the early 1880s, Elliot held a large stake in Nova Scotia's Albion Mines, and visited it accompanied by Sir William Thomas Lewis.[2] In Canada, Elliot offered miners, subject to payment and ownership provisos, 'half an acre of land as his own freehold, which he could cultivate and build one house upon'.

The Pontypridd, Caerphilly & Newport Railway

The Pontypridd, Caerphilly & Newport Railway (PC&N) was a further scheme pursued by the County Durham baronet. By 1884, the PC&N double track railway linked Pontypridd to a Rhymney Railway connection for Caerphilly.[3] He had earlier taken charge of PC&N's negotiations with railway companies whose tracks made the delivery of coal from East Glamorgan Valleys, via the company's track, to Newport's Alexandra Dock possible. By 1884, his hopes for the P&CN's success rested upon reaching agreement with the Taff Vale Company. Possibly the most powerful Valley railway company in Wales, the Taff Vale owned the railway artery that enabled great quantities of mined coal from the valleys of the Rhondda, Aberdare, and Taff, to be delivered to the docks, mainly Cardiff's.

Sir George Elliot

If Sir George Elliot's negotiations with the Taff Vale Railway Company began immediately following the Act of Parliament that made the PC&N possible, then he needed patience to secure his aims. After six years of meetings, on the 20th June, 1884, the Taff Vale Railway Company (TVR) entered into a 'Heads of arrangement' agreement with the PC&N. Moreover, the rivalry between Alexandra Dock, Newport and the Bute owned Cardiff docks was such that the Bute trustees fiercely opposed the PC&N.[4] Furthermore, around 1880, both dock systems shared a threat, new docks at Barry, Glamorgan.[5]

Nevertheless, the *Pontypridd Chronicle* saw value in the PC&N-Taff Vale agreement:

'We know that luck is usually measured by the piece, but where it is "feeding stuff," either for a dock or a railway, there can be no harm in using the term slice, and in this instance it means feeding a dock and a railway, but especially the latter. Wise in their day and generation, the directors of the Taff Vale Company are determined that, if the obstinacy of the Bute Dock authorities is likely to drive away trade from Cardiff, they, as carriers, will take the coal wherever the freighters want it to be taken to.'[6]

The PC&N-Taff Vale agreement enabled the TVR to man and so run PC&N's trains from Pontypridd to the Alexandra Docks. The PC&N opened on the 7th July 1884.[7] Consequently, the railway stimulated dock and transport cost reductions of benefit to the coal companies. The TVR and the GWR later reduced their prices by about 2d. per ton for their joint rate for traffic from this part of the coalfield to Newport.[8] However, the first train, carrying various top officials, halted at Bassaleg since 'the GWR would not let it through', on its line to Newport Alexandra Docks.[9] The GWR's ploy involved disputing that the Brecon & Merthyr had running powers on its line into Newport. 'After three weeks of argument, Paddington relented; soon after the PC&N laid its own tracks parallel with the GWR into Newport'.[10]

Cwmaman and Abercwmboi Railway

Between the years 1884 to 1886, Powell Duffryn built the Cwmaman and Abercwmboi Railway.[11] According to Edmund Mills Hann, the railway project was provoked by coal from Fforchaman Colliery incurring a very high railway rate to Cardiff and Newport, owing to a circuitous route, and a 'good deal used to be sent to Swansea, which was disadvantageous, both as market price, and the inability to mix with the coal from Aberaman and other Collieries, without incurring extra tolls'. He later judged that

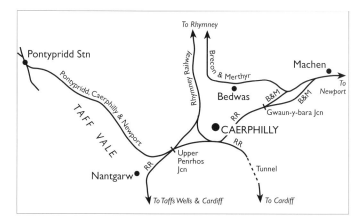

Pontypridd, Caerphilly & Newport Railway link between Taff Vale and Rhymney Valley. The Taff Vale Railway took charge of running the railway link from when it was opened in July, 1884. After 1906, the link was operated by The Alexandra (Newport & South Wales) Docks & Railway Company.

the railway project was a 'work of some consequence' since it saved railway rates, earned a profit, and saw improvement in mixing coals to meet market needs.

Such a private railway was not unique in the Aberdare Valley.[12] Nixon's Navigation Coal Company operated one. The southern limit of Powell Duffryn's railway network was at Middle Duffryn Colliery, where it connected with the Great Western Railway. Aberaman was the node of Powell Duffryn's railway network, with a branch line serving the Aman Valley. By 1914, the company operated its railway using sixteen of its own locomotives.[13]

The use of trustworthy brakes for railway wagons became basic equipment for an operator of a South Wales Valley railway. The gradient of the Aman Valley railway branch was a severe proving ground for brakes. Moreover, safe control of wagon movement on wet, or icy, rails was also needed. The brake system Powell Duffryn used won the respect of Cornelius Lundie of the Rhymney Railway Company.[14]

Lundie declared a preference for the Dean-Churchward design of 'either-side' brake, but admitted that his company fitted Powell Duffryn's brakes since they 'suited the Rhymney Railway inclines very well'.[15] He described the coal company's brakes as being 'either-side brake', and 'independent'. 'In the hilly country traversed by' the railway, 'it was very important to get a load of wagons safely down inclines'. He mocked the Board of Trade, and 'many of the great railway companies' for being blinkered, seeing only braking as a matter for shunting-yard operation, which rarely took place on steep inclines. Although the brake practice approved by such bodies worked for such a duty, it was inappropriate for steep inclines. 'It was obvious that if they stopped wagons to apply brakes on, or before an incline they might not be able to start again. Therefore for a

wagon descending there must be a brake which could be handled on the right-hand and run after as a wagon was in motion'.

Many of the wagons used by Powell Duffryn were supplied by Gloucester Wagon Company, later the Gloucester Railway Carriage & Wagon Co. This company had received its first orders from Powell Duffryn to supply two hundred and fifty 7-ton, and one hundred 10-ton wagons for the transport of coal to Cardiff and, for Rhymney Valley traffic to Newport Docks, in 1867.[16] Further orders were received in 1872 and 1873 for, in total, three hundred 10-ton, and thirty 8-ton wagons.[17] This second group of orders reflected excellent market conditions for coal as mentioned earlier. The wagon company eventually opened a small works near Hirwaun, north-west of Aberdare.[18] A photograph, taken in 1872, reveals the construction of one of its 10-ton wagons as steel framed, with dumb buffers, wooden brake blocks, and side and end doors. Lettered in plain white, on a black body, was 'POWELL DUFFRYN' and 'STEAM COAL'. Sometime afterwards this standard lettering was abbreviated to a large white 'P' on the left third of a wagon's side, and a large 'D' on the right. In 1910, the company's inventory of wagons was approximately, 7,800.

By 1914, Aberaman Works dealt with the maintenance of wagons. The former forge of Crawshay Bailey's ironworks being adapted for such a purpose.[19] The Works was equipped with a blacksmith's shop, carpenters' shop, fitting shop, and steel and iron foundries.

Perhaps the Cwmaman & Abercwmboi Railway became a statement about the extent to which Powell Duffryn governed the life of the population of the district that surrounded Aberaman. On the whole, nothing moved there by way of railway transport without the company's say. The incomes of people living around Aberaman largely relied upon the coal company. However, regardless of how

Photographed in February 1872 10-ton wagon number 1944 was built by the Gloucester Wagon Co. as part of an order for one hundred wagons taken on hire for three years. The six-plank wagon is fitted with side and end doors and is constructed on a steel underframe. The brakes are standard for this period - wooden blocks operating on one side only. *GRC&WCo.*

The later style of lettering is shown on this 12-ton wagon of 1910, one of three hundred ordered that year. By this date wagons were being built with brakes both sides, although still independently worked it did mean that shunters no longer needed to pass under wagons to apply the brake. Notice too, that the axlebox covers are marked for Powell Duffryn. *GRC&WCo.*

controlling a power the company was perceived to have been in the Aberaman locality, it was a servant of world market conditions.

The year 1885 featured a number of disappointments for the company's founder. The Redistribution of Seats Act erased the North Durham constituency, and when Sir George Elliot stood for election at the South East Durham constituency he lost.

Moreover, some of the company's shareholders did not necessarily approve of the way in which Sir George Elliot had established Elliot Colliery. Private command of related affairs exposed him to conflicts of interest, which could be resolved in favour of personal financial gain. He also flitted from one business activity to another leaving some administrative havoc in his wake. And so, according to Edmund Mills Hann, by the end of 1885, '*differences arose between Sir George Elliot and his co-directors with regard to dealings in wire ropes and various other matters*'.[20] The company's Board Minutes suggest that as early as the 1870s there were murmurs of disaffection about the manner in which the baronet conducted Powell Duffryn's affairs. Yet, an earlier attempt to curtail his 'practical direction' of the company had been reversed. Seemingly at odds with growing disenchantment in its founder, in 1886, Alexander Ogilvie retired as company chairman, and he was succeeded by Sir George Elliot. Ogilvie died the following year and so his son, Arthur Graeme, replaced him as director.

That year, Elliot, was again beneficent to the Church of England. As a result, he laid the cornerstone of a church at West Cliff, Whitby.[21] The year also saw Elliot's political career saved due to Gladstone's wish to introduce parliamentary measures for Irish Home Rule. The Conservatives were opposed to Irish Home Rule. However, the Irish Question was a factor that led Sir George Elliot to contest Monmouth Boroughs, and at the General Election, July 1886, he ousted (later Sir) E. H. Carbutt, a Gladstonian.[22] Perhaps,

to celebrate his return to the House of Commons, there was opened in Newport the Elliot Home for Seamen.

On Friday the 15th October, 1886, an outburst of firedamp at Aberaman Colliery demanded Edmund Mill Hann's attention.[23] At a location underground known as Draper's Heading, where a coal seam of over six feet was being worked, a squeeze began. Then, after ten o'clock that night, there was a noise 'louder than any shot'. Gas 'issued'. A 'rough calculation' estimated that 'the quantity of gas discharged in the following ten hours was just short of a million cubic feet'. An inspection of the colliery's 'self-registering' barometer chart found that the outburst '*took place whilst the barometer was making a heavy fall, and few hours before it touched the lowest records known for many years*'. Hann revealed that he had experimented with various barometers, from the mercury type to the aneroid, and so came to use the self-registering type.[24] However, the consensus of opinion among fellow mining engineers was that the falling atmospheric pressure was not a cause of the outburst. With hindsight, the fall in the barometric pressure at Aberaman Colliery could be said to represent a forecast concerning Sir George Elliot's future.

The Managing Committee of Directors

The year 1888 was a watershed year for the both the history of the Powell Duffryn Steam Coal Company, and its link with Sir George Elliot. Trevor Boyns found, on reading the Sankey Commission report of 1919, that '*Joseph Shaw then chairman of Powell Duffryn, stated that when he was appointed to the Board of Directors in 1888 he felt that the company was an absolutely bankrupt concern and advised the directors to wind the company up*'.[25]

On the 27th March, 1888, a five man shareholders' committee, comprising Joseph Shaw, Col. Lewin, W. P. Sutherland, E. A. Hedley, and William Appleton, was established to investigate and examine the past dealings and transactions and accounts of the Company. In the month of May, the committee revealed a number of unsatisfactory practices.[26] Apparent confusion between the costing of debts incurred either by the company, or by Elliot, due to him operating a private account, supposedly on behalf of the company, caused the committee to propose a new principle for handling any subsequent transactions. The committee found that the Board of Directors had failed to exercise sufficient control over the purchases made by two managers, the Commercial Manager (Bickerton Pratt) and the Mineral Manager (Edmund Mills Hann). The lack of control was judged to be 'no doubt due to the many other important occupations of Members of the Board'. A comparison made by the committee, between the prices of wire ropes supplied to the company by Messrs G. Elliot & Co. against other possible suppliers, found that the company had been overcharged. The report noted that the company's founder was prepared to give the company a rebate, and this was considered sufficient for the committee not to press further action. But this was a minor concession given to Elliot.

Regarding the Powell Duffryn founder's interest in other commercial undertakings, the committee's report asserted that some of them had been pursued 'in preference to the company' either 'intentionally or unintentionally'. An example cited concerned the cost of the coal traffic from the Aberdare collieries and 'Tredegar Collieries (sic)'. The committee judged that a saving of 3d. per ton upon an average of 900,000 ton could have been 'effected at Newport and Cardiff'. Dismissed also as 'not needed', by the committee, was a lease taken by the company of a wharf at Alexandra Dock, Newport, at £600 per year for twenty-one years from 31st March, 1882. The honorary Doctor of Law of Durham University might have been puzzled by the committee's claim that the legal expenses of the company were 'larger than necessary', but he may have been annoyed by their opinion that some leases, unspecified, were in an 'unsatisfactory condition'.

The report concluded, as if offering some reassurance about the company's future, that if there were: 'reductions in cost and more economical management ... improving prices ... the shareholders may reasonably expect a return on the large outlay that had been made upon their valuable property'. The report was in effect an indictment of Sir George Elliot's stewardship of Powell Duffryn.

Trevor Boyns later proposed: '*Elliot, however, seemed incapable of distinguishing, or perhaps had a positive interest in not doing so, his various interests from one another, or from his own personal interests, and hence one finds an extremely tangled web of financial inter-linkings and indebtedness between the various parts of Elliot's activities*'.[27]

The company's response to the committee of shareholders' report was to set up, in May 1888, a Managing Committee of directors, which comprised Henry Bolden, Graeme Ogilvie, and Joseph Shaw. Executive control of the operational affairs of the company passed to this body. Sir George Elliot kept the position of company chairman, but ceased to be managing director, a position left vacant.

The company's board meetings, up until then, were held at the company's London office, 23, Great Western Street, Westminster. The address was the base for Elliot's wire rope company and, most probably, for his other business interests. He may have also owned the property, and so earned rent from Powell Duffryn.

The founder of Powell Duffryn was hurt by the charges tendered against him by the committee of shareholders. On the 19th

December, 1888, a writ was issued against the company on his behalf by Messrs Marksby Stewart. The baronet did not attend the board meeting, held on the next day, where the writ was read out. A medical certificate was sent to the directors who 'expressed their regret at hearing of Sir George Elliot's indisposition'.[28] Around the time he may have learnt that the *George Elliot* had been wrecked at sea.[29] He did not consider the ship's loss as a bad omen for pursuing his case against the company.

In a letter, March 1889, Sir George Elliot defended his negotiations with the Taff Vale and Brecon & Merthyr Railway companies. He claimed he had made a 10 per cent saving to the good of Powell Duffryn.[30] Such a benefit was the 'outcome of a struggle which lasted for years', and had cost him 'great anxiety'. He contended that the use of Alexandra Docks had been to the company's good. Coal, he asserted, could be shipped out cheaper from Newport than Cardiff. He further implied that company coal sales had been boosted due to locating coal handling facilities at Alexander Docks which mixed the dry [steam] coal from the Aberdare Valley with the bituminous coal of New Tredegar Pits. Regarding the Pontypridd, Caerphilly & Newport Railway Company, he argued that it was a 'wise policy' for the company 'to continue' to support it since its construction had been 'the lever' which had enabled Powell Duffryn to barter 'advantageously' with the railway companies.

In June 1889, Elliot and Ogilvie were approached by William Abraham ('Mabon'), a leader of the South Wales Miners' Federation, with the aim of resolving a strike at Aberaman. Mabon was then the Member of Parliament for the Rhondda Valley. In 1888, William Abraham became idolized in the South Wales Coalfield due to negotiating a day's holiday, once a month, for the collier, and it became known as 'Mabon's Day'. Elliot's influence, though, within the company, was ebbing.

Maybe a sign of this emerged in July 1889. Meetings of the directors of the company removed from Great George Street to new company offices at 18, Leadenhall Street, London. The company's offices stood near Leadenhall Market, which had been the centre of Roman London. The market was a bustling place where meat, game, and provisions were sold. The directors meeting in Powell Duffryn Steam Coal Company's boardroom was deaf to the calls of buyers and sellers outside in the market. Like dutiful Roman senators, they objectively focused upon the affairs of the company.

The decades of the company being governed as if by an Egyptian pharaoh reincarnated as Sir George Elliot seemed to have reached closure. On the 26th March, 1889, his office as chairman of the company was ended, and he was replaced by Lord Brassey.[31] Elliot at least could look forward to, in the following winter, an extended sojourn in the 'warmer climate of the Riviera, or Madeira' as an inoculation against illness.[32]

Powell Duffryn's managing committee of directors, maybe surprisingly, sensed a healthy future for the company.[33] The company's total annual output had grown to 1,328,000 tons by 1886, but 'it remained nearly stationary for five years, during a rather slack state of trade'. Nevertheless, as Edmund Mills Hann later reflected: after 1888, '*a period of very great activity was initiated*'.[34] The activity was partly financed by an issue of £100,000 of 6 per cent Debentures. The most notable effect being the sinking of Elliot East, which according to Hann, 'made Elliot Colliery the most important of the Company's openings at that period'.

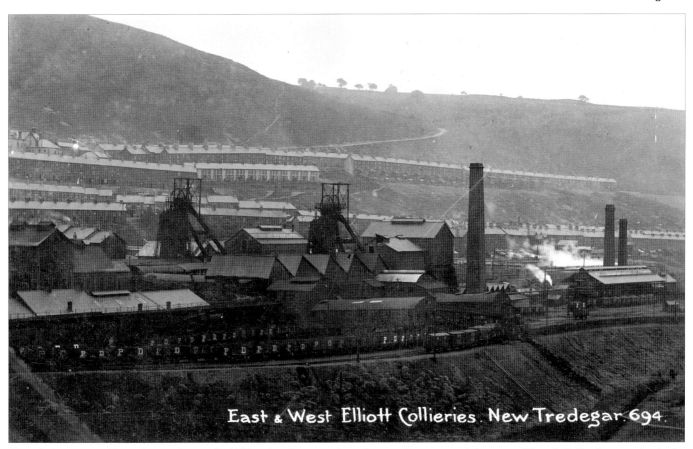

Elliot Colliery viewed from the north-west. In 1883 sinking began at the colliery, and represented the start of Powell Duffryn's expansion in the Rhymney Valley. The maximum depth of shaft that coal was worked from was 530 yards. The colliery became fully operational in 1890 according to its engineer, Edmund Mills Hann. In 1912, the colliery's manpower was 2,811. The terraced housing shown was the result of a local building boom.

Pope/Parkhouse Archive

A Coal Mining Community

Edmund Mills Hann judged that Elliot Colliery was completed ready for full operation around 1890.[35] That year, four hundred and eighty men were employed at Elliot Colliery to win coal. The results of colliery engineering, in simple terms, the quantity of coal lifted per cage, the rate at which cages were wound up a shaft, and the duration of the winding time per day, determined the limit of a colliery's underground manning level. Six years later, one thousand six hundred and eighty-seven men worked Elliot Colliery. Employment at the colliery reached a peak at 2,811 in 1912.[36]

The recruitment of workers for the colliery, from the late 1880s into the first decade of the 1900s, became an urgent need of the company. New Tredegar was born due to the opening of New Tredegar Colliery, and to work Elliot Colliery there was a need for more colliery workers than the original village could supply. Powell Duffryn addressed this matter in two ways.

First, in March 1896, the company entered into an agreement with the Brecon & Merthyr Railway Company (B&M) to run a workmen's train between Machen, at the southern end of the valley, and the colliery.[37] According to D. S. Barrie the railway company provided the engine, passenger brake-van, and train crew, the colliery company furnished the rolling-stock, and the platforms, 'some of which they also lit'.[38] D. S. Barrie observed that Powell Duffryn provided 'some bogie coaches of uncertain origin', and issued colliery workers free travel passes to use the passenger service.[39]

Railway train passes. The company issued these passes for Rhymney Valley rail travel to Elliot Colliery. *Courtesy of Mark Smith*

Workers were issued with metal brass checks bearing a counter-marked number and the colliery's name in an abbreviated form. This was not an unusual practice in Wales.[40] The railway company was expected to carry our 'strict checks' on the number of workers carried and those found travelling without a check or leaving the train whilst it was in motion', had to be reported to the coal company. D. S. Barrie perceptively observed: 'Anybody who has seen a hundred or more colliers bale out of a still-moving train as it draws into a small valley station lit only by oil-lamps will appreciate that this was one of several B&M rules which usually got no further that the rule book'. However, the railway scheme was secondary to building homes for colliery workers in the New Tredegar district.

Powell Duffryn 'built its own houses at the new sinkings at New Tredegar Elliot Pit, which were financed in the main from the issue of debentures. Here it also encouraged housing developments by acting as financial guarantor in building clubs'. Moreover, a New Tredegar Land & Building Company was financed with Powell Duffryn as a shareholder who would also act 'to ensure the successful completion of the dwellings'. 'Housing could thus be an inseparable extension of [company] expenditure on colliery plant'.[41]

The New Tredegar house building boom involved some speculation on the part of investors. Emigration was a feature of the locality as was migration. A slate quarry strike in North Wales in 1896-97, and another in 1903, saw many people remove to South Wales, and so to places like New Tredegar. However, many of these people apparently returned north once slate working recommenced. From 1904, some local people, including Welsh speaking families, left New Tredegar for the United States of America. They moved to states like Pennsylvania, Ohio, and Illinois, and those in the West. People from the shires of Hereford, Gloucester, Somerset, Devon, and 'even Staffordshire' replaced those that had emigrated. The district's Welsh culture of the mid-nineteenth century gave way to an Anglo-Welsh one by the start of the twentieth century.[42] House building in New Tredegar revived in 1905, and continued until 1912 when, as a town, comprising 'the Village', Elliot Town, Cwmsyfiog, and Phillipstown, it reached, more or less, its greatest extent.

The Colliery Machine

Elliot Colliery as an engineered machine, and men drawn essentially from a new community, united to win coal. The colliery manager was responsible to the company for coal production, and legally accountable for the safety of the colliery's workers. The managers' succession at the colliery consisted of at least the following: in or from 1884 the post was held by D. Evans; in or from 1891, A. Phillips; Nehemiah Phillips held the position in 1896 and 1900; F. Wilcox held the post in 1908 and 1911; J. A. Price in or from 1913 up until at least August 1921; O. L. Gibbon, in or from 1927; T. Bailey, in or from 1930, having been the colliery manager at New Tredegar Colliery around 1910; J. Shenton in 1934; M. Davies, in or from 1938; and from 1943 to 1945 it was T. Farrell.[43]

Colliery engineers accepted that it was the manager's decisions that governed the operation. Mechanics and electricians pursued routine maintenance. The colliery machine normally hummed, droned, hissed in the background as a familiar symphony of noises, which bored most listeners, except the engineer and the mechanic. The disruptive effect of an occasional engineering failure of an equipment item, or malfunctioning machinery on the colliery machine brought them curses from the manager, his officials and miners. Yet, such events rarely hit the newspaper headlines unlike a strike by miners.

Regarding Elliot Colliery, in 1895, The *Colliery Guardian* noted that '*the development of the [colliery's] lower Four-Feet and the east shaft*' had been delayed 'by three and a-half years'. The delay was partly due to a prolonged dispute at the colliery maybe in 1887.[44] The colliery's development was further hampered by underground floods, which are described later. When coal was won, free of miners' disputes, the considerable pervasive influence that engineering had on the successful running of the colliery could be all too easily overlooked. The journal forecasted for Elliot Colliery that 'the output from the [east] shaft will reach 1,200 tons per day within two years'. The steam coal raised was the 'best quality'.[45]

Cwmsyfiog, part of New Tredegar, with the four-wheeled carriages of the Powell Duffryn 'Paddy Train' used by workers stood in the sidings awaiting another change of shift.
Pope/Parkhouse Archive

Fading Powers

Around the cusp of the 1890s, Sir George Elliot's power as an industrialist began to fade. His grip upon Messrs Elliot & Co weakened. He failed to halt a souring of the company's relationship with Telford Batchelor due to an interpretation of an 1858 patent taken out by John Wallace Duncan for a submarine cable.[46] The wire rope company was motivated, according to T. H. Davies, by 'some individuals in the firm of Elliot's who were inimical to the two patentees or who scented that an opportunity to take advantage of them by supplanting their master patent'. Although the matter was settled through arbitration, the parties' business interests became separated when Messrs Latch & Batchelor Ltd was formed, which initially operated from Cardiff, but later Birmingham.

T. H. Davies, employed by Latch & Batchelor Ltd, later observed: 'It does seem clear that Sir George, now advanced in years and in poor health, not only was not cognisant of this move but if he had been would not have permitted it'. Davies' observation reveals a failing Sir George Elliot. Moreover, his words suggest that the conduct of the managers at Messrs Elliot & Co. would have been different if they acted in accord with duty to Sir George Elliot.

In 1889, Sir George Elliot sponsored at All Saints Church, Penshaw, the fitting of a stained glass window. This gift preserved the memory of his brothers, and a son of his who had died in 1874. At home in County Durham he may have felt detached from his duties as a Powell Duffryn director, and remote from the travails of mining of coal in the Aberdare and Rhymney Valleys. However, in Parliament, he crusaded to improve the lot of the coal miner in terms of the passage of an Employer's Liability Bill of 1889.

In 1890, the founder's influence in the boardroom of Powell Duffryn weakened further. Henry Bolden was elected company chairman in place of Brassey. Maybe more significantly, Graeme Ogilvie was not only an advocate at board meetings for colliery developments, but a future chairman in the making. The date of Graeme Ogilvie's entry into the management of the company was not identified, but an outcome was he became a mining engineer. At some stage he worked as a colleague of Henry Martins, which linked him with the 'oversight of Middle and Lower Duffryn and George Pit'. In some respects his destiny as chairman was a fitting sequel to having spent a period participating in the management of the company, which ended in 1885 when, it seems, he joined the board. In Edmund Mills Hann's opinion, after he became general manager of collieries, he nurtured an excellent working relationship with Ogilvie. Writing in a deferential manner, he later noted that sometime after 1883 that he 'became associated with him, and I believe obtained, and retained, his confidence'.[47]

Indeed, Graeme Ogilvie appears to have acted as a keen sponsor of Edmund Mills Hann's ideas. In March 1890, Ogilvie proposed at the company's meeting of directors a development for Elliot Colliery, estimated at £26,550, which involved the colliery's washery machinery and coke ovens referred to earlier, and described later.[48]

In July, 1891, some company's directors viewed the Elliot's 1888 writ against the company as 'frivolous'.[49] By 1891 litigation became more complicated since it not only involved Elliot and the company, but also Lord Tredegar. Shortly before the eve of the legal judgment of Elliot vs. Powell Duffryn, Lord Tredegar issued a writ against Elliot. However, Justice Shiling ruled in the company's favour. Moreover, any hope that Sir George Elliot clung onto for regaining the chairman's office was dashed when, in November, Lord Brassey was re-elected company chairman due to Henry Bolden's death.

Aberdare Valley Collieries' Development

The congregation of St. Margaret's Church, Aberaman, had witnessed the growth of the general manager of collieries, Edmund Mills Hann's family. During the 1880s his issue reached seven: Frank Percival was born in 1885, Douglas Alfred in 1887. There appears to be some confusion in the records concerning the birth of his family's eighth and final child, Graham. One source gives the birth of Graeme (sic) as 1889,[50] with another for Cyril Graham as 1893.[51]

Edmund Mills Hann's colliery engineering work included improving the Aberdare Valley operation. The company's financial straightjacket seemed to have eased by the end of the 1880s. Perhaps this was due in part to the fact that during the period from 1880-1890 the company's output leapt from 750,000 tons to 1,305,000 tons.[52] In 1888, he oversaw the deepening of Lower Duffryn Winding Pit to the Seven Feet seam, which 'with other necessary works' was begun so as to 'put it on a paying basis'.[53] By 1891, partly due to experience at Elliot Colliery, a 40ft diameter Waddle fan was installed at Aberaman Colliery to replace furnace ventilation.[54]

The period between 1890 and 1893 saw, Hann later recollected, 'the centralization of pumping operations by the deepening of the Middle Duffryn Winding shaft and its equipment with duplicate pumps each capable of raising 85,000 gallons per hour from a depth of 275 yards'.[55] At Middle Duffryn, the eight pump engines substituted were 'mostly in bad order, and with most wasteful boilers'. His objective was to make annual savings in the cost of raising water by guarding the working of the colliery's Seven Foot Seam from floods arising from five different areas of drowned workings. This work cost £35,000 and proved to be, in his judgement an 'excellent investment'. Experiences at Elliot Colliery was to make him acutely aware of the importance of pumping plant.

Outburst of Water

An 'outburst of water', in late 1891, had flooded Elliot Colliery's underground workings. Edmund Mills Hann wrote a report about the event.[56] Relative to the bottom of the Elliot East's shaft, a passageway was driven several hundred yards north to work the Lower Four-Feet seam. The Lower Four-Feet seam was opened by sinking 'a staple pit' from the Red Vein at 440 yards. By the end of October 1891 'about half an acre of coal had been worked' at Lower Four-Feet seam.

Rees Shore worked as a mechanic at Elliot Colliery.[57] The 5th of November, 1891, saw some celebration at his Elliot Town home to mark the third birthday of his son, Aldridge Guy Shore. The new Elliot Town stood immediately north of the colliery. Guy would later be nicknamed 'Mack' by his classmates at Elliot School before following his father's trade at the colliery. The mechanic learnt that day about the 'heavy squeeze' underground. Edmund Mills Hann recalled: 'During the night it became evident it was the bottom that was heaving and not the top coming down'. At 'about 9 o'clock a.m. on the 6th November a loud noise accompanied the formation of a long rent in the bottom'. Then, 'out of which came a puff of gas, followed immediately by a large volume of water'. 'This at once eased the pressure, and instead of the place being alive it became at once perfectly still'.

Regarding the 'outburst' of water, it 'was at once recognised that the quantity was beyond anything that the pumping … could

Plan of East Elliot Colliery – 1891 Outburst of Water.
Proceedings, SWIE, Vol. XIX, (1895)

cope with, and the men and horses and the most portable articles were removed. By noon all spaces had filled, and there were two feet on the pit bottom by 2 p.m., and rising very rapidly'.

Powell Duffryn's colliery officials and mechanics reacted. Two water tanks, each of 700 gallon capacity, were placed in Elliot East's cages and used like buckets to winch up water. However, this action had little effect upon the subterranean flood. Five days later, the water tanks were substituted with a pair of 1,100 gallons capacity tanks, and plumbed so that water was discharged on the surface at a faster rate. Yet, 'still the water rose six or seven feet per hour in the shaft'. 'The "feeder" for the first day or so was reckoned to be 70,000 gallons per hour, and afterwards, and for nearly three weeks, 60,000 gallons per hour'.

The force of the initial outburst of water also wrecked colliery equipment. A notable example being the collapse of a cast iron pipe used to supply compressed air to underground haulage engines. The company 'procured' the services of divers to help recover the cast iron pipe. Afterwards the pipes were assembled and fixed in the vertical position.

In the wake of the water being 'successfully got under control', materials and equipment, which included temporary pumps, were lowered in a cage down Elliot East's shaft. 'Unfortunately, an engineman drew the cage to the sheave and pulled the rope out

of the cap, so that the cage went to the bottom of the pit, but did no more damage to the guides than the breakage of one wire in a guide at the pit bottom'. The cage was damaged beyond repair, so was replaced with another one, but the broken wire in the guide went undetected. Then, on the 'following night', the 'shoe of the cage caught' the end of the broken wire in the guide, and so it was brought up to the meeting of the cages. Curing the jamb caused a delay of six hours. It was 'not possible' to repair or replace the damaged guide rope. However, 'had another guide on the same side been injured winding would have become unsafe'. So, after such an appraisal, winding continued. 'In spite, however of the best exertions the water gained upon the winding, and rose until it filled and stopped one of the main intakes of the west pit in the Ras Las seam'.

Then, eventually, a 'perceptible slackening of the flow did manifest itself'. 'For a week or more, however, it was so nearly a balance between the winding power and the water'. Fortunately, 'the water continued to abate, and after being idle from November 9 to November 27 coal working in the Red Vein was resumed'.

As salvage events took their course, Edmund Mills Hann re-assessed the colliery's pumping requirement. He gave 'very careful consideration to the question of how to deal permanently with the inflow of the water, and the comparative merits of all the chief systems were discussed'. Afterwards, a decision was made to order a Duplex Triple expansion Worthington pump supplied by Messrs Jas. Simpson & Co., Ltd, of Pimlico, 'to force water direct in one column 530 yards to the [colliery's] surface'.

Usefully, sometime before the November 1891 outburst of underground water, the company had ordered a pump from the Worthington Pumping Engine Company. The pump's allotted duty was as a 'stand-by' in case 'of accidents to the pumps' in order that 'the working of coal might not be interfered with'. The order was for an ordinary Worthington pump, with 29-inch cylinders, 8-inch rams and 10-inch stroke. The site chosen for the pump's lodge room was at 400 yards below the colliery's surface. At the time of the November outburst of water, preparatory underground work had not advanced to a stage where the pump's engine room was made, or associated pipework fixed. Nevertheless, after the outburst, it was judged 'requisite', during the period until the Simpson made Duplex Triple expansion pump was installed, to place a pump at a lower level, circa 530 yards, to raise water to the ordinary Worthington pump. So, a Duplex Pearn pump, 24-inch cylinders, 8-inch rams and 14-inch stroke, compressed air, was also 'set to work' at the lower level.

Elliot Memorials

In 1892, an event of interest to Sir George Elliot was the securing of a small granite tablet to an internal wall of St Margaret's Church, Aberaman. The granite had been taken from the Great Pyramid of Ghizeh 'with the permission of Ismail Pasha Khedive of Egypt'. The children of Aberaman, who down the years had enjoyed parties at Elliot's expense, may have learnt much as a result.[58] The plaque linked readers of the Bible's Exodus to the forced labour of the Israelites, by the 'throne of Egypt', to build the 'Pharaoh's store cities, of Pithom and Rameses'. The inscription on the tablet recorded not only that Lady Elliot had died on the 14th December, 1880, but also the death of his daughter Elizabeth on the 29th September, 1861, aged twenty years. Sir George Elliot's surviving son was George William, born on the 13th May, 1844,

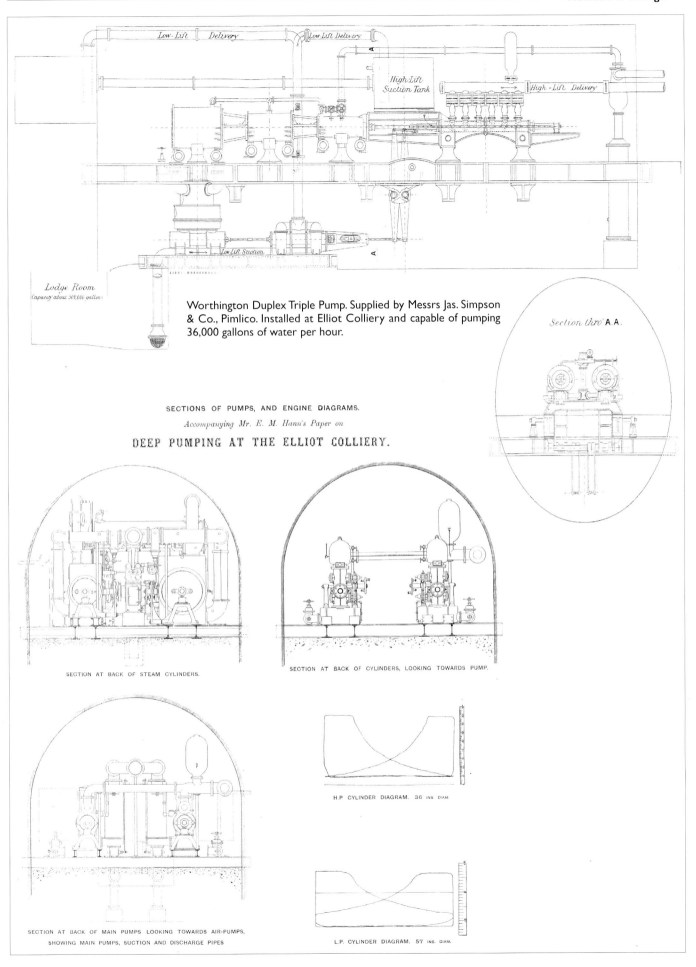

Worthington Duplex Triple Pump. Supplied by Messrs Jas. Simpson & Co., Pimlico. Installed at Elliot Colliery and capable of pumping 36,000 gallons of water per hour.

Section thro' **A.A.**

SECTIONS OF PUMPS, AND ENGINE DIAGRAMS.
Accompanying Mr. E. M. Hann's Paper on

DEEP PUMPING AT THE ELLIOT COLLIERY.

SECTION AT BACK OF STEAM CYLINDERS.

SECTION AT BACK OF CYLINDERS, LOOKING TOWARDS PUMP.

SECTION AT BACK OF MAIN PUMPS LOOKING TOWARDS AIR-PUMPS,
SHOWING MAIN PUMPS, SUCTION AND DISCHARGE PIPES

H.P CYLINDER DIAGRAM. 36 INS. DIAM.

L.P. CYLINDER DIAGRAM. 57 INS. DIAM.

and he had married Miss Sarah Taylor, daughter of Charles Taylor of Sunderland, in 1866. George William sat as MP for the Richmond Division of North Riding of Yorkshire, and was also a director of Powell Duffryn.

The motto on Sir George Elliot's armorial stated '*Labour et Veritas*' – Industry and Truth. But there existed one jury, the directors of Powell Duffryn, who held a less than favourable opinion about his facility for honesty in business. Maybe such an opinion caused the Powell Duffryn's directors to elect Graeme Ogilvie to the office of company chairman when Lord Brassey resigned, in June 1892, instead of Sir George Elliot.

Nevertheless, also in 1892, Sir George Elliot repeated his Aberaman deed in County Durham. First, West Rainton church saw the dedication of a tablet of granite also sourced from the great pyramid of Ghizeh. The tablet's inscription recalled Elliot's gift of the church's tower and spire, erected in 1877, and it served to commemorate the baptism of his six children at the church. Furthermore, at All Saints Church, Penshaw, another tablet of Ghizeh granite was blessed. This tablet informs that Elliot's father and mother, Ralph and Elizabeth Elliot, and his four brothers William, Ralph, Thomas and John, were buried in the churchyard. Recalled also on the tablet is the life of his elder son, Ralph Elliot who had died on the 23rd January, 1874. A Biblical text quoted on the tablet is difficult to read, but is thought to be from The Song of Solomon Chapter 2 Verse 17: 'Until the day breaks and the shadows flee away'. In the context of Sir George Elliot's life at the time the verse suggests that it was chosen by a defiant optimist. These early years of the 1890s were his life's nemesis.

Voting at the General Election of 1892 saw him lose his Monmouth Borough seat to Albert Spicer, a Gladstonian. Yet, his talent for conceiving imaginative schemes continued as an idea for a national insurance fund for mine workers. 'In September, 1893, he proposed a gigantic coal trust, the working of which was largely based upon the principle of according the workmen a voice in the regulation of their wages and the selling-price of coal, and also a share of the profits'.[59] However, in 1893 Powell Duffryn might have believed that measures had been engineered to cure flooding at Elliot Colliery.

Another 'Feeder'

Underground at Elliot Colliery an engine house was finished on the 1st April, 1893, and so the installation of the ordinary Worthington pump began. During the period from April 1892 to February 1893, the flow of underground water fell and settled at a rate of 21,000 to 22,000 gallons per hour, and dropped further to 'not more than 16,000 gallons' per hour during the month of June. Then, possibly around the middle of June, as the erected ordinary Worthington pump stood awaiting the completion of its pipework, there was a 'fresh burst of water'.

During the period that had seen the fall in flow of underground water, Edmund Mills Hann had been encouraged by the trend to instruct the driving of fresh headings and coal-getting resumed. Moreover, it was 'conjectured' that such work 'may have closed the old cracks'. However, as the coal work progressed, 'a quick weighting [a term for movement in the underground strata] was succeeded by a fresh long crack in the bottom, and the "feeder" rose at once to 38,000 gallons per hour'.

Emergency action was taken. 'The two water tanks were at once put to work on the winding engine'. But there was a repeat

of an earlier mishap: 'An engineman unfortunately made another over-wind, by which the rope became disconnected by the safety hook causing the water inside it to rip open the tank from top to bottom'. In addition, the delinquent tank also managed to twist and buckle the pulley legs. Hann considered that this item, designed for robust service, was the strongest that he had seen. '*Fortunately*', he reported, '*there was a spare tank, which was again put to work in a very short time*'. And, the 'water again abated'. Indeed, about six weeks later the ingress of underground water steadied at 22,000 gallons per hour. Moreover, the ordinary Worthington pump was successfully started in July 1893, and was destined to be 'worked regularly' thereafter and give 'complete satisfaction'.

The Duplex Triple expansion Worthington pump supplied by Messrs Jas. Simpson & Co was installed underground sometime afterwards. The pump's steam engine applied the triple expansion principle.[60] The engine was designed for 120 lb/in^2 steam pressure. Although the engine could operate using steam at 50 lb/in^2 pressure, it was normally operated using steam at 80 lb/in^2. The pump was described as 7^1/$_8$-inch diameter rams, with a stroke of 3ft 6in. The pump was capable of raising 36,000 gallons an hour of water up a height of 530 yards to the colliery's surface. A primary necessity of running such an engine was to keep the temperature of the water moderate, so as '*to avoid the shocks that occurred on the valves of high lift pumps when working on hot water*'. The date when the Simpson made Duplex Triple expansion Worthington pump became operable is not known, but surviving records of engine performance tests, as indicator diagrams, are dated January 1895. The *Colliery Guardian*, in August 1895, noted that the Simpson made pump was placed near the [East] shaft 'for pumping from the Farewell rock'.[61]

With the pumping capability at Elliot Colliery increased ready to cope with future outbursts on a scale of those experienced in 1891, only curiosity needed to be satisfied: what was the natural source of the outburst? Chemical analysis of the flood water in 1892 found only a minute trace of lime. This implied that 'the source of the water could not be from the limestone', and so suggested that it 'was probably from the Farewell rock, which was usually 38 yards below the Lower Four-Feet'.

This idea caused Edmund Mills Hann to consider the geology of the land at the head of the Rhymney Valley. Here the Farewell Rock [Millstone Grit] was exposed 'at a level of 1,800 feet above the point of the outbreak', where, 'into holes and fissures of the strata large quantities of water were known to disappear'. The 'extensive workings' of coal and ironstone of the Rhymney Iron Company had not 'encountered any considerable quantities of water, and were still kept well drained'. He learnt '*that further east, at Sirhowy, Ebbw Vale, and Cwm Tillery, similar occurrences on a much smaller scale had been known*'.

The development of Elliot Colliery though had been held back due to the underground floods of 1891. Indeed, the scale of the outburst of water at Elliot Colliery, on the 6th November, 1891, might have been the greatest experienced by a South Wales Coalfield colliery up until that time. The ground under the Rhymney Valley, at the colliery's location at least, had proved to be a very wet place. Powell Duffryn was forced to invest much more in pumping measures at Elliot Colliery than was originally intended. Yet, the subterranean Rhymney Valley would prove shy about revealing to Powell Duffryn the scale of the hazard posed by water outbursts.

Washery & Coke Ovens

Nevertheless, the general manager of collieries had 'urged the company to install a modern washery and ovens of the Copeé (sic) type capable of producing 100,000 tons of coke per annum, [with] the most usual mixture being three parts of steam coal small and one part of Brithdir small' at Elliot Colliery. Coppée ovens were popular in the South Wales iron and steel industry for blast furnace coke since they 'suited the local coal'.[62]

Evince Coppée, a Belgian, invented his coking process in 1861. It was 'one of the first retort ovens, in which the rectangular coking chamber was totally enclosed and the heat produced by burning in surrounding flues all the volatile gases discharged (but without any recovery of by-products). The yield of an oven was 70-75 per cent of the weight charged, compared with 55-65 per cent from the beehive oven', that was invented in 1620. The Otto Company of Germany improved Coppèe's invention, and it became popular in both Germany and Belgium. The 'first British battery of Coppèe ovens was installed in Sheffield in 1872, but had to be closed because of the crucible steelmaker's preference for iron smelted with beehive coke'. Yorkshire collieries took to using them, and in 1874 they were installed at Ebbw Vale as they then became more popular.

In 1893, Powell Duffryn started up at Elliot Colliery a Humboldt Coal washery of 650 tons per day, and fifty longitudinal ovens of the Coppèe type.[63] The Babcock & Wilcox boilers were installed at the colliery as a result. The washery, probably the first of its kind operated in the South Wales Coalfield, was said to be the first in England even though it stood in Glamorgan.[64] In 1914, the washery dealt with 70 tons per hour and operated to separate nuts, beans, peas, duff, and slurry.[65] Edmund Mills Hann recorded that the colliery's coking plant 'was ultimately increased to 180 ovens, and the plant was for a good many years successful.'

Black Times

The year 1893 also saw the Coalfield Hauliers' strike. The cause of the strike was the Sliding Scale agreement, and the coalowners' refusal to provide a guaranteed minimum wage. Work at the Aberdare collieries, and Elliot Colliery was disrupted as a result. The hauliers halted work on the 1st August. Civil unrest was anticipated in at least the Aberdare Valley since on the 19th August troops were assigned to duties in South Wales. Aberaman House became the military's headquarters for the Aberdare district.

'Black' times also hit Powell Duffryn. In 1893, Cwmneol and Abercwmboi Collieries were put on short-time working due to trade conditions not being 'good'. The company sought a loan from the Rock Insurance Company. The insurance company's representatives, T. Foster Brown and Arthur Sopwith, issued a report about their impression of the financial status of the company. They came up with a 'low figure of £265,000 as a valuation for the whole of the company'. Edmund Mills Hann recalled later: the report's contents berated the company for having an 'unsatisfactory character'.[66] Possibly prompted by the receipt of the insurance company's decision not to agree to give the company a loan, Graeme Ogilvie remarked to Foster Brown that the report 'was one' that Powell Duffryn 'should live down'. Ogilvie, who had succeeded Bolden as company chairman in 1892, felt he had grounds for optimism about the company's future.

Elliot Colliery's washery and coke ovens. Commissioned in 1893. The washery was possibly the first of its kind operated in the English and Welsh Coalfields.
Paul Jackson Collection

Sir George Elliot's life drew to a close. He caught a chill whilst attending Lord Salisbury's 'great' election campaign meeting' at Cardiff. A bout of pneumonia followed the chill, and he died on Saturday, 23rd December, 1893, at seventy-eight years of age.

Elegy

Powell Duffryn had some grounds to extol its founder. In the year of his death, the company produced two millions tons of coal. However, his period of 'practical direction' receives no praise, or critical assessment, in the company's history published in 1914. This may seem to be a rather mean act. He had, though, made a notable contribution to the development of the South Wales Coalfield.

Newport saluted Sir George Elliot. A flag was flown at half-mast on its Town Hall, other public buildings, and some of the shipping companies' offices.[67] The Newport Docks, partly due to his 1875 intervention, had seen its coal trade increased fourfold, to nearly 4,000,000 tons annually at the time of his death.[68]

The obituary of the *Western Mail* described the breadth of his career as an industrialist, but only gave his Powell Duffryn role a brief mention.[69] Neither did the newspaper elaborate upon the effect he had upon the Welsh economy. Perhaps this may have been due to him being 'counted as a north country coal-owner'.[70] If parochial partiality had conspired to obscure his importance in one part of the United Kingdom, then his will-o'-the-wisp lifestyle could have seen him suffer a similar fate in the North of England.

Sir George Elliot earned his wealth, and he warranted recognition in both the Durham and South Wales Coalfields. His achievements as both a manager of coal mining interests, and as a coal mining entrepreneur were considerable. Securing the support of private self-made wealth for particularly the founding of Powell Duffryn in 1864 was a feat. Maybe his fertile imagination had been persuasive.

'Bonnie Geordie', as county Durham miners reputedly called him, was also said never to have forgotten his humble beginnings. He put himself more than occasionally in an invidious position between the two sides of the coal industry. Thus, at times like the 1875 South Wales Coalfield strike, he risked being classed as a traitor to the interest of coalowners. Trade unionists only recognised their own kind as heroes, particularly those who confronted the owners. So, serving as a conciliator between two sides of the industry, brought him little or no credit from either side.

The Times observed that Sir George Elliot's work as a politician '*was simply in connexion with financial and other subjects falling within the range of his special experience*'.[71] Indeed, as a Member of Parliament, he worked for and gained some improvements for the benefit of the miner in a climate of deep hostility between both sides of the mining industry. He endeavoured to the end to improve the lot of the miner by trying to create a Workmen's Insurance Fund. The *Western Mail* appraised that his Parliamentary career experienced 'varying fortune'.[72]

Sir George Elliot's last known London address was 1, Park Street, Park Lane, in the centre of Mayfair.[73] This illustrated the gigantic leap in lifestyle he had made during his lifetime. The impact of his legacy was felt by people being employed in the mining of the Durham and South Wales Coalfields, in dock and railway ventures, and in the manufacture of wire ropes. What helped him attain such a position of authority in industry? One view was 'possibly he owed as much to a homely northern strain of fidelity to interests which had once engaged his serious attention as to any other single quality'.[74]

The Engineer judged that:

'Sir George Elliot was progressive as an engineer, and ready to give any new invention a reasonable and fair trial. Among other innovations he introduced iron wire pit ropes in the collieries, and became a

Sir George Elliot (1815-1893)
A commentary on his career. The date of the cartoon is not known.
Baker Baker Prints, with the courtesy of Durham University Library

manufacturer of them as a partner of the firm Glass, Elliot, & Co. The patents this firm had acquired included one for making submarine cables and this proved subsequently a source of large profit. The greatest undertaking of the firm was the construction of the first Atlantic cable which was accomplished in 1866, an achievement which brought distinction to all concerned. The success of this great undertaking was in a great measure due to Sir George Elliot; for although high scientific authorities, practical electricians, and a most able seaman were connected with the preparations and operation of laying the cable, it required a master-mind with great powers of organisation to carry so difficult and complex matter to completion.'[75]

By the mid 1860s, Elliot ranked among a class of Victorians that initiated and shaped enterprise as 'gentlemanly capitalism'. The baronet also strove to win for himself a public reputation as a giver of gifts. Whitby was claimed to owe 'its present importance as a watering-place largely to his liberality'.[76] Elliot donated an Egyptian mummy to the town's Pannet Park Museum.[77] A fascination with pagan ancient Egypt seemed not to trouble a devoted member of the Anglican Church. Church buildings in both his native county, and one in South Wales, still contain relics associated with him and his family

On a day of continuous heavy rain, the 28th December, 1893, Sir George Elliot was buried.[78] A cortège escorted his body from his County Durham home, Houghton Hall, Houghton-le-Springs, to a memorial service at St Michael's Church. There was a 'very large gathering' of mourners and friends of the family. The family received 'numerous' wreaths sent by, among others, Lord Londonderry, and Alexandra Docks, Newport. Among those present at the funeral, in addition to immediate relatives, were Lord Durham, Colonel Erainson, Matthew Fowler MP, Thomas Milvain QC, Dr Murphy (Sunderland), and Mr Appleby, secretary to Lord Londonderry. Powell Duffryn Steam Coal Company appears neither to have sent a wreath to the family, or had a representative at the funeral.

After the church service, the cortège proceeded up the gradual ascent of Sunderland Street to the town's elevated Hillside Cemetery. Men skilled in mining had excavated into a cliff face, which serves as a wall of the cemetery, a family burial vault. So, Sir George Elliot was entombed like a notary of a civilisation he had come to admire, the ancient Egyptians.

The Martin family acquired Houghton Hall sometime after Sir George Elliot's death. A son of the family, Edward Martin, recalled, in 1960, that a ghost of Captain Hutton was said to have stalked his former bedchamber in the Hall. This room had been kept furnished exactly as it was in Hutton's time, and the door to it kept locked.[79] This practice must have been observed during the decades when the Elliot family occupied the house.

Sir George Elliot ensured that at least his name and surname would live on after his death. A weather worn cast iron street sign in Aberaman announces 'George Street', which is not far from 'Margaret Street'. More notably the name of Elliot is synonymous with the Rhymney Valley town of New Tredegar. Its Elliot Town, with its Elliot Street, stand on the threshold of Elliot Colliery. The County Durham baronet might have felt that he had earned some right to adoration, or it partly satisfied his liking for self-promotion. He had though not yielded to vanity in 1864, when the Powell collieries were acquired. He ingeniously saw that the company's name, Powell Duffryn Steam Coal Company, would serve to market its product, and did not name the company after himself.

The minutes of the first meeting of the directors of the company in 1894, on the 9th January, noted: '*The death of Sir George Elliot Bart who was founder of the Company in 1864, having been reported, it was unanimously resolved: That a vote be recorded of the deepest sympathy with the family of the late Sir George Elliot Bart in their recent heavy bereavement*'.[80] The absence of any praise for the company's founder might give a clue to the low regard held about him among directors of the company.

Coal Mining Expansion

By 1894, the directors of Powell Duffryn had a firm grip upon the affairs of the company due to the work of the Management Committee. The coal potential of the Rhymney Valley also commanded their interest. The Rhymney Iron Company had sunk, south of Pontlottyn, Rhymney Merthyr Number 1 in 1889-90, followed by Rhymney Merthyr Number 2 in 1892.[81] Then, in 1891-93, the Rhymney Valley's southern appendix, the Aber Valley, situated north-west of Caerphilly, saw the sinking of the Universal Colliery Company's colliery, at Senghenydd.[82] The Rhymney Valley, though, was not alone in seeing an inrush of capital investment in new collieries.

The sinkings in the steam coal areas of Glamorgan, after 1890, saw constant employment for sinkers. In the Rhondda Fawr area four collieries were sunk: Great Western Colliery Company Limited's Tymawr in 1891; Naval Colliery Company Limited's Ely and Nantgwyn pits in 1892; and Lewis Merthyr Navigation Colliery Company Limited's Cambrian Number 4 in 1894.[83] In the Rhondda Fach area sinking took place at D. Davis & Son Limited's Ferndale Number 8 in 1892, and between 1891 and 1893, Locket's Merthyr Steam Coal Company Limited's Mardy Number 3.[84] The Taff Valley saw, between the years 1890–1896, the sinking of Dowlais Iron Company's Dowlais - Cardiff Colliery, at Abercynon.[85] In the Ogwr Fach and Ogwr Fawr Valleys there was between the years 1894-6 the arrival of Christmas Evans' Dinas Main New Pits, and Britannic Merthyr (Gilfach Goch, Cwm Ogwr Fach).[86] The Llynfi Valley saw the sinking of North's Navigation Collieries Limited, Caerau 1 and 2 between the years 1891-1893.[87] There would appear to have been no end to exploration for coal in Glamorgan.

In the Aberdare Valley Powell Duffryn's general manager of collieries Edmund Mills Hann, pursued three tactics: colliery improvements, colliery acquisition, and technical innovation, which is revealed later. The year 1896 saw the wooden headframe of Aberaman Colliery felled, and replaced with a Nevill of Llanelly (sic) wrought iron structure 55ft in height. The colliery's original steam winding engine was replaced.[88]

The year 1896 also saw Edmund Mills Hann hold office for one year as High Constable of Miskin (Higher). In 1894, he had been elected 'top of the poll' as a councillor on the Aberdare Urban District Council.[89] In the late nineteenth century, the High Constable was empowered to call, and chair meetings in Aberdare about local issues.

There was possibly one part of Powell Duffryn's operation that ranked low in the general manager of collieries' priorities: the Aberaman Brickworks.[90] The clay it used to make bricks and earthenware shapes, sanitary pipes etc. was obtained from a nearby level. By 1914, ground clay was fed automatically into three Fawcett Stiff Brick Machines, each were capable of making 60,000 bricks per week. There were also three pipe making machines. The bricks were baked in twenty-one kilns, nineteen being of the Beehive pattern, and two of the Continuous type giving an output capacity of 160,000 to 180,000 tons per year. The operation of Elliot Colliery received priority attention ahead of the brick works.

South Wales Coalfield's Largest Underground Pump

Flooding became a persistent nuisance at Elliot Colliery.[91] In 1896, there was a spate of 'feeder' incidents that were dealt with. Then in, July 1897, 'a considerable outburst occurred, and the total quantity ran up to 72,000 gallons', which was slightly greater than that estimated for the water outburst of November 1891. Chemical analysis found that the water's source was the limestone, which lay under the Farewell rock.

Regardless, Edmund Mills Hann decided that 'the winding of coal had to be stopped', and an unwanted 'long period of great difficulties occurred'. It became 'necessary' for him 'to consider most carefully what would be the best means of raising the increased quantity of water, and after an inspection of various appliances, a Reidler pump was decided upon, mainly owing to the numerous large plants in successful work in the German collieries'. '*One chief reason for this preference was that a rotative engine seems to allow more margin of capacity in case of partial breakdown, and this has since been demonstrated by the high speeds at which (for the sake of the trial) the pump was driven*'.

Messrs Fraser & Chalmers, Erith, was 'entrusted' with making, and installing the Reidler pump. The pump's specification was to deliver 60,000 gallons per hour against a head of 1,600ft when running at normal speed.[92] The date when the pump was commissioned is unknown. Nevertheless, the Reidler pump was 'probably the largest to have been placed underground at that time' in the South Wales Coalfield.[93] The pump proved successful in operation.

Edmund Mills Hann gave credit to Graeme Ogilvie for the notion about establishing a central washery for small coal to serve the company's Aberdare Valley collieries.[94] 'Shortly before his death', which occurred on the 14th September, 1897, in a manner venerated by engineers, Ogilvie had provided a pencil note of the notion to Joseph Shaw.[95] Ogilvie and Hann had, between 1890 and 1892, visited mainland Europe to inspect washery and coking plants. The Humboldt Coal Washery at Elliot Colliery, started up in 1893, was the immediate outcome. The approved Aberdare Valley central washery idea was erected in the vicinity of Middle Duffryn Colliery in 1900. It began operation by 1903, and in Hann's words: '*I think, conduced a good deal to the profitable results shewn*', and he anticipated that it would '*continue to assist* [the company] *in finding the most advantageous market for our produce*'.

The Central washery was a sign of Powell Duffryn's lead in the South Wales Coalfield regarding this aspect of colliery engineering. It was a fitting complement to the combined efforts of the company's general manager of collieries, and its late chairman. Years later, Hann wrote a short epitaph: '*Mr Arthur Graeme Ogilvie … devoted so much care attention to the progress of this concern* [Powell Duffryn]'.

Joseph Shaw

Joseph Shaw succeeded Ogilvie as Chairman of the Company. At forty-one years of age he was six years younger than Edmund Mills Hann.[96] He was a barrister, whose father, Joseph Shaw from Celbridge, County Kildare, Ireland, had relocated to Cheltenham, Gloucestershire. Schooled at Malvern College before going up to Trinity College, Cambridge University, he graduated with a BA in 1879. After being admitted to the legal profession at the Inner Temple, he was called to the Bar on the 26th January, 1884. He became a director of Powell Duffryn in 1887. Sometime afterwards he resided at Kentchurch Court, Herefordshire. Thus he lived on the border of Herefordshire with Monmouthshire. The railway linking the English Midlands with South Wales ran near to his residence. From Pontrilas Station he could also travel by rail to London via Newport. The knowledge and experience he obtained from working on Powell Duffryn's Managing Committee made him fit for chairmanship.

Reidler's Pumping Engine – Installed underground at Elliot Colliery in the late 1890s. Capable of pumping 60,000 gallons. Possibly the largest pump ever installed underground in the South Wales Coalfield. The pump was made by Messrs Fraser & Chalmers of Erith, Kent.

Joseph Shaw KC
Chairman of Powell Duffryn Steam Coal Company 1897-1928.

The high regard that company's shareholders had for Edmund Mills Hann was known by Joseph Shaw. Minuted for a meeting of the directors, in September, 1897, was the granting of eighty ordinary shares in the Capital of the Company to its general manager of collieries.[97] The shares had been transferred to his name by three shareholders: Griffin, Gassby, and Guy. Sir George Elliot, son of the founder also resigned from the board of directors around the same time. Due to the early deaths of the male inheritors of Sir George Elliot's title, the baronetcy quickly became extinct. The Elliots' left a legacy: Powell Duffryn had to resolve matters arising from Sir George's stewardship of the company, and some were still pending when the twentieth century began.[98]

Nonetheless, Edward Mills Hann was not held back from revitalising and improving the company's colliery operation. In 1898, Cwmneol Colliery, in the Aberdare Valley, 'idle' since April 1893, saw the start of shaft deepening work, and an engineering makeover. Cwmneol's engine and boiler were improved, new screens were erected, railway sidings were extended, and new buildings for stores and lamp room were erected. A parallel drum of 12ft was installed. So the colliery was not used to test a drum design idea of Hann's dealt with immediately below. Nonetheless, he later reflected that the improvements made at Cwmneol Colliery made 'the place much better fitted for economic working'.[99]

Improving Winding Appliances

An aim of Edmund Mills Hann's innovative work, during the early to mid-1890s, was to achieve improvements in winding at Powell Duffryn's collieries. In 1898, he presented a paper to the South Wales Institute of Engineers that reported some of the associated work.[100] He offered a reservation: the work was 'of very imperfect character'. Nevertheless, his 'desired end' was clear: to raise the largest amount of coal via a colliery's shaft during the hours assigned to coal winding so as to lower the cost of coal

production. He led the company's technical work concerning winding drum design, winding engines operation improvement such as experimenting with valve settings, evaluating the use of balance ropes for winding, and trialling pit bottom arrangements.

The company considered a number of winding drum design ideas. One idea involved a spiral winding portion on a drum. The idea envisaged using a spiral course for wrapping the winding rope during the initial stage of the cage's lift from pit bottom. The smallest diameter of the spiral course was to be used to wrap the rope at the start of a wind. After a number of wraps around the spiral portion of the drum, the rope would wrap around the drum's maximum diameter to complete the final stages of the lift of a cage. However, the prospect of an 'enormous weight' for a spiral drum led Hann to consider a radical concept: using a compound engine to drive such a drum design. The 'slow starting' aspect of a compound engine was at least another problem he faced.

Yet, he continued to contemplate 'whether a combination of compound engine with a drum specially designed to give an easier start would not be the best, thus by using a drum doubling its diameter in four strokes a compound engine would get a better start away, and have got into speed and the full pressure on all pistons, before its maximum load comes on; whilst by using cylinders of somewhat larger diameter and shorter stroke than the most usual proportions, the diameter of the drum might be kept down without detriment to the speed of winding and with economy of steam'. In 1898, Hann claimed that the design 'could be constructed, without the usual enormous weight, by strutting the spiral portions' [see diagram below].

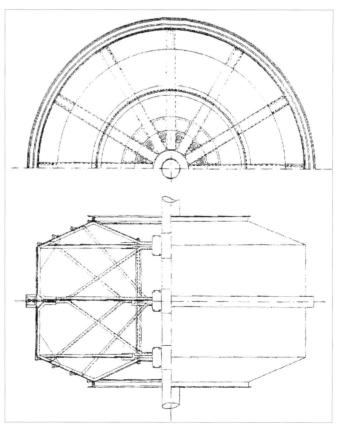

A pioneering semi-spiral drum design which was later classed as a 'bi-cylindro-conical' drum. Edmund Mills Hann led the design and development of the drum during the 1890s.
E. M. Hann, 'Improvements in Winding Appliances', SWIE, Vol. XX, (1898).

William Wight, a Durham Coalfield trained mining engineer, then making his mark in the Rhondda Valley, observed that what Hann had described was 'rather a departure from the usual practice'.[101] Wight judged that 'Mr Hann seemed to be in the right direction' away from some of the drums in South Wales which were of 'enormous size'.[102]

Significantly, the proposed use of a compound engine for winding was also a departure from the norm, simple engines. In a compound engine, steam expanded through two or more cylinders. As an example, a single tandem compound engine comprised two cylinders, in line, one behind the other. Steam was first admitted to one cylinder, termed a high-pressure cylinder. The exhausted steam from the high-pressure cylinder was then piped to power the other cylinder, the low-pressure cylinder. 'Compounding enabled steam to be expanded in the engine to many times its original volume with less [energy] loss from condensation on the cylinder walls. It also reduced leakage losses and the stresses in the engine'.[103]

The first compound horizontal steam winding engine used in the British coalfields was introduced in 1888.[104] Apparently of 'limited power', it suffered the indignity of being replaced by an 'ordinary horizontal engine, and converted into an underground haulage-engine'. Such ignominy may have been a gift for the supporters of simple steam winding engines. However, this did not dissuade Hugh Bramwell, manager of the Great Western Colliery Company, which owned collieries around the mouth of the Rhondda Valley, from taking up the compound engine design.

Consequently, he was responsible for the installation of a compound winding engine at the Great Western Colliery Company's Tymawr Colliery. The engine was designed and made by Messrs John Fowler & Co., Leeds, and 'commenced raising coal in August 1892'.[105]

The Tymawr Fowler engine also featured expansion-gear. The simple Thornewill & Warham winding engine at Elliot East Colliery, installed around the same time, also enjoyed such a means of steam control. The first instance of the use of expansion-gear on a winding engine in the South Wales Coalfield had taken place at the Great Western Colliery Company's Hetty Pit. According to Maurice Deacon, writing around 1893, that 'except in the case of large pumping and fan engines', expansion-gear had not received the attention it deserved for colliery winding engines.[106]

Expansion-gear offered a means for improving an engine's steam economy. Relatively greater power, as steam pressure energy, was needed for the short phase associated with starting a winding engine. For this period of the engine's operation cycle, steam was admitted to an engine to move its piston for a full stroke, with this mode being called 'non-expansive working'. Expansion gear enabled steam supply to be cut-off at maybe one-third of the stroke. Then, with steam locked in the cylinder, steam proceeded to expand as heat being converted into work to complete the winding cycle.

Of special interest, the Tymawr engine, according to Hugh Bramwell, was 'one of the few compound winding-engines in this country [United Kingdom]'.[107, 108] Notably, the engine was the first of this type used for winding in the South Wales Coalfield. William Galloway also used compound engines at Llanbradach Colliery, a short time later. During the colliery's sinking, Galloway experimented with a small one, and then proceeded to install at the colliery's Number 2 Pit one made also by Messrs John Fowler & Company, which became operational around 1894.[109]

Around 1896, Galloway and Bramwell cited the growing practice overseas of using compound steam winding engines. The Great Western Colliery Company's manager noted: 'Abroad, both on the Continent and in the colonies, compound winding-engines are becoming more common'.[110] Galloway, though, was somewhat more cautious in his claim: the compound engine 'appears to be receiving attention on the Continent'. Yet, they knew, as pioneers of this type of winding engine in Britain, only through experiment and satisfactory experience could any criticism from adherents to the simple winding engine be allayed. Hann was very familiar with Bramwell and Galloway's use of compound engines.

For Hann, it seems the factor that determined his preference for compound engines concerned advances in steam boiler design that had yielded increased steam pressures and higher thermal efficiencies. In 1898, he declared: '*In starting a new colliery they [colliery engineers in general] raised the boiler pressure very considerably over what they had been accustomed to; and as far as the use of the simple engine is concerned, he was bound to say that any expectations they had of saving fuel were dissipated, but not where compound engines were used*'.[111] Then after hearing disadvantages raised by members of South Wales Institute of Engineers on discussing the 'question of the relative economy of simple engines as against compound engines', he was inclined to 'the belief' that 'the two-cylinder compound engine was inadmissible', and significantly: '*If they [Powell Duffryn] had to use compound engines at all, they had much better be four-cylinder engines, and it would be a great improvement to have two sets of cylinders at right angles to each other, thus getting two cylinders horizontally and two vertically*'. The Aberdare Valley's Cwmneol Colliery, at the time when it was deepened in 1898, may have been where Powell Duffryn used a compound engine for winding for the first time.[112]

Possibly in 1898, Hann was on the verge of approving the specification of the winding appliances for Bargoed Colliery. As described more fully later, he committed the company to using compound winding at this new Rhymney Valley colliery. In his 1898 paper he makes reference to 'the practical problem of the best winding engine for a pit 600 yards, or over in depth', which anticipates Bargoed Colliery. However, the practical work of the mid-1890s, to improve winding, reaped a notable immediate benefit for the company.

Hann did not name company collieries where improvement work had occurred in his 1898 paper to the South Wales Institute of Engineers. Regarding the colliery where the first trial of a 'spiral drum' occurred, he gave the depth of wind as '220 yards'.[113] Such a shaft depth points to an Aberdare Valley colliery. A check of data about the depths of company colliery shafts suggests that the trial took place at Fforchaman Colliery. The colliery held its place as being vital to the prosperity of the company. The trial was aimed at increasing 'the output of the pit beyond what the engine could do'. Evaluated was 'whether a new engine was necessary', or whether 'modifications could be made to effect the desired end'.

Notably, in 1898, Hann reported that '*it was found that by using a spiral drum, the power requisite to lift a two tram cage, at the start, would be very little greater than when one was raised on a plain drum; and this was done, being considered in the end, under the circumstances of this particular case, preferable to condensing arrangement, or a balance rope*'. The outcome of the trial appears to have yielded a satisfactory improvement in tonnage raised at Fforchaman Colliery since, as will be dealt with later, its redevelopment was postponed.

1898 Strike

In 1898, there was a major strike. The collieries of the South Wales Coalfield stood idle for twenty weeks due to the men's reaction to a Workmen's Compensation Act of that year. South Wales Coalfield miners demanded the abolition of the Sliding Scale, and the introduction of a Conciliation Board, a minimum rate of pay, and payment for small coal. What particular part Hann played in defining the stance of the Monmouthshire and South Wales Coalowners' Association is not known, but there is not a hint of any dissent against the stance taken by the coalowners in his record of the strike.[114] He apportioned the blame for it to 'the men' since 'they declined to give their representatives full powers to settle, and the owners objected to negotiate with a body that had not such powers'.

The strike saw hostile confrontation, which Edmund Mill Hann described as being 'a great deal of very fatuous marching and speech-making and the Military had to be brought in on account of some attacks'. The strike ended with the 'defeat of the men', the Sliding Scale was kept for a further four years, 'at the end of which it was given up', and he considered that the 'owners were considerable gainers'. The presence of a 'company' of infantry, of 1,000 men, and a meagre strike fund, conspired together to break the strike. The Powell Duffryn general manager of collieries thought that the strike could have been avoided.

Keenness for learning

A personal mission of Hann's was to improve coal mining practices through conducting practical trials, and study. He had become a committed member of the South Wales Institute of Engineers by the 1890s. The Institute's Proceedings contain many comments that he raised in discussions, and the technical papers he delivered. After 1894, the Institute's meetings were held at a 'fine building at Park Place', Cardiff, 'containing commodious premises for the use of members, a fine library well stocked with books, and an excellent lecture hall'. In the 1890s, he produced two papers about managing the flooding at Elliot Colliery, which have been referred to earlier. Around Christmas, 1897, he prepared 'Improvements in Safety Explosives'.[115] This described 'practical trials' with 'High Explosives', which were done around 1894. An aim of his was to 'make those explosives' which were 'unsafe safe', and 'those which' were 'considered fairly safe still safer'.

The writing of papers exhibited Hann's keenness for learning. Around 1899, he gained the directors' approval to trial, at both Elliot and Aberaman collieries, a reading room for officials. He hoped to create 'something in the nature of an *espirit de corps*'. He was 'to an extent disappointed' to find that 'the majority of the officials' were 'not active minded enough to utilise such things, but a not inconsiderable minority' made 'use of them regularly and beneficially', and so he did not feel 'it advisable to discontinue them'.[116] When he recollected this experience he added a disparaging assessment: 'The Welsh genius does not run very much in the engineering direction, nor does it delight in the organisation or in co-ordination of details'. Although this assessment might suggest frustration with officials who lacked a desire for learning, it reveals that he did not shirk from reproving officials.

In 1899, the company's general manager of collieries was forty-nine years of age. At the same age, George Elliot led a group of investors to buy a number of Thomas Powell's collieries, and so formed Powell Duffryn. Elliot, for comparison, was as an entrepreneur, mobile in the pursuit of his interests, and wealth. Hann, though, had been anchored at Aberaman for sixteen years, and seems to have found riches in engineering collieries.

In 1900, the company authorised Edmund Mills Hann to buy Llety Shenkin Colliery from Messrs Burnyeat Brown & Company for £22,000.[117] Located north-east of Aberaman, its workings of 320 acres were entirely surrounded by Powell Duffryn's. The purchase price included some house property. The colliery was in 'poor order', but under Hann's management it later 'proved to be of great advantage'. However, the importance that the company's Aberdare Valley collieries once held was being challenged. In the 1890s, Powell Duffryn continued its explorations of the coal reserves of the Rhymney Valley

Llety Shenkin Colliery – Aberdare Valley. Purchased by the company in 1900 from Messrs Burnyeat Brown & Company. In 1914, coal was raised from 275 yards. In 1918, the colliery's manpower was 800.

Pope/Parkhouse Archive

NOTES

1. D. A. Farne, *op. cit.*, p.310. This Association, and its associated steering committee, was formed that year as a reaction to events in Egypt. An idea mooted by this Association, was the building of a second, and a British owned, Suez Canal.
2. Charles Wilkins, *op. cit.*, p.117.
3. John Hutton, *op. cit.*, p.64.
4. W. W. Price, *op. cit.*, p.13.
5. Sir George Elliot spoke at a Parliamentary Committee inquiring into the Barry Dock Railway Bill. Pontypridd Chronicle, 'The Working of the Pontypridd & Caerphilly Railway', 28 June 1884, p.6
6. *Pontypridd Chronicle, op. cit.*, 'Notes on Passing Events', p.5.
7. The Taff Vale Railway Company discontinued its involvement with the railway in 1906. The Alexandra (Newport & South Wales) Docks & Railway (AD&R) then provided the service having acquired the PC& N in 1897. See John Hutton, *op. cit.*, pp.64-65.
8. D. S. M. Barrie, *A Regional History of the Railways of Great Britain*, Vol. XII South Wales, *op. cit.*, pp.104-6.
9. R. W. Kidner, *The Rhymney Railway.* (The Oakwood Press, 1995), p.24.
10. The GWR subsequently took over the working of the line from 1st January, 1899. Consequently the GWR, AD&R, and RR worked the trains. R. W. Kidner, *op. cit.*, p.24.
11. E. M. Hann, *Brief History of The Powell Duffryn Steam Coal Company Ltd*, pp.12-13.
12. D. S. M. Barrie, *op. cit.*, pp.157-8.
13. *The Powell Duffryn Steam Coal Company 1864-1914, op. cit.*, p.44.
14. Barrie described Lundie as a 'notable Victorian strong man', who 'arrived from the Blyth & Tyne Railway [circa 1865] to stiffen the management [of the Rhymney Railway], virtually taking charge for the next forty years'. D. S. M. Barrie, *op. cit.*, p.118. Lundie in addition to being the general manager of the Rhymney Railway, a post he retired from in 1904 aged 90, served as chairman of Cardiff Collieries until his death in 1908.
15. Discussion, 'Railway Brakes', *SWIE*, Vol. XXIV (1904-1906), p.85.
16. Order Book, Gloucester Wagon Company.
17. D. S. M. Barrie, *op. cit.*, p.118.
18. Cynon Valley Historical Society, *Cynon Coal, op. cit.*, p.61. It possibly existed before 1908 when wagon companies of the region combined to rationalise the repair service network.
19. *The Powell Duffryn Steam Coal Company 1864-1914, op. cit.*, p.44.
20. E. M. Hann, *op. cit.*, p.13.
21. This might be St. Hilda. Pevsner does not mention Elliot's part in its founding, but proposes that the church's 'real date as 1884-6'. Nikolaus Pevsner, *op. cit.*, p.395.
22. *Western Mail*, 'Death of Sir George Elliot', 26 Dec 1893, p.5, col.5.
23. E. M. Hann, 'Notes on an Outburst of Gas at Aberaman Colliery', *SWIE*, Vol. XVI (1888-1889), pp.262-5.
24. 'Notes on an Outburst of Gas at Aberaman Colliery', *op. cit.*, p.292-9.
25. Trevor Boyns, 'Growth in the Coal Industry: the Cases of Powell Duffryn and the Ocean Coal Company, 1864-1913', *Modern South Wales Essays in Economic History*, eds. Colin Baber and L. J. Williams (University of Wales Press, 1986) p.161.
26. GR-PDMBDM No. 3, Placed between pp.19-20 and printed in booklet form. It concerned a report of the committee appointed 27 March 1888 for 1 May 1888.
27. letter Trevor Boyns to Writer, 21 July 2005.
28. GR PDMBDM No. 3, p.99.
29. It was registered as being wrecked during the period 1888-89. *Lloyd's Register of Ships.*
30. Letter, Sir George Elliot to Mr Parkinson, GR PDMBDM No.3, pp.120-122.
31. Sir Thomas Brassey was made a baron in 1886, and later, in 1911, an earl.
32. *Western Mail*, 'Death of Sir George Elliot', 26 Dec 1893, p.5, col.6.
33. GR PDMBDM No. 3, p.183.
34. E. M. Hann, *Brief History of The Powell Duffryn Steam Coal Company Ltd*, p.13.
35. E. M. Hann, 'A Recent Plant for the Utilisation of Small Coal', *SWIE*, Vol. XXV (1906-1908), p.470.
36. Trevor Boyns, Elliot Colliery-Employment Figures. (Annual List of Mines). 2,507 men were employed underground (East 1,191; West 1,316), and 304 on the surface.
37. GR-PDMBDM No. 3, p.98.
38. D. S. M. Barrie, *The Brecon & Merthyr Railway, op. cit.*, p.131.
39. Noel and Alan Cox, *The Tokens, Checks, Metallic Tickets, Passes and Tallies of Wales 1800-1993.* (1994), p.192.
40. Letter, Mark Smith to Writer, 4 March 2007. He informed that such passes were issued by other companies in Wales like the Dinorwic Slate Quarries, Cardiff Steam Coal Collieries Co. Ltd, Cwmaman Co. Ltd, Dowlais Iron Company, John Lancaster & Co. Ltd, and Tredegar Iron Company. Regarding English coal companies, he found that the practice was rare, and, as 'far as' he 'was aware, non-existent in Scotland'.
41. R. H. Walters, *op. cit.*, pp.135-6.
42. G. M. Harries, *op. cit.*, pp.5-7.
43. Research Notes as at March 2007, Raymond Lawrence. Colliery Manager details.
44. That year saw a dispute over the coal cutting price and allowances for clod [clay]. 'List of disputes', Records of the several Coal Owners' Association of Monmouthshire and South Wales 1864 to 1895. (Monmouthshire and South Wales Coal Owners' Association), pp.109-119.
45. 'The Monmouthshire Coalfield, VIII–The Elliot Pits, New Tredegar Collieries', The *Colliery Guardian*, 23 Aug 1895, p.362.
46. T. H. Davies, *op. cit.*, pp.35-43. The patent featured a locked cover to 'envelope the cable'. A subsequent legal case ended with a judgment that Duncan had not anticipated Batchelor's locked-coil wire rope invention.
47. E. M. Hann, *Brief History of The Powell Duffryn Steam Coal Company Ltd*, p.11.
48. GR PDMBDM No. 3, p.166.
49. GR PDMBDM No. 3, p.222.
50. Hann Research Notes, Edwin Greening. This information was taken from a Hann Family ancestral tree, drawn up by John Hann of Gloucestershire, undated, but maybe circa 1990, and sourced by the late Edwin Greening.
51. David Hann, 'The Hann Family–A Mining Dynasty of South Wales part 1', Glamorgan Family History Society, *Journal* No. 38, (June, 1995) p.39.
52. *The Powell Duffryn Steam Coal Company 1864-1914, op. cit.*, p.22.
53. E. M. Hann, *op. cit.*, p.13.
54. Cynon Valley History Society, *op. cit.*, p.200.
55. E. M. Hann, *op. cit.*, p.17.
56. E. M. Hann, 'An Outburst of Water, and the Means of Dealing With It', *SWIE*, Vol. XIX (1894-1895), pp.143-154. Unless otherwise noted the source for the description regarding Elliot Colliery's floods for the period 1891-1893.
57. Rees Shore (1860-1912) was the great-grandfather of the Writer who has taken the liberty to mention him in the description without documentary evidence. According to the Electoral Register, in 1889 Rees Shore lived at 3, Elliot Town, but by 1894 had moved into 1, Elliot Terrace. The sequence of his residence in Elliot Town, recorded in the Electoral Register, contains a break that coincided with the opening of Bargoed Colliery.
58. Every year Sir George Elliot entertained the children of the Industrial School, Trecynon at the Aberaman Park, grounds adjacent to Aberaman House. W. Price, *op. cit.*, p.13.
59. Obituary, Sir George Elliot, Bart., Institution of Civil Engineers Minutes of Proceedings, *op. cit.*, pp.356-7.
60. The triple expansion principle involved steam passing through, in sequence, high, intermediate, and low pressure cylinders, the cylinders having the following diameters 16-inch, 25-inch, and 39-inch respectively. Each cylinder featured a piston stroke of 3ft 6 inches.
61. 'The Monmouthshire Coalfield, VIII–The Elliot Pits, New Tredegar Collieries', The *Colliery Guardian*, 23 Aug 1895, p.362.
62. J. C. Carr and W. Taplin, *History of the British Steel Industry.* (Basil Blackwell, 1962), p.54.
63. E. M. Hann, *Brief History of The Powell Duffryn Steam Coal Company Ltd.*, p.15.
64. The plant was later described as being the first Humboldt Coal washery erected in 'England', and was 'set to work in 1893, making nuts, which at that time had only been attempted at very few and mostly with very old-fashioned wasteful plant'. The source was a book, title and date of publication unknown, although clues suggest circa 1905, p.17; facsimile of pages from the book in Writer's possession.
65. *The Powell Duffryn Steam Coal Company 1864-1914, op. cit.*, p.51.
66. E. M. Hann, *op. cit*, p.16.
67. *Western Mail*, 'Death of Sir George Elliot', 26 Dec 1893, p. 5, cols. 5 & 6.
68. Death of Sir George Elliot, Bart., *Engineering*, Vol. 56, (1893), p.791.
69. *Western Mail*, 'Death of Sir George Elliot', 26 Dec 1893, p.5, col.6.
70. J. H. Morris and L. J. Williams, *op. cit.*, p.131. Footnote 1: gave this impression of Sir George Elliot in the context of coal owners as Members of Parliament.
71. *The Times*, Obituary-Sir George, 26 Dec 1893, p.4, col.3.

72 *Western Mail*, 'Death of Sir George Elliot', 26 Dec 1893, p.5, cols.5 & 6.

73 Members' List, *Transactions, Institute of Mining Engineers*, Vol. 1, (1889-90), p.XX.

74 Obituary, Sir George Elliot, Bart., *Institution of Civil Engineers Minutes of Proceedings*, op. cit., p.357.

75 'Sir George Elliot', *The Engineer*, Vol. 76, 29 Dec. 1893, p.617.

76 Obituary, Sir George Elliot, Bart., *Institution of Civil Engineers Minutes of Proceedings*, op. cit., p.356.

77 In 1930, the mummy was sold to Hull Municipal Museum. Joann Fletcher, 'Edward Heron-Allen, His Friends and their Mummies: EHA and ancient Egypt', Opusculum VIII: *Journal of the Hero-Allen Society*, (2005), pp.18-19.

78 *Sunderland Daily Echo*, 'The Late of Sir George Elliot: Funeral Today', 28 Dec 1893.

79 *Sunderland Echo*, 3 Nov 1960, p.9.

80 GR PDMBDM No. 4, p.41.

81 R. H. Walters, op. cit., p.18.

82 R. H. Walters, op. cit., p.18.

83 R. H. Walters, op. cit., p.26.

84 R. H. Walters, op. cit., p.28.

85 R. H. Walters, op. cit., p.14.

86 R. H. Walters, op. cit., pp.31–3.

87 R. H. Walters, op. cit., p.35.

88 John Cornwall, *Collieries of South Wales*: 2. (Landmark, 2002), p.10.

89 W. W. Price, Card Records, Hann 2, item 5. National Library of Wales.

90 *The Powell Duffryn Steam Coal Company 1864-1914*, op. cit., pp.44-5.

91 E. M. Hann, 'Deep Pumping at Elliot Colliery', *SWIE*, Vol. XXI (1898-1899), pp.248-256. Unless otherwise stated, the source for what follows including the Reidler pump.

92 The pump comprised a horizontal cross compound Corliss engine with duplex pumps. Steam pressure at 90 lb/in². The high-pressure cylinder's diameter was 36-inch, and operated with a 48-inch stroke, and the-low pressure cylinder's dimensions were 57-inch diameter by 48-inch stroke.

93 *The South Wales Institute of Engineers – Sesquicentenary Brochure 1857-2007*, (SWIE, 2007), p.54.

94 E. M. Hann, *Brief History of The Powell Duffryn Steam Coal Company Ltd*, p.21.

95 E. M. Hann, op. cit., p.17. Hann states July, 1897. Marginalia, in the handwriting of W. W. Price, on a copy of this reference, gives 14th September, 1897 as the date of Ogilvie's death.

96 *The Times*, Obituary - Mr Joseph Shaw KC, 25 Dec 1933, p.4, col.1.

97 GR PDMBDM No. 4, p.158.

98 GR PDMBDM No. 5, pp.2-4.

99 E. M. Hann, op. cit., p.20.

100 E. M. Hann, 'Improvements in Winding Appliances', *SWIE*, Vol. XX (1898), pp.519-525.

101 Discussion, 'Improvements in Winding Appliances', *SWIE*, Vol. XXI (1898), p.24.

102 Discussion, 'Improvements in Winding Appliances', *SWIE*, Vol. XXI (1898), p.124.

103 R. J. Law, *The Steam Engine*. (HMSO, 1965), p.23.

104 H. Bramwell, 'The Raising of Coal from Vertical Shafts', *SWIE*, Vol. XXX (1917), p.17. An interpretation of a note of his is that it took place at Allhallows Colliery, Cumberland Coalfield, England.

105 Hugh Bramwell, 'The Compound Winding Engine at the Great Western Colliery Company's Tymawr Pit: with notes on its comparative steam economy', *Transactions, Federated Institution of Mining Engineers*, Vol. XII (1896-1897), p.282. The engine was a horizontal type, twin compound, one cylinder either side of the drum. Its high-pressure cylinder was 32-inches diameter; low-pressure cylinder, 48-inches diameter; stroke of each cylinder, 5ft; and it was operated using double-beat Cornish equilibrium–valves. The average boiler steam pressure was 120 lb/in².

106 Maurice Deacon, 'The use of Expansion Gear as applied to Colliery Engines', *Transactions, Federated Institution of Mining Engineers*, Vol. VII (1893-1894), p.672.

107 Maurice Deacon, 'The use of Expansion Gear as applied to Colliery Engines', op. cit., p.681-2. The Tymawr engine used a trip-gear for its Cornish valves, and were so arranged that steam expansion could take place at any point in the winding, and could act from one-seventh of the piston stroke.

108 Hugh Bramwell, 'The Compound Winding Engine at the Great Western Colliery Company's Tymawr Pit: with notes on its comparative steam economy', op. cit., p.282.

109 W. Galloway, 'A Compound Engine', *Transactions, Federated Institution of Mining Engineers*, Vol. XII (1896-1897), p.207. The engine consisted of two high-pressure cylinders, 24-inch diameter; two low-pressure cylinders 44-inch diameter, strokes 4ft 6in. Boiler steam pressure varied between 120 lb/in² and 150 lb/in².

110 Hugh Bramwell, 'The Compound Winding Engine at the Great Western Colliery Company's Tymawr Pit: with notes on its comparative steam economy', op. cit., p.282.

111 Discussion, 'Improvements in Winding Appliances', op. cit., pp.125-6.

112 *The Powell Duffryn Steam Coal Company 1864-1914*, op. cit., p.38. The engine was a Fraser Chalmers cross-compound engine with cylinder diameters of 28-inch, and 46-inch, with a 5ft stroke.

113 E. M. Hann, 'Improvements in Winding Appliances', op. cit., pp.519-520.

114 E. M. Hann, *Brief History of The Powell Duffryn Steam Coal Company Ltd*, p.19.

115 E. M. Hann, 'Improvements in Safety Explosives', *SWIE*, Vol. XX (1898), pp.409-413.

116 E. M. Hann, *Brief History of the Powell Duffryn Steam Coal Company Ltd*, pp.24-5.

117 E. M. Hann, op. cit., p.21.

The 1893 South Wales Coalfield strike caused a detachment of troops to be assigned to at least the Aberdare Valley. The officers were: standing (left to right): Major Young (2nd Beds). Lt. Ely (2nd Beds), Lt. Col. T. Phillips (3rd V.B. Welsh Regt.), Capt. Coates (2nd Beds); sitting: Capt. Hamilton (14th Hussars), David Davies Esq. JP, Colonel Vernon (2nd Beds).

Courtesy of Rhondda Cynon Taf Libraries

Bargoed. Colliery.

Looking eastwards over Bargoed Colliery with South Pit on the left and Brithdir Pit on the right. Extreme left on the horizon between the hillside and the sky is seen the tower of the Norman church of St. Sannan, Bedwellty. In later years such a view of the church would be lost due to a second coal rubbish tip growing on a site between the church and the village of Aberbargoed shown.

Pope/Parkhouse Archive

Chapter Five
HANN'S MARK

The mining at New Tredegar Colliery and Elliot Colliery gave Powell Duffryn Steam Coal Company first-hand clues about the possibilities of finding further coal under the floor of the Rhymney Valley. Only the Cardiff Steam Coal Collieries Company's Llanbradach Colliery and the Rhymney Iron Company's collieries had such knowledge. Curiously no other rival company intruded into the central length of the valley, which lay between Elliot Colliery and Llanbradach Colliery, to sink for coal deep underground. Perhaps rival coal companies were discouraged from mining coal in the Rhymney Valley due to flooding at Elliot Colliery. Powell Duffryn, though, expanded its operation in the Rhymney Valley. Trevor Boyns identified: '*In addition, the boom of 1890-1 and the coming to fruition of the sinking operations at Elliot pits helped the company substantially in the early 1890s. With the reversal in fortunes the company embarked on a massive campaign of expansion*'.[1]

The company's invasion of the Rhymney Valley, southward from Elliot Colliery, began with a modest manoeuvre. On New Year's Day, 1893, the sinking of Coed-y-moeth Pit began about a mile south of Elliot Colliery. 'By September of the same year coal was being sold, and a very successful career commenced [at Coed-y-moeth Pit], which is just closing as these memoranda are being written [1909]'.[2] The Coed-y-moeth Pit was sunk, according to Hann, to supply coal for the coking ovens at Elliot Colliery, but much more crucially, it was a means of managing underground water. Coed-y-moeth Pit served 'to avoid leaving a long barrier with the water of other concerns against it if this area was worked from' a planned colliery further south, Bargoed Colliery. The site for Bargoed Colliery stood just over two miles south of Elliot Colliery.

Bargoed Colliery

The prelude to Bargoed Colliery involved patient business negotiations by Edmund Mills Hann. The mining area eventually settled upon for the colliery was 2,400 acres, and it was leased from some twelve owners.[3] The finance for the colliery was partly raised through an issue of £300,000 5% Debentures, of which £253,900 was subscribed.[4]

Coed-y-moeth Pit. Sunk by Powell Duffryn in 1893.   *Courtesy John Smith, Welsh Collieries website*

Percy S. Philipps, Bargoed.

Bargoed Pits.

The lamp check was made by Halwood & Ackroyd
Ltd, Morley, Leeds.   *Courtesy of Mark Smith*

An early postcard view of Bargoed Colliery from the south-east. The maximum number of men ever employed at the
colliery was 3,353. The colliery's sinking began in 1896. The highest headgear is the South Pit that accessed the Nine Feet
seam at 628 yards. The headgear used to sink the North Pit stands to the left of the South Pits. The colliery's offices are
seen behind the South Pit's headgear.   *Pope/Parkhouse Archive*

A look at the Ordnance Survey's 2nd Edition 25-inch map, dated
1901, will find that a hamlet known as Charleston predated the
growth of the town of Bargoed. Moreover, Pont Aber Bargoed
marks the junction of the rivers Rhymney and the Nant Bargoed
Rhymney. Near to this river junction, in 1885, a woollen mill
used the hydro power supplied from the Nant Bargoed Rhymney
River. Perched at the top of an extremely steep hill track, east of
Pont Aber Bargoed, was the small hamlet of Aber-Bargoed. The
locality's main industry was farming. Dispersed across the locality
were a few small coal mines. One mine, Gilfach, that stood just
south of Bargoed Colliery, was in 1893 owned by the Rhymney
Iron Company as a source for house coal. After closing its iron
and steel making plant at Rhymney in 1891, the Rhymney
Iron Company chose coal mining as its main business.

Powell Duffryn's colliery site was crowded by the valley's sides.
The colliery took its name from a railway station, Bargoed Junction.
The Rhymney Railway Company opened the station in 1858. Civil
engineers left a notable landmark immediately north of the station,
an eight-arch, stone viaduct, 360ft in length. The viaduct spanned
the tributary valley to the Rhymney Valley, down which flowed,
from the north-west, the Nant Bargoed Rhymney. The northern
abutment of the viaduct dug into a hillside spur that was formed
during the Ice Age. Two lateral glaciers met there, one from the
Bargoed Rhymney Valley, whilst the other inched south from the
northern part of the Rhymney Valley. The medial glacier, so formed,
gouged a very narrow stage of the valley, which as the site for the
colliery constrained the design of its surface plant and buildings.

Sinking at Bargoed Colliery began in 1896 a distance east from
the Monmouthshire bank of the Rhymney River.[5] The work
yielded 'two shafts sunk to the steam coal measures intersecting
the 'Nine Feet' seam at 628 yards, and one shaft to the Brithdir
seam at 200 yards'.[6] Found, in 1901, was the steam coal of the Rhas
Las, otherwise called the Nine Feet seam.[7] The Brithdir (house
coal) shaft was sited to the south of the two shafts sunk to the
steam coal, which due to their relative positions, were known as
North [the upcast] and South [the downcast] Pits. The diameters
of the shafts were: the two steam coal pits 21ft; and 19ft for the
Brithdir pit. Compared with Elliot Colliery, it was essential to sink
the steam coal shafts to a greater depth, by around 100 yards, so as
to find the desired seam.

Bargoed Colliery's Brithdir seam was classified as bituminous
coal, and mined for household and coking purposes.[8] The seam
was 'heavily watered', that is prone to water seepage, and it was
'calculated that eight tons of water' were 'pumped for every ton of
coal raised'.[9]

Edmund Mills Hann reported 'no difficulties of any note
were met [sinking] except from feeders of water, but these were
numerous if not exceptionally large, and in consequence, from
a depth of about 200 yards down to 545 yards, the sinking was
carried on mostly with considerable water-making at the bottom.
The strata being so largely of hard rocks, in which heavy charges
of high explosives have to be used, there is, with ordinary sinking
pumping-sets, a great risk of interruption by breakage; and
consequently the mode of pumping adopted was direct-acting

horizontal steam pumps carried on the walling-stage pumping up to others placed at convenient positions in the shaft.[10]

The company, though, recognised that difficulties were overcome sinking the colliery.[11] In January 1901, Powell Duffryn granted Edmund Mills Hann, a special gratuity of £250. He was rewarded for 'the extra work involved which must have been greater than expected, his personal interventions underground', and the 'tact and care' he showed 'dealing with the difficulties' that arose, 'from time to time', with the company's workmen.

For raising coal from underground at Bargoed Colliery, Hann decided upon four trams per cage each having two decks with two trams per deck.[12] Each tram contained 28 to 30 cwt. of coal. With the total lift per cage at around six tons, this represented just over a doubling of the amount of coal raised per cage at Elliot Colliery. However, the total weight of a fully loaded cage lifted-off the pit bottom was 20 ton 12 cwt, which meant, in his words, 'The design of the winding-engine to raise this load was naturally a matter of great importance'.

Winding – Bargoed Colliery

Powell Duffryn's search for improvements in colliery winding during the mid-1890s shaped the associated operation at Bargoed Colliery. Moreover, Hann travelled 'to Germany and other places to see some of the latest engines' before making his final decision. The winding engines and drums installed at the colliery were:[13]

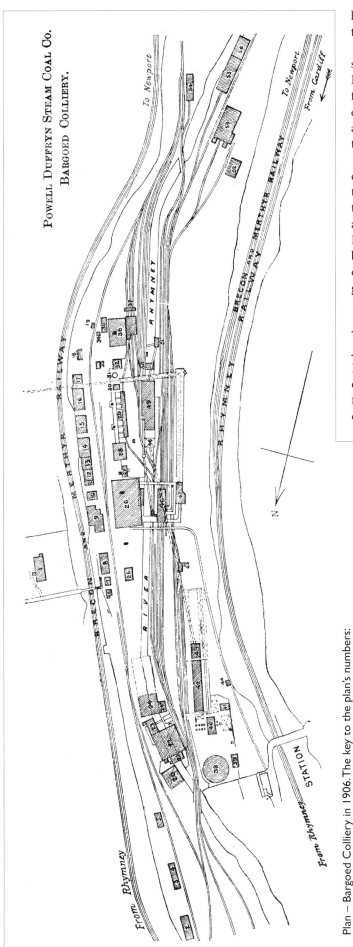

Powell Duffryn Steam Coal Co. Bargoed Colliery.

Plan – Bargoed Colliery in 1906. The key to the plan's numbers:

1. Colliery Office
2. Corn Stores
3. Saw Mill
4. Mortar Mill
5. Rope Shed
6. Pay Office
7. Overman's Office
8. Lamp Room
9. Fan Engine
10. Small Stores
11. Electrician's Workshop
12. Carpenter's Shop
13. Fitting Shop
14. Smith's Shop
15. General Stores
16. Electric Power House
17. Air Compressor
18. Air Receivers
19. Cabin
20. Purifiers
21. Oxide Burner
22. Sulphuric Acid Chambers
23. Sulphate Plant
24. Gas Engine and Electric Generator
24a. Sub-Station
25. North Pit Winder
26. South Pit Top
27. Hawthorn Davey Pump
28. South Pit Winder
29. Boilers
30. Boiler Feed Pump
31. Kennicott's Water Softner
32. Brithdir Pit Winder
33. Brithdir Sub Station
34. Crab. [?]
35. Brithdir Shops
36. Brithdir Screens
37. Weighing Machine
38. Gasometer
39. Laboratory
40. Exhauster House
41. Pumps
42. Coke Ovens
43. Bunker
44. Time Office
45. Coke Screen
46. South Pit Screens
47. Rubbish Bunker
48. Washery Bunker
49. Washery
50. Centrifugal Pumps
51. Robin's Belt Conveyor
52. Pattern Shop
53. Foundry
54. Loco Shed
55. Fitting Shop
56. Smith's Shop.

E. M. Hann's paper to the Institution of Mechanical Engineers, (October, 1906). Courtesy of Institution of Mechanical Engineers

Bargoed Colliery's South Pit Winding Engine – A four-cylinder cross-compound Corliss, made by Thornewill & Warham. The engine was powered by steam at 120 lbs per square inch The drum was a semi-spiral, with a diameter of 14ft to 24ft.

The Watkins' Collection, courtesy of English Heritage

North Pit Winder   Two cylinder cross compound Corliss, made by Yates & Thom, Blackburn. The drum was a semi-spiral, with a diameter of 14ft to 22ft

South Pit Winder   Four cylinder cross compound Corliss, made by Thornewill & Warham. The drum was a semi-spiral, with a diameter of 14ft to 24ft

Brithdir Winder   Two high pressure Corliss cylinders. The drum was a semi-spiral, with a diameter of 6ft to 9ft

The 1904 *Proceedings* of the South Wales Institute of Engineers described the Thornewill & Warham engine to be a four-cylinder compound with two horizontal high-pressure cylinders 32-inch by 72-inch stroke and two low-pressure cylinders, vertical, placed directly below the cranks, 50-inch by 72-inch stroke, and it drove a drum of a modified conical form.[14] Hann was confident that the Thornewill & Warham design gave 'sufficient power to dispense with any live steam in the low-pressure cylinders, which seemingly was the cause of much of the inefficiency of the then existing compound-engine'. Half a century later, in 1954, one of Britain's authorities on stationary steam engines, George Watkins, inspected the engine, and remarked that it was 'an unusual design, for high power and good balance', and noted that it featured Corliss valves – each side.[15]

In 1906, Edmund Mills Hann defended his use of compound engines at Bargoed Colliery before an audience of some of Britain's leading mechanical engineers. '*A very large proportion of mining engineers have disputed the superiority of the compound engine for winding, owing to its very short runs and frequent stoppages, and the large proportion of its power taken up accelerating its load*'.[16] However, '*the performance of the* [Thornewill & Warham] *engine had been very satisfactory, both practically and as to steam economy*'. A plant mishap at Bargoed Colliery had enabled him to reveal such an evaluation of the engine's steam economy. Steam, supplied from a 'group of boilers' to the engines, had made it difficult to 'present' a measure of the coal consumption results specific to any winding engine. However, an 'accident to the high-pressure cylinders of the [Thornewill & Warham]' engine' forced the colliery 'to wind for a time with two low-pressure cylinders'. The colliery's engineers found that as a result the 'coal consumption was most marked, amounting to over one hundred tons of coal per week, or one per cent of the output'.

Bargoed Colliery's winding engines drove 'semi-spiral' drums, which was Powell Duffryn's term for them in 1914. The drums were the 'combination of the spiral and cylindrical form' developed by the company as described earlier. Decades later, Powell Duffryn's semi-spiral drum would belong to a general category known as the 'bi-cylindro-conical' drum. One of the design feats of the semi-spiral drum was that the feared difficulties of a drum's weight and size were curbed. In the case of the South Pit winding drum, the rope was wound by way of the conical portion in three revolutions, and the rope coiled for the remaining twenty-two revolutions on the 24ft diameter.[17]

Edmund Mills Hann made no claim about being the creator of such a novel design.[18] However, just over a decade later, Hugh Bramwell noted that the South Wales Coalfield saw the adoption of the cylindro-conical drum around 1905. He acknowledged that the drum had been introduced in 1902 due to 'the direction of Mr E. M. Hann (Powell Duffryn Co.)'.[19] This date agrees with the drum design put into operation at Bargoed Colliery. The winding drum at Bargoed South Pit was capable of raising a load from a depth of 625 yards in forty-five seconds. So, although the design quest for winding had been aimed at raising weight rather than giving precedence to speed, the winding system was no slouch.

For Bargoed Colliery detailed attention was also given to how mine cages were guided when in motion in the shaft. Edmund Mills Hann revealed that 'consideration of the best form of cage-guides in dealing with the great weights and the considerable depth of shaft involved … occupied much attention'. 'Wire ropes', admitted Hann, 'are the cheapest and handiest' means, but 'are not very satisfactory in shafts where there is much water to be dealt with, and are at increasing disadvantage with deeper pits with heavier loads'. Powell Duffryn applied the guide rail method, which according to Hann, its design was 'different to any previously used'. The outcome was 'most satisfactory, and the 'smoothness and quietness of running' was 'remarkable'.[20]

The optimisation of shaft size, and cage capacity, was a perennial matter for Hann to consider when engineering Powell Duffryn collieries. Shaft conditions, and other influential factors, varied from place to place. He countenanced other approaches:

> 'Were it not for the heavy crush experienced in the South Wales coal measures, it might be more convenient to have four decks, and one tram only on each deck; but the author [Hann] thinks that most mining engineers in the district would share his hesitation in making openings at the bottom of a pit at such a depth with so great a height of practically unsupported side-wall as would be entailed by the arrangement. Owing to the smallness of the shaft not admitting of two trams being placed end to end in the cages, the author is installing, at another colliery which he is connected, a third deck, where only two were originally intended, and without any additional space being excavated at the pit-bottom; but it may be regarded more as an arrangement of compulsion than one selected for a new construction.'

The last aspect of winding at Bargoed Colliery that received attention from Powell Duffryn's engineers concerned preventing over-winding. The winding calamities in the 1890s that marred Elliot Colliery's flood rescue attempts were experiences to be avoided. Edmund Mills Hann adapted an idea that 'French engineers had been using for a long time' as an over-winding device for Bargoed Colliery engines. The device regulated a throttle valve which 'gradually' 'applied 'the brakes, if the speed when approaching the top of the shaft' was 'excessive; and should the cage not be brought to rest by the time' it reached 'the top of the shaft', the brakes were 'put full on, and the engine at once stopped'.

Bargoed Colliery's Plant and Facilities

One of Hann's aims for Bargoed Colliery was to achieve the best plant energy utilisation possible. Sixteen Babcock & Wilcox boilers were erected to raise steam for colliery use.[21] He observed that 'one disadvantage frequently found in colliery arrangements, [was] the distances to which steam has to be carried to the various engines', adding that 'the narrowness of the site in this instance considerably increased that bad feature'.

An option he considered for the colliery was to extend the use of electricity. However, in 1906, he admitted it 'was considered advisable to delay the introduction of electricity on a large scale, [at Bargoed] until the colliery was more developed'. Nevertheless, 'at an early stage, about 1898, it was decided that to work all smaller machinery on the surface [of Bargoed] by electricity, and a Marshall compound engine of 300 hp, with three 100 hp dynamos, were installed for the purpose, which supply at present about forty-one motors, ranging from 1 to 5 hp'.[22] As an interim measure, an air-compressor was installed to power underground haulage.

The company's general manager of collieries directed a rigorous review of ventilation equipment before making a choice for Bargoed Colliery. Chosen was a 30 foot diameter by 9ft wide Walker fan driven by cotton ropes by a vertical Corliss valve-engine. The fan was capable of moving 500,000ft^3 of air per minute at six-inches water gauge. For comparison, in 1906, sinking began in the South Yorkshire Coalfield to establish Brodsworth Main Colliery, near Doncaster.[23] This colliery was planned to raise 1 million tons of coal per year, a greater expectation than for Bargoed Colliery. Coal was eventually proved at Brodsworth Main Colliery at 595 yards, which was a slightly shallower depth than the 628 yards find of the Nine Feet seam at Bargoed Colliery. At the Yorkshire colliery, two Capell fans, one steam driven, the other using electrical power, provided the ventilation system. The Capell fans, united in operation, moved 300,000ft^3 per minute. So, miners at Bargoed Colliery were provided with more fresh air underground than miners at Brodsworth Main Colliery.

The nature and extent of the investment in plant and equipment at Bargoed Colliery caused Edmund Mills Hann to gift the place first class engineering workshop facilities. Moreover, Bargoed became the central engineering workshops for the company's Rhymney Valley collieries. The workshops included a fitting shop, smith's shop, foundry, and pattern shop. At the time Elliot Colliery seemed to be the logical place for such a works since it lay, roughly, half way between Bargoed and New Tredegar Collieries. As a dedicated engineering works, Powell Duffryn's Bargoed works had only one rival in the Rhymney Valley, the Caerphilly Locomotive

Works of the Rhymney Railway, opened a number of years earlier in 1901.[24] Quality maintenance work was seen by Edmund Mills Hann as vital to ensuring that Powell Duffryn's collieries operated efficiently with minimal downtime.

During 1904, 1,421 men were employed at Bargoed Colliery.[25] That year, working underground were 1,080 men and on the colliery's surface 341. Two years later just over 2,000 men worked at the colliery. The transition to becoming a fully operational colliery was well advanced by 1904. For Edmund Mills Hann the test of all his earlier technical preparation for the colliery had begun. The year also saw the start to the raising of house coal from the colliery's Brithdir pit.

The decision made to sink Bargoed Colliery seems to have co-incided with a break with Sir George Elliot's policy of using Newport docks to ship Rhymney Valley coal. Access to the Brecon & Merthyr Railway was an option retained, but a branch line was constructed to link the colliery to the Rhymney Railway.[26] Moreover, in 1900, an Act of Parliament enabled the Rhymney Railway to build branch lines so as to move coal from New Tredegar and Elliot collieries.[27] The Rhymney Railway enabled Powell Duffryn to ship Rhymney Valley coal out through, not only Cardiff docks, but also Penarth docks and the ambitious Barry docks, opened in 1889. Southampton also became a shipping point for the company's coal.

Eye-catching on Bargoed Colliery's surface, when in motion, were two aerial ropeways. 'The rubbish unavoidably raised from the mine, and that washed out of the coal' was 'taken up the [eastern] hill-side' by one of the aerial ropeways. The other ropeway transported 'the coal from the washery to coke-ovens'. Waste from Bargoed Colliery, after decades of miners work, created two massive coal tips. The coal tips became the largest in the Rhymney

Bargoed Colliery maybe circa cusp of the 1920s and the 1930s. South Pit on the left with the washery building on the right. The size of the colliery's tips became famous due to the quantity of coal rubbish moved by the aerial ropeway shown.   *Pope/Parkhouse Archive*

Valley, and were locally believed to be the biggest coal tips in Britain, but only the second largest in Europe. A Belgium colliery was reputed to hold the dubious honour of producing Europe's largest coal tip. Those Aberbargoed miners' families whose homes backed up against such a black mountain found no joy in any boast about the size of Bargoed Colliery's coal tips.

However, this was one penalty of building terraced houses for workers, and other homes for officials for Bargoed Colliery. As a result, the town of Bargoed was created on the west side of the valley with the village of Aberbargoed opposite on the valley's eastern hillside. The maximum number of men ever employed at the colliery was 3,347, and this occurred in 1914. That year saw working underground at the colliery 2,768 men supported by 579 on its surface.[28] Over the decades, Powell Duffryn appointed a succession of qualified men to manage Bargoed Colliery.

Managers' Proving Ground

Edmund Mill Hann's executive leadership of Powell Duffryn's collieries contrasted with that given by the plutocrats among the coalowners of the South Wales Coalfield. He had, of course, worked for one, Sir George Elliot. Hann, though, as a manager, was a servant of the company, and his style of management appears to have been that of a technocrat. He derived his operational plans, aimed at raising production efficiency for the benefit of the business, after considerable technical thought and analysis.

Most of the people attracted to live around Pont Aber-Bargoed, so as to work at Bargoed Colliery, were also unlikely to appreciate Edmund Mills Hann's skill in, and inclination for, innovative colliery engineering. Denied an adequate education in say mathematics and science, when such people were younger, they lacked the grounding to value the colliery's design, and the work of its engineer. Instead, the general manager of collieries was for them a remote figure, at worst reviled, and at best respected from afar. They may have learnt something about him from colliery officials who had transferred to Bargoed Colliery from Elliot Colliery.[29] But most people can spot acts of nepotism.

The twenty-three year old George Gilroy Hann was made the manager of Bargoed Colliery for its opening out phase, between 1902 and 1904. George was educated initially in Aberaman before being sent, at thirteen years of age, to boarding school at Haileybury and Imperial Service College, Hertfordshire.[30] He was described as being an energetic student who played rugby. In 1896, at seventeen years of age, he joined Powell Duffryn 'to work alongside his father learning the business over the next six years'. His 'ability to learn', and meet the high standards of performance required of him by his father, 'enabled' his move to Bargoed.

After his Bargoed Colliery assignment, George Hann returned to Aberaman to become the company's assistant general manager of collieries, and the Agent for the company's Aberdare Valley collieries. He was succeeded, as manager of Bargoed Colliery, by his brother, Edmund Lawrence, who took up the post in 1905.

Edmund L. Hann was born at Aberaman in 1881. He was the first of the Hann family to be born in Wales. Before he was thirteen, he was educated in the Aberaman coal mining community, becoming familiar with its culture and customs. He was then sent, like his earlier two brothers, to Haileybury and Imperial Service College.[31] He was 'a popular pupil, and immediately showed his enthusiasm and skills in the rugby XV, both his house and his college'. The *Haileybury Magazine* recorded that the '11 stone 8 lbs.' developed

George Gilroy Hann.
His career in colliery management began at Bargoed Colliery and he would rise to become the company's assistant general manager of collieries.

into a 'hard working forward with a family aptitude for the game'. At eighteen years of age he returned to Aberaman, and was apparently unsure about what career to follow, but eventually chose to join Powell Duffryn. With his father as his mentor, he followed a similar induction into the company as his brother George. In terms of his technical education, he may have enjoyed one advantage over his brother with respect to his subsequent developments as a mining engineer. He attended lectures in Cardiff, at the fledgling mining department of University College of South Wales and Monmouthshire, today Cardiff University.[32] William Galloway was the mining department's first professor, serving between 1891 and 1902.[33]

Douglas Alfred Hann was the next son to be assigned to the colliery.[34] At twenty-three years of age, in 1910, he was listed as a mining student living at West View, Bargoed.

Edmund Lawrence Hann's successor as Bargoed Colliery manager appears to have been Lewis Watkins, in 1908, who was succeeded at least by: F. Wilcox from 1913 and 1916, who appears to have shared a year with Thomas Griffiths who served in the post from 1915 to 1919, or even later; J. R. N. Kirkwood held the post in 1921 with T. B. Fisher made manager of the Brithdir Pit; in 1930, the colliery's manager was J. Tait; in 1935, the colliery's manager was G. D. Corfield; and from 1938 to 1945 the post was held by D. Williams.[35]

The manager of Bargoed Colliery resided at 'The Laurels', a large semi-detached house, set in Aberbargoed, a short walk from the colliery's offices perched on the eastern hillside overlooking the colliery. The other occupant of The Laurels was the colliery's engineer who, in 1914, was Ivor Williams.[36] It was exceedingly rare for a colliery manager in the South Wales Coalfield to share his accommodation in this way. Generally a colliery manager lived in a large detached house, in the vicinity of the colliery, but isolated from the community. That manager and engineer were immediate neighbours was a sign, maybe, that Edmund Mills Hann anticipated that the management of the colliery's engineering technology was as important to the future success of the colliery as was the management of officials responsible for the work of the miners employed there to win coal.

According to the 1931 census, the population of the Glamorgan 'mining town' of Bargoed was 12,177.[37] The corresponding population of its neighbour, Aberbargoed, has not been identified, but was about 2,000. Thus, the combined population of Bargoed and Aberbargoed was around 14,000 people. New Tredegar's population, for comparison, was estimated at 4,500 for 1950.[38] Yet, in 1911, the maximum population attained in the New Tredegar's district was reckoned to be 22,547.[39] Nonetheless, and notably, Powell Duffryn's march south down the Rhymney Valley, to found Bargoed Colliery, had caused the creation of new communities.

The Aberdare Collieries' Electricity Scheme 1903-1905

In the first decade of the 1900s, the opening of Bargoed Colliery, though, was just one among many colliery development activities pursued by Powell Duffryn. In June 1903, Edmund Mills Hann presented a proposal to the company's directors that scoped how Powell Duffryn could embrace electrical engineering on an ambitious scale at the Aberdare Valley collieries.[40] A special meeting of the directors was then held in July, and he was present to give more details about the proposal, including cost estimates.[41] The proposal was approved by the company's board of directors who in 1906 comprised: Joseph Shaw, Arthur March Tapp, William Woolley, the Hon. Thomas Alnutt Brassey, Charles Edward Hunter, Campbell P. Ogilvie, George Bevan Heyworth, and Francis Kennedy McLean. In 1906, the members of the company's Managing Committee were Joseph Shaw, Arthur March Tapp, and Campbell P. Ogilvie.

According to Charles P. Sparks (1866-1940) the electricity scheme for Powell Duffryn's Aberdare Collieries 'was projected in 1903'. Charles Sparks was chosen by Edmund Mills Hann as the consulting electrical engineer for the scheme.

The subsequent career of Charles Sparks showed that Hann made a wise choice. Charles Sparks became one of the few members of the Institution of Electrical Engineers to hold office as its President for two years, in his case in 1915 and 1916. In 1941, after his death, he was acknowledged as being 'one of the band of pioneers ... who under the leadership of [Lord] Kelvin, Ferranti, John Hopkinson and many others laid the foundations of electricity supply as we know it today'. In 1891, Charles Sparks was appointed Manager of Messrs Ferranti Ltd, and prior to forming a consulting partnership, he was the Chief Engineer of the County of London Electric Supply Company. [42]

Byatt's study of the British electrical industry between the years 1814-1914 judged that the coal industry was comparatively slow to adopt electrical power. He blamed the colliery manager for the slowness: *'Colliery managers were ex-pitman – not engineers – and there is justice in the contemporary complaint that they had only enough training to think of objections to the innovations which came to their notice'.*[43] Indeed, in 1904, Hugh Bramwell was quoted as saying that the South Wales Coalfield was *'ten years behind the Germans in applying electricity to mining operations'.*[44] However, in April 1907, D. Selby-Bigge, of Newcastle-on-Tyne, claimed to be the first engineer in Europe to design and install a meaningful electrical scheme at a colliery to power its plant and equipment.[45]

D. Selby-Bigge reflected that *'between the years 1885 and 1890 comprehensive electric mining schemes were practically unknown, and for the most part the applications of electricity were purely tentative ones, and consisted in individual cases of driving surface machinery, pumps and occasional haulage'.* In 1891, his electrical scheme was laid down at the Margaret Pit, owned by the Earl of Durham. His application of electricity 'was at the time regarded as

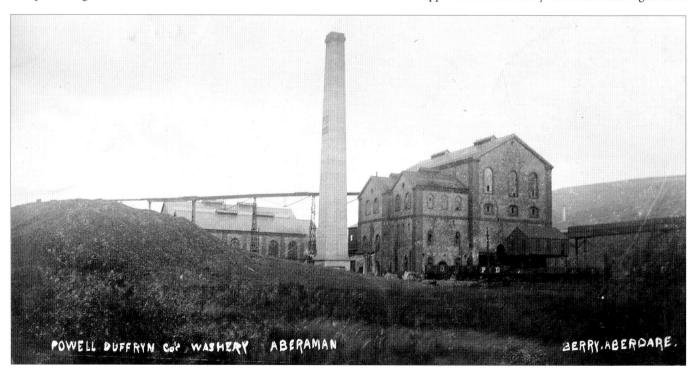

The washery at Middle Duffryn with the power station beyond. Both the washery and the brick chimney have the date 1902 and the initials PD built-in in different colour bricks.

Pope/Parkhouse Archive

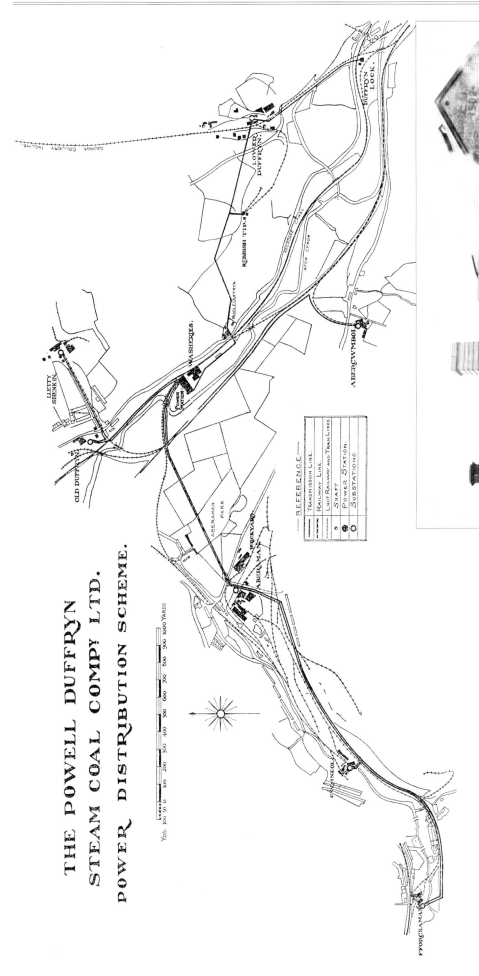

THE POWELL DUFFRYN STEAM COAL COMPY LTD.
POWER DISTRIBUTION SCHEME.

Yds. 100 50 0 100 200 300 400 500 600 700 800 900 1000 YARDS

REFERENCE
	Transmission Line.
	Railway Line.
	Light Railway and Tram Lines.
⊙	Shaft
■	Power Station
⊙	Substations

Aberdare Collieries Electricity Scheme. Operational by 1905. Described as 'one of the most perfect installations of its kind in the United Kingdom'. The geographical area it covered was eight square miles, with some of the collieries being two miles from the power station at Middle Duffryn, which in 1913 was called Aberaman Power Station.
Journal, Institution of Electrical Engineers, vol.36, (1906)

Right: Middle Duffryn Washery and Power Station in the early 1920s.
Paul Jackson collection

one of the largest and most complete in the country'. 'Continuous current' electricity was used at Margaret's Pit to power a pump, a haulage engine, electric lighting underground 400 yards from pit bottom, a telephone and electric-bell system, electric rock drills, and 'primitive' coal-cutting machines.

The Margaret Pit electrical scheme was seen to be suitably important for 'Continental engineers' to visit the colliery to inspect the installations.[46] D. Selby-Bigge reflected that *between the years 1891 and 1901, the progress which was made in the application of electricity for mining purposes was very slow, and consisted of constructional improvements in machinery*. However, he notably observed that with *the advent of three-phase machinery in a practical form that a real and stimulating impetus was given to the electric mining industry*.[47]

In the South Wales Coalfield, the pioneer of three phase alternating current [AC] electricity supply for colliery plant and equipment applications was the Tredegar Iron & Coal Company.[48] W. A. Scott was responsible for the installation of an electrical system that served three of the Tredegar Company's Sirhowy Valley collieries: Bedwellty Pit, Pochin Colliery, and Ty Trist. Electricity was transmitted at 500 Volts. The 'periodicity' of electricity supply, which was the term used in Scott's paper for frequency in cycles per second, was 40 Hz, which later became an exception to the norm of 50 Hz.[49]

Hugh Bramwell, of Great Western Colliery Company, judged that the Tredegar Iron & Coal Company's electrical scheme was the 'first large installation of three-phase current transmission in the South Wales Coalfield'.[50] The Tredegar Company's electrical scheme was erected over the period 1901-2, and powered underground haulage, and pumping instead of using compressed air for such purposes. Maurice Deacon was the consulting engineer employed by the Tredegar Company to design the electricity scheme. In 1904, Scott observed: *Electric power* had been *steadily growing in favour for mining operations during the past ten years, and in the North of England and Scotland many large plants* had *been installed for both pumping and haulage underground*.[51]

Powell Duffryn's Aberdare Valley collieries scheme's geographical coverage was 'eight square miles in area, some points being two miles from the proposed power station'. The power station was located near Middle Duffryn Colliery and so adjacent to the central washery. The scheme applied the 3-phase AC system, and generated 3,000 V at 50 Hz. The plant comprised: one 2,000 kVA engine and generator; and two 1,000 kVA engines and generators. The installed Yates & Thom, of Blackburn, horizontal, cross compound jet condensing engines, were coupled to alternators supplied by Allemeine Elecktricitäts Gesellschaft, of Berlin. Ten Babcock & Wilcox water tube boilers were erected to meet steam requirements, which condemned thirty-two Lancashire boilers to the scrap yard.

A tour of the scheme, in 1905, found electrical power being distributed to seven collieries: Lower Duffryn, Abercwmboi, Old Duffryn, Lletty Shenkin, Aberaman, Cwmneol, and Fforchaman. B. J. Day toured the scheme that year, and reported that overhead wires ran for a distance of thirty-three miles.[52] The furthest distance between a colliery, which was Fforchaman Colliery, and the power station was 3,770 yards.[53]

The electrical engineering consultant was aware that 'many people' considered electricity to be a 'dangerous agent'.[54] Indeed, at the meeting of the South Wales Institute of Engineers meeting that discussed D. Selby-Bigge's paper about the Margaret Pit

electricity scheme, T. H. Deakin recalled a series of accidents involving electricity at Vipond & Company's Varteg Collieries, Monmouthshire. The concern, he said, among 'colliery people' about 'the question of sparking and flame' was acute. The pump house at Varteg, on two occasions became a 'furnace', 'full of flame', and that 'the electricians – if they knew – would not tell them the cause'.[55] D. Selby-Bigge informed T. H. Deakin that investigations had shown that 'nearly the whole of the accidents that had been recorded had been caused on low-tension installations' due, he thought, 'to a comparative lack of attention to that which was given to high-tension installations'.[56]

Charles P. Sparks told members of the Institution of Electrical Engineers that Powell Duffryn had 'not spared expense' where they saw that it gave 'added safety' to their employees. He even speculated that 'electricity' was going to give 'added safety to employees'. He also observed that the 'few fatal accidents' associated with electricity, were nothing like the 'enormous death toll' faced by the coal industry.

The Aberdare Collieries' scheme distributed electricity to power electric motors that drove a wide range of colliery equipment. On the surface, twenty-eight haulage engines, and underground five haulage engines were so powered. One advantage of the electric driven engines was that speed of movement was maintained on steep gradients engines unlike the steam driven equivalent. Three fans and six pumps were also electrically powered. The fans' air pressure was found to be more uniform than had been obtained using steam-driven fans. Forty-six motors were used for a variety of general duties. Two aerial ropeways were powered by electricity: 'One ropeway' dealt 'with all the small coal from Lower Duffryn over the mountain; a second ropeway' moved 'all the small coal from Lletty Shenkin and Old Duffryn; the small coal from Fforchaman, Cwmneol, and Aberaman pits being conveyed in trucks over the Company's railway sidings'. One other consequence of the scheme was that the original colliery lighting system, DC, was substituted with AC, and fed from substations above ground.

Powell Duffryn's electricity scheme for its Aberdare collieries collected plaudits. At a meeting of the Institution of Electrical Engineers, March 1906, W. C. Mountain saluted Charles Spark's Powell Duffryn Aberdare Valley collieries electrical scheme by rating it 'one of the most perfect installations of its kind in the United Kingdom'.[57]

B. J. Day helpfully described the visual effect of the scheme:
'At first sight one would imagine that Old Duffryn pit was feeling the bad effects of a depression in the coal trade, and was "on stop" as there is an entire absence of clouds of steam visible at all times at nine out of ten of the pits in South Wales; but at a second glance one notices clouds of black dust rising from the screens, and there are the men about the yard.
As a matter of fact, there is no steam to be seen, because all of the boilers have been removed: everything, including the main winding engine and fan, is driven electrically....
...There can be no doubt', that the scheme, was 'by far the boldest, most comprehensive and interesting private installation in the country, or on the Continent today'.

Two hundred members of the South Wales Institute of Engineers alighted from 'special trains' of the Great Western Railway, Taff Vale Railway, and Rhymney Railway companies, at Aberaman Station on the 22nd November, 1905, to inspect the Aberdare collieries' electrical scheme.[58] Powell Duffryn's 'own engines and servants took charge of the trains, and conveyed members directly

Elliot East Colliery's Thornewill & Warham twin tandem compound steam engine. The engine, a 1904 modification of a simple engine, was powered with steam at 160 lbs psi. The engine's modification saw Corliss valve cylinders of 28-inch installed behind the original cylinders. The engine has been preserved as the prime exhibit of the Caerphilly County Borough Council's museum, the Winding House. The photograph was taken in 1967.
The Watkins' Collection, courtesy of English Heritage

to the power house adjoining the new washery at Middle Duffryn pumping pit'. The visitors also discovered that Powell Duffryn had implemented electric powered winding of coal.

The three electric powered winding engines, installed for Powell Duffryn as part of the scheme, may have been technical novelties as far as the South Wales Coalfield was concerned. One electric winder raised trams up a 70 yard pit. An electric winder was also installed to lift men 100 yard up a pit, and 'was capable of raising 400 tons of coal in eight hours from 200 yards'. The third application of an electric winder was associated with a 100 yard deep, staple shaft.[59] Except Old Duffryn B. J. Day did not name the other collieries where these electric winding engines were used.

The praised Aberdare Collieries electrical power scheme also won Edmund Mills Hann further credit. After the South Wales Institute of Engineer's November 1905 inspection of the scheme, T. H. Deakin's salute drew a revealing reply from Hann. Deakin toasted the 'Directors and staff of the company and the health of Mr Joseph Shaw, the Chairman of Powell Duffryn, and Mr Hann'. B. J. Day reported that 'having been drunk with musical honours', Edmund Mills Hann, in reply, said he was 'a man of action and not words'.[60]

Elliot Colliery – Winding Redevelopment 1904-1908

The year 1904 has been judged to be the year when the simple Thornewill & Warham engine at East Pit, Elliot Colliery was modified by its maker to a twin tandem compound.[61] Installed behind the original simple steam engine cylinders were high-pressure cylinders, each of 28-inch diameter. The original simple steam engine cylinders, at 42-inch diameter with a stroke of 6ft, were utilised as the low-pressure cylinders. Expansion gear was installed to operate the engine. The Elliot East Colliery's high-pressure cylinders' steam control was achieved using Corliss valves.

Clearly, Elliot East Colliery's Thornewill & Warham engine, as an adaptation, did not conform to Edmund Mills Hann's ideal for a four-cylinder winding engine, with two sets of cylinders at right angles to each other with one pair placed horizontally. Although the use of a twin tandem winding engine at the colliery appears to have been a new development for the company, the company's engineers at Aberaman might have acquired some useful practical knowledge from a nearby colliery.

Early in the first decade of the 1900s, the winding engines at Cory Brothers Company's Penrikyber Colliery, south-east of Aberaman, near Mountain Ash, underwent radical technical change. At Penrikyber Colliery's Number 2 shaft, a 'powerful' Thornewill & Warham compound winding engine was erected. Its earliest engineman was 'very well known – the bewhiskered David Gethin who came in 1876 and retired in 1913'.[62] 'The big Thornewill & Warham engine played a large part in the Colliery's history and was among the most efficient engines in the South Wales Coalfield'.[63]

Fortunately providence has seen the Thornewill & Warham engine at Elliot East preserved in situ. The engine is now a rare survivor, not only of its type, but also of the legion of steam winding engines that were once used in the British coal industry. As a monument, the Elliot Colliery winding engine represents Hann's commitment to the use of the compound engine for the benefit of Powell Duffryn. Moreover, the Elliot East twin tandem engine further serves as a reminder of an engineer's courage in breaking with an industry's norm, simple winding engines, so as to try and make a colliery's operation more efficient.

With the benefit of hindsight, Edmund Mills Hann's action to use compound winding engines at Bargoed Colliery represented the start of a major technical policy change at Powell Duffryn collieries. At Elliot West Colliery the shaft may have been deepened a further 40 yards around 1907 and at the same time the Joicey horizontal engine was replaced by an inverted vertical cross compound non-condensing engine made by Andrew Barclay & Company, Kilmarnock, in Ayrshire, Scotland, and it was equipped with Corliss valves.[64]

The Elliot West Colliery's Barclay engine comprised cylinder diameters of 34-inch and 56-inch, with 4ft 6in. stroke, and its design featured 'the cylinders overhead and the crankshaft and drum at floor level'.[65] George Watkins found that they *were not widely used … [yet there] were fine examples at Harris* [Deep Navigation], *Elliot and Tirpentwys collieries in South Wales, and at Wath Main in Yorkshire*.[66] The Joicey engine was replaced for

sound engineering reasons, but sadly the Barclay engine, after many decades of excellent service, was also scrapped when Elliot Colliery closed in the 1960s.

Nevertheless, when Edmund Mill Hann presented his 1906 paper about Bargoed Colliery to the Institution of Mechanical Engineers, he enjoyed privileged knowledge about the performance records of a number of compound winding engines in use in the South Wales Coalfield. His advocacy of compound winding engines was based upon proven experience, and he obtained the support for it from other engineers.

W. H. Patchell submitted: 'the saving on a compound engine as against simple running non-condensing was somewhere in the neighbourhood of 25 per cent'. Mr Tannett-Walker contended: 'At the present time a good compound engine with a high pressure steam and condensation, or a good compound engine for a rolling a rail or plate, or a good compound engine for a blowing machine, was the most economical appliance known'. He also advised that some trials had found that compound engines used 30 per cent less steam. Edmund Mills Hann was unimpressed by such findings. With 'regard to the difference between a plain engine and a compound engine was, as far as [Hann's] experience of winding was concerned, well under the mark. He should be inclined to say it was over 30 per cent'.

Indeed, in 1906, the stance that the Powell Duffryn general manager of collieries took regarding the use of compound steam winding engines was both clear and certain. He was 'convinced of the superiority of the compound not only for steam economy but because a single engine cutting off very early in its stroke brings upon the winding ropes very much greater inequalities of strain, which is a bad feature and conducive to danger'.[67]

Regarding the history of steam winding technology, George Watkins wrote: '*By the 20th century, the steam winder had developed into a highly advanced machine that met the conflicting demands of the*

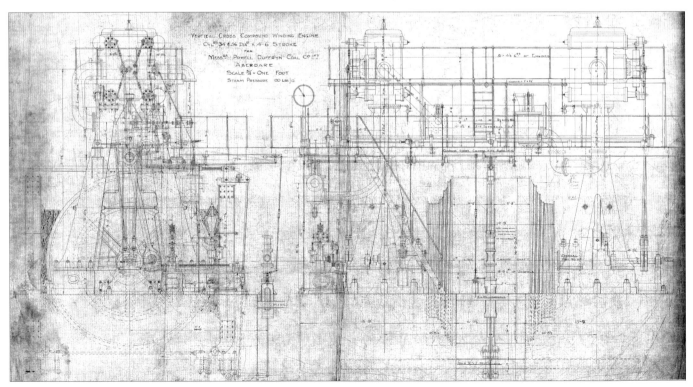

Undated drawing by Andrew Barclay & Co., Kilmarnock of the engine supplied to Elliot West Colliery.
RHP66306/1 Andrew Barclay Collection. Courtesy Glasgow University Archives Service

Elliot West Colliery's Andrew Barclay & Co., Kilmarnock, inverted vertical cross-compound non-condensing steam engine, which was installed around 1907. The engine worked at 160 lbs psi.

The Watkins' Collection, courtesy of English Heritage

mining industry'.[68] He judged that '*the steam winder really reached its peak with the twin tandem, which, able to start and come to bank [where the cage halted on the colliery's surface] rapidly, was also fast and economical'.*[69]

Regarding the 'semi-spiral' drum the design became a company standard. Indeed, the drum driven by the Barclay winding engine at Elliot West Colliery featured such a design.[70] However, the design did not represent the end of winding drum design development within Powell Duffryn.

At the company's Aberaman offices, during the first decade of the 1900s, the semi-spiral drum design was developed further. A semi-conical or semi-spiral drum, 'Diabolo' configuration was the outcome. Seen from the front, the centre span of a Diabolo drum was shaped as a vee, like a valley. The valley sides created the tapers for guiding the rope in its movement from the middle of the drum, when starting a wind to lift a cage from the foot of a shaft, outwards to the cylinders positioned at the outer parts of the drum's span. So the winding rope's journey during winding was in the opposite direction to that featured in Hann's first cylindro-conical drum design.

At Elliot East Colliery Winding House a priceless Diabolo drum has survived and is preserved in situ.[71] The drum serves as a further exhibit of Edmund Mills Hann's inclination for technical experiments so as to improve a colliery's winding operation. The Elliot East Colliery drum's relatively light construction gives an

The Diabolo drum used at Elliot East Colliery viewed from outside the winding house through the rope aperture. Aberaman Colliery is believed to be where the first one was trialled successfully in 1905. Then, in 1913, the drum design was put into operation at Elliot Colliery where it has been preserved. *Courtesy Brian Davies*

impression of a frail piece of equipment, but it withstood the robust duty of coal mining for decades. The Elliot East Colliery Diabolo drum might have been installed in 1913. The installation date of the Diabolo drum at Elliot East Colliery confirms that it occurred after successful trials of the first drum at Aberaman Colliery, which is dealt with shortly.

In 1910, Powell Duffryn's George Hann reported that the use of balance ropes had been dispensed with at Elliot Colliery.[72] This suggests that in addition to a bi-cylindro-conical drum being used at Elliot West Colliery, one was used for a period before the installation of the Elliot East Colliery Diabolo drum. The installation of bi-cylindro-conical drums at the colliery made balance ropes unnecessary. Balance ropes were attached to the underside of cages in many collieries as a means of steadying their rise and fall particularly when winding used a cylindrical drum.

The 'Diabolo' drum never became a coal industry standard like Edmund Mills Hann's original bi-cylindro-conical drum. George Watkins noted, in 1954, one was in use at Bargoed Colliery, being driven by the Thornewill & Warham engine.[73] The only known Diabolo drum used in the South Wales Coalfield outwith Powell Duffryn collieries was operated, until around the 1950s, at Cwmtillery Number 1 Colliery, Abertillery, Ebbw Fach Valley.[74]

Renewal of 'The Old Pits' 1905-1906

Circa 1903, Edmund Mills Hann decided that a new shaft was needed at New Tredegar Colliery. The colliery's two old shafts 'were very small and out of perpendicular'.[75] In operation at the colliery, circa 1888, was a vertical cylinder non condensing type steam winding engine with 45-inch cylinders and 6-foot stroke. The winding drum was 10-foot in diameter and wound a flat tapering rope averaging five-inches in width.[76] The desired site for the new shaft lay on land owned possibly by the Tredegar Estate. Powell Duffryn was no doubt irritated to find that some company agreement with the Marquis of Bute required that 'any additional Pit at New Tredegar' had to be on Bute land. A resettlement was negotiated, some years before 1905 to sink 'a large shaft for winding purposes' with the old shafts as upcasts.[77] Powell Duffryn's general manager of collieries considered that the work 'ought to have been done a long time previously'.

New Tredegar Colliery saw Robert Lonie, the colliery manager in 1875, succeeded by C. Frame in 1878. Nehemiah Phillips became the colliery's manager in 1888, and held the post until 1900. So, for some four years, he held the post simultaneously with serving as the manager of Elliot Colliery. New Tredegar Colliery became known locally as the Old Pits, apparently after 1888. In 1900, supported by 140 men on the surface, 948 men and boys were employed underground at New Tredegar Colliery, and the Yard and the Four Feet seams were worked.[78] Five years later, chaos struck the colliery.

In March 1905, 'a serious landslide' hit New Tredegar Colliery. Demolished were 'three officials' houses, several workshops', and 'the air compressor house, boiler seatings, walls, and the new winding engine house for the new shaft [No. 3 Pit] were damaged'. W. E. Jaynes, an official at New Tredegar Colliery, later recalled that he had 'the misfortune to witness' the landslide. He described that '*there was a large stack at the colliery which, at daybreak on the morning following the landslide, was lying over very dangerously, at the top in the direction from which the slide had come, showing clearly that the foot of the stack had moved downwards in the*

Damage done to No. 3 Pit at New Tredegar Colliery by the 1905 landslip.

Pope/Parkhouse Archive

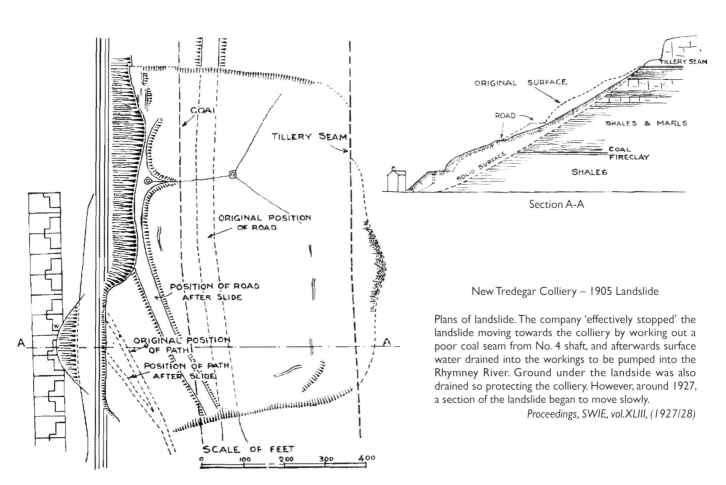

Section A-A

New Tredegar Colliery – 1905 Landslide

Plans of landslide. The company 'effectively stopped' the landslide moving towards the colliery by working out a poor coal seam from No. 4 shaft, and afterwards surface water drained into the workings to be pumped into the Rhymney River. Ground under the landside was also drained so protecting the colliery. However, around 1927, a section of the landslide began to move slowly.

Proceedings, SWIE, vol.XLIII, (1927/28)

Above: New Tredegar Colliery Officials' Houses damaged by the 1905 Landslide.
Left: The area around the No. 3 pithead.   *both Pope/Parkhouse Archive*

direction of the slide. This inclination, however, seemed to decrease as the day wore on', but days later, 'showed very little deviation from the vertical'.[79]

The company was not daunted by the landslide. Powell Duffryn spent £20,000 to fix the colliery's buildings. Moreover, mining measures were contemplated aimed at arresting the landslide. The company saw the restoration of No. 3 pithead as vital since it came into operation in 1906.

Edmund Mills Hann also authorised measures to try and safeguard the colliery from landslip. During the sinking of the No. 3 shaft, excellent seams of coal were found at 45 yards. A fourth shaft was then sunk to mine what was hoped to be a bonus seam.[80] During sinking the Number 4 shaft a thin coal seam was found that lay at '110 yards below the Tillery (No. 2 Rhondda) Seam'. However, this seam had 'little commercial value, but it was thought that by working out the coal and allowing the water to drain into the underground workings it could be collected and pumped directly into the river'.[81] The workings of this thin coal seam were then extended to 'cover an area wide enough to protect the colliery'. The action 'resulted in draining' the underground area worked from the Numbers 1, 2 and 3 pits, and 'effectively stopped' the landslide.

However, by 1909 the 'asset value' of No. 4 shaft had yet to be justified due 'to a lot of water under the roof'. Hann, though, hoped that 'good results' would be obtained once the workings reached 'drier conditions' under the mountain.[82]

The steam winding engine installed at No. 3 shaft appears to have been a compound one made by Thornewill & Warham. The engine was possibly the culmination of a fruitful working relationship between the engine maker and the coal company.[83] A Powell Duffryn history, up to 1914, notes that the winding at New Tredegar Colliery utilised a four cylinder engine, the high-pressure cylinders being horizontal, and the low-pressure being vertical, which offered an estimated 2,000 horsepower. It would seem that the engine's power enabled double deck cages to be used at the colliery, with two trams per deck.[84] The engine's data, and description, made it the equal in terms of power of the Elliot East engine, but its design was like the Thornewill & Warham engine at Bargoed Colliery.[85] New Tredegar No. 3 winding engine drove a semi-spiral winding drum, diameters ranging from eleven to eighteen feet.

Based upon reflection, decades later, Thornewill & Warham engines at possibly New Tredegar Colliery, Elliot East Colliery, and Bargoed Colliery can be proposed as being candidates for consideration as high-points in the history of the steam compound winding engine in the British coal industry.

The renewal of New Tredegar colliery also saw the ventilation improved. The engine driven ventilating fan was 24 foot in diameter by 8 foot wide. Significantly the system supplied 180,000ft[3] per minute of air, which was five times more air for ventilation than available at the time of the 1875 explosion.

In the year 1914, the company reported that only three shafts were being used at New Tredegar Colliery. It would appear then, that before 1914, the colliery's No. 4 shaft ceased winding coal, but was probably kept for pumping purposes.

Aberaman and Fforchaman Collieries – Redevelopment 1905-1908

During the period of years from 1905 to 1908, two Aberdare Valley collieries were chosen for major redevelopment. At Aberaman Colliery, in 1905, the winding engine was re-engineered by Thornewill & Warham, as their number 928, a horizontal Corliss type two cylinders, each of 24-inch diameter, with a stroke of 5-foot which delivered an internal horsepower of 763.[86] Such re-engineering provided a suitable occasion to install a pioneering Diabolo drum at the colliery, and one operated there for decades afterwards.[87]

Sometime around 1905, the Aberaman Colliery saw its Waddle fan replaced by three fans of the Walker type each driven by a Lenz compound engine.[88] A fan of 24-foot diameter was located at the Old Duffryn shaft of Aberaman Colliery. One fan 12-foot in diameter was also installed at Abercwmboi shaft, a mile to the east of the Aberaman shaft, so that the colliery's eastern, and south-eastern workings were ventilated. One fan, 9-foot in diameter, was positioned at Abergwawr, just over a half a mile to the north of the Aberaman shaft for the ventilation of the northern workings. The Longwall system was used, and the width of each stall was twelve yards. Around 1905, Aberaman Colliery's output attained 11,000 tons per week, and the coal was raised from the Yard and Seven Feet seams which lay around a depth of 220 yards.

Fforchaman Colliery, according to Edmund Mills Hann, was '*like a country with no history – in the happy state of making profits out of the 4 foot and 6 foot seams, and to a small extent the 2ft 6in. seam*'.[89] Maybe in 1904, he decided that this 'could not go on'. Then, in 1905, he issued instructions which involved deepening

Aberaman Colliery, the centre of redevelopment around 1905, was where Powell Duffryn introduced the Diabolo winding drum.

Pope/Parkhouse Archive

the winding shaft, and to 're-fit the place in a several respects', and to 're-open on the seams below the 9 foot'. The work was 'done in 1905 and 1906' and in 1908, became 'the last of the company's collieries in the Aberdare Valleys' to be 'carried down to the lowers seams'. The company's description of the colliery, in 1914, gave some idea of the resulting redevelopment: '*The seams at present worked include the Bute, Yard, 6 feet, 7 feet, and Gellideg, all being steam coal*'. The Gellideg seam was the lowest workable coal seam in this part of the Aberdare Valley, and at Aberaman Colliery, it was found at 710ft 7in., approximately 237 yards.[90]

The redevelopment of Fforchaman Colliery was, perhaps, belated reward for having aided the funding of Elliot Colliery. Erected at Fforchaman Colliery was a new winding engine, made by Fraser & Chalmers, having 28-inch by 5-foot high-pressure cylinders.[91] The engine drove a semi-spiral drum with diameter range of 8 feet to 14 feet. The associated shaft, the colliery's No. 2, was deepened to 305 yards, but the colliery's No. 1 shaft's depth was left at 227 yards.[92]

Rhymney Valley Electricity Grid Scheme, circa 1906

In 1906, Edmund Mills Hann informed members of the Institution of Mechanical Engineers about an electricity grid scheme that linked Bargoed up to Elliot Colliery, and thence to New Tredegar Colliery. The purpose of the Rhymney Valley electricity grid was to 'minimize the effect of stoppages of any of the electrical plant' at Bargoed Colliery. His Institution of Mechanical Engineers paper about the electrical grid scheme was less than clear, and this was probably due to its design not being finalised. In 1914, it was described as a generating plant consisting of a two-cylinder cross compound Corliss engine, of 750 kW, by Yates & Thom, and a 2,000 kW Rateau Patent mixed pressure turbine, made by Fraser & Chalmers, and having a Siemens generator.[93]

The Rateau turbine enjoyed a good reputation mainly due to its use in marine propulsion. Designed by Professor Rateau, and made initially by Messrs Sutter-Harlé of Paris, it was categorised as being a multi-cellular or compartment class of turbine.[94] Professor Rateau's turbine recovered some of the work usually wasted in the exhaust steam of non-condensing engines. A Rateau turbine was installed not long after 1906 at Elliot Colliery.[95] The Elliot Colliery

Rateau Patented turbine as used at Bargoed and Elliot Collieries that enabled further work to be obtained from steam exhausted from colliery winding engines. *Proceedings, SWIE, vol.XXIV, (1904-06)*

winding engine united with the Rateau turbine is not known but, by 1914, both winding engines were so equipped. Steam exhaust from both the winding engines was harnessed to generate electricity.[96] The use of a Rateau turbine caused a working steam engine to fall silent.

The first Rateau turbine used at Elliot Colliery powered a generator of 500 kW and it ran in parallel with a 750 kW set located at Bargoed Colliery. A 750 kW generating set was, in addition, located at Elliot Colliery with equipment, rated at 300 hp, capable of converting alternating to direct current, or vice-versa. Hann informed that 'electric power was put in to reduce the requirements of compressed air which [was] becoming too heavy for the existing plant, and because it could supply Bargoed temporarily until the place got its own gas driven plant erected, and also as a permanent reserve'. So, the arrival of Bargoed Colliery influenced the working of the company's neighbouring colliery, and obtained operational safeguards in return.

Bargoed's Gas and By-Product Plant, circa 1906

Whereas the miners of the Elliot, Fforchaman and New Tredegar collieries experienced the effects of respective redevelopments, Bargoed Colliery's miners became spectators of a major chemical engineering project. Edmund Mills Hann issued a paper to members of the South Wales Institute of Engineers about a new by-product plant at Bargoed Colliery, and discussions about it began on the 29th October, 1907.

Hann opened his paper by reflecting about experiments he had done in 1881. These involved small-scale coke making using what was known as the rectangular Welsh oven. 'Brithdir' small coal was mixed with some steam coal small, so as to increase the yield of coke, and lower the sulphur. However, the test results were disappointing. Only a small proportion of steam coal could be used in this type of oven, and it produced weak coke. Nevertheless, the experiments left him 'favourably impressed' with the possibilities, and the knowledge useful for when specifying the coke ovens for Elliot Colliery. Moreover, with approval from the company's directors, he was enabled to take his 1881 experiments much further.

Edmund Mills Hann's quest was to 'improve the value of small coal'.[97] He reasoned that one way forward was to utilise by-product coke ovens, and use the gas produced by the process as a fuel for gas fired engines coupled to drive electric alternators. The Bargoed by-product plant included: the mechanical conveying of small coal to a 120 ton per hour washery that fed a block of fifty Koppers ovens to yield coke. The plant's gas and tar output was supplied to a by-product plant consisting of air coolers, water coolers, bubblers, water, tar and ammonia pumps; and a sulphate plant. One consequence of operating the Bargoed plant was that the coke ovens at Elliot Colliery were later closed.

As a precursor to agreeing the design of the Bargoed by-product plant, the general manager of collieries inspected 'all the best-known types of by-product ovens and was impressed with the newer regenerative ovens, in which great improvements had then recently been made, the economy being considerable when compared with the additional expense incurred'.[98] So, when he authorised purchase of what had been judged to be the best plant and equipment, he was assured that they would earn Powell Duffryn economic benefits. In February 1906, Bargoed saw the first block of fifty Koppers regenerative ovens in use, and a second block of fifty ovens, was added in October 1907.

Bargoed By-product and coking plant. The laboratory stands in the foreground with process distillation towers to its right. The prominent building beyond the line of coke ovens housed sulphate acid chambers and sulphate plant.

However, obtaining acceptable results from operating the Koppers ovens was governed by the mix of coals. Experiment found that the appropriate mix was three parts [Rhas Las] steam coal small, and one part Brithdir coal small.[99] The quality of the Bargoed's 'Ras Las' was one reason why the regenerative oven type was selected. Hann observed, that an 'unusual quantity of gas' was produced from it, 10,000ft³ per ton, with a thermal value of 460 Btu/ft³.[100] Elliot and New Tredegar Collieries were also directed to supply Bargoed with small coal 'to meet with irregularities in working provision'.

Concerning Bargoed's first installed ovens, based on early tests, 60,000ft³ gas per hour was produced.[101] Each oven produced 1,536 tons per annum of coke, so for the fifty ovens the total maximum was around 76,800 tons per annum.[102] The yield of ammonia sulphate was 19.2 lb/ton of raw coal, and tar 36.5 lb/ton.[103]

Powell Duffryn's selection of Koppers oven was approved of by Professor William Galloway. In June 1908, he visited Germany to inspect coking-ovens built by Messrs Koppers, of Essen, at Rheinpresussen Colliery. He was impressed with the coking system, and process of recovering by-products used at the German colliery. So he advised members of the South Wales Institute of Engineers to study Powell Duffryn's Bargoed development. Professor Galloway judged that German coking-oven development was ahead of Britain's.[104]

Bargoed Colliery Coke Ovens.

The first by-product coking plant erected in the South Wales Coalfield was due to Bramwell. He achieved this, circa 1902-3, at the Great Western Colliery Company's Maritime Pit, located south-west of Pontypridd.[105] He candidly admitted that 'for some four and a half years it had worked satisfactorily in every way except perhaps as regards make money'. He then disclosed the year 1907's total output figures for the Maritime plant. It had made 53,690 tons of coke, 595 tons of sulphate, and 1,747 tons of tar. Bramwell reckoned: '*The yield of bye-products (sic) was very much the same as Mr Hann's; more tar was got at the Maritime, and the same amount of sulphate. Mr Hann got gas, and he (Mr Bramwell) steam'*.

Gas Engines

Hugh Bramwell's observation caused a steam versus gas debate. A. E. Chorlton, an expert on gas-engines, declared that he favoured the two-cycle gas-engine ahead of the four-cycle one for industrial and factory purposes.[106] He noted that it was 'only in the last five years or so that the large gas-engine had come to the front, and all must agree that the progress made was truly remarkable, especially when compared with the steam engine, that had been developing for a century'. Provocatively, he observed: 'The future of the gas-engine was a far greater one than the ordinary engineer was inclined to think, and there was little doubt that in time they would oust the steam-engine for all except very special duties'.

This ruffled Thomas Sugden. His motto, he asserted, was: 'More Steam and Less Gas'.[107] He bluntly said: '*When they came down to real facts, and found out what guarantees they could get, they discovered there was little, if anything, in the claims of the gas advocates to put it upon an equality or say that it was superior to steam. He did not think they could get any type of large size gas-engine which in the long run would prove either as reliable or efficient as, or would produce power more cheaply, everything taken into account, than, a high-class steam-engine or turbine'*. Maybe mindful of the regard there was in the South Wales Coalfield for Hann's judgement, whom he considered to be a 'gentleman who approached the subject with an open-mind and from a business point of view', he rationalised that the Bargoed example had 'a special purpose'.[108] However, his entrenched support for the steam side of the debate did not necessarily have Hugh Bramwell's vote.

The Great Western Colliery Company man had an open-mind to innovation, and applied acute powers of analysis to select engineering projects for his company to pursue. Bramwell reckoned: '*The choice between regenerative ovens with a large surplus of gas and no steam, and non-regenerative ovens with no, or only a small, surplus of gas (depending on the coal coked) and a supply of steam, was still an open question. It depended on the choice between gas-engines and steam engines as a means of utilising the available power. The balance-sheet between the two would, in his opinion, as often favour the one as the other depending on special circumstances'*.[109] Bramwell shared his Maritime plant's cash balance for comparison with Hann's.[110] The cash balances for the plant at Bargoed and Maritime were almost identical.

An ambition of Edmund Mills Hann's for Powell Duffryn's Bargoed Colliery was as an electric power generator. However, to use gas engines for power generation, he was troubled by the chemical analysis of the gas made, which in percentage terms was: carbon dioxide 2.01; oxygen 0.42; carbonic oxide 5.21; ethylene 0.8; hydrogen 63.42; methane 23.14; and nitrogen 5.0. The high percentage of hydrogen risked pre-ignition by compression in an engine. Yet, the explanation Hann gave for installing gas engines was to utilize a residue of gas arising from using retort regenerative coking ovens.[111] He wrote that half of the gas so produced had been used 'under the ovens' but the residue had been used 'at the steam boilers'. This was judged by him to be economic folly.

In 1908, Thomas Sugden, 'believed that the best design of steam turbine and boiler plant working under the most favourable conditions would run the modern gas engine very closely'.[112] He further observed that the adoption of gas fired engines 'on the Continent' was due to the higher value of its coal compared with 'English coal', which may have also implied Welsh coal. Yet, William Wight was of the opinion that 'a gas engine has a consumption of fuel of only half the cost of that of the highest class of reciprocating or steam engines'. He had concluded that 'the gas engine' was 'already a formidable rival of the steam engine'.[113]

Powell Duffryn, though, experienced great difficulty in sourcing a gas engine maker prepared to supply an engine that met the duty desired for the Bargoed Colliery application. After what seemed to be an anxious search, the Vereinigte Mashinfabrik Augsberg und Maschinenbaugesellschaft Nürnberg A. G. Nürnberg came up with a 'satisfactory proposition'. A contract was sealed on the 12th September, 1905, with Electric Co. Ltd, to enable them to act as contractor for the installation of the engine.[114] The outcome was the operation, in February, 1907, of an engine and electrical generator alternator set rated at 825 kW. The engine itself operated at 100 rpm and developed 1,200 bhp. The set was electrically linked up, in parallel, with the Rateau turbine generator at Elliot Colliery.

The gas engine's satisfactory performance encouraged the company to further the application of the technology. A second set was made by the Nürnberg Company, and installed at the colliery sometime, either in late 1907, or early 1908. This engine delivered 2,400 bhp. By 1914, the colliery featured three gas engines made by Messrs M. A. N. Nuremberg. One gas engine was described as a single Tandem, producing 825 kW, and the two gas engines as double-Tandem, 1,650 kW.[115] These gas fired engines appear to have proved their worth to Edmund Mills Hann.

However, using a gas engine to drive the ventilating fan at Bargoed Colliery was less than successful. Messrs Richardson, Westgarth & Co., of Middlesbrough, supplied this gas engine. Hann 'conceded' that unless it was 'employed fairly continuously and with a good load factor' that it 'was not commercially economical'. Through experimentation, Powell Duffryn explored the limits for the use of gas engines at a colliery. This speaks once more for an engineer, Edward Mills Hann, who was prepared to give licence to technical adventure.

Steam Turbines

The Aberdare Valley electrical scheme, in around 1908, saw further change. Edmund Mills Hann directed that the compound steam engines, used to generate its electricity, be replaced by steam turbines.[116] Thomas Sugden may have felt flattered that his motto, 'more steam and less gas', had been partly heeded. Sugden's self-esteem was further bolstered when he learnt about company developments that took place over a period of years.

Beginning in 1910, compound steam engines at Middle Duffryn Power Station were replaced in sequence by four turbines. Turbine unit number 1 was installed perhaps by early in 1910, and was of a Curtis design, and yielded 2,200 kW and 3,300 V AC.[117] Units numbered 2 and 3 were Zoelly turbines, and each generated 2,000 kW and 3,300 V AC. The Lalimeyer Electrical Company supplied the generating package, which included the Zoelly turbines, by, maybe, late 1910, or early 1911.[118] Unit 4, was another Zoelly turbine, and was installed after May 1913, and in operation produced 5,000 kW and 3,300 V AC.[119]

In 1905, the makers of the Curtis turbine were the General Electric Company of America and the British Thomson-Houston Company who supplied the one to Middle Duffryn Power Station, also called the Aberaman Power Station, in 1913.[120] The turbine was an impulse type designed by Curtis, an American engineer. Messr Escher, Weiss & Company, of Zurich made the impulse type Zoelly turbine. Investing in steam turbines was a further indication that technically Powell Duffryn was at the forefront of progress. Furthermore, in 1908, Powell Duffryn was also making use of gas engines as the prime mover for electricity generation.

On the 6th April, 1908, the South Wales Institute of Engineers held a further discussion about Hann's paper, 'A recent Plant for the Utilisation of Small Coal'. Hugh Bramwell ended the discussion by saying: '*Mr Hann's paper was one of very great interest and value, as the Council had very properly shown by awarding it the President's gold medal*'.[121] Upon receiving the medal, Hann said that it '*was the greatest honour which had fallen to him*'. He added that he would '*highly prize it as long as he lived, and hand it down to one of his sons to treasure in the years to come*'. Which son? His fifth son, Frank P. Hann, then twenty-three years of age, had that day been welcomed as a new Student member of the Institute.

Edmund Mills Hann's writings about the Bargoed coke and by-products plant dealt with a new and complex technical development.[122] They reveal a mastery of basic chemical engineering, then an emerging art, so that he could lead in an informed way Powell Duffryn's quest to utilise small coal. Undoubtedly his intelligence and inclination for learning enabled him to gain such knowledge. Yet, for a busy man, holding the equivalent of a chief executive's position, such mastery was a feat. Hugh Bramwell's act in tabling information about the Great Western Colliery Company's by-products plant at the South Wales Institute of Engineers' meeting did not go without notice. William Wight, the Institute's President remarked that their actions 'evoked highly interesting and practical comparisons'. He further expressed

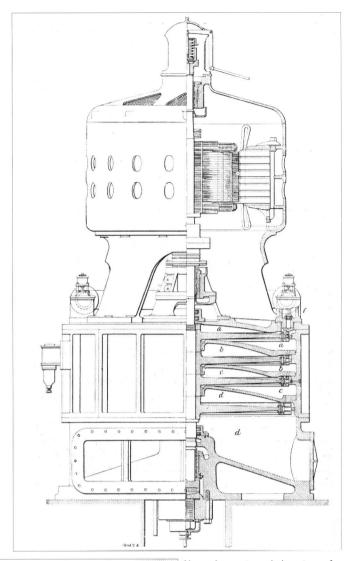

Above: A sectioned drawing of a Curtis turbine.
Proceedings, *SWIE*, Vol XXIV, (1904-06)

Zoelly turbine as used at Middle Duffryn Power Station.
Proceedings, *SWIE*, Vol. XXIV, (1904-06)

an opinion that Hann's paper *'was one of the most valuable ever submitted to the Institute'.*[123]

White Rose Level Closed

In 1908, mining at New Tredegar's White Rose level ended.[124] The 1885 Ordnance Survey map shows two levels in operation in the vicinity of the Brecon & Merthyr's White Rose Station that served New Tredegar people. The name 'White Rose Colliery' was given to the level sited a cricket ball's throw southward from White Rose railway station. About a quarter of a mile north from the railway station, at a higher elevation, and near the road that led to New Tredegar Colliery, stood the second level. To the south of White Rose Colliery the map shows coke ovens. Although it is clear that Powell Duffryn operated and closed White Rose Level, the history of the other level remains to be found.

In 1888, clay was extracted from the White Rose level maybe as brick-making material. However, in 1899, the level yielded 40,220 tons of coal, the year when the employment of miners at the level reached its peak, at 106. By 1907, miners' numbers had declined to around forty. The closure of the level broke a link with Thomas Powell.

Record Breaking – 1908 and 1909

A. Z. C. James mentions that under Edmund Lawrence Hann's management Bargoed Colliery's output rose to 3,300 ton per day in 1907. He claimed that this was then 'the record output for a single shaft in Great Britain'. An attraction for record breaking is endemic in most industries, and coal mining was no exception.

A spur for Bargoed Colliery to put its coal raising performance to the test could have been the performance posted after the reopening of Cambrian Collieries' Clydach Vale Colliery, situated in the Rhondda Fawr Valley, in July 1906.[125] This coal company's chairman was David Alfred Thomas MP. The colliery had been restored after a major disaster on 10th March, 1905, when thirty-one men were killed. Leonard Wilkinson Llewellyn, the grandson of George Wilkinson who served as Powell Duffryn's general manager of collieries under Sir George Elliot, held the post of general manager of Cambrian Collieries.[126]

The winding machinery of Clydach Vale's No. 1 pit raised 2,000 tons per day.[127] 'In one week [probably six days] they had out 12,000 tons of coal, 2,500 tons' in one day, whilst 'on one occasion in No. 2 pit they dealt with 2,700 tons in nine hours'. Messrs Llewellyn & Cubitt, of Ton-Pentre, Rhondda supplied the winding engines for No. 1 and No. 2 pits. The No. 1 pit worked the 6-feet seam at a depth of 394 yards, and also what was called locally the 'Coronation seam' that lay at a depth of 509 yards. The No. 2 pit mined the Red Vein seam at 415 yards. So, the coal workings were at a shallower depth than Bargoed Colliery's. The No. 3 pit raised Coronation seam coal using a Thornewill & Warham winding engine.[128] The output performance at Clydach Vale No. 2 pit, for what appears to have been a nine hour shift, might have become the target for other companies in the South Wales Coalfield to beat.

Nevertheless, it was tempting for a manager of a 'state of the art' colliery to carry out a trial to find out what it could actually achieve in one day, or one shift. However, it was the successor to Edmund Lawrence Hann as Bargoed Colliery's manager, probably Lewis Watkins, who took up the challenge. On the 3rd December, 1908, the colliery set a world record by raising 3,562 tons of coal in a ten hour shift.[129]

Edmund Mills Hann's approval would have been secured before the trial took place. He would have expected a thorough review of the trial so that useful lessons were learnt for raising the efficiency of winning coal. The findings of the record breaking trial persuaded him to sanction another one.

On the 23rd April, 1909, the Bargoed 'colliery machine' was again the scene of a record breaking attempt. The outcome was that in one shift 4,020 tons of coal was raised to the surface of the Rhymney Valley.[130] This performance was for raising coal up the South Pit for a ten hour period.[131] The *Western Mail* report about this feat noted also an hour's record 'in raising 70 bonds containing four trams conveying, 30 cwt of coal each tram, this equals to 420 tons'.[132] The Bargoed colliers, and other miners, returned home that day to sit in small tin baths, filled with kettle-heated water, taken from hearths fired by coal. After washing the grime and sweat off their tired bodies, they might have felt additional pleasure in believing that they had set another world record. The *Western Mail* reported the event the next day under the headline 'Coal-Winding Records at Bargoed', but omitted any claim to a world record.[133] Moreover, Powell Duffryn, in 1914, referred to this performance 'as not having been equalled by any other colliery' without any qualification. However, until at least 24th June, 1949, it was a record for collieries in the South Wales Coalfield.[134]

COAL-WINDING RECORDS AT BARGOED.

No less than 4,020 tons of coal were raised in ten hours at the Bargoed Steam Coal Pit (Powell Duffryn Company) on Friday. This company carried off the world's record on the 3rd of December, 1908, when 3,562 tons were raised in a similar time. Another hour's record was in raising 70 bonds containing four trams, conveying 30cwt. of coal in each tram. This is equal to 420 tons.

A *Western Mail* news item regarding Bargoed Colliery in 1909. No further reference to the world record set at Bargoed Colliery in December 1908 was found.

But, of course, holding any record can be a fleeting achievement. On the 24th April, 1910, at the Crown Park Colliery, Mansfield, Nottinghamshire, a world record was set at 4,524 ton in a shift timed at 7 hours 40 minutes.[135] Nevertheless, Bargoed Colliery's annual total output performance proved to be noteworthy. In 1911, this was about 775,000 tons. This may have been greater than the Hann's expectation for the colliery which W. H. Patchell deduced was half a million tons per annum from the steam coal part of the colliery.[136]

Hann's Mark

The period, between 1897 and 1909, was devoted, in Edmund Mills Hann's words, to *'the sinking and development of that very important work, the Bargoed Colliery'.*[137] The design and selection of its plant and equipment had seen its architect make scouting trips to potential suppliers, including some on mainland Europe. He paid exacting attention to detail. He even chided the brick makers of Britain for not using 'expert chemists', like the Germans, so that they could make bricks to meet his standards for oven construction.[138] His thorough approach to colliery design yielded exacting specifications for equipment suppliers.

The sourcing of plant and equipment involved procuring what he judged to be the best available. Innovation in terms of the application of gas engines, and turbines, which resulted in imports of equipment from Germany, also occurred. The *Colliery Guardian* stated, in 1928, that Powell Duffryn was the 'first concern' in coal mining to use large gas-engines.[139] Chemical engineering was then not recognised as a separate discipline, but was manifest in Bargoed's by-product plant. For Edmund Mills Hann, such plant advanced the extraction of commercial value from small coal for the company's benefit. In 1914, Powell Duffryn boasted that the Bargoed by-product plant 'constituted the most complete plant of its kind in the United Kingdom at that time'.[140]

By 1907, Bargoed Colliery was appreciated by a wide technical audience through *The Engineer*, which printed a facsimile of Hann's Institution of Mechanical Engineers paper about the colliery.[141] Thomas Sugden, the advocate for steam, and not gas, reflected in a written response to that paper: '*It used to be commonly remarked that any kind of machinery was good enough for a colliery, but it would be seen from this Paper that all the up-to-date appliances which had been applied to work of raising coal had been adopted by the author [Edmund Mills Hann] in the collieries of which he had charge*'.[142] Emerson Bainbridge further remarked, concerning Hann's paper: '*it would be a great pleasure for him to compare notes of what had been done in the Midlands with what Mr Hann, as one of the most enterprising engineers in South Wales, had done in that coalfield*'.[143] So, the design and engineering of Bargoed Colliery was viewed as a statement of both technical and business enterprise. The colliery, during the first decade of the twentieth century, was a model for at least British coal companies to emulate.

NOTES

1 Trevor Boyns, 'Growth in the Coal Industry: the Cases of Powell Duffryn and the Ocean Coal Company, 1864-1913', *op. cit.*, p.162-3.

2 E. M. Hann, *Brief History of The Powell Duffryn Steam Coal Company Ltd*, p.15.

3 'Joint Meeting, September 13 to 15', *SWIE*, Vol. XXVII (1910-1911), p.572.

4 E. M. Hann, *op. cit.*, p.18.

5 OS grid reference ST 153998.

6 'Visit of Belgian Engineers to South Wales', *SWIE*, Vol. XXIV (1904-1906), p. 102.

7 In *The Powell Duffryn Steam Coal Company 1864-1914, op. cit.*, p.52, Powell Duffryn's analysis of Bargoed Colliery's Rhas Las coal, in percentage terms, was given as: 80.2 of fixed Carbon; 2.9 of Ash; 16.25 of Volatile Matter; and 0.65 Moisture. The method used to arrive at such an analysis is unknown, which does not help for making comparisons. However, according to the 1942 classification, like that at New Tredegar Colliery and Elliot Colliery, it is ranked as a bituminous I: volatiles 17-23%, carbon ranged from 90-92%, hydrogen 4.3–5%, and calorific value 15,650 to 15,800 Btu/lb. Data from the *South Wales Coalfield (Including Pembrokeshire) Regional Survey Report, op. cit.*, pp.20-21.

8 Powell Duffryn's analysis of the Brithdir coal was by percentage: 70.5 Carbon; 2.6 Ash; 26.0 Volatile Matter; and 0.9 Moisture, see E. M. Hann, 'A Recent Plant for the Utilisation of Small Coal', *op. cit.*, p.476. Since the method used for the analysis is unknown, coalfield wide comparisons have to be treated with caution. However, since Powell Duffryn's tests were the same for the Rhas Las and the Brithdir seams, a clear difference in their properties is shown.

9 Utilised were two Sulzer 475 hp pump, one 330 hp Worthington pump, and one Mather & Platt 150 hp pump. At the 'North Pit' two 800 hp Sulzer pumps did duty.

10 E. M. Hann, 'Some notes on the Mechanical Equipment of Collieries', *Proceedings*, Institution of Mechanical Engineers, Vol. 71, (1906), pp.729-730.

11 GR PDMBDM No. 4, 8 Jan 1901, p.282.

12 E. M. Hann, 'Some notes on the Mechanical Equipment of Collieries', *Proceedings*, Institution of Mechanical Engineers, *op. cit.*, p.722.

13 *The Powell Duffryn Steam Coal Company 1864-1914, op. cit.*, p.58.

14 'Visit of Belgian Engineers to South Wales', *SWIE*, Vol. XXIV (1904-1906), p.102.

15 George Watkins, *Stationary Steam Engines of Great Britain, The National Photographic Collection, Volume 4: Wales, Cheshire & Shropshire, op. cit.*, p.56.

16 E. M. Hann, 'Some notes on the Mechanical Equipment of Collieries', *Proceedings*, Institution of Mechanical Engineers, *op. cit.*, pp.722-723.

17 *The Powell Duffryn Steam Coal Company 1864-1914, op. cit.*, p.58.

18 *The Powell Duffryn Steam Coal Company 1864-1914, op. cit.*, p.37. In this history it states that the semi-conical type of drum was 'developed by Mr. E. M. Hann about 20 years ago'. This suggests that the idea initiated development around 1894.

19 'President's Inaugural Address', 'The Raising of Coal from Vertical Shafts', *SWIE*, Vol. XXX (1917), pp.5-15.

20 E. M. Hann, 'Some notes on the Mechanical Equipment of Collieries', *Proceedings*, Institution of Mechanical Engineers, *op. cit.*, pp.727-728.

21 E. M. Hann, 'Some notes on the Mechanical Equipment of Collieries', *Proceedings*, Institution of Mechanical Engineers, *op. cit.*, pp.719-720. Each boilers was rated at 180 hp, with 1,826ft^2 of heating surface, each with its own superheater, the steam pressure being 120 lb/in^2 and the average superheat 90^0 F.

22 E. M. Hann, 'Some notes on the Mechanical Equipment of Collieries', *Proceedings*, Institution of Mechanical Engineers, *op. cit.*, p.719.

23 'Summer Meeting in South Yorkshire', *SWIE*, Vol. XXVII (1912), p.122.

24 D. S. M. Barrie, *op. cit.*, p.265.

25 Trevor Boyns, Bargoed Colliery-Employment Figures. (Annual List of Mines)

26 R. W. Kidner, *The Rhymney Railway*. (The Oakwood Press, 1995), p.27.

27 See R. W. Kidner, *op. cit.*, pp.34-35, and p.149.

28 Trevor Boyns, Bargoed Colliery-Employment Figures. (Annual List of Mines). In that year the steam coal pits employed 2,771 men (2253 underground and 518 on the surface), and 576 were employed at the Brithdir pit (515 underground and 61 on the surface).

29 G. M. Harries, *op. cit.*, p.5.

30 David Hann, 'The Hann Family–A Mining Dynasty of South Wales part 2, G. G. Hann (1879-1918)', *Glamorgan Family History Society, Journal No. 39*, (Sept., 1995) p.5,

31 David Hann, 'The Hann Family–A Mining Dynasty of South Wales part 3, E. L. Hann (1881-1968)', *Glamorgan Family History Society, Journal No.40*, (Dec., 1995) p.10.

32 Document, A. Z. C. James, '1957 Draft of Powell Duffryn History', p. 163. A. Z. C. James was described as being the former Editor of the *PD Review*. Item from Edwin Greening Collection, inspected December 2005.

33 Arnold Lumpton, 'The Coal Resources of the United Kingdom-Economy and Waste', *SWIE*, Vol. XXXII (1916), p.149.

34 List of Student Members, *SWIE*, Vol. XXXII (1916).

35 Research Notes as at March 2007, Raymond Lawrence. The colliery manager information.

36 E. M. Hann, *Brief History of The Powell Duffryn Steam Coal Company Ltd*, p.45.

37 C. J. O. Evans, *Glamorgan*. (Cardiff-William Lewis, Second Edition 1943), p.196

38 C. J. O. Evans, *Monmouthshire*. (Cardiff-William Lewis, 1952), p.436.

39 Hilda M. Evans, *New Tredegar in Focus*. (Starling Press, 1977), p.20.

40 GR PDMBDM No. 5, p.51.

41 GR PDMBDM No. 5, p.56.

42 Obituary Notices, Charles Pratt Sparks CBE, *Journal, Institution of Electrical Engineers*, Vol. 88, (1941), p.318.

43 I. C. R. Byatt, *op. cit.*, p.94.

44 W. A. Scott, 'Electric Motive Power in Mines and Collieries', *SWIE*, Vol. XXIII (1904), pp.179-182.

45 D. Selby-Bigge, 'The Development of Electricity in the Mining Industry', *SWIE*, Vol. XXV (1906-1908), pp.275-6.

46 'The Development of Electricity in the Mining Industry', *op. cit.*, p.278.

47 'The Development of Electricity in the Mining Industry', *op. cit.*, p.279.

48 W. A. Scott, 'Electric Motive Power in Mines and Collieries', *SWIE*, Vol. XXIII (1904), pp.225-303.

49 Comment, A. J. Edwards to Writer, 18 Feb. 2007. The use of 40 Hz prevailed at these collieries until at least 1947. In around 1950, W. A. Scott acted as Seconder for A. J. Edwards's application for Associate Membership of the Institution of Mechanical Engineers. With respect to identifying use of 40 Hz, see Electric Motive Power in Mines and Collieries', *SWIE*, Vol. XXIII (1904), p.285 & p.290.

50 Discussion, 'Electric Motive Power in Mines and Collieries', *SWIE*, Vol. XXIII (1904), p.439.

51 W. A. Scott, 'Electric Motive Power in Mines and Collieries', *SWIE*, Vol. XXIII (1904), p.236.

52 B. J. Day, 'Visit to Powell Duffryn Collieries and Works in the Aberdare Valley', *SWIE*, Vol. XXIV (1904-1906), pp.560-570.

53 At sometime before 1914, Ysguborwen Colliery was also connected into the Aberdare scheme, and at a distance of $2^1/_2$ miles became the Aberdare Valley colliery furthest away from the power station. *The Powell Duffryn Steam Coal Company 1864-1914, op. cit.*, p.30.

54 Joint Discussion of Messrs Spark's, Mountain's, and Hooghwinkel's Papers, *Journal, Institution of Electrical Engineers*, Vol. 36 (1907), p.565.

55 'The Development of Electricity in the Mining Industry', *op. cit.*, pp.348-350.

56 'The Development of Electricity in the Mining Industry', *op. cit.*, p.355.

57 Joint Discussion of Messrs Spark's, Mountain's, and Hooghwinkel's Papers, *Journal, Institution of Electrical Engineers, op. cit.*, pp.514-5.

58 B. J. Day, *op. cit.*, p.560-579.

59 B. J. Day, *op. cit.*, p.573.

60 B. J. Day, *op. cit.*, p.574.

61 This date is stated in *A Guide to Stationary Steam Engines*, (Moorland Publishing, 1981), p.125. In Hann's 1906 paper to the Institution of Mechanical Engineers, he states that 'quite recently at another colliery where a four-cylinder compound-engine was started in lieu of a plain engine'. This is judged by the Writer to be the Elliot East Colliery's Thornewill & Warham engine. Indeed, a surviving Powell Duffryn engineering drawing, dated March 1904, part of a collection held by Nigel Brake, Penybryn Engineering, Ystrad Mynach, shows structural strengthening of the original drum. Such strengthening served to deal with the increased forces on the drum once a more powerful winding engine became operational. The strengthened drum proved to be an interim measure until a choice was made about what type of spiral drum was to be used. Chosen finally was a Diabolo drum. The drawing for the Elliot East Colliery Diablo drum in the collection is dated 1912, which helped date its installation.

62 Document, G. F. Bond, 'The History of Penrikyber Colliery', April 1964, (National Coal Board, 1964), Aberdare Library I 2/16/2, p.2.

63 Document, G. F. Bond, *op, cit.*, p.3.

64 Dating the Barclay engine to around 1907 was derived from a near arithmetic mean of dates. The photograph of the colliery on p.54 shows no Barclay winding house cf. with the one of the colliery on the title pages. Page 54's photograph shows the colliery's Rhymney Railway branch line, which sets circa 1903 as the earliest date for Barclay engine work. However, the reengineering of the Elliot East engine, as the main winding engine, took precedence so making 1905 as the earliest date for site work on the Barclay engine. The company's plan of the colliery, p.52, shows the Barclay engine's winding house in place by the end of 1910 making this the latest date.

65 George Watkins, *Stationary Steam Engines of Great Britain, The National Photographic Collection, Volume 4: Wales, Cheshire & Shropshire, op. cit.*, SER 680a, p.128.

66 G. M. Watkins, 'The Development of the Steam Winding Engine', *op. cit.*, p.14.

67 E. M. Hann, 'Some notes on the Mechanical Equipment of Collieries', *op. cit.*, p.724.

68 G. M. Watkins, 'The Development of the Steam Winding Engine', *Transactions, Newcomen Society*, Vol. 50 (1979), p.15.

69 G. M. Watkins, 'The Development of the Steam Winding Engine', *op. cit.*, p.17.

70 Andrew Barclay & Co. engine drawing 'Vertical Cross Compound Winding Engine, cylinders 34- & 56-in. dia. x 4ft 6in. stroke' for 'Messrs Powell Duffryn Coal Co. Ltd', undated Andrew Barclay & Co. records, University of Glasgow Archives, RHP 66306/1.

71 One other Diabolo drum survives in component form in the keeping of the Foxfield Railway, Blythe Bridge, in Staffordshire. The drum was once used at Penrikyber Colliery. The Robey winding steam engine, used to drive the drum, has also been saved in component form by the Foxfield Railway.

72 George Hann, 'The Sinking and Equipping of Penallta Colliery', *SWIE*, Vol. XXVII (1910-1911), p.279.

73 George Watkins, *Stationary Steam Engines of Great Britain, The National Photographic Collection, Volume 4: Wales, Cheshire & Shropshire, op. cit.*, p.56.

74 Comment, A. J. Edwards to Writer, Feb. 2005.

75 E. M. Hann, *Brief History of the Powell Duffryn Steam Coal Company Ltd*, pp.22-3.

76 Research Notes as at March 2007, Raymond Lawrence.

77 *The Powell Duffryn Steam Coal Company 1864-1914, op. cit.*, p.10.

78 Research Notes as at March 2007, Raymond Lawrence. The source of manager details and employment numbers at the colliery.

79 George Knox, 'Landslides in South Wales Valleys', *SWIE*, Vol. XLIII (1927-1928), p.239.

80 E. M. Hann, *op, cit.*, pp.22-3. The maximum depth of the shaft was 438 yards. Research Notes as at March 2007, Raymond Lawrence.

81 George Knox, 'Landslides in South Wales Valleys', *SWIE*, Vol. XLIII (1927-1928), pp.248-249. The details on the method adopted at New Tredegar Colliery to retard the 1905 a landslide by draining underground works was presented by W. E. Jayne who later held many key management roles in Powell Duffryn. Comment, A. J. Edwards to Writer, August 2007: following the Aberfan disaster of 1967, Knox's paper became vital reading for National Coal Board engineers. Tipping colliery refuse on an 'unstable ground' was raised by Robert James; see p.272 and also p.280.

82 E. M. Hann, *op, cit.*, pp.22-3.

83 *The Engineer*, 'Some Notes on the Mechanical Equipment of Collieries', by E. M. Hann, 25 Jan. 1907, p.98. A puzzle concerns the No. 3 Pit winding engine installed at New Tredegar Colliery. George Watkins referred to an engine, see 'The Development of the Steam Winding Engine', *Transactions*, Newcomen Society, Vol. 50 (1979), p.22, 'special designs [of winding engines] were rarely used in English collieries, but one was built for New Tredegar pit, South Wales, about 1900'. This date agrees with the new shaft. 'Designed by Mr Hann … it was built by Thornewill & Warham, works no. 834, and was an inverted Manhattan type. These details are the same in his description of Bargoed Colliery's engine; see G. M. Watkins, *Stationary Steam Engines of Great Britain, Vol. 4: Wales, Cheshire & Shropshire, op. cit.*, p.56. However, a drawing of a Thornewill & Warham engine at New Tredegar Colliery appears in an article about Bargoed Colliery, *The Engineer*, 'Some Notes on the Mechanical Equipment of Collieries', E. M. Hann, 25 Jan. 1907, figures 4 & 5.

84 Research Notes as at March 2007, Raymond Lawrence.

85 *The Powell Duffryn Steam Coal Company 1864-1914, op. cit.*, p.48.

86 *The Powell Duffryn Steam Coal Company 1864-1914, op. cit.*, pp.36-7. With date and other details from Brian Davies, 20th Jan. 2007.

87 Comment, Brian Davies to Writer, Jan. 2007.

88 Information sourced from a remnant of a Powell Duffryn advertising leaflet, title unknown (undated but before 1905), p.7.

89 E. M. Hann, *Brief History of the Powell Duffryn Steam Coal Company Ltd*, p.23.

90 A. W. Woodland & W. B. Evans, *Geology of the South Wales Coalfield Part IV: The country around Pontypridd and Maesteg*. Explanation of One-inch Geological Sheet 248. *op. cit.*

91 *The Powell Duffryn Steam Coal Company 1864-1914, op. cit.*, p. 37.

92 Cynon Valley History Society, *Cynon Coal, op. cit.*, p. 214.

93 *The Powell Duffryn Steam Coal Company 1864-1914, op. cit.*, p.23.

94 S. A. Everett, 'Turbine Machinery', *SWIE*, Vol. XXIV (1904-1906), pp.344-347.

95 Trevor Boyns, 'Contracts Sealed by Company for Electrical Equipment', (Unpublished). Contract being sealed on 12th June, 1906 with Messrs P. J. Mitchell.

96 *The Powell Duffryn Steam Coal Company 1864-1914, op. cit.*, p.52.

97 E. M. Hann, 'A Recent Plant for the Utilisation of Small Coal', *SWIE*, Vol. XXIV (1906-07), p.469.

98 E. M. Hann, 'A Recent Plant for the Utilisation of Small Coal', *op. cit.*, p.472.

99 E. M. Hann, 'A Recent Plant for the Utilisation of Small Coal', *op. cit.*, p.476.

100 E. M. Hann, 'A Recent Plant for the Utilisation of Small Coal', *op. cit.*, p.473.

101 E. M. Hann, 'A Recent Plant for the Utilisation of Small Coal', *op. cit.*, p.474.

102 E. M. Hann, 'A Recent Plant for the Utilisation of Small Coal', *op. cit.*, p.476.

103 E. M. Hann, 'A Recent Plant for the Utilisation of Small Coal', *op. cit.*, pp.477-8.

104 Discussion, 'A Recent Plant for the Utilisation of Small Coal', *SWIE*, Vol. XXVI (1908-1910), p.105.

105 Discussion, 'A Recent Plant for the Utilisation of Small Coal', *SWIE*,

Vol. XXV (1906-1907), pp.668-9.

106 Discussion, 'A Recent Plant for the Utilisation of Small Coal', *SWIE*, Vol. XXVI (1908-1910), pp.109-113.

107 Discussion, 'A Recent Plant for the Utilisation of Small Coal', *op. cit.*, Vol. XXVI, p.118.

108 Discussion, 'A Recent Plant for the Utilisation of Small Coal', *op. cit*, Vol. XXVI, p.122.

109 Discussion, 'A Recent Plant for the Utilisation of Small Coal', *SWIE*, Vol. XXV (1906-1907), p.671.

110 Regarding Powell Duffryn's cost tabulation see E. M. Hann, 'A Recent Plant for the Utilisation of Small Coal', *op. cit.*, Vol. XXV (1906-1907), p.478. Regarding the Maritime plant see Discussion, 'A Recent Plant for the Utilisation of Small Coal', *op. cit.*, Vol. XXV, p.672. Bramwell also presented his calculations with reference to conditions that may not have been identical to those used by Hann's engineers.

111 E. M. Hann, 'Some notes on the Mechanical Equipment of Collieries', *Proceedings of the Institution of Mechanical Engineers*, (1906), p.731.

112 Discussion, 'A Recent Plant for the Utilisation of Small Coal', *SWIE*, Vol. XXV (1906-1907), p.664.

113 Presidential Address', *SWIE*, Vol. XXV (1906-1907), p.664.

114 Trevor Boyns, 'Contracts Sealed by Company for Electrical Equipment'. (Unpublished).

115 *The Powell Duffryn Steam Coal Company 1864-1914*, *op. cit.*, p.23.

116 *The Powell Duffryn Steam Coal Company 1864-1914*, *op. cit.*, p.32.

117 Trevor Boyns, 'Contracts Sealed by Company for Electrical Equipment'. (Unpublished). The contract was sealed by the company, on the 10th November 1908, for £9,980.

118 Trevor Boyns, 'Contracts Sealed by Company for Electrical Equipment'. (Unpublished). The contract sealed by the company for unit 2 was dated 19th October 1909, and the one for unit 3 dated 12th April 1909 for £3,892 and £3,887 respectively.

119 Trevor Boyns, 'Contracts Sealed by Company for Electrical Equipment'. (Unpublished). The contract sealed by the company for unit 4 was dated 20th May 1913 for an unknown cost.

120 S. A. Everett, 'Turbine Machinery', *SWIE*, Vol. XXIV (1904-1906), pp.335-344.

121 Discussion, 'A Recent Plant for the Utilisation of Small Coal', *SWIE*, Vol. XXV (1906-1907), p.673.

122 In addition to his paper to the South Wales Institute of Engineers, see Discussion, 'A Recent Plant for the Utilisation of Small Coal', *SWIE*, Vol. XXVI (1908-1910), pp.199-205.

123 Discussion, 'A Recent Plant for the Utilisation of Small Coal', *op. cit.*, Vol. XXVI, p.209.

124 Research Notes as at March 2007, Raymond Lawrence.

125 Trevor Price, 'Visit to Cambrian Collieries, Clydach Vale', *SWIE*, Vol. XXV (1906-1907), p.38-46.

126 His father, Llewelyn Llewellyn, who worked as George Wilkinson's assistant, was born in the same house as the younger sons of Edmund Mills Hann. Leonard Wilkinson Llewelyn was later knighted. W. W. Price, *op. cit.*, p.19.

127 Trevor Price, 'Visit to Cambrian Collieries, Clydach Vale', *op. cit.*, p.38-46.

128 No. 3 pit's Thornewill & Warham engine was of the horizontal type with its cylinders being 36-inches diameter, 6ft stroke, and raised 800 tons per day. George Watkins gave the No. 3 pit engine an uncertain date of 1900; George Watkins, *Stationary Steam Engines of Great Britain, The National Photographic Collection, Volume 4: Wales, Cheshire & Shropshire, op. cit.*, p.68

129 *Western Mail*, 24 April 1909, p.6, col.6. This article mentioned the world record, but it is not reported in the *Western Mail*, or *The Colliery Guardian*, for the appropriate date in 1908.

130 *The Powell Duffryn Steam Coal Company 1864-1914*, *op. cit.*, p.52.

131 'Joint Meeting, September 13 to 15', *SWIE*, Vol. XXVII (1910-1911), p.574.

132 *Western Mail*, 24 April 1909, p.6, col.6.

133 *Western Mail*, 24 April 1909, p.6, col.6.

134 Briefing Notes, 'Bargoed Steam Coal Colliery', (National Coal Board, 1949) for the visit to the colliery by HRH Duchess of Kent, 24th June 1949.

135 'Summer Meeting in South Yorkshire', *SWIE*, Vol. XXVII (1910-1911), p.161.

136 E. M. Hann, 'Some notes on the Mechanical Equipment of Collieries', Proceedings, Institution of Mechanical Engineers, *op. cit.*, p.736.

137 E. M. Hann, *Brief History of The Powell Duffryn Steam Coal Company Ltd*, p.18.

138 E. M. Hann, 'A Recent Plant for the Utilisation of Small Coal', *op. cit.*, Vol. XXV (1906-1907), p.475.

139 *The Colliery Guardian*, Vol. CXXXVI, No. 3508, 23 March 1928, p.1154.

140 *The Powell Duffryn Steam Coal Company 1864-1914*, p.23.

141 E. M. Hann, 'Some Notes on the Mechanical Equipment of Collieries', *The Engineer*, 25 Jan 1907, pp.96-8.

142 E. M. Hann, Some notes on the Mechanical Equipment of Collieries', *Proceedings of the Institution of Mechanical Engineers*, (1906), p.744.

143 E. M. Hann, 'Some notes on the Mechanical Equipment of Collieries', *op. cit.*, p.741.

New Tredegar 1905 landslide's effect upon at least the Brecon & Merthyr Railway's 'Old Rumney' line. One of the colliery's two chimney stacks rocked during the landslide.

Pope/Parkhouse Archive

Aberaman Colliery. Aberdare. 992

During the first decade of the twentieth century the importance to Powell Duffryn of its Aberdare Valley collieries, represented here as Aberaman Colliery, was eclipsed due to the company's colliery expansion in the Rhymney Valley. However, the rich colliery engineering knowledge and skill that the company acquired under Edmund Mills Hann still resided at the company's Aberaman offices as did the central management of the company's collieries.

Pope/Parkhouse Archive

Chapter Six
MANAGEMENT DELEGATION

The burden of work carried by Powell Duffryn's general manager of collieries during the first half of the 1910s was immense due to his wide scope of work. Edmund Mills Hann monitored the coal output performance of the company's collieries. He dealt with industrial relations. He led an extensive colliery development and redevelopment programme, which prompted him to travel abroad on technical information gathering missions. As the company's Agent, concerning mining leases, he engaged with associated legal and commercial matters. He handled negotiations between the company and railway companies. Railway rates, railway extensions, like new branch lines to collieries, for the transport of coal, miners' passenger services, and coal haulage logistics gave rise to such negotiations.[1] All these activities were regularly reviewed by the company's Management Committee, which he attended subject to an invitation from its members.

The administration of Hann's management work involved some kind of bureaucracy. For financial control, a cost accountancy function kept him informed. A function dealt with the commercial department's coal orders and sales forecasts for the planning of coal production. He kept a close eye on each colliery's coal production, and visited the company's collieries to learn about the state of affairs. Underground inspections of his played a part in a colliery's visit. Such visits enabled him to assess the mettle of a colliery's manager. The administration of the collieries took up a proportion of his time as general manager of collieries.

Edmund Mills Hann participated in industrial relations at two levels. Joseph Shaw, as chairman of Powell Duffryn, had precedence over him regarding the company's dealings with the Monmouthshire & South Wales Coalowners' Association. Concerning coalfield-wide industrial relations issues at least, Hann seems to have given support to Shaw. In general, the unforeseen aspect of industrial relations both at coalfield and colliery operation level meant that Hann dealt with each particular issue, or dispute, as they arose. Obviously dealing with the affairs of industrial relations was at the expense of other aspects involved managing the collieries. Moreover, a penalty of dealing with the industrial relations matter of the moment was that he gave less time to at least thinking about shaping the company's future.

The time he allocated to overseeing the company's extensive colliery development and redevelopment programme was also precious for the company's future. The scale of his work in this area may be appreciated by taking stock of the portfolio of projects he was engaged in during 1903. That year he controlled: developments for Bargoed Colliery like the gas and by-product plant, the redevelopments at Aberaman, Fforchaman, and New Tredegar collieries, and the redevelopment of winding at Elliot Colliery. Moreover, helped by Charles Sparks, he initiated the Aberdare Valley collieries' electricity scheme.

Regarding planning for the company's future, his priorities included expanding Powell Duffryn's coal property, serving as the company's agent, and seeking engineering technology that could further his quest to produce coal as cheaply as possible. In 1903, as will be detailed later, he was engaged in matters arising

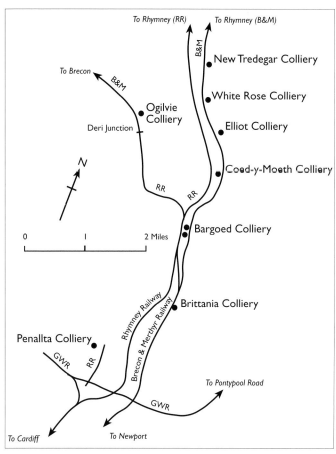

The map shows Powell Duffryn collieries in the upper part of the Rhymney Valley that Edmund Mills Hann was responsible for engineering or planning their sinking. Circa 1902, the company envisaged sinking Penallta and Britannia collieries. Around 1914, the company leased Bargoed Rhymney Valley mining property from the Marquis of Bute that was exploited after 1923 following the sinking of Ogilvie Colliery.

from the acquisition of Rhymney Valley coal property that lay south of Bargoed Colliery's property. His membership of the South Wales Institute of Engineers aided his search for engineering technologies.

The technical ethos of Powell Duffryn was shaped to some extent by what Edmund Mills Hann learnt through being a member of the South Wales Institute of Engineers. Conversely, the Institute's members learnt about Powell Duffryn's developments, which may have influenced technical development throughout the South Wales Coalfield. Surprisingly perhaps, in 1903, Hann, no doubt after seeking and getting the approval of the directors of Powell Duffryn, agreed for his name to be put forward as a candidate for the Institution's presidency. And so, from 1904, for a two year period, he served as the Institute's President. A description of his period of office offers a means for appreciating Powell Duffryn's activities in the context of the South Wales Coalfield. Moreover, a glimpse is also obtained of the general technical state of the coalfield, and the attitudes and outlooks prevailing within coal companies are partly revealed.

South Wales Institute of Engineer's Headquarters, Park Place, Cardiff.
Proceedings, SWIE, Vol. XXV, (1905)

Presidential Address

On Thursday, 21st April, 1904, the Annual General Meeting of the South Wales Institute of Engineers was held at its Park Place, Cardiff, building.[2] T. Hurry Riches, Locomotive Superintendent of the Taff Vale Railway, having completed his term of office as the Institute's President, announced that its Council had elected 'unanimously' Edmund Mills Hann to be his successor.

In the 1970s, theatre and opera audiences arriving at, or leaving, the New Theatre may have glanced at the Institute's building opposite. The Institute's building could catch the eye since it was a large red brick building having ornate features in the Queen Anne style. Through the large windows that faced the theatre, could be seen a gallery of large portraits of men, lit by chandeliers. The celebrity status of these men was unknown to the general public. The place looked like a gentlemen's club of faded importance.[3]

However, in 1904, this building could have been considered to be the senate house for the government of the South Wales Coalfield. The Institute rented some of the building's rooms to the Monmouthshire & South Wales Coalowners' Association. Association meetings were conducted with the degree of confidentiality needed to guard the coal company shareholders' interests. Moreover, a public announcement of the Association had the potential to cause ill-will among colliery workers. Nevertheless, many of the Association's members were also members of the Institute. Indeed, Edmund Mills Hann was involved with the Association as a representative of Powell Duffryn.

The Institute conducted its affairs in a more open fashion than the Association. The Institute's lecture theatre was where the expressed views of its members were recorded in its *Proceedings*, and made available for an interested public to be read. Such an airing of technical and business economic issues risked affecting the fortunes of the coalowners. Moreover, reports of Institute meetings provided clues useful for appreciating the character, mental capacities, and values of some of the men who led the South Wales coal industry contemporarily with Hann.

T. Hurry Riches offered an appraisal of Edmund Mills Hann at the Institute's Annual General Meeting. He was 'thorough' in 'all he did'. 'Mr Hann was well known and highly respected in the engineering world, and it was eminently in the interests of the Institute to have such a man at the head of affairs'.

Edmund Mills Hann then delivered his Presidential address. The main theme of the address was 'the principal changes' that had 'occurred in the winning and raising of coal' over the previous thirty-seven years or so. Helpfully, the contents of his address gave a considered picture and review of the state of the South Wales Coalfield for the period, and identified milestones in progress. He began his address by observing that technical change was 'due to the general progress of the arts, that is the adaptation to mining purposes of ordinary mechanical and scientific appliances. Yet the mining engineer can point to a goodly array of reforms and improvements of prime importance'.

'The supersession of furnaces for ventilation', was at the top of his list of changes he attributed to mining engineers. He believed that 'owing to the greater impediments', that existed in the South Wales Coalfield to 'splitting of [underground] air currents', there had been 'more necessity' for change 'than any other British district'. He lauded the Institute for its role in encouraging this change, and mentioned particularly William Price Struvé and John Roberts Waddell, who were deceased members.

Next he praised the mining engineer for extending the 'application of steam power [to drive the fan] instead of a column of heated air'. Yet, with regard to mechanical ventilation systems, he hoped that there would be still more progress, and put forward his thoughts on the use of 'subsidiary fans'.

The third and last item he attributed to mining engineers concerned 'safety lamps and the manner of securing them'. But he 'hoped for greater safety, both in the explosives and in the lamps', and predicted that they would be realised in both items in the 'near future'.

Perhaps not surprisingly, he used the Cleveland ironstone miner's former days of 'hand work' as his reference for a review of change in sinking shafts through hard strata. Then he acknowledged that 'probably the most notable advance', in the process of sinking shafts, was the use of more powerful explosives. Chemistry had helped man's craft and graft increase the rate of sinking.

But science had not found an answer to feeders of water. He tabled a dilemma: whether, or not, to use temporary pumping or to bail the water by winding, which he saw as a 'revival of an old idea'. Feeders at Bargoed Colliery were identified by him as having 'forcibly' revealed the 'deficiencies of our present appliances'. He then shared his doubt about there being one elegant solution for coping with feeders. Scathingly he observed that 'the best kinds of pumping' left 'much to be desired both as to hardiness, reliability, and economy'. The mining engineer was urged by him to 'balance the probable troubles from sinking setts, from underground steam pumps, or from winding appliances, or the wastefulness of compressed air plant, but the electric-driven centrifugal pump for high lifts, lately [used] in Germany', he judged, was a promising alternative.

Concerning winning coal, he was pessimistic about the application of the coal-cutting machine. He found it 'difficult to imagine any machine that would have any general and useful application' in the steam coal part of the South Wales Coalfield as achieved 'in the case of America, and other countries too'. In the South Wales Coalfield, Longwall, he acknowledged, held 'the field', noting that with perhaps exception of the introduction of the 'Nottingham system', there had been no important changes. The 'rules for laying out [underground] districts and conduct of working faces' were difficult to apply with consistency since the variation in 'roof and floor, thickness and section of coal seam, the amount and direction of the dip, vary as much or more frequently than in any other British coal-field'. He was though irritated by the lack of effort being made to collate the experiences gained working the South Wales Coalfield.

Sharing Experience

Although alert to the intense rivalry between coal companies, he rebuked his South Wales Coalfield colleagues for failing to collect data for comparison purposes. The County Durham man quoted the founding president of the Institute, William Menelaus, to characterise their behaviour: 'each working single handed' – 'alone in his own corner of the coal-field'.

The *Proceedings* of the Institute reveal that Hann regularly reported Powell Duffryn's developments and experiences. So, he held to a belief that pooling experience and knowledge would yield improvement in 'methods, means, and safety', which 'could not but be advantageous alike to the employer, to the workman, and the nation'.

As a general manager of collieries, he proceeded to call for 'some system of payment that will call forth the best energies of the men and provide for a fair division of the advantages'. The collier, according to him, was 'better remunerated for the unproductive parts of his work' than 'getting the coal itself, which is the sole source from which all expenses are first to be defrayed, and a profit earned if possible'.

He then declared that he was troubled by the poor return on the labour expenditure side, and the effect that it had on the attitude of Britain's financiers towards investing capital in coal companies. He thought that this malaise, as a general thing, had its roots in the attitude of the company's directors: 'The engineer often finds his principals unwilling to embark the capital required to install improved appliances', which he considered to be 'serious matter telling against our ability to compete'. He spoke having had his schemes supported by the directors of Powell Duffryn. Yet, he feared that the general state of affairs made the British capitalist less likely to invest in 'the trade'.

So, he warned that investors were inclined to back the coal mining industry's international competitors since their use of investment made the capitalist more confident about getting financial returns. By 1904, he possessed first-hand knowledge of the financial return expectations of investors. Bargoed Colliery was partly financed due to an issue of company debentures. The substance of the colliery's capital assets, he might have learnt, had attracted the investors who bought the debentures. Moreover, he appears also to have heard critical opinions expressed by investors about unappealing investment plans touted by other South Wales Coalfield colliery companies. But, he hoped that 'the causes of this discouragement and mistrust could be removed', otherwise the industry's 'decadence' would became 'decidedly apparent'. This gloomy warning would, decades later, prove prophetic for some of the coal companies of the South Wales Coalfield.

Powell Duffryn's business with great steamship lines had also alerted him to another benchmark for gauging change. He recalled a statement made by a chairman of one of these ship owners about the growth in size of ships, over the previous thirty years. This

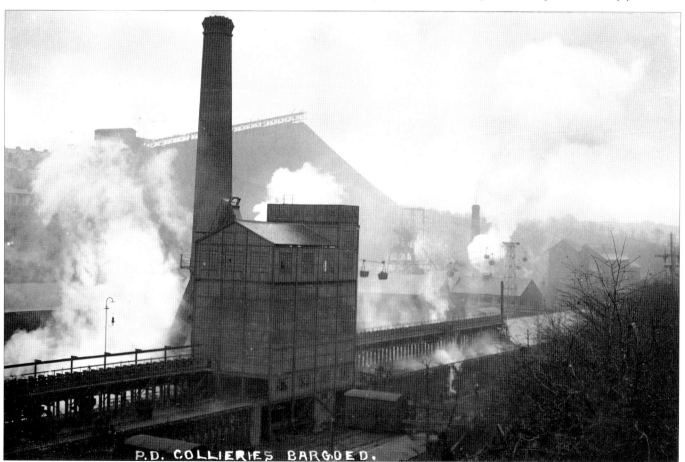

A custom of Edmund Mills Hann's, approved of by Powell Duffryn, was to share with company rivals knowledge gained from developments such as those at Bargoed Colliery.
Pope/Parkhouse Archive

P.D. COLLIERIES BARGOED.

period had seen improved economy of ship's engines and boilers, and 'traffic, reckoned in ton-miles, had quadrupled without any material increase in the coal burned'. Such a reference made him doubt if 'coal mines could show any such remarkable result'.

Nevertheless, he noted that 'a very creditable, if smaller improvement' had 'been attained' in colliery engineering. He cited the move from the Cornish boiler to the largest size of Lancashire and water tube boilers, in which economisers and superheaters had become 'numerous'. Regarding underground haulage in deeper mines, where longer distances were traversed, this had 'stimulated the introduction of the endless rope with double road and the use of double roads with main and tail rope having two journeys in motion'. He observed that 'a very commendable endeavour to replace horses at the face by engines' had 'been going on'. Lubricating grease was becoming a substitute for oats, or hay.

Concerning the pumping of water, he pronounced that 'compounds and triples' had seen off the Cornish engine 'good as it was'. Moreover, he was probably aware that the 'triple-expansion engine was at the heart of shipping development during the final two decades of the nineteenth century', and would learn that this continued to be the case 'for the first two of the twentieth century'.[4]

The tone of his address might have been serious, perhaps even dry, but it contained a flash of effusion when it came to electric power. 'In age', he said, 'it is still a child, and a few years since was a mere infant and a good deal of a pet, set to play strange tricks. Now we are looking eagerly for the performance of its manhood, already feeling sure that even very great expectations will not be disappointed'. As a general point, he mentioned that its application was 'busily' underway in ventilation, and pumping, and that the electric winding of coal was 'on trial'.

During his address, he revealed Powell Duffryn's plan for the Aberdare Valley electricity grid, which was described earlier. He proposed that a 'Group of collieries evidently afford a more promising field for self supply [of electricity] than a single mine' and so the company had decided 'to put down, at a central point among their Aberdare pits a modern three phase plant, of about 4,500 h.p., to supply about 85 motors at seven different pits'.

He also used his address to highlight the 'great strides' made, and 'still in progress with regard to steam winding-engines, and the auxiliary appliances, at the top and bottom of the shaft'. He thought that the winding of 300 tons per hour had been made possible, partly due to improvements in the way that 'larger' cages could be loaded and unloaded, but he called upon engineers to study the 'great variety of these arrangements' and to 'simplify them'. He observed: '*The single-cylinder vertical condensing engine most frequently provided with a counterbalance chain, was on the whole a credible plant from an engineering and economic point of view in the days of low-pressure steam, and it is probable that even with better boiler results obtained when the pressure was materially raised, the want of expansive and condensing and balancing arrangements at the double horizontals which came into vogue more than outweighed the gain, and there was a decided falling off in steam economy, which was sacrificed for speed. A further rise in steam pressure has bought to the front the compound-engine, of which quite a number of interesting examples now exist here, and in America and on the Continent, presenting a great variety of design and promising great economy for the deeper shafts'.*

Edmund Mills Hann advocacy of compound winding engines was based upon Powell Duffryn's experience. The company had

implemented and tested technical ideas that he had encouraged the development of during the 1890s, and which he had earlier shared with Institute members.

His mind still contained a store of technical ideas, some of which he made public. He speculated, with regards to coke ovens, about 'the rapid' development of the gas engine. 'It will probably now be but a very short time before we shall – with the aid of the by-product coke oven, gas engine and the electric dynamo – [see] collieries where no coal is burned for the production of power, but on the contrary the colliery may be a seller of power not in the potential only but the actual'. His listeners were left to ponder if Powell Duffryn was envisaging a future as a seller of electricity.

Edmund Mills Hann closed his address by calling upon 'local industries … to provide without delay the means of a systematic training for our future managers and engineers'. Adding an appeal: 'that this Institution will do all in its powers to assist in keeping South Wales to the fore in mining engineering by means of improved educational facilities as well as other ways it may find within its sphere of action'.

The office of President of the South Wales Institute of Engineers was seen by Edmund Mills Hann, not in terms of granting him superior status, but as a privilege. For the period of his office, he could lead discussions in south Wales about the practical significance of both scientific and technical change for its industries.

Presidential Office

Edmund Mills Hann, as president of the South Wales Institute of Engineers, led its meetings. On Thursday, 7th July, 1904, Professor William Galloway presented a paper to the Institute about a 'Portable Tank for Watering the Roadways in Mines'. He believed it was a means for dampening coal dust so as to reduce the risk of underground explosions. William Galloway had resigned from Her Majesty's Inspectorate of Mines after disputing his superiors' views about the causes of underground explosions. Fire-damp, they held, was the cause. He had accepted this view until the Llan Colliery explosion. However, his subsequent studies, and practical research in a south Wales colliery, led him to propose that the coal dust in the atmosphere of underground workings was a means by which an explosion could occur. Moreover, if 'blowers' of gas were also ignited as a consequence, a considerable underground disaster became likely.[5] He presented a paper on his coal dust theory about a cause of explosions to the Proceedings of the Royal Society in 1887

Hann supported Galloway's Institute paper that proposed a preventive measure. Hann mentioned experiments that he had done in 1882, to use salt to dampen dust.[6] He then announced that he would trial Galloway's proposal at one of the company's pits since he thought that Professor Galloway's tank system 'seemed to be a solution'.[7] Improved safety in coal mines was important as far as Powell Duffryn's general manager of collieries was concerned. Alas subsequent trials appear to have been less than successful.

The inventor of the Patterson Safety Lamp, W. Patterson, then took the floor at the Institute's Park Place building. The Institute had been a forum for inventors of safety lamps for decades. Up to 1904, the Institute's *Proceedings* recorded reviews of the Foster and Fluess Safety Lamp (see Proceedings of 1881); Crossley's Patent Compressed Air Safety Lamp (1881); Morgan's Lamp (1884); Clapp and Sandbrook's Improved Safety Lamp (1886); the Mercier (1887); Portable Electric Safety Lamp (1887); Vaughton's Electric Miner's Lamp (1888); Bristol's Miner's Electric Safety Lamp (1892);

the Miner's Piston Safety Lamp (1892); Sussman's Electric Safety Lamp (1893); and Best's Safety Lamp (1895).

Patterson claimed that his was the 'safest of all safety lamps'.[8] The Institute's members had probably heard similar claims before, and greeted them with both courtesy and some doubt. But, considering the humane objective, each new lamp deserved a fair trial. And Hann announced from the chair, that he was 'trying' out the lamp, and had found that it had 'many things to recommend it'. He added, however, that though he was sympathetic to a view expressed at the meeting by William Thomas, 'that there was no lamp existent that was really a safety lamp', he thought that the ones then available 'were entitled to the name when they were compared with the lamps of thirty-five years ago'. He further remarked about the prejudice in the counties of Durham and Northumberland against the Clanny lamp because its glass surround had tended to crack. However, a better joint between glass and the Clanny lamp body had been achieved.

An item about the geology of the South Wales Coalfield followed the Patterson lamp discussion. A paper submitted in late 1902, by Henry K. Jordan about the 'South Trough of the Coalfield' was discussed.[9] The paper was notable for winning for its author the first Gold Medal awarded by the Institute. Henry Jordan had correlated 'the Caerphilly vein with No. 3 Llanwit', and this had led to a revision of the national Geological Survey maps. In an Institute discussion, a year earlier, Hann had taken Jordan to task over what was called the Gadlys fault, a geological feature of the Aberdare Valley.[10] His remarks showed, as did that of other speakers, that mining engineers were as familiar with the pattern of faults in their area of the coalfield as they were with the lines on the palms of their hands. Nevertheless, Hann closed the paper's discussion by recommending that members should study Jordan's work to further improve their knowledge of the geology of the district.

One highlight of Edmund Hann's time as president was an exchange of knowledge and experiences between the engineers of south Wales and Belgium. In September 1904, a party of Belgium engineers, and graduates of the University of Liége, arrived in South Wales.[11] Hann led the Institute's reception committee. On Monday, 19th September, the party visited the Dowlais Cardiff Steel Works of Guest Keen & Nettlefolds. On the Tuesday, a visit was made to Llwynypia and Clydach Vale Collieries. The next day a party toured the Ocean Company's (formerly Harris) Deep Navigation Colliery, and then proceeded to Bargoed Colliery. The party was welcomed at Bargoed Colliery by Joseph Shaw and Hann, where, after lunch, the 'modern and up-to-date machinery installed at the colliery' was inspected.

Cardiff then became the evening's venue for events. Hann first entertained the visitors and members of the Institute for dinner, which was followed by an evening performance of the Cardiff Musical Festival. Maybe the visitors learnt that in South Wales there was a link between coal and music. Nonetheless, the visitors returned home to Belgium with knowledge about the best that Welsh industry offered the world.

On the 19th January, 1905, Hann chaired a meeting which he considered to be 'one of the best discussions' that the Institute 'had had for many years'.[12] The discussion's subject was 'Electrical Coal Winding' with its source material being an essay by Horace D. B. How,[13] and notes by Graham Stevenson giving examples of electrical winding engine.[14] Graham Stevenson had inspected collieries in Westphalia, Germany, where both DC and AC

power systems were being used. Hugh Bramwell suggested at the meeting that if electricity was taken from a central generator, to power not only winding but other colliery equipment as well, then the economic case for electric winding would be proven.[15] Hugh Bramwell's suggestions could be prophetic, and he was inclined to turn his thinking into something practical.

At the time, Edmund Mills Hann's position as regards electrical winding engines appeared somewhat ambivalent. Nevertheless, during the Institute's discussion, he criticized Horace How's opinion that an 'Ilgner system was the only system which could be advantageously used for coal winding'. But Horace How censured Hann for seeming to be more interested in appraising the Koepe rope system that was not 'essential to electric winding'.[16] Hann's apparent defence against this reprimand was that he had 'the benefit of seeing several electrical winding engines'.[17] Significantly though, Hann declared that 'he could not say that he was in favour of electrical winding yet, but it was evident it was making exceedingly rapid strides, and objections to it were being quickly removed'.[18]

Instructively, Edmund Mills Hann declared what he wanted to know so he could be persuaded to adopt electrical winding. 'What mining engineers wanted from electrical engineers was the comparison in cost between the latest mechanical plant that could be bought today and electrical installation'. Adding, maybe disparagingly: 'Some of the figures that had been quoted, he was bound to say, were not such as commended themselves to his mind'.[19] Powell Duffryn's investment in compound steam windings engines represented an acceptable business economic position as far as he was concerned.

The start of his second year of office as president was marked by him chairing the Institute's Annual General Meeting, on the 13th April, 1905.[20] The meeting proceeded with discussions about papers on compressors for colliery work, electric power distribution, and timbering and arching in mines.

Some of the members departed from the meeting eagerly looking forward to a summer's outing. The Institute had accepted an invitation of the President and Council of l'Association des Ingénieurs sortis de l'Ecole de Liége. Institute members, led by its president, arrived in Liége on the 17th June.[21] The Belgian engineers had returned the favour of their tour to south Wales. Each member of the Institute left Belgium with their own impressions, and ideas. Hann's are not known, but maybe those written by W. O'Connor were of interest to colliery engineers in the South Wales Coalfield. He mentioned inspecting a number of electrical winders in operation, raising, via deep shafts, coal won from thin seams.[22]

A Melancholy Meeting

On Thursday, 13th July, 1905, a sad task fell to the South Wales Institute of Engineer's president when opening a meeting.[23] Edmund Mills Hann moved a vote of condolence, regarding fatalities at No. 2 Pit, National Colliery, Wattstown, in the Rhondda Fach Valley. One hundred and twenty-one men were killed at the colliery, including its manager.

The meeting's gloom may have lifted briefly when T. H. Deakin proposed a vote of thanks to 'the President for his admirable arrangements' regarding the visit to Belgium. T. H. Deakin raised laughter, and applause, from Institute members, since he claimed that the earlier visit of Belgian engineers to south Wales had seen them 'take the "measure" of Mr Hann', and so the Institute had benefited from the 'President's reflected glory'. The president's retort was that if he had known what Deakin was going to say, he would not have allowed him to speak. Two papers were then presented to the Institute, one concerning boilers, by C. E. Stromeyer of the Manchester Steam User's Association, and the other was a member's essay on turbine machinery, by S. A. Everett.

The manner and style in which Edmund Mills Hann steered a South Wales Institute of Engineer's meeting was on show at an October meeting.[24] Regarding compressors, he sought many explanations, and appealed for someone 'better up in physics' to help raise his understanding. In a discussion about the 'economic working of boilers', he admitted that he did not have 'any great experience of mechanical stokers, but he had known them to fail in certain circumstances'. This suggests that he was referring to chain grate stokers since he also observed, in summary, that mechanical stokers worked better with an 'inferior grade of coal' than for a first-rate coal like steam coal from the South Wales Coalfield.

Hann's conduct at the October meeting of the Institute revealed some aspects of his nature. That he declared that he was ignorant of physics suggests he possessed humility. He was a relentless and probing questioner. His behaviour showed a keenness for learning, and might partly explain his annoyance, several years earlier, with the indifferent reaction of some Powell Duffryn colliery officials about a move of his to provide them with reading rooms.

Edmund Mills Hann's two years of office as president of the South Wales Institute of Engineers ended at its Annual General Meeting, 24th April, 1906. Mr T. H. Deakin succeeded him as president and offered the ritual thanks to the outgoing president: 'Mr Hann had by untiring energy coupled with great natural ability and acquired knowledge, made his way to the top of the mining profession in this district'. Applause followed, before he added that Hann had 'ungrudgingly placed at the service of the Institute' all 'his powers and all the advantages of his important position'.

Overstretched General Manager of Collieries

The first decade of the 1900s was a hectic one in the life of Edmund Mills Hann. In addition to managing Powell Duffryn's collieries, serving as President of the South Wales Institute of Engineers, in 1904 he took office as the Chairman of the Aberdare Urban District Council.[25] He was first elected as a local councillor in 1894. He participated in the work of the council's sub-committees. Notably, in April 1905, a council motion acknowledged his 'valuable' service at the end of his one and only period of office as chairman.[26]

In May 1905, his fellow councillors elected him chairman of the Council's Parliamentary Committee. This authorised him to attend the House of Lords, 'if deemed advisable', to lobby about an Amended Bill which stood to affect the Council.[27] This was

A record of the first meeting of the Aberdare Urban District Council in 1895. Edmund Mills Hann stands centre front of the doorway. R. H. Rhys, seated centre, was the council's Chairman.
Courtesy of Rhondda Cynon Taf Libraries

possibly the nearest that Edmund Hann ever came to imitating Sir George Elliot's parliamentary career.

However, an effect of his company, South Wales Institute of Engineers', and civic commitments, was that he became overstretched. He admitted, years later, that Powell Duffryn implemented organisational changes around 1906 to 'relieve' himself 'from the growing strain and overwork produced by the increase of the business from about 750,000 tons per annum in 1879', to attain '3,552,431 tons' in 1909.[28] In addition to being the general manager of collieries, he 'occupied the responsible position of Agent' for the company, 'the like of which', he thought, had 'never been attempted by anyone else'. Around 1906, he eased his workload through delegation. An action of his was to make Nehemiah Phillips the company's Agent for the Rhymney Valley Collieries.

Nehemiah Phillips

Edmund Mills Hann described Nehemiah Phillips as being 'a most capable and energetic official'.[29] He had spent an early period of his mining career as a Mountain Ash colliery manager. After serving as manager of New Tredegar Colliery, he became the manager of Elliot Colliery in 1896. Nehemiah Phillips then resided at Bryn Syfi [Strawberry Hill] House, New Tredegar.[30] Bryn Syfi House was a large home, and stood close to, but isolated from, Elliot Town, by a high boundary wall and screened by a thicket of trees and bushes. The house's driveway gates faced on to the crown of ground marking the highest elevation of Elliot Town. He became the self-appointed squire of the surrounding community, and so, in some local people's judgment, its absolute ruler. His only rival as a self-appointed squire was Dr T. E. Rhys Davies, the local general practitioner, who lived as his neighbour in a large house, 'Caeglas', which was later renamed 'Brooklands'.

The Phillips's grip on the community had a nepotistic dimension. His brother and his brother's wife held the posts of headmaster and headmistress of Elliot Town School.

However, according to Hilda Evans, Nehemiah Phillips 'ruled' in a gracious way. 'Nothing departing from the ordinary was organised in the village [of New Tredegar and district]' without his approval. She recollected that 'anything likely to corrupt the morals of the people' was not permitted. An 'ardent Baptist', he was a member of Saron Welsh Baptist Church. He performed Sunday School teacher duties at the church. Most of the men worshipping at Saron Welsh Baptist Church worked for Powell Duffryn and their faces at least became known to Nehemiah Phillips.

Considerable deference was shown to him in public. It was said that when the Powell Duffryn manager walked down a street of the town, pedestrians left the pavement to give him clear passage. Such courtesy was enacted as an obligation due to some fear.

Yet, he appears to have garnered genuine respect for himself in New Tredegar. He was elected as a County councillor, and later became an alderman. In 1913, a community subscription paid an artist to paint his portrait. The painting's caption acknowledges his: 'valuable service' concerning civic duties, his 'labours for a period of 27 years and of his interest in and support of all ethical, philanthropic, and educational work'. An estate of terraced housing, built to the north of his residence, became known as Phillipstown. As the company's agent for the Rhymney Valley he became the manager of all its collieries in the valley in 1906: New Tredegar, Elliot and Bargoed, so making him a very important

Nehemiah Phillips. Company's Agent for Bargoed, Elliot, New Tredegar Collieries for the years 1906-1918. Had previously served as colliery manager at both New Tredegar and Elliot Collieries.
Photograph of painting courtesy of Brian Griffiths

person in the Rhymney Valley. Powell Duffryn was planning an additional colliery for the valley, and Edmund Mills Hann delegated responsibility for its founding to his son, George Hann.[31]

Penallta Colliery

At the start of the first decade of the 1900s Edmund Mills Hann contemplated establishing 'Penalltau' [head of the hill; or cliff; or wood] colliery. In 1902, Powell Duffryn leased about 5,000 acres of mining property immediately south of Bargoed, at Penallta and Pengam, which was twice the area leased for Bargoed Colliery. The action was, he wrote, due to 'prudence' by the company's directors in 'view of the approaching exhaustion of the best seams at Aberdare and New Tredegar Pits'.[32] The preceding statement probably belittles the scale of his influence upon the action taken by the company. He further noted that the acquisition was 'effected on very fair terms, viz. about 7d. per ton on large coal and 3½ d. per ton on small, with open average clauses and easy payments for wayleaves'. The matter-of-fact way in which he noted the outcome of terms he had negotiated adds to a picture of a man who was modest about his own business acumen.

Sinking work began at 'Penallta', the colliery's eventual name, in late 1906, a mile or so, as the crow flies, east of Thomas Powell's Gelligaer Colliery.[33] Penallta Colliery stood roughly on the 600 foot contour of a small subsidiary valley of the Rhymney Valley. The subsidiary valley was drained by the Nant Cylla [stomach]. Water drawn from the brook's springs, to the north, might once have quenched the thirst of Roman military engineers as they built a fort at Gelligaer. The Nant Cylla became a tributary of the Rhymney River just south of today's town of Ystrad Mynach at the 325ft contour.

Illustrating Mr. George G. Hann's Paper on
'The Sinking and Equipping of Penallta Colliery.'

A plan of Penallta Colliery's surface arrangements at its founding.

Penallta Colliery. Sinking of this Rhymney Valley colliery began in October 1906. The colliery's two shafts were the deepest sunk by the company. The photograph was taken during the construction of the colliery's surface facilities. In 1932, the colliery's manpower was 3,208. The colliery's winding house was a British colliery first: two winding engines housed under one roof. *Pope/Parkhouse Archive*
Inset: A Penallta Colliery token. *Courtesy of Lyndon Rees*

In July 1910, George Hann wrote a paper about 'the sinking and equipping of Penallta' for the South Wales Institute of Engineers. This paper and the ensuing discussions was used to write the following account about the founding of the colliery.[34]

Reconnaissance work in the Nant Cylla valley included a trial pit 'put down to find the solid rock' that proved the 'Mynyddislwyn' seam. Although finding the Mynyddislwyn seam bolstered George Hann's hopes regarding what coal seams lay at a greater depth, the area's geology also gave him a quandary. The colliery's site lay an 'estimated 400 yards to the south of the main synclinal which traverses the South Wales Coalfield'. He admitted that it would have been 'preferable to have placed the shafts in the bottom of the basin, but this was not attainable without sinking on properties of small area'.

The layout of the colliery accommodated site factors, and featured innovation. The engine house, placed to avoid old mine workings, captured attention since it was 300 feet long by 70 feet wide, and accommodated: two winding engines, the fan motor, two 750 kw electrical generators, and an air compressor of 4,000ft^3 of free air per minute. The engine house became the first two shaft colliery in the British coal industry to house its winding equipment under one roof. The Yorkshire Main Colliery, which began production in 1911 near Doncaster, and owned by Staveley Coal Company Ltd, appears to have been the first English colliery to use such a design of winding house. At Penallta, the engine house was sized not only to accommodate the equipment detailed above, but 'considerable floor space' was provided 'for future developments'. Down-to-earth engineering saw Pennant sandstone removed from the shafts during sinking used as the main construction material

for colliery buildings. One of the engine house's generators was powered by a Yates & Thom Corliss steam engine removed from the company's Aberdare Collieries Power station where it had become a redundant piece of equipment. In general, though, the engineering of Penallta Colliery was not stinted due to meanness.

As at Bargoed Colliery, steam pipe run minimisation was an aim of Penallta Colliery's design. Eight Babcock & Wilcox boilers, each of 3,080ft^2 heating surface with a working pressure of 160 psi, were erected, and adjoined the engine house's north facing wall. T. Sugden noted that Penallta's boilers were 'a large installation', and supported the 'plan to adopt … larger units of boilers', which would be the case in the future he forecasted. He reckoned that Lancashire boilers could be made to raise such quantities of steam, but judged that they would prove too difficult to transport by rail. He mentioned an instance of a Lancashire boiler being stuck in a tunnel during transit.

Electrical engineering at Penallta featured 3-phase current, 50 Hz, and 3,000 V, with the voltage transformed down to 500 V for all motors of less than 50 hp. Yet, by 1908, some South Wales colliery engineers probably had higher expectations for the use of electricity at a new Powell Duffryn colliery: electric winding of coal.

Steam versus Electric Winding

Powell Duffryn considered using electric winding at Penallta Colliery. In 1905, or just earlier, Hugh Bramwell made a notable technical decision for the Great Western Colliery Company. He chose electric winding of coal for a re-equipped Maritime Pit, located south-west of Pontypridd.[35] The company contracted Gerald Hooghwinkel, a consultant electrical engineer, to design

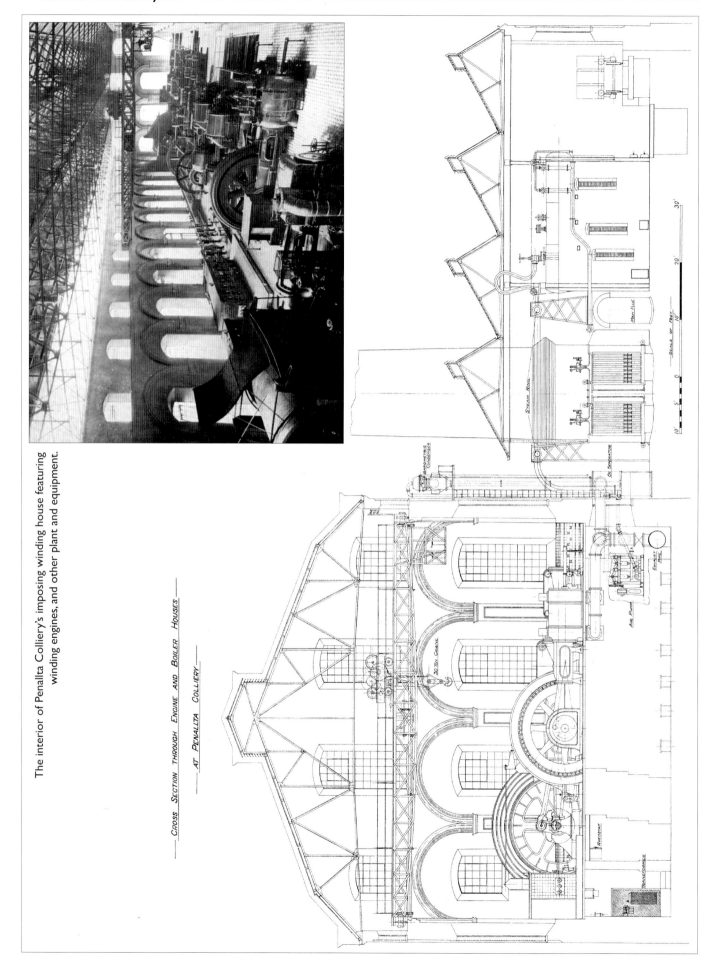

The interior of Penallta Colliery's imposing winding house featuring winding engines, and other plant and equipment.

CROSS SECTION THROUGH ENGINE AND BOILER HOUSES

AT PENALLTA COLLIERY

Penallta Colliery power station.

and manage the associated work. The Maritime Pit electric winder was put into operation in 1908.[36] Hooghwinkel then confidently reflected that he was responsible for the first electric winder 'of moderate capacity at work in South Wales, and for that matter in England'.[37] A Westinghouse system was used at Maritime Pit and enabled a three-phase motor to be run direct from a local mains electricity supply.[38] The depth of wind was 1,110ft and this was considered to be a 'shallow depth'.

In 1906, Powell Duffryn invited tenders from 'some of the largest electrical and steam engineering firms'. This enabled George Hann to make a cost comparison between steam and electric winding. He concluded that for Penallta Colliery 'the electric winding engine could not compete with the steam, either in capital cost, or in economy of running'. George Hann submitted that the 'capital cost of the electric winder, with the further cost of providing electric generators, amounted to nearly three times the cost of a four-cylinder compound Corliss winding engine, while the steam consumption guaranteed by the makers was slightly in favour of the latter engine when working in conjunction with an exhaust turbine'.[39]

Edmund Mills Hann mentioned this also in 1906 regarding the thought he had given to such a choice for Penallta. He wrote: 'The differences between the best figures that were given to him by those who respectively made steam-engines and electric engines was so small, that it would be impossible to pay interest upon the extra capital expenditure involved in putting down electric winding'.[40] This was written in the year when his advocacy of compound steam winding engines reached beyond the South Wales Coalfield to gain the attention of other British colliery engineers.

In a prelude to the foregoing comment, Edmund Mills Hann acknowledged that it was a response 'to seeing whether the great improvements which were going on in electric winding would be an inducement to change' from the plan to use at Penallta an 'ordinary steam-winder'. In sharing the conclusion derived from their cost comparison reckonings, the Hanns appeared confident about rejecting electric winding. Yet, this decision might still have caused some members of the Institute to wonder: why had Powell Duffryn not taken a revolutionary technical step regarding winding at Penallta?

Penallta Colliery – Fraser & Chalmers' twin tandem non-condensing steam winding engines powered with steam at 160 pounds per square inch. The photograph was taken in 1954.
The Watkins's Collection. Courtesy of English Heritage

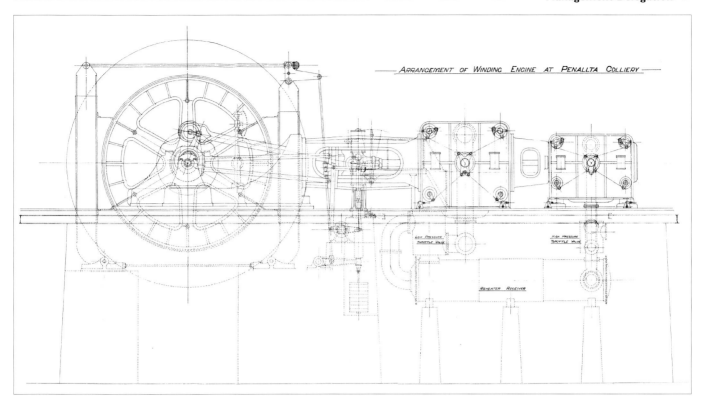

ARRANGEMENT OF WINDING ENGINE AT PENALLTA COLLIERY

The company's enterprise in terms of electrical engineering was apparent to members of the Institute after inspecting its Aberdare Valley collieries' electrical scheme in late 1905. There they had also seen small electric winders in use. B. J. Day's vision, presented earlier, of a steam-less Powell Duffryn colliery, foresaw ambitious innovation by the company. Moreover, if the comparatively smaller Great Western Colliery Company could commit itself to larger scale electric winding, then why not Powell Duffryn?

Powell Duffryn opted instead to inch forward with regard to the application of electric winding. In September 1908, the company sealed a contract with Electric Co. Ltd to install such plant at its Abercwmboi Colliery, located south east of Aberaman.[41] The colliery's No. 1 electric winder was 400 hp, and its No. 2 electric winder was 125 hp.[42] Although this colliery had been acquired to provide pumping and ventilating support to at least Aberaman Colliery, a small amount of coal was raised there from the '2 Feet 9 Inch' seam found, approximately, at 250 yards below ground. Some members of the South Wales Institute of Engineer may have viewed electric winding at Abercwmboi Colliery as only a modest technical step forward by the company.

Powell Duffryn's apparent hesitancy to apply electric winding at a new colliery was highlighted even further by an action taken by Messrs D. Davis & Sons, Ltd at Ferndale Colliery, Rhondda Fach Valley. Installed at Ferndale Colliery, in 1907-1908, was a 4,800 kW 3-phase generating plant that operated a 2000 hp electric winder.[43] The Ferndale Colliery's motors were DC and, for control purposes were coupled to an Ilgner motor generator, and fly-wheel system.[44] The depth of wind was 516 yards, and the duration of a complete wind was 52.91 seconds.[45]

Cross Compound Steam Winding

For Penallta Colliery, Powell Duffryn purchased two steam winding engines from Messr Fraser & Chalmers. This make of engine seems to have been used at the company's Cwmneol

Colliery sometime earlier than at Penallta, but dates that might confirm this were not found. The installation of Penallta's engines proved to be less than straightforward. For the sinking of No. 1 Pit, a cross compound Corliss engine was installed, with cylinder diameters 28-inches and 46-inches by 5ft stroke, having a cast iron cone drum, small diameter 8ft increasing to 12ft in twenty-eight revolutions, and although the design could be deemed to be 'of small dimensions, it was easily able to deal' with its assigned task.

Sometime later the cross compound Corliss engine was substituted with the permanent engine, a double tandem compound operated using Corliss vales. The permanent engine's low-pressure cylinders were 53-inches in diameter and its high-pressure ones were 32-inches diameter with a stroke of 6ft. The No. 1 Pit was the downcast and the main winding shaft. The winding engine substitution caused Arnold Lumpton to query the selection of a double-tandem engine ahead of a cross-compound.

Describing himself as a 'rough colliery man', Lumpton thought that 'putting two cylinders at the back of the other cylinders – an arrangement of plant with eight stuffing boxes – must entail the consumption of a good deal of horsepower in driving the machine empty, and that some arrangement by which two cylinders and two stuffing boxes would certainly reduce what might be called as the friction of the engine'. He then referred to a 'continuous-flow steam engine' devised by a German professor [Stumpf], which he thought was a way of 'enabling us to get that expansive use of high-pressure steam without having to use two cylinders'. Even as electric winding pressed for recognition, steam engine innovation remained in progress.

J. W. Price, of Rhymney, commented upon Lumpton's thoughts. He observed that the Stumpf engine appeared to 'require development in connection with valve gear and steam distribution to make it suitable for winding purpose'. George Hann registered surprise about Lumpton's view since the 'reason for adopting a four cylinder' was 'to keep the cylinders to moderate dimensions'.

He predicted that if a cross compound engine had been used 'the low-pressure cylinder would have been 74-inches in diameter'.

Arnold Lumpton was also intrigued by 'the highly inclined drum'. George Hann told him that the drum had been used with the sinking engine of No. 1 Pit to 'balance the weight of the rope as the shaft became deeper'. The drum permanently installed was of the modified conical type, 15ft small diameter, rising to 16ft in eight coils, five of which were working coils. The diameter then increased to 24ft in five revolutions, with the remainder of the drum's revolutions being made on that diameter.[46]

The associated winding operation was designed to raise a load of six tons from a depth of 800 yards in 45 seconds. The usual winding time though was expected to be 50 seconds. So it was faster than the Ferndale Colliery's electric winding engine that hoisted cages from a lesser depth. In January 1911, George Hann told a meeting of the South Wales Institute of Engineers that: 'In the upcast at Penallta the tachograph on the winding engine recorded a maximum speed of 83 feet per second, equal to 56 miles per hour'. He added, for comparison, that a winding speed of 76ft per second had been measured by a tachograph at Bargoed Colliery.[47]

Penallta's No. 2 Pit winding engine was a cross compound. The engine drove a parallel drum, and was installed prior to sinking work ready for opening out the workings prior to the availability of No. 1's permanent engine, a double tandem compound. The design of the No. 2 Pit winding engine allowed it to be converted later into a four-cylinder engine to function like the permanent No. 1 engine. The No. 2 Pit winding engine was capable of winding two trams at a time from 750 yards in 45 seconds, and dealing with an output of 180 tons per hour. So, for a 9 hour day, it was expected

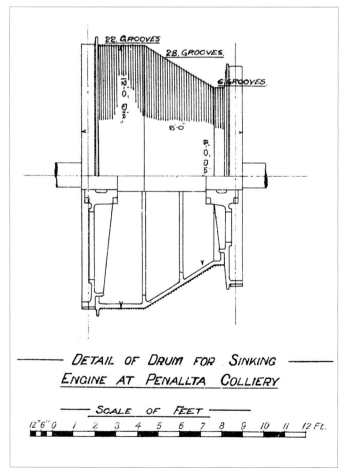

——— DETAIL OF DRUM FOR SINKING ———
ENGINE AT PENALLTA COLLIERY

——— SCALE OF FEET ———

to raise 1,620 tons compared with Ferndale Collieries' expectation of 1,800 tons. Throttle valves were assembled on the high and low-pressure cylinders of No. 1 and No. 2 engines in 'order to obtain a starting torque equal to a pair of engines without the admission of live-steam into the low-pressure cylinders'. George Hann, in 1910, reported that they became economical, and easy to handle as permanent engines.

The vocal Arnold Lumpton raised a concern about noise in Penallta's winding house, due to its range of machinery. He thought that although the engine men would each be screened within an iron shelter, he feared that they would be distracted by noise. J. W. Price, who had first hand knowledge of the conditions proposed that 'too much had been made of the supposed distracting noises'. His remark might have had a double meaning.

George Hann was party to a decision to sink the colliery's two shafts, both 21ft in diameter, 70 yards apart. On the surface the shafts lay on a line which was 'supposed to be nearly on the level course line, namely, east to west'. He explained that the distance between the shafts was the result of resolving 'the opposing requirements, of making convenient arrangement at the pit bottoms and of reducing the distances to avoid long connecting headings for ventilation and for dealing with the water during the sinking'. The ventilation aspect of the colliery's design did not appeal to an important person.

'Sirocco' Ventilation

His Majesty's Inspector of Mines, W. H. Pickering, thought that the positioning of the ventilating fan at Penallta Colliery was 'rather peculiar'. The distance between the two shafts 'appeared' to him 'to be rather excessive', and enquired if 'Mr Hann had made such arrangements underground so that in the event of an accident in one shaft the other could be used to draw coal'. However, he conceded that there were certain advantages in placing the fan between the shafts if the system was designed so that 'the ventilation could be reversed at a minute's notice'. A variant of such a ventilation system, he advised, was a feature of Shamrock Colliery, Westphalia, where the ventilation could be reversed.

George Hann informed W. H. Pickering that the pit bottom's arrangements enabled coal to be diverted to either pit as required. Moreover, for the operation of Penallta Colliery it had not been considered necessary to reverse the ventilation. However, he observed that if 'it is desired to reverse the ventilation it appears to be a better plan to use the fan for forcing the air into the mine, instead of exhausting'. The company also had plans that enabled the fan to provide air into the colliery 'sufficient for rescue work'.[48]

The ventilating fan installed at Penallta was a "Sirocco", designed and made by Messrs Davidson & Co., Ltd, Belfast. In late 1904, Stevens described the Sirocco as being 'conspicuous' due to its 'shape, size, and number of blades'.[49] He also mentioned an interesting application for the fan. Since 1901, one had been used to extract 75,000ft³ per minute of foul air from the Law Courts, London.[50] So, due to technical development, the pursuit of justice and coal mining had least one thing in common.

In early 1905, Edmund Mills Hann chaired a South Wales Institute of Engineer's discussion about the Sirocco design. The example given of a Sirocco in use was Pelton Colliery, in the Durham Coalfield, which might have been the first of its kind installed at a British colliery. Pelton Colliery's fan was 75-inch in diameter, and a test measured its air discharge performance as

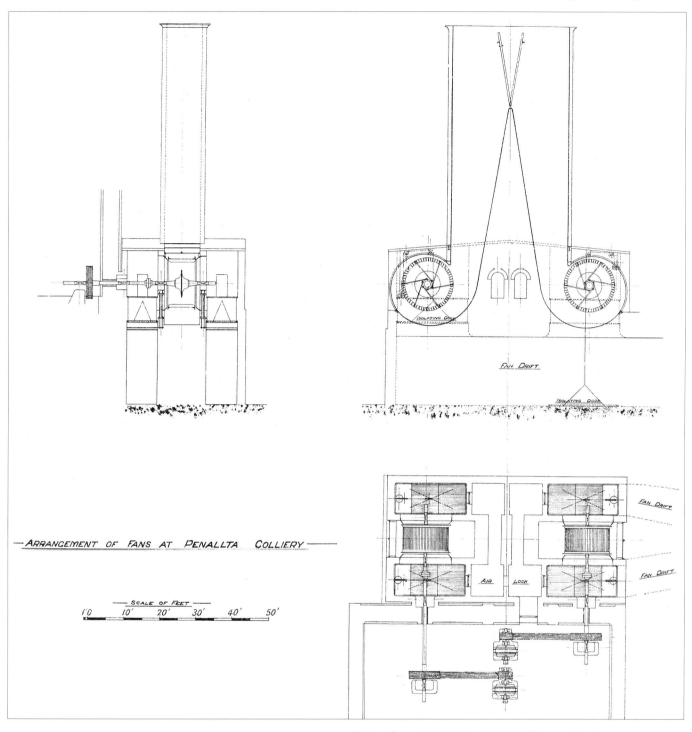

ARRANGEMENT OF FANS AT PENALLTA COLLIERY

SCALE OF FEET
1'0   10'   20'   30'   40'   50'

A Sirocco design of ventilating fan was installed at Penallta Colliery.
Proceedings, *SWIE*, vol.XXIV, (1904-06)

being from 221,000 to 226,000ft³ per minute at water gauge pressure of 2¹/₂ inch.

Mr MacGuire, who appeared to represent Sirocco, claimed that 'the Sirocco fan was the youngest of all the ventilating fans, but while an infant in years, it was rapidly developing in to a veritable giant'. Penallta's Sirocco fan was possibly the second application of the fan in the South Wales Coalfield. Powell Duffryn must have been impressed by what they heard from MacGuire. Shortly afterwards the company purchased a giant Sirocco fan for Penallta Colliery with a 154-inch diameter multiblade runner, was 9ft wide, and running at 200 r.p.m. was capable of exhausting 500,000ft³ of air per minute. Hugh Bramwell, of Great Western Colliery Company, also paid due notice, and one Sirocco at least was installed, at Hetty pit, Great Western Colliery, and it currently survives.

Section of Strata
as sunk through
by the
No I SHAFT

A section through Penallta Colliery's Number I Shaft. The shaft's depth, 783 yards, was the deepest ever sunk by Powell Duffryn.

SWIE Proceedings Vol. XXVII (1910)

Deep Shafts

The sinking of the shafts at Penallta was notable for a number of reasons. First, George Hann advised that the company had been determined, 'as far as possible', to avoid using temporary engines and structures in order that 'with the completion of the work', the winding of coal could proceed with 'but little delay'. So the 'permanent steel head frames were erected at once'.

William Benjamin Lloyd was the sinking contractor.[51] After completing the work, he was entitled to boast about a number of achievements. His sinkers began No. 1 shaft in October 1906 and, two years and eleven months later, in September 1909, they halted work at 783 yards depth. This set a record for the depth of a Powell Duffryn colliery. Llechog, a top found on Wales's highest mountain, Snowdon, rises approximately to the same height above sea level.[52] Lloyd began No. 2 shaft on 10th June, 1907, and work occupied seventeen sinkers for two years and four months until a depth of 750 yards was achieved. The sinking of Penallta found seams of steam coal for Powell Duffryn, which raised hopes that the colliery would earn a profitable return on the capital invested in its engineering.[53]

According to W. Stewart, the sinking of the colliery was 'probably one of the most successful sinkings in modern times'. 'The time occupied over the sinking, for such a depth, was … less than any instance which he could recall'. George Hann noted that during the sinking of No. 2 shaft the greatest distance sunk and walled in a fortnight was 22 yards. He further mentioned that at the start of sinking No. 1 shaft, 'the old method of hammer and drill' was used, but a fortnight later, a hammer drill supplied by Flottman Engineering Company was introduced instead. Although the cost of 'upkeep of the machines and drill steel' was 'considerable', the 'cost of sinking' was 'largely reduced owing to the greater speed

attained and the greater amount of ground removed per man; also the drills' did not 'require such highly skilled labour'.

The sinking work encountered feeders of water. So, George Hann discovered that sinking was an adventure, and he muddled through to success like his predecessors had done in the past. With regard to the engineering of the shaft, he caused a debate.

The use of fixed rail cage guides at Bargoed Colliery was adopted at Penallta Colliery. The details of his father's views on this topic given to the Institution of Mechanical Engineer raised no controversy. Arnold Lumpton pointed out that, for the mining engineer, making a choice between rail guides or wire ropes was a 'burning question'. He added: 'There were two schools of thought. He remembered that South Wales used to be the most prominent advocate of the rail-guide system, and there were gentlemen present who could tell them better than he – who only made casual visits to South Wales – which had now the majority on its side there. In South Yorkshire there seemed to be a division of opinion, but he thought the rope guide had the majority on its side in that neighbourhood'.

W. Stewart agreed that the 'rail versus rope guides was a vexed question', and that 'South Wales was very much divided in opinion'. He thought, though, that there 'was something to be said' for each method. The use of rail guides had been successful 'in deep shafts where' it was 'necessary to raise great loads at high speed'. The prevailing objections to rope guides were not detailed, but he claimed that they could be overcome by the introduction of a balance rope. George Hann's stance was unequivocal: 'it was safer to run rail guides in a deep shaft'.[54] He cited the associated speeds attained by cages due to guide rail use, and the experience of a cage's ride in support of his stance.

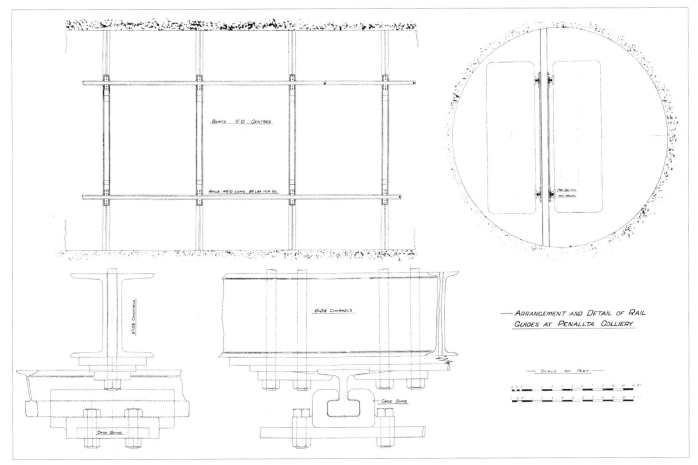

ARRANGEMENT AND DETAIL OF RAIL GUIDES AT PENALLTA COLLIERY

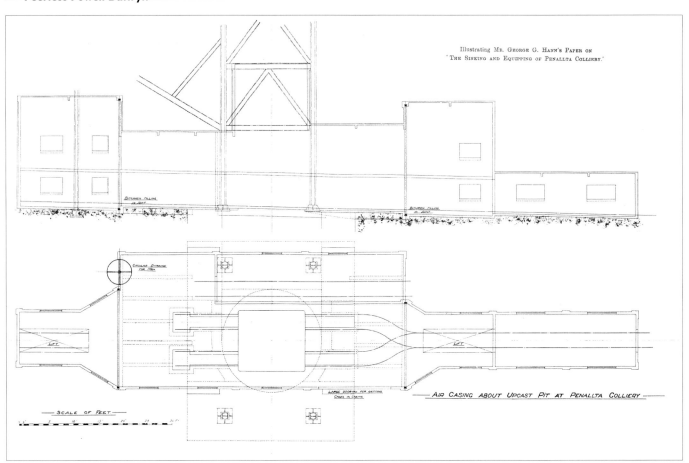

Illustrating Mr. George G. Hann's Paper on
'The Sinking and Equipping of Penallta Colliery.'

AIR CASING ABOUT UPCAST PIT AT PENALLTA COLLIERY

SCALE OF FEET

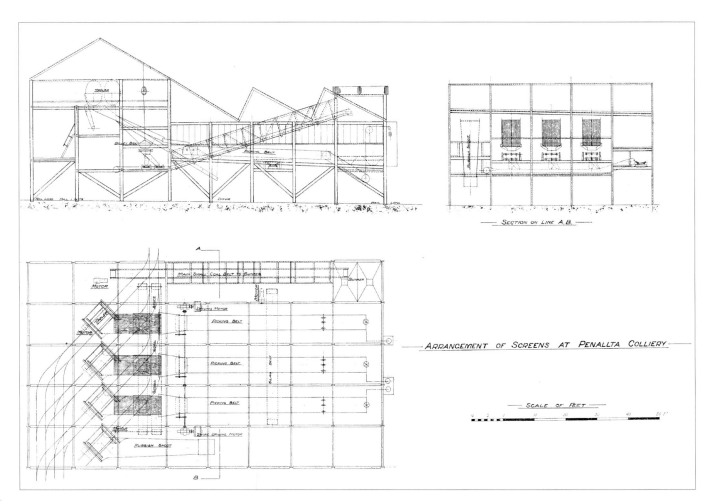

SECTION ON LINE A.B.

ARRANGEMENT OF SCREENS AT PENALLTA COLLIERY

SCALE OF FEET

4595. Penallta Colliery & Washery, Ystrad Mynach.
Ernest T. Bush.

Penallta Colliery sometime after the First World War. The Baum washery is shown on the right of picture. The foreground features, as a network of rails, a spur of the Cylla branch of the Rhymney Railway.
Pope/Parkhouse Archive

Although the matter of using guide rails prompted an argument during the South Wales Institute of Engineers' discussion about Penallta, the subject was minor one for valuing the engineering of the colliery. Yet, the discussion about guide rails aroused speculation about Powell Duffryn's next planned colliery investment in the Rhymney Valley, at Pengam, in Monmouthshire, which would be called Britannia Colliery. George Hann let it be known that the 'question of guides will again arise in connection with the sinking at Pengam'.

Aberaman Rescue Station

The year 1909 saw a notable pioneering action of the company's: a colliery rescue service opened at Aberaman. In January 1908, Gasgoyne Dalziel advised that the Monmouthshire & South Wales Coalowners' Association had been 'impressed with the recommendations' of a Royal Commission, and so had appointed a committee to enquire into mines rescue, and Edmund Mills Hann had been elected as its chairman.[55] The committee consisted of twenty-one mining engineers who set up a sub-committee to survey the rescue services deployed elsewhere in the British coal industry. The committee recommended to the coalowners that central rescue stations should be set up to serve 'some thirteen geographical areas' of the South Wales Coalfield. Edmund Mills Hann was tasked with assessing mining rescue apparatus. Dalziel observed that 'in the hands of Mr Hann's committee' that 'the interests of both employers and employed with regard to practical measures of exploration and rescue would be perfectly safe'.

A year later, Powell Duffryn, supported by other Aberdare Valley based colliery companies, Nixon's, Cwmaman Coal, and the Bwllfa Colliery, opened the first colliery rescue station in the South Wales Coalfield. The building's architect was Messrs Tether & Wilson of Cardiff. The rescue station was sited not far from Powell Duffryn's offices at Aberaman.

The station's opening occurred on 23rd January, 1909, with Edmund Mills Hann delivering an address.[56] The ceremony's guests included leading figures of the South Wales Coalfield, and local doctors such as Finney and Asbury.[57] The guests heard Hann say that he 'hoped that the result would be the establishment of similar installations in other parts [of the South Wales Coalfield]'. The cost of the building was declared at around £1,450 with additional expenses incurred for fixtures and other requirements.

Guests at the opening further witnessed a briefing, due to Hann, about three makes of breathing apparatus for rescuers chosen for evaluation at the Aberaman Rescue Station. Breathing apparatus gave a colliery rescuer the means to work in an underground atmosphere that contained 'foul gases'. Mr Garforth described how his invention, the Weg apparatus, operated, and mentioned that it had been used in recent rescue work at Hamstead Colliery [in the South Staffordshire Coalfield]. He was also the managing director of its maker, Messrs Pope and Pearson, West Riding Collieries, Normanton, Yorkshire. However, another report noted that British Rescue Apparatus Co., of Leeds made the Weg apparatus.[58] Nonetheless, the Weg apparatus comprised a headpiece that enclosed the mouth and nose, but it had the facility to allow the

Aberaman Rescue Station team. The rescue station was opened in 1909. The South Wales Coalfield's first rescue station. Powell Duffryn combined with Nixon's, Cwmaman and Bwllfa Coal Companies to establish this rescue service.   *Courtesy of Rhondda Cynon Taf Libraries*

user to 'breath just as freely with it as without it'. The apparatus also had a dual valving system to prevent a person sucking in exhaled breath. The air circulated for the user to breathe was purified by caustic soda, contained in a tin, which absorbed 'carbonic acid gas'. The Weg apparatus weighed about 35 pounds, and unlike the other types being evaluated, its oxygen supply was provided intermittently in harmony with a user's breathing rate.

Draeger was the second type of breathing apparatus chosen for trial. The Draeger type could be worn either with a mouthpiece, or a 'smoke helmet'. A Draeger engineer, Richard Jacobson, explained that the apparatus's oxygen supply lasted for two hours, and was capable of meeting the maximum demand of its user when performing hard work. Potash cartridges were installed to purify the circulating air. This apparatus had been purchased by a number of rescue stations in the English coalfields.

The final apparatus chosen for evaluation at Aberaman Rescue Station was an invention by Henry Albert Fluess. The key feature of Fluess's invention was the storage of oxygen as a compressed gas in steel cylinders, which was coupled to a gauge, via a flexible metallic tube, that measured the amount of oxygen available. He claimed that the apparatus was very light and simple to use, and circulating air was purified using caustic soda. The inventor did not mention any record of its application. Both the Fluess and the Draeger apparatuses were supplied from Germany. Edmund Mills Hann's search for the best equipment had again taken into account what European suppliers could offer.

The crucial facility at Aberaman rescue station was a gallery built as a mock-up of 'a Colliery after an explosion'. The gallery was fed with noxious fumes supplied from a special plant. A simulated rescue saw a 'dummy' man used so that breathing apparatus wearing 'workmen' could 'learn the best way to convey a person through the gallery'. Following Hann's opening address, and the words of Messrs Garforth, Jacobson, and Fluess, a 'body of men, dressed as if engaged in rescue work after a colliery catastrophe', enacted a rescue.

Henry Morris was the station's superintendent and trainer.[59] His rescue training had taken place at the collieries of Messrs Pope, Pearson & Co., Normanton. Three proficient rescuers of Messrs Pope, Pearson & Company had been drafted into help Morris train men at Aberaman. His training plan envisaged the recruitment of four or five men, 'consisting of officials and intelligent workmen' drawn from each of the 'respective [Aberdare Valley] pits in rotation'. They would be 'drilled' until they were 'thoroughly familiar with the intricacies of the various apparatuses. The target after training was a 'corps of at least 50 persons' who would be 'efficiently equipped with the knowledge of the various gases in mines, and the means of penetrating through these gases in cases of explosion'. Rescue training was expected to accomplish in 'a few hours' what had previously taken 'two to three weeks'.

So, due to Edmund Mills Hann's leadership, a humanitarian service was established by Powell Duffryn and other Aberdare colliery companies for their rivals in the South Wales Coalfield to copy. Henry W. Martin, of the Dowlais Iron Company, thanked Hann for allowing those present to 'witness the opening of the first rescue station in the South Wales Coalfield'. He paid 'high tribute to [Hann]' for the 'invaluable service' that he had 'rendered to the coalowners through the initiative', and that much could be learnt from it 'in the event' of other coalowners 'deciding to follow Mr Hann's great example'.

With candour, Edmund Mills Hann later admitted that colliery rescue would not have come about without the insistence of the Home Secretary, who between December, 1905, and February, 1908, was Herbert Gladstone. According to Hann, 'a strong circular was issued in 1907, and intimation made that if the Colliery owners did not move voluntarily, probably it would be made compulsory'.[60] He was to note afterwards that 'within 10 months' following the opening of Aberaman Rescue Station its staff rendered assistance at Abernant, at Darren, and at Penrikyber Collieries. In 1909, he remarked: 'I cannot say that the results justify the optimism of the Home Secretary, but yet I feel I would be very loath indeed to do away with it, and hope better results will be accomplished if cases of need arise'. The coalowners of the South Wales Coalfield had needed a Government threat to force them to introduce colliery rescue station services. Regardless, the risks to life and limb that a miner faced to physically win coal had not altered. Alternative means for winning coal were also available.

Conveyors and the Iron Collier

During the first decade of the twentieth century Powell Duffryn made limited use of mechanised coal mining underground. In 1906, Edmund Mills Hann decided to introduce coal-cutting machines into Powell Duffryn's Aberdare Valley collieries.[61] Coal-cutting machines worked the Gellideg seam of Lower Duffryn, Lletty Shenkin, and Aberaman; the Graig seam at Abercwmboi; and the Seven Foot seam at Cwmneol.[62] Their introduction was due to 'the exhaustion of the thicker seams, and the success in other Coalfields by the use of coal-hewing machines and face conveyors'.

Just before 1909, conveyors were used to move coal from the coalfaces of: Bargoed's Red Vein Seam, New Tredegar's Yard seam, and Elliot East's new seam.[63] The company appears to have been among the pioneers of conveyor use. Trevor Boyns' observed that between the First and Second World Wars that 'in one respect, that is the introduction of mechanical conveying, south Wales was initially in the forefront of technological advance' in the British coal industry.[64]

Nonetheless, Powell Duffryn, and most of their rivals in the South Wales Coalfield, proved less than eager to use coal-cutting machines. In late 1909, Sam Mavor delivered a paper to the South Wales Institute of Engineers on 'Machine Mining with Special Reference to South Wales'.[65] Mavor was an inventor of a coal-cutting machine that carried his name. At a discussion of the paper, C. W. Jordan made an informative claim: the paper 'was the first paper ever presented to the Institute' with coal-cutting machines as the main subject.[66] He then declared that 'this lack of interest was all the more remarkable seeing that in some respects the colliery managers of South Wales lead the world; and he hoped that Mr Mavor's paper would have the effect of immediately stimulating a desire to introduce coal-cutting machine all over the coalfield'.

The response of the Institute's President, William Wight, revealed a dilemma that might explain why it was taking time for coal-cutting machines to become established in the South Wales Coalfield. The first coal-cutting machine used in the coalfield may have been due to James Barrow at Maesteg, in 1865.[67] Wight's opening remark was: 'The day must come, he was satisfied, when some great and radical change would have to take place in the working of their seams in South Wales'.[68] Then he admitted that 'he came into the category of those who had worked coal-cutters and had given them up, and had recommended using them'.[69]

Throughout the year of 1910 the Institute saw an epic series of discussions about Mavor's paper. He presented for discussion disc, bar, and chain types of coal-cutters. He had a preference for the bar design. The participants in the discussion meetings learnt that coal-cutters were then in use in the collieries of the United States of America, Prussia, and in Britain in Durham, Fife, Lancashire, the Midlands of England, and Yorkshire.

Reports were heard about recent trials of mechanical coal winning trials in the South Wales Coalfield. J. W. Hutchinson introduced coal-cutting machines into the Coedcae pit some six and a half years earlier [thus 1903] than the discussions about Mavor's paper. 'They were still in use', he reported, and mentioned that disc and bar machines had worked along side each other at the Hafod Pit.[70] He had also trialled chain machines. The bar machine, he found, took less power than the disc or chain, was suitable for friable coal, and created less dust. Moreover, disc and chain machines operations had to stop when falling coal blocked their mechanisms. However, he believed 'there was a great future for coal-cutting machines in the South Wales Coalfield but it would be in the thinner and upper seams of coal'. Indeed, Mavor submitted that the 'principal sphere for machine mining', in the South Wales Coalfield, was 'without doubt in seams under 3 feet 6 inches thick'.[71]

However, in general, the discussions revealed that in the South Wales Coalfield the 'Iron Collier' was treated with much scepticism. Doubts were held with regarding to a coal-cutting machines rate of work, and inability to work inclined seams. Engineers also moaned that coal-cutting machines were not durable since they vibrated in use.

'Great opposition from the men' had beset the introduction of coal-cutting machines into Powell Duffryn's collieries.[72] Edmund Mills Hann further claimed that 'an amount of dishonesty [was] practiced by them, which deserves to be strongly characterised as both a crime and a blunder'. Such discord was not a feature of steps taken to introduce hospital care into the Rhymney Valley

Aberbargoed Cottage Hospital

In 1909, due to the shared determination of the men of Bargoed Colliery, and Powell Duffryn, a cottage hospital was opened at Aberbargoed. The company had made an earlier attempt in the Rhymney Valley to set up a hospital. In 1902, a cottage hospital for New Tredegar was mooted.[73] In 1909, Edmund Mills Hann reflected: a 'scheme was formulated for the erection of a hospital and an hotel on site' with 'the object in view' being 'that the profits of the hotel' would 'go to assist the maintenance of the hospital'.[74] But the scheme was 'strenuously opposed by the Monmouthshire County Council and the police', and, apparently also by magistrates. Nevertheless, alert to the suffering experienced by seriously injured miners 'carried by rail to Cardiff Infirmary', the company and their employees at Bargoed Colliery persisted.

The outcome was an agreement that the company paid the capital needed to build Aberbargoed Cottage Hospital while the miners accounted for the operational and maintenance costs. The cost of the building, furniture, and fittings was about £6,000.[75] Just before the opening of the hospital, the miners had saved a balance of £589 6s. 8d., and this was deemed to be sufficient for starting the hospital 'under very good auspices'.[76]

'The weather was inclement and heavy rain fell' on the 10th December, 1909, the day of the hospital's opening. Maybe the weather denied guests at the opening a chance to admire that

Aberbargoed Cottage Hospital was opened in 1909 by Viscount Tredegar. The company provided the funding for its building and equipment, and the colliery workers paid for its running costs.
Courtesy of Old Bakehouse Publications

Inset: 'Charity healing the sick' by T. A. Jones

the building, built upon high ground, did not deter 'sun from playing upon its walls'.[77] Furthermore, the guests might not have appreciated the outlook from the hospital's 'principal rooms, wards, and verandah', which gave 'an extensive pleasant view of the Rhymney Valley in the southerly direction'. And not wanting to linger in the rain, the guests only glanced to see 'above the main entrance archway ... a carved Portland stone panel of Charity healing the sick' by a 'well-known Welsh sculptor', T. A. Jones.[78] Viscount Tredegar and Joseph Shaw performed the opening ceremony, and a modest brass plaque, situated on a wall of the entry passageway into the hospital, acted as a record of the event.[79] Guests, after the ceremony, removed to the nearby Workmen's Institute to hear speeches. Joseph Shaw's 'graceful speech' included a disclosure that 'he had always had a keen interest in cottage hospital work'. '*Nothing, indeed, was more of a necessity in mining villages than a cottage hospital*' since '*it was desirable to get a place where operations could be conducted and proper care given to the injured nearer home*'.[80] The year marked his twelfth year of office as Powell Duffryn's chairman, and the hospital became the first that the company had played a part in founding. Shaw also paid tribute for the 'excellent work' of the hospital's architect, Bargoed's George Kenshole.

Some observations of Lord Tredegar's, in his address, gave clues to social and welfare matters of the period.[81] 'He knew that for some time the question of cottage hospitals had been rather in the nature of a doubtful experiment'. The 'want of finance' seemed to him to be the root of such opposition. Indeed, he also recognised that the 'same objection was raised against public libraries'. He saluted the medical profession, 'the finest in the world'. There was 'none equal to them in point of generosity and self-sacrifice'. Although he wondered if the 'doctors had anything [money] at all' since 'some nine out of ten letters' he received 'contained an excuse that the doctor's bill had to be met' possibly ahead of the

Tredegar Estate receiving its debt. His speech closed to applause no doubt due in part to his certainty that the hospital 'would be of the greatest benefit to the district'.

Powell Duffryn's role in founding Aberbargoed Cottage Hospital drew praise from Walter Lewis, the miners' agent. 'Although at times they as workmen had conflicts with the company, he was glad to find them there that day in the common interest of the people'.[82] Joseph Shaw responded to Walter Lewis's remark by saying that '*in spite of the industrial conflicts and squabbles, the company always joined in the work of endeavouring to minimise suffering*', and with a mention of a 'recent disaster ... in the valley close by made them realise that they belonged to a common stock'.[83]

According to a later reflection by Edmund Mills Hann, the Rhymney Valley men had begun to subscribe to a fund aimed at establishing 'a very fine hospital' in 1908.[84] Aberbargoed Hospital fulfilled such an ambition, and featured two large wards that, in total, accommodated fourteen beds. The hospital's ground floor comprised a surgeon's room, with a receiving room adjoining, entered from a vestibule, an operating room, a matron's room, a nurses' room, and a staff dining room, complete with kitchen, and offices. Featured in the hospital's basement were a large ambulance room, X-ray facilities and a heating chamber. Moreover, on the upper-side of the hospital's site there was a laundry, mortuary, and post-mortem rooms.[85] The building was centrally heated using a low-pressure hot water system, naturally ventilated, and lit by electricity taken from the company's mains. The builder employed had been John Lloyd, of Ystrad Mynach, and his workers had finished the exterior walls of the hospital 'above the ground floor level with rough cast white wash', which, it was claimed, made the 'building a landmark for miles around'.[86]

Powell Duffryn acted benevolently. The associated leases and assignments initially held by the company were handed over to trustees. The trustees comprised: Messrs Reuben Gould and A. Lawrence, representing the workmen, and C. E. Foreister Walker and the Rev. T. Jesse Jones, Rector of Gelligaer. In effect, the company had delegated the responsibility for running the hospital to colliery workmen.

The opening of both the Aberbargoed Cottage Hospital, and Aberaman Rescue Station, occurred at a time when the company's business performance was excellent.[87] The year 1909 saw company coal output at 3,552,431 tons.

Concerning the Aberdare Valley colliery operation, the Board of Directors supported Edmund Mills Hann's proposal to buy Ysguborwen Colliery from John Howard Thomas for £3,000, which occurred on 1st November, 1909.[88] Although an old operation with 'a probability of further profitable working', for around three years, the colliery's importance lay in that it had a drainage level to the Afon Cynon. The level was used to carry underground water so safeguarding other company workings from flooding. An event of greater significance for the community around Aberaman occurred in October 1910.

A Cwmaman Cottage Hospital Proposal

Edmund Mills Hann met a delegation of men who tested Powell Duffryn's support for an idea of theirs: to build a cottage hospital at Cwmaman.[89] The idea's origin has been dated to late 1906 when a meeting of friends took place at Cwmaman Public Institute 'for the purpose of organising an Eisteddfod'. Such a festival, or session of music, and poetry, was viewed as being capable of 'brightening up the drab existence of the inhabitants'. The group of friends' first aim was to raise funds to establish the eisteddfod as an annual event. A few months before the first eisteddfod, a spate of serious accidents occurred at local collieries.

There existed in the Aberdare district only a small cottage hospital, maintained by the Marquis of Bute, and the 'conditions and the inadequacy of provisions at the workmen's homes for the proper care and treatment of accidents … distressed' two members of the Cwmaman group. They were 'determined' to improve matters, and proposed to the group that proceeds from the eisteddfod be used to found a cottage hospital in their village, which was 'willingly agreed'. The first eisteddfod occurred on Whit Tuesday, 1907.

By Whit Tuesday, 1910, £600 had been raised, and so the group proceeded to seek support for their idea. A public meeting gave their idea an 'enthusiastic' support, and a committee was formed. Representatives of this committee met Edmund Mills Hann, and also separately, the general manager of the Cwmaman Coal Company, W. J. Heppell.

Powell Duffryn's general manager of collieries was a receptive listener. An earlier attempt of his to establish a hospital in the Aberaman area had failed. He later chronicled that it had been in the 'minds of the Directors for some years to provide something in the way of Hospital accommodation, and with their sanction in 1903 I made an offer to the workmen, that the Company would build a new hospital if the men would maintain it'.[90] A likely model for such a project was Mountain Ash Cottage Hospital, opened in 1896.[91] However, the company's offer 'was not taken up'.

Nevertheless, when, in 1910, the delegation met Edmund Mills Hann it received his 'full sympathy'. Moreover, W. J. Heppell was similarly supportive. Hann suggested that representatives of the committee visit Aberbargoed Cottage Hospital and such an inspection 'confirmed the Committee's views as to the great benefits which could be obtained' for such a facility in the Aberdare Valley.

The project then gathered momentum.[92] 'The committee canvassed the workmen's support with 'a circular letter – explaining the scheme-printed in English and Welsh', asking them to state 'on a form provided' whether they 'favoured a contribution of half-penny per week towards the Hospital's maintenance'. The canvassing occurred on 7th October, 1910, and found that workmen at Powell Duffryn and Cwmaman Collieries were 'prepared to maintain the Hospital'. Edmund Mills Hann and W. J. Heppell next won approval for the project from their respective company's directors. However, almost immediately afterwards, work halted on the project due to local industrial relations troubles. The origin of the troubles appears to have been a dispute between Powell Duffryn's colliery workers and its management.

The Strike of 1910

The emergence of civil unrest in the Rhondda Fawr Valley might have also been an influential factor. This valley lies roughly five miles south of Aberaman, over mountains. Geography played a part in creating independence in the running of local affairs in South Wales Valley districts. Yet, aspects, and consequences, of a dispute at the Rhondda Valley's Cambrian Combine's Ely pit of the Naval Colliery, seemed to affect the behaviour of men working at Powell Duffryn's Aberdare collieries.

In August 1910 a collieries' dispute endemic began that spread through parts of the South Wales Coalfield. Some days after the 1st August, Leonard W. Llewelyn, general manager of the Cambrian Combine, served notice of termination of colliery workers' employment at the Ely Pit. His action was due to a breakdown in months of negotiations about coal cutting prices that affected wages.[93] The issue of notices not only riled Ely Pit's miners, but other Rhondda Fawr miners as well. Without giving warning to their employers, miners withdrew their labour from work at all the Cambrian pits. Later, in September, the Glamorgan and Brittanic Merthyr Colliery also came to a halt due to strike action.[94]

'The more moderate of the miners' leaders' of the South Wales Miner's Federation [SWMF] tried to find a solution to the Ely pit issue. Yet, by the end of September, their efforts failed. The Cambrian Combine rejected their suggestions. Moreover, a split of views appeared within the Federation about whether, or not, to pursue a course of militancy such as a general coalfield strike.[95]

David Evans, who afterwards chronicled the events that follow, claimed that the split was due to 'a severe contest for supremacy' being 'waged between the younger and older leaders' of the miners' trade union. The 'younger leaders were Socialist imbued with Communistic theories concerning the relations of Capital and Labour'.[96] In his opinion, 'hotbeds of discontent were the mid-Rhondda, Aberdare, and Maesteg districts', and implied that this was due to men being motivated by 'extreme socialism'.[97]

In part due to the authority of the union's leadership being subverted, chaos spread beyond the Rhondda. In September, 20,000 men were involved in stoppages at collieries in the Rhondda, Rhymney, and Monmouthshire valleys.[98] The 900 men dismissed from the Ely pit had won support, but latent trouble was unleashed, which was inflamed on the 1st October when 12,000 workmen of the Cambrian Combine's collieries were served notice.

On the 20th October, a strike occurred at Powell Duffryn's Lower Duffryn Colliery without 'a day's notice' and 'without the

During the 1910 strike, Cwmneol Colliery officials with their colleagues at other Aberdare Valley collieries continued to work. The matter of their protection was raised by Edmund Mills Hann at a Cardiff meeting about Government measures to deal with civil unrest in the Rhondda and Aberdare Valleys.

Courtesy of Rhondda Cynon Taf Libraries

knowledge of the [miners'] agent of the district', C. B. Stanton. The strike was apparently provoked by a company notice banning the removal of pit timber for home firewood purposes except with the permission of the company and by making a payment at a very nominal charge.

Edmund Mills Hann, on the 26th October, met a 'large deputation of the men' led by C. B. Stanton, the miners' agent. Hann told the deputation that 'the strike was a violation of the Wages Agreement'. Stanton responded by asserting that since he was no longer a member of the Agreement's governing body, he was not bound by its regulations. Hann advised that the company 'had not yet decided whether or not to take action against the men for breach of contract'. Stanton's riposte was 'that the men would refuse to pay any damages that might be imposed upon them'. Hearing 'defiant declarations', the general manager of collieries asked those present to 'state their grievances'. The meeting ended with no 'arrangement'. Hann travelled to London for an appointment.

On the following day, an 'unfounded' report about coal being wound at Cwmneol Colliery caused a telephone conversation between C. B. Stanton and Edmund Mills Hann. The miners' agent objected to a violation of agreed procedures, that the union's 'checkweighers had not been advised that this activity was planned'. The telephone conversation ended with the agent saying that *'if there is going to be 'blacklegging' over this, there is going to be murder'*, which caused Hann to take a stance: not to meet Stanton

"on this or any other business." The stance 'provoked passion in the district to fever heat'.

Also on the 26th October, in the Rhondda Valley, the men at the Cambrian Combine's Naval Colliery rejected the advice of the Federation's Executive to accept a settlement offer, and went on strike on November 1st, at the Cambrian Combine collieries.[99]

In the Aberdare Valley, the next day, a Great Western Railway workmen's train was 'stormed'. This happened at the Tonllwyd Crossing, Aberaman, on the night of the 2nd November.[100] Then, on the 3rd November, the strike was extended to other collieries in the Aberdare valley, and most of the residences of colliery officials were picketed. Afterwards both Valleys shared a link.

An 'urgent meeting' was arranged in Cardiff between the Coal-owners' Association and the Chief Constable of Glamorgan, Capt. Lindsay, to discuss the protection of company property, and personnel. By the 6th, marshalled were one hundred mounted men ready to reinforce the police force in the Rhondda and Aberdare valleys.[101] Meanwhile, for a number of days after the 4th November, in response to fears among the strikers of the import of labour, 'frenzied and desperate' attacks were made against the Cambrian collieries.[102] Police constables assigned to maintain order in the Rhondda became casualties of fighting with strikers on the night of the 7th November.[103]

Anxiety within the civic authorities caused them to appeal to Government for more police resources. So, assigned to the troubles, were 'small bodies of police', from Bristol, Swansea, and Bridgend, and, a short time afterwards, a large contingent of London's Metropolitan police. The Home Secretary, Winston Churchill, further heard of a worry of the Chief Constable of Glamorgan's, that 'owing to hilly character of the district at and about Glamorgan Colliery he would not be able with police alone to prevent another night attack on the pit'.[104] Churchill did not authorise the despatch of troops to South Wales but on hearing about their march west he stopped them at Swindon. He also instructed the Chief Constable, in a telegram, that the 'infantry should not be used till all other means have failed'.[105]

Such preparations lagged behind events. 'The sack of Tonypandy' began on the 8th November due to strikers, retreating from Glamorgan Colliery, Lywnypia, after a battle with police. The rioters vented their rage on local property that saw extensive damage to buildings, and shops were looted.[106] The event's notoriety with its traumatic effect seems to have deflected interest away from what happened on the same day in the Aberdare Valley.

The first sign of trouble brewing was when '200 or 300 people assembled outside the Aberaman Institute'.[107] Two detachments of Aberdare Valley strikers, with women and children in train, made Powell Duffryn the target for action. Five hundred people gathered to demonstrate outside Aberaman Colliery. Although they were 'kept at bay' by two policemen, the threat to Aberaman Colliery was a diversion.[108] The strikers' main protest occurred at the Middle Duffryn washery and electric power station, key to operating company collieries.

The baying of about one hundred and fifty people was a clarion call for the marshalling of a crowd estimated at between 2,500 and 3,000 people. The crowd confronted twenty-nine policemen guarding the Middle Duffryn facilities. Some miners swarmed the facilities' fences. A storm of hurled stones, and other missiles, fell upon the company's property, and its defenders, the police, made a counter charge. Some of the rioters then fled along the towpath of the canal. A section of the rioters made an overture to the police, so as to seek a peaceful withdrawal, but were caught in a police pincer move.

The *Aberdare Leader* 'stated' that 'about 60 strikers were more or less injured. One person had his hand seriously burnt by contact with live electric wire, while another fractured his leg. The injuries of most of the others consisted of serious wounds to the heads'.[109] All the police were 'either slightly or seriously injured'.[110]

Edmund Mills Hann attended a conference in Cardiff, on the 11th November, regarding the civil disorder.[111] Present also at the conference were: David Alfred Thomas and Leonard Llewelyn of the Cambrian Combine, General Macready (in charge of the military), Capt. Lindsay, Sir Marchant Williams (Aberdare Stipendiary) and Lleufer Thomas (Pontypridd Stipendiary). The coal companies expressed worries about the prospect of a withdrawal of the bulk of the 802 Metropolitan police mustered in south Wales. General Macready told the conference that he would not assign soldiers to guard the homes of any workmen still working at the collieries, and that the troops would become active only 'in the event of the civil police having exhausted all their available resources'. Hann 'protested strongly against their having been called together to consider, not the best means of preserving the peace and the protection of property, but to make the best arrangements with a restricted force given to them'. He would have known that on the previous day that 'the windows of a PD official's house in Regent-

1910 Strike Relief Committee, Aberdare Valley.

Courtesy of Rhondda Cynon Taf Libraries

street were smashed to atoms', and that company officials had taken 'precautionary measures by barricading their windows'.[112] The Cambrian representatives added their protest. General Macready replied by advising them that he was acting 'under the instructions of the Home Secretary', and regardless of their views, he would prepare a scheme for 'holding the valleys and maintaining order during the next three weeks'.

Troubles continued in both Valleys, and 'outrages', as David Evans later termed them, took place in the Aberdare Valley. A Taff Vale passenger train, passing between Mountain Ash and Abercwmboi, was stoned on 17th November.[113] On Sunday, 20th November, a service at Aberaman's Saron Welsh Congregational Chapel was 'broken up owing to the conduct of members who objected to the presence of a member who remained at work'.[114] Serious rioting took place at Aberaman on the night of 22nd November, and this was 'suppressed by baton charges'.[115] Barracked at Aberaman, after the 24th November, was one troop of cavalry of the 18th Hussars, and infantry comprising one company of the Loyal North Lancashire, and a half company of West Ridings.[116] Winston Churchill had agreed to the deployment of soldiers. A striker may have felt that the might of an Imperial Empire stood-by to weaken his resolve. Regardless of these fears, incensed indignation could only be partly doused by a settlement to the dispute that had triggered the local disorder.

C. B. Stanton appealed to the Executive Council of the South Wales Miners' Federation on 7th November for a general conference of the coalfield so that strike pay could be made available from a levy on its membership. The idea of the general conference met opposition within the Federation. However, the Federation raised the 'Aberdare question' on 14th November with the Conciliation Board, a body, it might be inferred, not recognised by Stanton.[117] The Council Executive pressed Powell Duffryn to offer a proposal of terms that would enable colliery operations to

begin. The coalowners of the South Wales Coalfield countered by demanding an apology, from Stanton to Hann, 'for the part he had taken in recent proceedings and undertakes to abide by the Conciliation Board Agreement in future'.

The call for an apology to Edmund Mills Hann was then tabled at a meeting of over 8,000 men at Aberdare's Market Hall, on the 15th November. A resolution was proposed, and 'adopted unanimously', that their agent should express his regret to Hann for his statement made in their telephone conversation of the 27th October. However, the meeting rejected all other suggestions of the Conciliation Board. Moreover, some Aberdare Valley men 'were determined not to allow the letter of the constitution of their Federation to defeat their purposes'. Stanton proceeded to fight 'hard' for 'temporary aid to the Aberdare miners'. Nevertheless, on the 20th November, an exchange of letters of his with Hann included his apology. He withdrew his earlier 'words', claiming that an 'erroneous view' had been made of them, since they were 'capable of misrepresentation'.

In a letter, 22nd November, Hann accepted the apology of the miners' agent, demanded that Stanton abide by the Conciliation Board Agreement, and invited the men to return to work so that 'grievances' could be 'dealt with in the usual way'. He added, though, that this only applied to 'such workmen whose services the Company requires, as it was explained at that meeting [Conciliation Board on 14th November] that the Company intended stopping certain workings which had proved remunerative (sic)'. He repeated his call for 'a cessation of the ill-treatment to which the officials of the Company were being subjected'.[118]

C. B. Stanton's reply to Hann's letter included an objection to the 'insinuation' regarding 'the intimidation' of company officials, and a reminder that it was the Board's decision 'that the men should return to work, and afterwards that the alleged grievance be dealt with in usual way'. He also recalled hearing Hann say that 'no-start

Aberdare valley Miners 1910 strike – Women and children.

Courtesy of Rhondda Cynon Taf Libraries

would be made until all the grievances were settled'. David Evans's impression, from reading the company's correspondence, was that the 'original purpose of the company … insisted on a settlement of all outstanding disputes at the Aberdare pits before work was resumed'.[119] So, the outcome of the exchange of letters was a stalemate, and no 'immediate improvement in the situation'.

This impasse featured a tussle between the Aberdare strikers, and their SWMF Executive. The Executive did not want to expose the union to the charge of supporting men who were engaged in an illegal strike.[120] The men persisted, and were later to receive money from a relief fund. However, on the 5th December, at a Conciliation Board meeting, an Executive Council spokesman, Mr Onions, stated 'that before the men should return to work the Company should withdraw the notices they had put up with regard to taking firewood and that the Company should negotiate on this matter after the resumption of work'.[121] The Coalowners' Association rejected this proposal. A union delegates' conference was then held on the 7th December, at which the Executive repeated its earlier recommendation, of 14th November, that the Aberdare, and Cambrian workmen for that matter, return to work. The recommendation was eventually carried at an adjourned meeting, on 14th December.

A Joint Committee of strikers, representing not only colliery workers of Powell Duffryn, but also rival company collieries at Bwllfa and Blaennant, took place at Aberdare sometime between these two meetings. Debated was a recommendation that each colliery committee should meet the managers of their respective companies to obtain guarantees for reinstated workmen upon returning to work. The men feared victimisation by the coal companies. The meeting broke up without agreement, but the Joint Committee acted independently, and so communication was made with Powell Duffryn.[122] Hann replied by advising them that in 'withdrawing the stokers and others', it had 'made it impossible to re-start some, and others [collieries] are unremunerative'. This message 'rekindled the smouldering discontent of the strikers', and at a meeting of theirs, on 16th December, adopted was a resolution to 'express' their determination' to stand by their agent, and 'not to accept the tyrannical conditions sought to be imposed'.[123] David Evan's judged that this was 'a travesty' of the general manager's attitude. Nonetheless, by the 21st December the 'back of the strike' had been 'broken'. The Aberdare Valley strike leaders at last accepted the Federation's Executive's recommendation, and work was resumed on Monday, 2nd January, 1911.

According to some much later local opinion, the strike saw 'personal antagonism between the two negotiators, C. B. Stanton and E. M. Hann, exacerbated the situation'.[124] A clash of personalities might occur between two men of contrasting natures. Edmund Mills Hann was a man of action not words, and inclined to be more self-effacing than showy. He was, though, confident in his position of managerial authority, whereas C. B. Stanton relied upon the vote of miners to keep his office. Stanton's attitude towards the miners' Federation leadership suggests that he was eager for militant action. He verbally abused the leadership by calling it a 'faint-hearted, over-cautious, creeping, crawling, cowardly set'.[125] The apparent natural effusion of Stanton won the loyal support of the miners in the Aberdare district for militant action, but if his style was inclined more to bombast than reason, Hann could have been aroused to anger. The ambitions of both men also proved to be different.

Five years later, Charles Butt Stanton succeeded Keir Hardie as Member of Parliament for Merthyr Tydfil. A later opinion of Stanton was that he was 'the most flamboyant of the local Members of Parliament, and underwent a complete metamorphosis from being an extremely militant union leader, to become a most jingoistic politician – hence his nickname "John Bull" Stanton'.[126] If Stanton's popularity flourished due to the strike, it fell to Powell Duffryn's general manager of collieries to deal with its consequences. His subsequent actions caused some miners to believe that they were the victims of company malice.

The stoppage at Powell Duffryn's Aberdare collieries lasted ten weeks and four days.[127] Just 3,500, of the nearly 5,500 men in work before the strike, were re-employed. The company abandoned some underground workings, and other workings took nearly a year's labour to bring them back into safe productive use. The Treaman Colliery, nicknamed the Nici-Naci, was closed, and so 1,300 men lost their jobs.[128] The distress, in terms of poverty in the community, 'was acute and widespread'. The cottage hospital project was suspended.[129] These items were casualties of a dispute about kindling for household fireplaces.

David Evans judged that the men gained 'absolutely nothing'. Moreover, he claimed that it was 'probably one of the most wanton strikes in the annals of the coalfield'. This was some claim. The Cambrian Combine collieries' men did not resume work until 1st September, 1911. The legacy of starvation, and misery in the Rhondda left considerable bitterness. Although during the strike the military remained in barracks, such restraint curried little favour with people of the Rhondda, and their descendants.

In contrast, the 1910 strike that hit the company's Aberdare Valley collieries is not mentioned by Powell Duffryn in its fifty year history. The history only notes that the Conciliation Board Agreement of the South Wales Coalfield had expired on the 30th March, 1910, and that 'fresh agreement was made for a further five years'.[130]

The company's main focus at the time was colliery developments in the Rhymney Valley. As a measure of the relative importance of the Rhymney Valley to Powell Duffryn, in 1910, the company's area of takings were 10,670 acres whereas it was 4,801 acres in the Aberdare Valley.[131] Also in 1910, the directors decided to raise more investment finance for Powell Duffryn to open Britannia Colliery, south of Bargoed, at Pengam, Monmouthshire. The decision saw an issue of 206,250 new Ordinary Shares valued at £1 each, and, according to Hann 'there was a great rush to obtain' them. The action boosted the company's authorised capital value to £1,187,045.[132] Moreover, that year, an order was issued by the company to build a colliery rescue station in the Rhymney Valley.

However, in 1910, the start to Penallta Colliery's operation was rated as 'disappointing' by Edmund Mills Hann.[133] 'Great trouble' was experienced 'in opening out' due to 'steep gradients and disturbances in the Red Vein on the South Side'. Worryingly for him, there was a chance of the 'total disappearance of the seam in that direction'. The screening plant, designed by the colliery company and made by Messrs Head Wrightson & Co., looked set to be underused. A belief was that the 'upkeep of this plant will be small, owing to the reduction in the amount of belting and shafting, and that there will be a greater immunity from breakdown than in older kind of screening plant'.[134] Fortunately for the company, Penallta Colliery's setbacks were overcome.

In 1913, the colliery's steam coal output reached 120,000 tons. Then, in 1914, with the colliery's operational problems solved, the annual output level of steam coal rose steeply to about 500,000 tons.[135] The business of running the Rhymney Railway's Cylla (Penrhiewfelin) branch to the colliery became lucrative due to coal traffic, and the running of workmen's trains.[136] Over a decade later, in December 1930, Penallta Colliery achieved, on one Friday, a 'coal winding feat' of 5,586 tons.[137] The colliery also attained a new weekly output record of 22,700 tons. Praise for this performance was credited to its colliery manager, J. Basset, his staff, and the men. The colliery's manpower reached its zenith the following year at 3,208.[138] The colliery ultimately achieved an average annual output of 'around 860,000 tons', a measure of the rewards achieved over a longer-term as a result of a Hann engineered colliery.[139]

NOTES

1 The logistics of moving coal by rail in the coalfield involved the 'wait and order' system. Railway wagons loaded with coal were consigned to storage sidings until required for shipment, or movement. A high demand for Powell Duffryn's coal, and their rivals for that matter, severely tested the system. Tension between Powell Duffryn and the railway companies could be exacerbated by friction between railway companies. Powell Duffryn's general manager of collieries no doubt met the senior management of the railway companies to resolve serious disputes.

2 'Introducing the New President and Presidential Address', *SWIE*, Vol. XXIII (1904), pp.503-19.

3 This was the Writer's opinion when he as an undergraduate student in Mechanical Engineering at the University of Wales Institute of Science & Technology (UWIST), Cathays Park, Cardiff. UWIST was later amalgamated with University College of South Wales and Monmouthshire. In 2005, following Privy Counsel approval, the united colleges were granted independence from the University of Wales, and became Cardiff University.

4 Denis Griffiths, *op. cit.*, p.116. Moreover, 'Even then it [triple-expansion engine] played a major role in marine matters for years to come and mainly tramp steamers, particularly during the 1940s and 1950s'.

5 *Oxford Dictionary of National Biography, Volume 21*. (Oxford University Press, 2004), pp.332-3.

6 'The Watering or Damping of Dusty Mines', *SWIE*, Vol. XXIV (1904-1906), pp.103-5.

7 'The Watering or Damping of Dusty Mines', *op. cit.*, pp.316-7.

8 'Ordinary General Meeting', *SWIE* Vol. XXIV (1904-1906), p.10.

9 'Ordinary General Meeting', *op. cit.*, pp.13-15.

10 'Adjourned Discussion on Notes on the South Trough of the Coal-Field, east Glamorgan', *SWIE*, Vol. XIII (1902-1903), pp.361-363.

11 'Visit of Belgian Engineers to South Wales', *SWIE*, Vol. XXIV (1904-1906), pp.97-106.

12 'Discussion Electrical Coal Winding', *SWIE*, Vol. XXIV (1904-1906), pp.71-80 & pp.120-140.

13 Horace D. B. How, 'Coal Winding Machinery', *SWIE*, Vol. XIII (1902-1903), pp.548-569.

14 Graham M. Stephenson, 'Notes on Examples of Electrical Winding', *SWIE*, Vol. XIII (1902-1903), pp.462-476.

15 'Discussion Electrical Coal Winding', *SWIE*, Vol. XXIV (1904-1906), pp.74-5.

16 An eminent German mining engineer, Koepe, developed this colliery winding system. In the system a large diameter pulley was used in place of the winding drum. A rope was extended all the way from one cage, up over the sheave on the headgear, around the engine driven pulley, wound around a second sheave on the headgear, to fall down to be attached to the other cage, and then continued to the bottom of the shaft, where it formed a loop, and finally it was connected to the initial cage. When the engine pulley revolved, one cage ascended the shaft, whilst the other descended the shaft.

17 'Discussion Electrical Coal Winding', *SWIE*, Vol. XXIV (1904-1906), pp.139-140.

18 'Discussion Electrical Coal Winding', *SWIE*, Vol. XXIV (1904-1906), pp.131.

19 'Discussion Electrical Coal Winding', *SWIE*, Vol. XXIV (1904-1906), pp.139-140.

20 Annual General Meeting, *SWIE*, Vol. XXIV (1904-1906), pp.159-231.

21 W. O'Connor, 'Notes on Summer Outing to Liége- June 17 to June 23, 1905', *SWIE*, Vol. XXIV (1904-1906), pp.282-308.

22 W. O'Conner, 'Summer Outing to Belgium, Part III-The Belgian Coalfields and Collieries', *SWIE*, Vol. XXIV (1904-1906), pp.457-506.

23 'Ordinary General Meeting', *SWIE*, Vol. XXIV (1904-1906), pp.233-364.

24 'Ordinary General Meeting', 19 October 1905, *op. cit.*, pp.365-506.

25 W. W. Price, Card Records, Hann 2, item 5. National Library of Wales.

26 Glamorgan Record office, Urban District of Aberdare, Minute Book [hereafter GR-UDCAMB], No. 4, p.101.

27 GR-UDCAMB No. 4, p.388.

28 E. M. Hann, *Brief History of the Powell Duffryn Steam Coal Company Ltd*, p.23 & p.28 respectively.

29 E. M. Hann, *Brief History of the Powell Duffryn Steam Coal Company Ltd*, p.60.

30 The additional details about Nehemiah Phillips from Hilda M. Evans, *New Tredegar in Focus*. (Starling Press, 1977), p.14, and *New Tredegar Again*. (Starling Press, 1979), p.20-1.

31 David Hann, 'The Hann Family – A Mining Dynasty of South Wales part 2', *Glamorgan Family History Society, Journal No. 39*,(Sept., 1995), p.6.

32 E. M. Hann, *Brief History of The Powell Duffryn Steam Coal Company Ltd*, p.25.

33 OS grid reference ST 140958.

34 George G. Hann, 'The Sinking and Equipping of Penallta Colliery', *SWIE*, Vol. XXVII, No. 1, (July 1910), pp.47-62, and the discussion pp.82-102.

35 Hugh Bramwell, 'Re-sinking and Re-Equipping the Great Western Colliery Company's Maritime Pit', *SWIE*, Vol. XXVI, (1908-1910), pp.138-151.

36 Hugh Bramwell, 'President's Inaugural Address', *SWIE*, Vol. XXXIII, (1917), p.17.

37 Gerald Hooghwinkel, 'Electric Winding at the Maritime Pit of the Great Western Colliery Company', *SWIE*, Vol. XXV, (1908-1910), p.345.

38 The motor's normal rating was 700 hp at 2,200 volts and 25 Hz see Gerald Hooghwinkel, *op. cit.*, p.350, which also informs that a DC compound rotary converter was used in the electrical system to balance the variation in power factors.

39 George G. Hann, 'The Sinking and Equipping of Penallta Colliery', *op. cit.*, p.48.

40 E. M. Hann, 'Some notes on the Mechanical Equipment of Collieries', *Proceedings of the Institution of Mechanical Engineers*, (1906), p.733.

41 Trevor Boyns, 'Contracts Sealed by Company for Electrical Equipment'. (Unpublished). The actual date the contract was sealed was 8th September 1908.

42 *The Powell Duffryn Steam Coal Company 1864-1914, op. cit.*, p.40.

43 W. H. Patchell, 'The Electrification of the Ferndale Collieries', *SWIE*, Vol. XXVI, (1908-1910), p.850.

44 W. H. Patchell, *op. cit.* pp.901-2.

45 W. H. Patchell, *op. cit.* p.896.

46 Comment, John Boucher to Writer, 21st Sept 2006. The Yorkshire Main Colliery used two duplex steam winders (cylinders 42-inch and 84-inch stroke), identical except that No. 2, the main coal winder, had a parallel drum 24ft diameter, and No. 1 had a BCC drum 34ft diameter, the largest in Britain (perhaps in the world)'.

47 Discussion, 'The Sinking and Equipping of Penallta Colliery', *SWIE*, Vol. XXVII, (1910-1911), p.361.

48 Discussion, 'The Sinking and Equipping of Penallta Colliery', *SWIE*, Vol. XXVII, (1910-1911), p.101.

49 A. Leighton Stevens, 'The Sirocco Fan', *SWIE*, Vol. XXIV, (1904-1906), pp.107-114, and 'Discussion' pp.176-194.

50 A. Leighton Stevens, 'The Sirocco Fan', *op. cit.*, 'Discussion' p.176. His reference: *The Engineer*, 12 April 1901.

51 In 1910, he lived at 'The Laurels', Cardiff Road, Bargoed. 'District List of Members', *SWIE*, Vol. XXVI, (1908-1910), p.xcix.

52 *The Powell Duffryn Steam Coal Company 1864-1914, op. cit.*, p.66. This measured Penallta's No. 1 shaft at 780 yards, and No. 2 shaft at 752 yards.

53   According to the 1942 classification, Penallta's coal ranked as a bituminous I: volatiles 17-23%; of remainder, carbon ranged from 90-92%; hydrogen 4.3–5%; and calorific value 15,650 to 15,800 Btu/lb. Data from the *South Wales Coalfield (Including Pembrokeshire) Regional Survey Report, op. cit.*, pp.20-21.

54   'The Sinking and Equipping of Penallta Colliery', *SWIE*, Vol. XXVII, (1910-1911), p.361. Regarding Stewart's opinion about the use of a wood liner, George Hann acknowledged its usefulness, but stated that the success of the rail method was dependent upon getting rails 'perfectly plumb from top to bottom', and the tolerated deviation was less than half an inch, which was a 'difficult matter' to attain but was achieved at Penallta.

55   Discussion, 'Mining Rescue Apparatus', *SWIE*, Vol. XXV, (1906-1908), pp.538-540.

56   *The Powell Duffryn Steam Coal Company 1864-1914, op. cit.*, p.46-7.

57   *Western Mail*, 'Colliery Rescue Station, Building opened at Aberdare, Demonstrations with Air Apparatus, 25 Jan 1909, p.6.

58   *The Aberdare Leader*, 'Rescue Station, Building', 30 Jan 1909, p.6, col.1.

59   *The Aberdare Leader*, 'Rescue Station, Building', 30 Jan 1909, p.7, col.2. Henry Morris held a first-class colliery manager's certificate, and lived at 18, Margaret Street, Aberaman.

60   E. M. Hann, *Brief History of the Powell Duffryn Steam Coal Company Ltd*, pp.26-7.

61   *The Powell Duffryn Steam Coal Company 1864-1914, op. cit.*, p.11.

62   E. M. Hann, *Brief History of The Powell Duffryn Steam Coal Company Ltd*, p.24.

63   E. M. Hann, *Brief History of The Powell Duffryn Steam Coal Company Ltd*, p.24.

64   T. Boyns, 'Jigging and Shaking: Technical Choice in the South Wales Coal Industry between the Wars', *The Welsh History Review: Cylchgrawn Hanes Cymru, Vol.17*, No. 2, (1994), pp.230-231.

65   Sam Mavor, 'Machine Mining with Reference to South Wales', *SWIE*, Vol. XXVI (1908-1910), pp.954-1053.

66   Discussion, 'Machine Mining with Reference to South Wales', *SWIE*, Vol. XXVI (1908-1910), p.1153.

67   'Machine Mining with Reference to South Wales', *SWIE*, Vol. XXIX (1913), p.386.

68   Discussion, 'Machine Mining with Reference to South Wales', *op. cit.*, p.1044.

69   Discussion, 'Machine Mining with Reference to South Wales', *op. cit.*, p.1051.

70   Discussion, 'Machine Mining with Reference to South Wales', *SWIE*, Vol.XXVI (1908-1910), pp.1200-4.

71   Sam Mavor, 'Machine Mining with Reference to South Wales', *op. cit.*, p.1000.

72   E. M. Hann, *Brief History of The Powell Duffryn Steam Coal Company Ltd*, p.24.

73   GR PDMBDM No. 5, p.6.

74   *New Tredegar, Bargoed and Caerphilly Journal*, 'Cottage Hospital-Aberbargoed buildings, speech by Lord Tredegar', 16 Dec 1909, p.3, col.2.

75   *New Tredegar, Bargoed and Caerphilly Journal, op. cit.*, 16 Dec 1909, p.3, col.3.

76   *New Tredegar, Bargoed and Caerphilly Journal, op. cit.*, 16 Dec 1909, p.3, col.1.

77   *New Tredegar, Bargoed and Caerphilly Journal, op. cit.*, 16 Dec 1909, p.3, col.1. Located at OS reference SO 157002.

78   Following the demise of the hospital, the 'Charity' panel was salvaged, and placed on display in Aberbargoed's refurbished Garden of Remembrance, which was opened on 11th November, 2011.

79   Godfrey Morgan, 2nd Baron Tredegar, was created a Viscount in 1905. A bachelor, he died in 1913, and was succeeded by his nephew, Courtnay. An equestrian statue of Godfrey Morgan stands in Cathays Park, Cardiff, to the front of the National Museum of Wales.

80   *New Tredegar, Bargoed and Caerphilly Journal, op. cit.*, 16 Dec 1909, p.3, col.1.

81   *New Tredegar, Bargoed and Caerphilly Journal, op. cit.*, 16 Dec 1909, p.3, cols.1 & 2.

82   *New Tredegar, Bargoed and Caerphilly Journal, op. cit.*, 16 Dec 1909, p.3, col.2.

83   *New Tredegar, Bargoed and Caerphilly Journal, op. cit.*, 16 Dec 1909, p.3, col.2.

84   E. M. Hann, *Brief History of the Powell Duffryn Steam Coal Company Ltd*, p.27.

85   *The Powell Duffryn Steam Coal Company 1864-1914, op. cit.*, p.68.

86   *New Tredegar, Bargoed and Caerphilly Journal, op. cit.*, 16 Dec 1909, p.3, col.3.

87   E. M. Hann, *Brief History of the Powell Duffryn Steam Coal Company Ltd*, pp.28-9.

88   E. M. Hann, *Brief History of the Powell Duffryn Steam Coal Company Ltd*, p.28. Hann used a phonetic spelling of the colliery's name, Sguborwen. In 1983, members of the Cynon Valley History Society 'rediscovered' an entrance to the level of Ysguborwen, and noted that on the keystone of its stone arch was engraved: T(homas) J(oseph) S(guborwen) W 1850; see Cynon Valley History Society, *Cynon Coal, op. cit.*, p.37. Maybe useful as a further guide to the area of coal takings leased by coalowners in the Aberdare valley during the mid-1800s, the colliery's takings were 394 acres; E. M. Hann, *op. cit.*, p.31.

89   Arthur W. Humphreys, 'Brief History of the Aberdare and District General Hospital', *Souvenir Report -Thirtieth Annual Report and Statement of Accounts.* (Aberdare & District General Hospital, 1947), p.6. Copy retained at Aberdare Library

90   E. M. Hann, *Brief History of The Powell Duffryn Steam Coal Company, Lt, op, cit.*, p.27. This aspect of his history was written in 1909.

91   Roberta Ross Powell, *A Miners' Hospital-An Illustrated History of Mountain Ash General Hospital.*(No details), p.1 & p.3. The opening date is inferred from reading these pages.

92   Arthur W. Humphreys, *op. cit.*, p.7.

93   David Evans, *Labour Strife in the South Wales Coalfield 1910-1911*, (Educational Publishing, Cardiff, 1911), p.5 & p.9.

94   David Evans, *op. cit.*, p.12.

95   David Evans, *op. cit.*, p.16.

96   David Evans, *op. cit.*, p.1.

97   David Evans, *op. cit.*, p.17.

98   David Evans, *op. cit.*, p.17.

99   David Evans, *op. cit.*, p.18, and pp.23-5.

100 David Evans, *op. cit.*, p.38.

101 David Evans, *op. cit.*, pp.39-40.

102 David Evans, *op. cit.*, pp.40-1.

103 David Evans, *op. cit.*, p.42.

104 David Evans, *op. cit.*, p.43.

105 David Evans, *op. cit.*, p.43.

106 David Evans, *op. cit.*, p.43.

107 *The Aberdare Leader*, 'The Strike', 12 Nov 1909, p.6, col.1.

108 David Evans, *op. cit.*, pp.51-2.

109 *The Aberdare Leader*, 'The Strike', 12 Nov 1909, p.6, col.1.

110 David Evans, *op. cit.*, pp.49-52.

111 David Evans, *op. cit.*, pp.69-70.

112 *The Aberdare Leader*, 'The Strike', 12 Nov 1909, p.6, col.3.

113 David Evans, *op. cit.*, p.82.

114 David Evans, *op. cit.*, p.87.

115 David Evans, *op. cit.*, p.101.

116 David Evans, *op. cit.*, p.96.

117 David Evans, *op. cit.*, pp.117-122.

118 David Evans, *op. cit.*, p.121.

119 David Evans, *op. cit.*, p.127.

120 David Evans, *op. cit.*, p.125

121 David Evans, *op. cit.*, p.126.

122 David Evans, *op. cit.*, pp.128-9.

123 David Evans, *op. cit.*, p.130.

124 *Aberdare, Pictures from the Past*, (Cynon Valley History Society, 1986), photo.199.

125 David Evans, *op. cit.*, p.35.

126 *Aberdare, Pictures from the Past*, (Cynon Valley History Society, 1986), photo.90A.

127 David Evans, *op. cit.*, pp.131-133.

128 Closed in 1912. Cynon Coal, *op. cit.*, p.240.

129 Arthur W. Humphreys, *op. cit.*, p.7.

130 *The Powell Duffryn Steam Coal Company 1864-1914, op. cit.*, p.26.

131 E. M. Hann, *Brief History of the Powell Duffryn Steam Coal Company Ltd,* p.31. The figure for the Aberdare Valley excludes the take for Ysguborwen Colliery.

132 The Powell Duffryn Steam Coal Company 1864-1914, *op. cit.*, p.26.

133 E. M. Hann, *Brief History of the Powell Duffryn Steam Coal Company Ltd*, p.38.

134 George G. Hann, 'The Sinking and Equipping of Penallta Colliery', *SWIE*, Vol. XXVII, pp.54-5.

135 *The Powell Duffryn Steam Coal Company 1864-1914, op. cit.*, p.66.

136 R. W. Kinder, *op. cit.*, pp.120-121.

137 *South Wales Argus*, 22 December 1930, p.10.

138 Trevor Boyns, Penallta Colliery-Employment Figures. (Annual List of Mines). 2,863 men worked underground and 345 on the surface.

139 John Cornwell, *Collieries of South Wales: 1*, (Landmark, 2001), p.206.

Senghenydd, from Station Terrace.

Universal Colliery, Aber Valley. In 1905, Sir William Thomas Lewis (1837-1914) took control of the colliery. He was maybe, during most of his lifetime, the most fearful coalowner in the South Wales Coalfield. The colliery became infamous in Britain during the early decades of the 1900s for a huge toll of miners deaths caused by underground explosions. In 1911, he was created a baron. His title, Lord Merthyr of Senghenydd, indelibly linked him to the colliery's traumatic history.

Pope/Parkhouse Archive

Chapter Seven
HANN BROTHERS' COLLIERIES

The Hanns' grip of the colliery management of Powell Duffryn became indisputable. Edmund Mills Hann's sons took advantage of privileged entry into careers with the company. One outcome was that, by the end of the first decade of the 1900s, George Hann emerged as his father's most likely successor as general manager of collieries. The thirty-one year old George Hann's paper about Penallta Colliery won for himself the South Wales Institute of Engineers' Gold Medal.[1] Maybe this was also a public statement of his wish to emulate his father.

The year 1911 also saw Frank Percival Hann made Penallta's colliery manager. Born in 1885, he was educated like his brothers at Haileybury and Imperial Service College.[2] 'Frank was good academically and showed skills of leadership; he became captain of a house rugby XV and was an aggressive forward'. He joined Powell Duffryn, in 1903, but following two years as Penallta Colliery's manager, he left the company to become agent for Penrikyber Navigation Colliery Company, owned by the Cory Brothers & Company Limited. In doing this he succeeded his brother, Edmund Lawrence, at Penrikyber.

Preceding Frank Hann as Penallta Colliery manager was G. H. Lowry who held the post in 1909. Douglas Alfred Hann then succeeded Frank Hann as the colliery's manager in 1913.[3] A continuation of managers then followed the Hanns: Abraham Moore in, or from, 1918 until around 1927; A. Tait was in the post

between 1928 and 1930, and he appears to have been followed by J. Basset; and from 1943 to 1945, it was C. H. Davies.[4]

Edmund L. Hann, a seemingly indecisive eighteen years old before joining Powell Duffryn, developed into an ambitious, independent minded man. He resigned from the company after his time as the colliery manager at Bargoed to become the agent for the Penrikyber Navigation Colliery Company. Being ambitious, he might have judged that his brother George was a bar to him making progress in Powell Duffryn. Upon resigning from the Penrikyber Navigation Colliery Company, he became a consulting engineer.

The Hann brothers who entered the mining operation's side of Powell Duffryn matured early as managers in the main due to Rhymney Valley experiences. Recruiting the services of a Hann also offered a way to tap into Powell Duffryn knowhow, and the establishment of Bedwas Navigation Colliery, in the Rhymney Valley, gained in this way.

Bedwas Navigation Colliery Company

On April 4th, 1910, the sinking commenced of the North Pit of Bedwas Navigation Colliery.[5] The colliery was sited two miles north-east from the mighty walls of Caerphilly's Plantagenet castle. At an identical distance east from the colliery, on the left bank of the Rhymney River, stands the village of Machen. If the town of Rhymney is used as the marker for the northern limit of the

Bedwas Navigation Colliery. Edmund Lawrence Hann was responsible for engineering this Rhymney Valley colliery, which was modelled upon Penallta Colliery. Sinking of the colliery began in April 1910. The colliery's South shaft, at 804 yards, was for a time, the deepest in the South Wales Coalfield.

Pope/Parkhouse Archive

South Wales Coalfield, in the Rhymney Valley, then its southern counterpart is Machen. David Emlyn Evan indicated that a boundary of the South Wales Coalfield' featured on the surface as the 'Machen Gorge, cut by the Rhymney [River] through the southern edge of the main coalfield syncline'.[6]

In 1866, Bassett claimed that before 1792 that 'coal and wood [was] brought on the backs of mules and horses from levels opened on the south crop of the basin between Machin (sic) and Caerphilly' for use by the inhabitants of the town of Newport.[7] The opening of the Rhymney Tramroad possibly encouraged more coal mining ventures around Machen.[8]

On the top of Mynydd Rudry, south-east of Caerphilly, outcrops of coal can be seen.[9] 'The footpath from the road to the [Mynydd Rudry] summit crosses a number of northward dipping coal seams. These include the Rhondda No. 2, or Big Rock Vein, and the Rhondda No. 1 or Little Rock Vein, the latter out-cropping beneath the summit of the hill'.[10]

The mountain's summit also gives an expansive view northwards over the Rhymney Valley. A capacious basin commands the foreground of such a view. The contrasting claustrophobic aspect of the Rhymney Valley, from New Tredegar to Bargoed is not obvious from such a viewpoint. The village of Llanbradach can be seen as a door post for where the valley's U-form eases into the large, shallow, basin, which accommodates the town of Caerphilly. Emlyn Evans's 1971 description of the scene from atop Mynydd Rudry mentions the Llanbradach Colliery as closed. Surprisingly, he omitted to mention Bedwas Navigation Colliery, which was then a fully functional colliery.

Bedwas Navigation Colliery Company was registered as such on the 7th December, 1908 "to acquire the lease of a coal-mining property at Bedwas, Mon."[11] The company had strong links with Powell Duffryn. Trevor Boyns identified in the Stock Exchange Book covering the years between 1908 and 1922, that Bedwas Navigation Colliery Company chairman was Joseph Shaw and one of the other directors was E. M. Hann'.[12] Moreover, Edmund L. Hann's services were used to found Bedwas Colliery, and his model was Penallta Colliery.

Edmund L. Hann's paper, 'The Sinking and Equipping of Bedwas Colliery', issued by the South Wales Institute of Engineers in 1911-12, declared that 'the sinking and layout of the Bedwas Colliery has to a large extent followed Penallta, there have been some considerable modifications, partly due to local circumstances and partly due to experiences gained at Penallta'.[13] However, the production plan for Bedwas Colliery was 2,000 tons of coal per day.

Like at Penallta Colliery, 'it was decided to install the permanent plant before sinking'. Robey & Co. received an order to deliver two pairs of 4-cylinder tandem compound drop-valve winding engines, and a cross-compound air compressor with a capacity of 5,000ft^3 of free air per minute at 90 lb/in^2. The winding engines dimensions were: high-pressure 31-inches; low-pressure cylinders 52-inches, and stroke of 72-inches.[14] Furthermore, the winding engines were erected inside one winding house, and it was 'fixed so that the pit bottom arches would be in line with the level course of strata'. The colliery was sited 'just south of the main anticlinal'.

Six Lancashire boilers and two Babcock & Wilcox units were installed behind the winding house for steam raising. The Lancashire boilers used treated 'water pumped from the pit'. The Babcock & Wilcox water-tube boilers were fuelled by what Edmund L. Hann described as 'a modification of the travelling

chain-grate stoker'. The boiler company began to supply stokers within Britain in 1897.[15] It seems that Powell Duffryn collaborated with Babcock & Wilcox in an attempt to make efficient use of Welsh steam coal in chain-grate stokers. With the advent of forced draught boiler furnaces, the introduction of stokers, and improved boiler plant, the range of coal for raising steam was widened from free-burning types, such as steam coal, to coals having strongly caking properties.

Chain-grate stokers

The furnace arch modifications for a mechanical stoker were actually introduced by Babcock & Wilcox after 'some years of experiment' at Penrikyber Navigation Colliery, situated near Mountain Ash in the Aberdare Valley. This Penrikyber Navigation Colliery Company had enlisted Edmund Lawrence Hann as its agent in 1907. This may partly explain how a co-operative working relationship between Babcock & Wilcox and Powell Duffryn evolved with Penrikyber Navigation Colliery being used as a venue for development work.

Edmund L. Hann described the design changes developed for stokers to burn steam coal more efficiently. 'Generally stokers used furnace arches (front and/ or rear) to improve combustion by reflecting heat on to the fuel bed'. 'The front arch served 'to break up and mix rich streams of volatile gases that might travel through the unit unburned'. But, 'the stoker for burning bituminous coals depended upon a front arch, which maintained in a state of incandescence by the combustion of the volatile hydrocarbon; whereas for burning Welsh coal it was found necessary to modify the brick arch setting, so that the same high furnace temperature necessary for complete combustion was established by the more direct radiant heat given off by Welsh [steam]coal'. And, so, as a result, the coal underwent 'gradual distillation entering the furnace in an absolutely level layer' … 'slowly carried forward into an increasing furnace temperature until it has been wholly reduced to ash and clinker'.

The modified mechanical stoker tests at Penrikyber yielded efficiencies that were 'in practice unobtainable by hand-firing'. An efficiency of 73 per cent was attained by a mechanical stoker, whereas, in the case of hand-firing efficiency was less than 60 per cent. The coal won at Penrikyber Colliery was smokeless steam

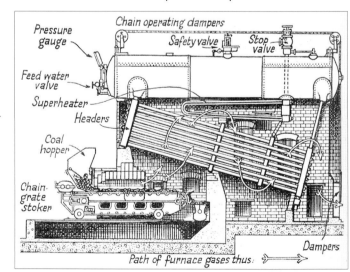

Babcock & Wilcox water-tube boiler fired using a chain-grate stoker.
T. R. Barnard, Coal Mining Series – Mechanical Engineering.

coal. The conclusion of the tests suggested that Welsh steam coal could meet the rising challenge from bituminous coals as a chain-grate stoker fuel. Moreover, in a complete coal-handling plant, it was conceivable that one fireman could 'easily' attend 'to five or six boilers, no matter how much coal is fired per boiler through using stokers'. The days of hand-firing of boilers seemed numbered.

Lessons learnt at Bedwas Navigation Colliery played some part in chain grate-stokers users buying Welsh steam coal. Although, in the case of Bedwas Navigation Colliery, the coal won was classed as bituminous manufacturing.[16] However, news of the benefits offered by using mechanical stokers did not reach Nine Mile Point Colliery, which was Bedwas Colliery's neighbour in the Sirhowy Valley, until decades later. Hand-firing was still being practised there at the end of the 1940s.[17]

Engineering Bedwas Navigation Colliery

Bedwas Navigation Colliery's other features of interest included ventilation, and compressed air use. The ventilation fan was of the 'Walker's indestructible type' that moved 400,000ft^3 of air per minute. The colliery's compressed air provision was planned to meet contrasting needs: stand-by in the case of breakdown, and economical operation during periods when the demand for power was small. However, air provision calculations entailed some speculation since it was 'impossible to foresee to what extent electric power will be used for haulage purposes'.[18]

Powell Duffryn's technical generosity, though, had not included extending its electricity grid to Bedwas Navigation Colliery. Edmund L. Hann advised that no link-up was possible for Bedwas due to its situation. So, as a one colliery coal company, the design of the colliery's electrical plant had to be capable of dealing with large fluctuations in the amount of exhaust steam being made available, and the electrical current demand, whilst achieving an acceptable load factor. Edmund L. Hann claimed that the plant at Bedwas Colliery was designed to 'get over this difficulty', but it was done at some cost. He revealed: 'Whilst such a plant' called 'for an increased expenditure' there appeared 'to be no doubt that power can be produced at a price considerably lower than it can be supplied by an outside source, and this should amply repay the increased expenditure, particularly in view of the large power consumption of the pumping plant which' had been installed. The DC system was largely used, though some small AC motors were installed. Electricity was generated using two units each comprising a mixed-pressure turbo alternator of 1500 kW, complete with Worthington jet condenser and rotary air pump. The turbine was of a Rateau design, and Messrs Brown, Boveri & Co. supplied the alternator.

Edmund L. Hann made Penallta Colliery his reference for appraising the sinking of Bedwas Navigation Colliery. The cost of coal, used as fuel for the colliery's sinking operation, proved to be cheaper, and the sinking was completed in a shorter period. The sinking of the colliery's North Pit, the upcast, began on the 4th April, 1910. On 11th November, 1911, the shaft work 'proved' the 'Black Vein'.

The excavation of the South Pit began on the 27th May, 1910, and the 'Black Vein' was 'proved' on the 16th February, 1912, at 789 yards. Sinking the South Pit took longer due mainly to some disruption from feeders. The South Pit was deepened further to 804 yards to make a sump, and so created the deepest shaft in the South Wales Coalfield, up until that date.

Caerphilly contractor, Fred Piggot, was responsible for sinking Bedwas Navigation Colliery. He owned a large house west of Caerphilly known as 'The Beeches', which will take on notable importance later in the work.

Edmund L. Hann's paper about Bedwas Colliery was discussed by members of the South Wales Institute of Engineers on the 1st September, 1913.[19] J. Fox Tallis considered the colliery to be 'admirable'. William D. Wight was 'impressed' that due to 'the valuable experience that the owner had they had come to the conclusion to stick to steam as the main motive power'.

On 20th November, 1913, the geology of Bedwas Colliery was revealed.[20] Henry J. Jordan, perhaps the most knowledge man regarding the geology of the South Wales Coalfield at the time, wrote about Bedwas Colliery as:

'The most interesting of all the shafts that have been sunk to the present time, because they are the first in the coalfield to intersect all the measures from the Mynyddislwyn seam down to the lowest workable seam in the sequence. The vertical section … shows the Mynyddislwyn seam (which goes by the name 'Bedwas Seam' in the Bedwas district, and is the No. 3 Llanwit seam in the Taff Valley and westwards) to have been intersected 22 yards from the surface, and the lowest seam, which probably is the Hard Vein of Rudry and the Lower Four-Feet of Aberdare, is shown to be at a depth of 838 yards 1 foot 11 inches.'

When Henry Jordan visited the colliery, to examine its geology, he was met there by Edmund L. Hann, and his host, Edmund Mills Hann. Bedwas Navigation Colliery appears to have been more than just an example of where Powell Duffryn's technical knowledge and experience was put into effect for the benefit of another coal company.

Nonetheless, Bedwas Navigation Colliery's status as the deepest colliery in the Rhymney Valley would ever remain fast. Moreover, the colliery was to be the deepest sinking ever managed by a Hann. For Edmund Lawrence Hann he had gained practical experience in founding a colliery, like his brother George had done at Penallta Colliery. Powell Duffryn had also been busy south of Bargoed at Pengam, on the Monmouthshire side of the Rhymney Valley, sinking Britannia Colliery. Moreover, the company had also taken measures in the valley to provide a colliery rescue service.

Rhymney Valley Rescue Station

On Monday, 30th January, 1911, Powell Duffryn's Agent for the Rhymney Valley collieries, Nehemiah Phillips, led the opening of the Rhymney Valley Rescue Station, which stood adjacent to the eastern side of Elliot Colliery.[21] The children of nearby Brynhyfryd Villas, like the youngest of Rees Shore's family, Beatrice and Florence, lost the use of 'swings and other amusements' when Powell Duffryn entered into a lease with the Bedwellty Urban District Council to build the station on their recreation ground.[22] Notably the rescue station became the third one opened in the South Wales Coalfield. The building's cost, £2,000, was shared between Powell Duffryn, the Tredegar Iron & Coal Company, and the Rhymney Iron Company.

The Rhymney Valley Rescue Station consisted of two blocks of buildings. 'One block containing the air tight galleries' was 'built round the observation hall for practicing with the rescue apparatus'. The other block contained offices, cleaning rooms, dressing rooms, stores, and a 'fan for supplying gas' to the first building's galleries used for rescue practice.

Believed to be a medal awarded for a Rhymney Valley inter-colliery ambulance and rescue competition.

Courtesy of Lyndon Rees

Instructor Henry Morris, of the Aberaman rescue station, supported by 'a selected squad', directed the practice demonstration at the opening of the New Tredegar station. He then answered questions put to him by members of the gathering. In one of his answers he admitted that a rescuer's breathing apparatus was 'heavy to carry'. After observing that rescue work was 'yet in its infancy, and no doubt in due time some invention would bring about the lessening of its weight', he informed that a man carrying an apparatus 'could remain about two hours in the mine, and work hard, but not at such work as putting up timber, and by its means they were able to restore ventilation in a few hours instead of, as in other times, in a few weeks'. Nevertheless, 'hear hears' greeted his vindication of the rescue service: 'those in the immediate vicinity of an explosion must be killed by its force and could not be saved, but if the apparatus were effective enough to reduce the percentage to 70 or 65 per cent it would be an excellent benefit'.

A 'large' gathering of 'mining engineers, directors, medical men, ambulance men and members of rescue parties' witnessed the 'galleries being charged with smoke and sulphur for the apparatus' practice. The Hanns present at the event were Douglas, and his brother, Cyril, more commonly called by his second name, Graham. Graham Hann, the final sibling of Edmund Mills Hann's family, was born in 1893, became a qualified mining engineer.

After the opening of the rescue station, guests moved to the Workmen's Hall, New Tredegar, where they were 'entertained to high tea', and listened to several speeches. F. B. Saunders, the secretary of the Rhymney Iron Company, acknowledged in his speech that 'the Powell Duffryn Company, who were the prime movers in this undertaking, 'had never been backward in doing anything that which they thought would be of benefit to their workmen'. However, 'from his impression of the apparatus he

A Rhymney Valley Rescue Station team exercise believed to have been at Groesfaen Colliery, Bargoed Rhymney Valley. The station's superintendent, J. M. Kitto, stands furthest right.

Courtesy of Caerphilly County Borough Museums & Heritage Service: Winding House

thought it would have to be greatly improved upon before it became any real use in collieries'. Walter Lewis, the miners' agent, noted: 'There was a time when the rescue subject was a controversial one in south Wales, and when suggestions on this subject were much criticised'. However, that day he was 'pleased to see in the Rhymney Valley that what had been a controversial one on which they [unions and coalowner] agreed'. Indeed, Henry Morris appears to have spoken for all at the station's opening: 'In the best ventilated collieries accidents occurred, and therefore they ought to be prepared for such emergencies by every able help'.

As an aside, the children of Brynhyfryd Villas and neighbouring terraced streets were provided with a new recreational ground on the site of Hope Colliery. Possibly few of these children saw the playground as a sign that orphans were less likely to be left as a result of Rhymney Valley station rescuers attending the aftermath of an underground explosion. Nonetheless, less than a year later, a fatal accident brought about an abrupt change in the lives of the Shore family.

On Sunday, 16th April, 1912, the fifty-one year old Rees Shore was killed at East Elliot Pit. He joined Powell Duffryn at Elliot Colliery in 1888. In March 1912, a six week long strike of members of the South Wales Enginemen, Stokers & Craftsmen Association began but it had 'fizzled out' with a return to work at least at Elliot Colliery ahead of a settlement with the coalowners.[23] He was probably not a member of the Association, but as a foreman of underground craftsmen, Rees Shore's duty was to ensure that mechanical equipment allowed coal to flow to the pit bottom once miners began work. His death was recorded as: 'Accidental … viz. injuries received by being run over by a journey of trams whilst following his employment'. The grief of the Shore family swiftly became a private matter. A national strike of miners took place in April and May 1912. Ship owners, fearing a shortage of steam coal, changed their ship bunkering plans. At Southampton, the White Star Line gave priority to the *Titanic* for the passenger liner's maiden voyage to New York. The sinking of the *Titanic*, on the eve of Rees Shore's death, was an international story. The coal miner's strike was for a minimum wage. The Government was prevailed upon, and a Minimum Wage Act was passed.

Pre-Britannia Colliery

The previous year, on 21st November, 1911, Lord Merthyr of Senghenydd, formerly Sir William Thomas Lewis, addressed a Special General Meeting of the South Wales Institute of Engineers convened to make him an Honorary Member. In 1905, the company he led, Lewis Merthyr Collieries, bought the Universal Colliery located at Senghenydd, Aber Valley, from the Universal Colliery Steam Coal Company. He had also been a leading instigator in the founding, in 1872, of the Monmouthshire & South Wales Coalowners' Association.

The Institute's occasion gave Lord Merthyr an opportunity to reflect upon the 'great change' that had taken place in the South Wales Coalfield between 1851 and 1911.[24] In 1851, the Coalfield's output of coal stood at 9 million tons, but in 1911, it was over 50 million tons. In 1851, the Coalfield's coalowners employed 32,143 workmen, and six decades later 220,887. With regard to his reflections, he chose mechanical ventilation as the most valuable aspect of engineering applied in the South Wales Coalfield during his long mining career. Nevertheless, another major technical change had reached a mature state in the Coalfield.

By 1911, steam power dominated colliery winding in the South Wales Coalfield just as water-balance winding headgear had done when William Thomas Lewis was a boy. George Hann observed later on that November day: 'It is quite obvious that to anyone who travels around the South Wales Coalfield, or any other coalfield, that there is a vast amount of steam being wasted which could be used'.[25] Preceding this he had said: 'I think that it would be generally conceded that if the collieries of the South Wales Coalfield were laid out again the most economical method of extracting the coal would be putting up central electric generating stations and electric plant at the collieries'. What can be implied from this statement was that such infrastructure made electric winding possible. Indeed, George Hann's words were a prelude to his reflection about a momentous step taken by Powell Duffryn. The company had sealed a contract with Siemens Brothers Dynamo Works Ltd on the 11th October, 1910, for the delivery of two electric winders for Britannia Colliery.[26]

The members of the South Wales Institute of Engineers had earlier learnt about this from George Hann on the 18th October, 1910, during a discussion about his paper about 'The sinking and equipping of Penallta Colliery'. Earlier in 1910, George Hann did not appear to be in favour of electric winding.

Hugh Bramwell, on hearing about Powell Duffryn's decision to order electric winders for Britannia Colliery, remarked that he was 'pleased to see that Mr Hann is more or less converted to' a view that the most economical winding plant was 'entirely electric'.[27]

George Hann responded on the 19th January, 1911: 'Mr Bramwell suggested that he (Mr Hann) was now converted to electric winding because the colliery now being sunk by the Powell Duffryn Company at Pengam was to be electrically equipped throughout. But this was not the case', as he explained:

'The Pengam proposition was not the same as that of Penallta, and were Penallta to be done over again, there was no question it would be done in the same way, viz., with steam as the winding power. To examine the conditions at the two places – Penallta Colliery had no Electric Power Station from which to derive its power from; and to wind with electricity meant putting much larger generating plant at the colliery. There was no electric power company in a position to supply it, and the cost per unit would have to be below $^{1}/_{4}$ d. in order that it might compete with the steam winder.'[28]

George Hann's explanation held to what he had given in his 1910-1911 South Wales Institute of Engineers' paper about the sinking of Penallta. However, Hugh Bramwell's observation that Powell Duffryn had undergone a conversion to electric winding at the Pengam sinking, otherwise Britannia Colliery, was true. Yet, it seems, an impression had formed in at least Hugh Bramwell's mind that Powell Duffryn had been somewhat hesitant about adopting electric winding. Was such an impression a fair one?

Writing in 1918, George Hann, tabled two reasons why electrical winding was favoured at Britannia Colliery.[29] First, that 'the colliery' was 'situated $1^{1}/_{4}$ miles to the south of Bargoed Colliery and 3 miles from Penallta Collieries'. 'Both these collieries had power available in the shape of exhaust steam from winding engines, compressors and fans, and Bargoed Colliery also had surplus gas from the coke ovens'. Then he stated: 'This was perhaps the main consideration which decided on electric power as the drive for the machinery'. He admitted though, that the waste power available was 'not sufficient to operate the colliery at a big output, but was nearly sufficient for the period of the sinking', when electrical winding was used.

Britannia Colliery– Electric Winding Engine that used the Ilgner System.

So, to power Britannia Colliery an extra amount of electrical generating capacity was needed at a developing Bargoed Power station, which was eventually provided. However, according to George Hann, the last reason 'that influenced the decision in favour of electricity, was the site of the [Britannia] pits was confined, and the electric equipment took much less room, as boiler house, cooling pond, etc., were not required'. However, had the company hesitated regarding the adoption of electric winding? Or, had it acted in its customary fashion when thinking about making technical change?

In 1904, T. Hurry Riches gave an insightful appraisal of that year's South Wales Institute of Engineer's president, Edmund Mills Hann. Powell Duffryn's general manager of collieries was 'thorough' in 'all he did'. Moreover, as a practical engineer, Hann became technically wise due to both rigorous study of old and new engineering technologies, and through encouraging experimentation with regard to incremental equipment development. His sense of duty to the company as a business was also acute.

Edmund Mills Hann had to be convinced about the financial value to Powell Duffryn of a proposed colliery engineering change before he sought board approval. When he dealt with the company's board, his modesty of manner served him well. Such a manner allowed him to act with patience and tact dealing with probing questions arising from board members unfamiliar with engineering. The board members must have also possessed a keenness to learn since they backed many of his proposals that envisaged considerable technical change. The Tredegar Iron & Coal Company led the way in the South Wales Coalfield with colliery electrification, and Powell Duffryn surpassed it not long afterwards with its Aberdare Collieries scheme. The Bargoed Colliery by-products plant supplanted the coalfield's pioneer, the Great Western Colliery Company. In the case of the advent of another major technical advance in the company's history, electric winding at Britannia Colliery, Edmund Mills Hann acted in his customary fashion. Although, as implied from the above, he put the onus upon George Hann to produce the Britannia Colliery case, he gave his son's work a stern test before it was proposed to the board.

It would be unjust to think that Hugh Bramwell's comment about the 'conversion' of Powell Duffryn to electric winding was a taunt. The Great Western Collieries manager was to the fore in sharing knowledge of his company's developments at forums of the South Wales Institute of Engineers, like Edmund Mills Hann. Maybe as the pioneer of colliery electric winding in the South Wales

Coalfield he was eager for other colliery companies to follow his lead. Perhaps, being confident about the value of electric winding, he remained puzzled by Powell Duffryn's decision to adopt steam winding at Penallta Colliery, and so George Hann became the butt of his comment. Nonetheless, he knew the ways of Edmund Mills Hann, and no doubt admired the advances made by Powell Duffryn in colliery engineering.

Indeed, in April, 1910, Ithel Treharne, a 'genial', President of the South Wales Institute of Engineers, had recorded his perspective:

'The immense advances and improvements that have been made within recent years, and compare the two coal-winnings of Harris's Navigation and those of Powell Duffryn Company at Bargoed and Penalltau. The first when it was sunk and equipped was considered to have been carried out in the most improved manner and with the best then known modern appliances, but the completion of the work took many years. Compare this with the celerity with which the winning has been completed at the two Powell Duffryn Company's undertakings, the modern methods and machinery there employed, and it will be at once appreciated what great strides have been made in the knowledge and ability of the mining engineer.'[30]

Ithel Treharne's appraisal of enterprising engineering by Powell Duffryn, under Edmund Mills Hann, was a profound one. Indeed, key to appreciating the company's progress was a grasp of technical knowledge. And major technical change was put into practice at Britannia Colliery in a form and size that some of Powell Duffryn's rivals had come to expect. Hugh Bramwell observed, in October, 1910, 'The [electric] winders to be installed at Pengam are, he believed, the largest ever ordered in this country.'[31]

Electric Winding Options

The electric winder chosen by Powell Duffryn came after a rigorous study of the available technology, and learning from shared experience. Hugh Bramwell judged it useful to warn Powell Duffryn about a 'great bugbear' of electric winding: 'the necessity to use an expensive piece of plant in the form of a heavy flywheel balancing set'.[32] The Great Western Colliery Company adopted for the winding engine at Maritime Pit the British Westinghouse Company's converter-equaliser system of electrical control.[33] In summary: the system comprised a three-phase motor on the drum shaft operated through a water resistance, and having a flywheel equaliser set "in parallel". The equaliser set enabled 'surplus energy' to be taken 'out of the transmission line' for use at crucial moments when the conditions demanded of the winding motor was greater than normal.

A crucial moment, commonly referred to as the 'peak load', was when it became necessary to lift the cage, plus its cargo, from a stationary position at the foot of a shaft as a wind to the colliery's surface began. To manage the peak load condition at Maritime Pit, calculations identified a need for a 1,450 hp electric motor if a cylindrical drum was driven.[34] However, by making use of Edmund Mills Hann's spiro-cylindrical drum, the use of a lower peak load condition, at 1,000 hp, was made possible.

Hugh Bramwell, in late 1910, announced the demise of the 'bugbear'. At Maritime Colliery, 'for more than twelve months [the electrical winder had] been working without the balancer. The Power Company is now able to take on all the peak loads, and the result has been that, having no balance running when the engine is standing, the [electrical] units used per wind have been greatly reduced'.

D. Davis & Sons, Ltd chose to use the Ilgner system at Ferndale Collieries.[35] The Ilgner system enabled the 'total fluctuating power demanded by the winding-engine' to be passed through the equaliser set which was "in series" with the winding motor'.[36] The equaliser set comprised a motor generator consisting of a three-phase motor (AC), a continuous current (DC) dynamo, and a flywheel. Physically the equaliser was located in the winding house some distance from the motor driving the drum. The loss of electrical power to a winder was an early fear for colliery engineers since miners could be stranded underground. Hooghwinkel acknowledged, though, that since the Ilgner system put energy back into the system, and was 'recuperative' in braking, it avoided 'heavy starting losses, and may be easily controlled'.[37]

Hooghwinkel was also alert to a 'controversial point' – the price of electrical power. This was determined by the cost of coal. He noted an 'apparent anomaly', of the period, that the value of small coal in South Wales was increasing whilst there was a decrease in the cost of electric power. The explanation for this was improved economy of boiler plant, and the introduction of large economical generating units. However, he suggested that the higher the selling value of the small coal used, the better the case for electricity. So, in principle at least, Powell Duffryn judged that at Bargoed Colliery was a reserve of electricity generated that offered Britannia Colliery the prospect of competitively priced electricity.

Moreover, the scale of Powell Duffryn's electrical generating capacity, being greater than its South Wales Coalfield coal company rivals, implied that it was capable of producing electricity at a much cheaper price than them. In 1910, the company, with installed generating capacity of 15,200 kW, produced 28,295,391 Board of Trade electrical units.[38] For rough comparison, the pioneer in the Coalfield of colliery electrical engineering, the Tredegar & Iron Coal Company, possessed a total generating capacity of 2,700 kW by 1911.[39] In 1913, the Cambrian Combine, by then an amalgamation of the Glamorgan Coal Company, Britannic Merthyr Coal Company and the Naval Colliery (1897), possessed 3,500 kW generating capacity.[40] The D. Davis & Son coal company operated by 1907-8 with 4,800 kW generating capacity.[41]

Britannia Colliery

Although Edmund Mills Hann gave the final approval on colliery engineering matters, George Hann led the engineering of Britannia Colliery. The Ilgner system was chosen for winding. The company stressed that it was installed to 'avoid the heavy loads coming on the Power Stations at the time the winding engines' were started.[42]

Edmund Hann wrote a brief description of Britannia Colliery's Ilgner system.[43] To handle the peak loads, the system used a motor generator, to convert 3-phase AC into DC, and it was located in series between the electricity supply mains, and a Siemens DC motor that drove the winding drum. The peak load arose winding 6-tons per minute, demanding about 5,000 horsepower. The Ilgner system involved a motor set and fly-wheel to satisfy this peak load condition by having 1,850 hp of energy supplied from Bargoed power station to the motor set with the balance of power from energy stored in a spinning 33-ton fly-wheel. When the electrical demand reached 1,850 hp an arrangement prevented any more electricity being taken from the power station. The fly-wheel subsequently lost speed. When the power supply was switched off, the AC motor was used to drive the fly-wheel so as to return it

Britannia Colliery. The first British colliery operated entirely by electricity. By 1915, 689 miners worked at the colliery. A shortage of horses, due to the First World War, partly caused the colliery to utilise underground conveyors to move coal. *Inset*: Britannia token.
Courtesy Paul Jackson Collection and Mark Smith

to full speed before the next wind was begun. The two winding engines installed at Britannia Colliery, complete with the Ilgner system, saw each one drive a spiral drum of 14ft to 22ft diameter.[44]

At the outset, Britannia Colliery was supplied electricity by way of two overhead lines, one from Bargoed Colliery, and the other from Penallta Colliery.[45] The Rhymney Valley electricity transmission scheme also included Elliot and New Tredegar Collieries, but by 1913, the company operated a grid that united the electricity resources of the Rhymney and Aberdare Valleys.

Britannia Colliery stood on the arbitrary boundary between steam, and smokeless steam coals.[46] Sinking began there in February 1911 with its two shafts being 21ft in diameter.[47] The electric winders were operational in September 1910, and so were available for the removal of spoil from the sinkers' excavation work.

George Hann reported that 'very great difficulties were encountered' sinking at Britannia Colliery. 'The quantity of water being greater' than had 'been experienced in any sinking at a similar depth'. According to Edmund Mills Hann, the scale of the feeders at Britannia was a surprise. The company believed that the pumping operation of Bargoed Colliery, and maybe Elliot Colliery, would have curtailed the flow of underground water at Britannia Colliery.

In September 1913, sinking work was completed at Britannia Colliery. Edmund Mills Hann reported that the depth of one shaft was 615 yards, and the other 715 yards. George Hann also quoted 730 yards for the deeper shaft. This may have been to the base of its sump, and not the depth from which double decked cages, with two trams to each deck, making a load of 6-tons of coal, were

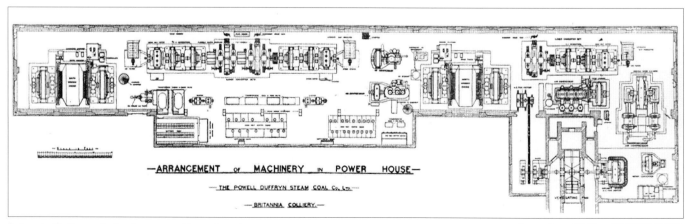

Britannia Colliery winding house machinery layout.
Proceedings, SWIE, vol.XXXIV, (1918)

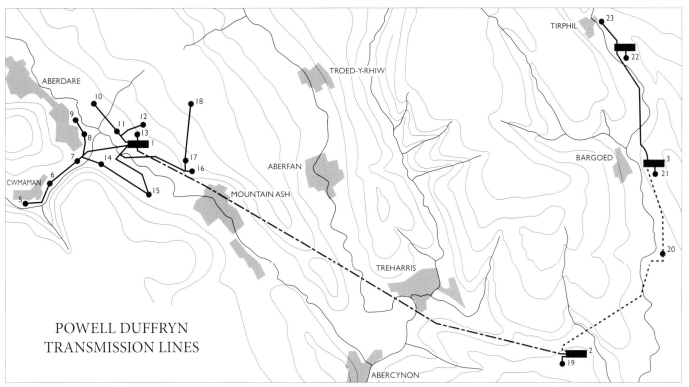

POWELL DUFFRYN
TRANSMISSION LINES

Powell Duffryn's electricity transmission grid connecting the Aberdare and Rhymney Valleys in 1913. Locations are represented by the following numbers: 1-Aberaman Power Station (formerly Middle Duffryn Power station; 2 & 19- Penallta Colliery; 3 & 21- Bargoed Power Station & Colliery and; 5-Ffforchaman; 6-Cwmneol; 7-Aberaman Colliery; 8-Treaman Pit (used for haulage); 9-Abergwawr (Plough Pit); 10-High Duffryn; 11-Old Duffryn; 12- Llety Shenkin; 13-Middle Duffryn Washery; 14-Aberaman Brick Works; 15-Abercwmboi; 16 & 17-Lower Duffryn; 18-George Pit; 20-Britannia; 22-Elliot; and 23-New Tredegar.
Electricity in Mining, Siemens Brothers Dynamo Works Ltd, 1913

The sinking of a shaft at Britannia Colliery, Rhymney Valley. Photograph taken by Arthur Wright.
Courtesy of Caerphilly County Borough Museums & Heritage Service: Winding House.

raised. The rail versus guide rope debate, which Penallta Colliery's engineering attracted, was provoked further at Britannia Colliery. Guide rails were erected in the colliery's south pit, while in the north pit (the upcast) rope guides of $1^3/_4$-inch diameter were fixed into position. However, the completion of the sinking of Britannia Colliery was overshadowed by a notable coal mining catastrophe.

'And there the canary died'

As referred to earlier, in 1905 the Universal Colliery at Senghenydd, at the top of the Aber Valley, became an asset of Lewis-Merthyr Collieries due to its acquisition of Universal Steam Coal Company.[48] The fifth year of the colliery's operation, 1901, was remembered for an underground explosion that killed sixty-one men. In 1913, the colliery was used 'exclusively for the production of steam coal for the Admiralty' and employed 2,200 men (term used hereafter but numbers included youths).[49] The colliery was described as being a 'dry mine'.

On Tuesday, 14th October, 1913 at 8.30 a.m. at a depth of around 507 yards, in a western district of the colliery, there was another explosion.[50] At the time there were 935 men underground on the 6 a.m. to 2 p.m. shift. The explosion's blast hit the colliery's surface. The headgear for the colliery's northern shaft, the downcast, called the Lancaster pit, was damaged, and two surface banksmen were killed.[51] 'Though weighing tons', the cage in the Lancaster pit had been 'hurled up like a ball, with a result that the ropes got entangled'. The colliery's upcast shaft, the York pit, lay southward from the Lancaster pit, was operable.

Immediately after the explosion, Edward Shaw, agent and manager of the colliery, with another official, descended the York pit. At pit bottom they began a search but fires and other hazards forced them to retreat. Shaw returned to the surface and, at 10 a.m.,

called for rescue station support by which time an underground evacuation was underway. By noon, nearly 500 men, with a show of calm that hid fear, escaped to the colliery's surface.[52]

The Rhymney Valley Rescue Station's team was the first of a number of such teams to arrive at Universal Colliery.[53] The team, eleven trained rescuers, led by the station's superintendent, J. M. Kitto, arrived at the colliery in a 'specially equipped car'.[54] They were joined later by teams from the rescue stations at Aberaman, Crumlin, and Porth.

The Rhymney Valley rescue team, equipped with breathing apparatus, added skilled support to the colliery's search and rescue work. Team members 'took down' canaries to 'test the air' for poisonous gases. A fire halted attempts to reach the men in the colliery's western districts. 'More work had to be done to reach the 400 entombed men in the Lancaster pit'. However, seventeen dead bodies were recovered.

A huge response to the colliery's explosion followed. The village of Senghenydd was 'soon filled with motor cars. Officials and mining experts arrived from all parts of South Wales', as did Government Mine inspectors. Doctors rushed to the colliery. A 'full strength' contingent of Red Cross sisters, Cardiff Infirmary nurses, and one hundred ambulance men, completed the medical support.

Underground the brave teams of rescuers from the Aberaman, Crumlin, Porth, and Rhymney Valley rescue stations worked in relay. The grimmest work for the rescuers involved recovering dead bodies, and horse carcasses. Exploratory work met dangers like the heat due to the fire, deadly fumes, dense smoke, the risk of another explosion, and roof collapse. Rescuers crawled along narrow passageways in many places.

The Wednesday saw Lord Merthyr, chairman of Lewis-Merthyr Collieries, chair a conference.[55] An outcome of the conference

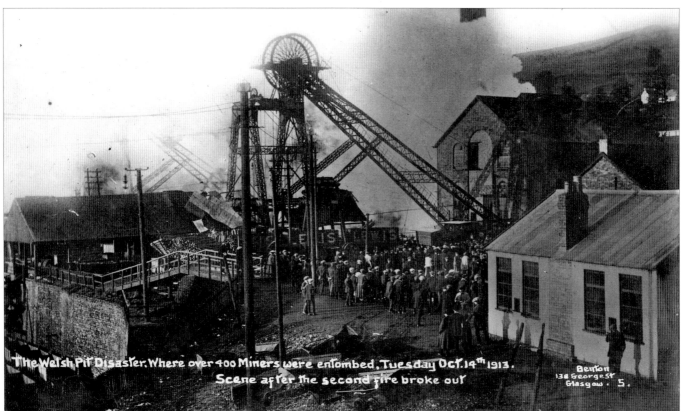

The Welsh Pit Disaster. Where over 400 Miners were entombed. Tuesday Oct. 14th 1913. Scene after the second fire broke out

Benton 138 George St Glasgow. 5.

Universal Colliery, Lancaster Pit top showing, to the left of the headgear, some structural damage due to an underground explosion on 14th October, 1913. Such bystanders would later recall being present at the greatest human catastrophe in the history of British coal mining. *Pope/Parkhouse Archive*

The Great Welsh disaster at Senghenydd. Removing some of the Victims.

A sombre mood prevails as stretcher bearers carry from possibly the Universal Colliery's York Pit one of the 439 men killed by an explosion in 1913.

Pope/Parkhouse Archive

was the formation of a 'committee of experts', which included Leonard Llewelyn, Cambrian Collieries, 'who has always taken a foremost part in rescue work at all Welsh colliery disasters in recent times'. The committee was set up to 'discuss' with the colliery's management and the inspectors of mines 'the best means of restoring the ventilation on the east side of the colliery and also to deal with the fire on the west side'.

One rescue in the colliery's Bottanic district won notice. Dr Dan Thomas, of Bargoed, Gelligaer Urban District Council's medical officer of health, 'headed' an advance rescue party. He was notable for being the first medical man to descend into the pit, and worked underground from 9 p.m. Tuesday until 3 p.m. on Wednesday.[56] Regarding the Bottanic district rescue effort, the doctor's party contained Greenland Davies (mines inspector), Lewis Watkins (Bargoed colliery manager), J. M. Kitto, J. W. Price, (Mechanical Engineer, Rhymney) and D. Watts Morgan (Miners' Agent). The advance party was supported by Robert T. Rees (agent to Lord Merthyr), J. A. Price (Elliot Colliery manager), and other members of the Rhymney Valley rescue team. The advance party men gained the 'highest credit'.[57]

Immediately after Dr Dan Thomas's advance party saved the lives of eighteen men from the Bottanic district there was an incident. At 'a spot on the Bottanic level' the party 'had' to desist from further exploration'. Later, the spot was pointed to on a plan of the colliery's workings, and was a cue for a 'practical expert' to say, "*And there the canary died.*"[58] The sacrifice of a bird's life warned the party of a threat to their lives.

However, the success of Dan Thomas's advance party rescue proved to be a rare moment in the attempt to save more men's lives at the colliery. On Friday, 17th October, the underground fire was brought under control. The search of the western districts of the

colliery for bodies took weeks since large roof falls, and blowers of gas were encountered. The final official death toll was 439 men, and one rescuer was killed by a roof fall.[59]

The 1913 explosion at Universal Colliery became the biggest disaster in British coal mining history. The cause and place of the explosion became subjects of expert speculation, but no consensus was reached. The disaster left an estimated at 542 children, 205 widows, and sixty-two 'father and mothers dependent' to grieve the loss of both loved ones and household wage earners.[60] The South Wales Coalfield's position at the top of a "miner's graveyard" league table was strengthened.[61] Concerning the Universal Colliery disaster, the jury at the Coroner's inquest gave an 'accidental death' verdict. A commission of inquiry into the disaster followed the Coroner's inquest.

Senghenydd's colliery, a contemporary of Bargoed Colliery, was claimed to operate using plant and equipment 'on the most up-to-date lines'.[62] However, an issue was whether, or not, the plant and equipment had been engineered to a standard, supported by methods and procedures, that promoted explosion prevention. Over a period of months, in 1914, Edward Shaw and the coal company were prosecuted at Caerphilly's Magistrate Court for breaches of the Coal Mines Act 1911. Universal Colliery's ventilation, contrary to the Act, which appeared to be a new requirement, did not have the ability to reverse the air flow. When Penallta Colliery was opened the ventilation's air flow was not designed as reversible, but a means was available to provide 'sufficient air for rescue work'.[63] However, as an idea of a preventive measure, Bargoed Colliery's ventilation system moved 500,000ft³ of air per minute versus 150,000ft³ of air per minute at Universal Colliery.[64] The inadequate administration of safety lamps and the use of non-approved types were also among the breaches found at

Senghenydd's colliery. The painstaking Edmund Mills Hann, wary about the limitations of safety lamps, directed Powell Duffryn to buy the safest lamp available, and his mind was open to safer lighting inventions. Indeed, in 1913, Powell Duffryn introduced electric safety lamps after satisfactory trials, which found they gave from two to three times more light than an oil safety lamp. 7,200 electric safety lamps were allotted to Powell Duffryn's collieries.[65]

Another breach of the Act at Universal Colliery was due to neglect in removing accumulations of coal dust on the 'roof, sides and timber' of the underground roadways. Edmund Mills Hann and William Galloway would have both been aghast on learning about the build-up of coal dust at Universal Colliery. Why had the management of Universal Colliery not fully heeded the work of William Galloway like, for instance, Powell Duffryn had endeavoured to do?

Britannia Colliery – Development Phase

One item of interest to Powell Duffryn's general manager of collieries for the period from September 1913 to August 1914 concerned reports from his son, George, about progress made to develop Britannia Colliery. The period saw lodge-rooms for pumps driven, the North Pit fitted out, arches erected at pit bottom, and driving out beyond the pit pillar so that Longwall mining commenced.[66] The actual work of opening out the colliery began 'in January 1914 in the Red Vein' coal seam that varied in thickness from 4ft to 4ft 6 inches.[67] Moreover, Edmund Mills Hann disclosed in 1914 that it was the company's intention to work first 'the Red Vein and the Ras Las ... the depth to the Red Vein in the downcast is 715 yards'.[68]

George Hann revealed: 'Very rapid driving was accomplished through the shaft pillar: as much as 86 yards were driven in a week with a puncher type of coal-cutter'. He further claimed introducing an innovation in mining practice to the South Wales Coalfield:

> 'When the workings were opened out it was decided to use conveyors of the jigging type, to be driven by compressed air. The use of conveyors in a thick seam was certainly a departure from the usual practice in the district. The chief reason for adopting conveyors was that a larger yield of coal per yard of face per day could be obtained than with the stall system; this allowed of a more rapid increase of output. The yield per yard of face per day could be obtained for the colliery averages 16 to 17 cwts, or for from 12,000 to 13,000 tons are got per week from 2,400 yards of working face.'

Also in 1918, in his paper about Britannia Colliery, George Hann reflected: 'the advent of the Jigging Conveyor' brought to an end ten years of disappointing experience with conveying.[69]

Another underground practice, borrowed from the Midland Coalfield, was introduced into the colliery. George Hann's hope was that there would be no need to send rubbish out of the pit. The practice introduced involved a 'system of packs [of rubbish] .... stowed in the region of the coal face' to allow 'for better control of the roof than if the face was filled'.[70]

The colliery's compressed air supply facility was backed up with a supply from Bargoed Colliery.[71] In case of failure of compressor plant, at either Bargoed, or Britannia, a 9-inch main, 6,000ft long connection was installed.[72] Contingency planning was an essential aspect of Powell Duffryn's 'modern' colliery engineering.

The experience of the feeders, though, may have caused more investment to be made in the colliery's pumping capability than was initially planned. The company treasured the resulting facilities. Altogether, six pumps, all of the centrifugal type were installed.[73] The thirst of these pumps, and the location of Britannia Colliery in the Rhymney Valley, had an unexpected consequence: they 'partially drained all the upper [Rhymney Valley] pits'. Edmund Mills Hann noted that the quantity of water pumped at Bargoed' fell by 'about 70%, at Elliot Pits 40%, and even at New Tredegar to a small extent, though nearly four miles away'.[74] Edmund Mills Hann speculated that 'the source of the water was the Pengam Fault which runs west of all these collieries but gradually approaches the line of the Collieries as one proceeds southward'. The geology of the Rhymney Valley still retained some mystery for the experienced mining engineer to solve.

In someway, Bargoed Colliery exchanged its future as a drier pit to become the coal depository for its southern neighbour. A short time after 1914, an aerial ropeway was commissioned to take Britannia Colliery's coal to Bargoed's washery.

Britannia Colliery would later justify the company's general manager colliery's optimism of 1914, that it would be a 'most valuable colliery'. Nevertheless, Edmund Mills Hann suffered a setback: the sinking did not find the Six Feet seam due to 'a local washout', which occurred earlier in geological time. However, with regard to the Red Vein and Ras Las seams, and with 'other seams above', perhaps 'not so favourable', he predicted a 'profitable life ... for a very long period'.

What though made Britannia Colliery different according to its engineer? George Hann wrote in 1918: 'There are two ways in which the colliery differs from the ordinary:

1. The whole of the machinery is electrically driven, there being no steam boilers at the colliery.
2. The whole output is got by conveyors; there are no horses, the haulage being mechanical throughout'.[75]

Although Britannia Colliery was exceptional in these respects, the colliery gave an opportunity to a further Hann to advance his management career. In 1913, Douglas Alfred became agent of Britannia and Penallta Pits.[76] In 1915, Britannia Colliery employed 689 miners underground and there were 172 colliery workers employed on its surface.[77] In 1921, sourced from the first employment data available after the First World War, the colliery employed 1,332 miners and 259 surface workers. The year 1924 saw the maximum number of miners employed at the colliery, 1,634. In 1934, the colliery's output was 400,000 tons.[78]

According to John Cornwell's review of Britannia Colliery, 'by the late 1970s, 800 men raised an annual saleable output of 244,953 tons of coal from 2 faces'.[79] He also recounted an anecdote, that although it was a 'very wet pit', it was one 'where nothing ever happened apart from raising coal'. This anecdote might have had its origins in ridicule, but it can also be read as a compliment. Sixty years after it had been founded, the colliery remained a statement about Powell Duffryn's quest to engineer efficient collieries. And, in Powell Duffryn's book about its fifty year history, Britannia Colliery was identified as being the first colliery in the British coal industry 'to be entirely worked by electricity produced by the owners of the Colliery, and not any boilers among the plant at all'.[80]

As another new colliery operating under the direction of Edmund Mills Hann, his fourth in the Rhymney Valley, it initiated a further lineage of colliery managers. In 1914, Britannia Colliery's manager was W. E. Jayne. He was followed by at least: D. Griffiths, around 1921; T. Thomas held the post in 1927; H. S. Jayne was manager in 1938; and C. H. Clark was in the post for the period between 1943 and 1945.[81]

Moreover, east from the colliery, another Rhymney Valley community was created so as to house miners and their families. Today known as Cefn Fforest, a suburb of Blackwood, its housing was semi-detached in style in contrast to the terraced homes of New Tredegar and Bargoed. Edmund Mills Hann served as chairman of a co-partnership society, using as part of its name Pengam Garden Village, to set up and develop the community.[82]

A Hard Piece of Dry Timber

In 1913, Powell Duffryn's general manager of collieries shared the company's experiences of underground mechanisation with rival coalowners. Edmund Mills Hann was disappointed with results obtained when coal-cutters and conveyors were used together.[83] With regard to conveyors, 'where they were put into operation on hand cut faces there has been some success, but even these results are not as good as were anticipated. In every case these conveyors were of the continuous-running type, and where the coal was got by hand this appears to be the most suitable type. Where the coal is machine-cut, my opinion is that the intermittent type is the better, but it must be of the most simple construction'.

Moreover, regarding conveyors, he thought, they were 'too delicate' for coal mining. He proposed that 'inventors of conveyors should endeavour to provide one which will handle coal, and also the rubbish necessary for storing the goaf [gob]'. These difficulties aside, conveyor use advanced much more quickly in Powell Duffryn collieries than coal-cutters.

The low productivity of coal-cutting machines restrained their use at Powell Duffryn's collieries. The state of the roof at the coalface, and time lost in Longwall when coal-cutting machines were moved and the 'gob' packed, were factors cited by Edmund Mills as causing a loss of coal output. Concerning a coal-cutter working a thin seam, he had calculated that the 'yield' of coal was $2^1/_4$ to $2^1/_2$ hundredweights per yard of face.[84] In his opinion, this was 'of course an exceptionally slow rate of advance; it meant that heavy timber was standing for a long time'. And he further pronounced: 'If machine mining was to be any success at all, this rate of progress per yard of face must be accelerated, and to achieve that they were bound to improve the general conditions of the roof'.

He had still to reach a conclusion about which coal-cutting method was best. The bar machine, 'under certain circumstances', was found to be 'better than the disc machine'. When coal fell on a disc, it jammed. He had found that 'the bar' machine 'took a big cut, whereas the chain machine cut down to $3^1/_4$-inch, which in a thin seam was an enormous advantage. The chain machine must have soft material to work in. It did not seem to be able to tackle hard material'.

Indeed, maybe not surprisingly, he echoed an observation made by G. D. Budge and W. E. Jayne in their joint paper about coal-cutting machine trials they had conducted at a south Wales steam coal colliery around that time. The trials were probably carried out at a Powell Duffryn colliery and may have preceded W. E. Jayne's appointment as manager of Britannia Colliery. G. D. Budge and W. E. Jayne's observation was: 'Coal-cutting in South Wales seams closely approximates to the work of cutting a hard dry piece of timber with a hatchet. A good coal-cutting subject corresponds to fresh moist timber being cut with the same tool. Obviously what is required is a special cutting-tool for South Wales coals'.[85]

Perhaps Powell Duffryn's experiences of machine mining spoke for the general outlook taken by other mining engineers of the

South Wales Coalfield. In January 1914, Henry Wales commented that 'the use of coal-cutting machinery and conveyors' in the South Wales Coalfield had 'not increased to any great extent, the numbers in use being, in 1912, 114 coal-cutters and forty-seven conveyors in forty-five collieries, where the quantity of coal cut mechanically was 590,000 tons, which represented just over one percentage of the coal produced.[86] During the second decade of the twentieth century, seams of steam coal worked by Powell Duffryn were not favourable to machine mining. Indeed, the character of Bargoed Colliery's coal seams, similarly at the collieries of New Tredegar and Elliot, apparently hindered the introduction of coal-cutting machines.

Yet, years later, underground mechanization was noticeable at Bargoed Colliery, for example. Trevor Boyns identified: 'At the house-coal colliery [the Brithdir pit] neither conveyors nor mechanical cutters were being used, whilst at the Bargoed steam pits [Bargoed North and South], which were described as highly mechanized with cutters and conveyors, three quarters of the coal was mechanically cut'.[87] So, eventually, a trend towards machine mining became a feature of Powell Duffryn's collieries. But what did the company gain from capital investment in electrical winding at Britannia Colliery in its early years of operation?

The Benefits of Electricity

In 1914, Edmund Mills Hann announced that '*the electrical equipment*', at Britannia Colliery, had '*been pronounced on all hands to be very fine, and it has performed exceedingly well*'.[88] Moreover, around 1912, George Hann disclosed forecasted performance data concerning both the Penallta and Britannia engines to members of the South Wales Institute of Engineers as part of a review of electric winding. As a way of comparing contrasting source data, steam usage in the case of Penallta Colliery's winders, and the units of electricity used by Britannia Colliery's winders, A. E. Du Pasquier adopted a measure of pound of steam per shaft horsepower.[89] For Britannia Colliery, the equivalent of steam per kilowatt hour was 360 lb of steam as against 440 lb for Penallta Colliery which included an adjustment for colliery shaft depth differences. This meant that the electric winder used approximately 20% less energy based upon steam equivalence.

In 1912, George Hann told members of the South Wales Institute of Engineers that he thought that the electricity price had to be at the around $^1/_4$d. per unit if the electric winder was to compete with 'a modern steam plant, using exhaust-steam turbines, and using the power recovered from its exhaust steam for pumping, ventilating, hauling, and, if there is any surplus, for supplementing the compressed air supply'.[90]

Trevor Boyns's study of 'the Electricity Industry in South Wales to 1949', revealed for 1911, that Powell Duffryn's Middle Duffryn generated electricity at 0.28d./unit compared with the South Wales Power Company's 0.81d. per unit.[91] This comparison, in addition to suggesting that Powell Duffryn's unit cost met its own economic test for choosing electrical winding ahead of steam winding, revealed that a dedicated generating company of the period could not supply electrical power at Powell Duffryn's cost.

George Hann had knowledge of this advantageous position when offering a warning: 'Colliery companies are well advised in not adopting electric winding and other large electrification until they can get a supply at a reasonable cost'. As an operation's manager, his immediate priority lay in measuring for Powell Duffryn the impact of electrical winding.

Years later, in 1918, George Hann disclosed Britannia Colliery's 'general results of operation as regards power consumption as compared with steam driven machinery' for 1917. Using the rate of consumption per unit of electricity generated at Middle Duffryn Power Station at $2\frac{1}{2}$ lb per kilowatt, he calculated that Britannia Colliery consumed the equivalent of 315 tons, or 3.1 per cent of its output in coal.[92] He then predicted that with 'boiler house improvements the consumption at the new station [not identified, but it anticipated a new power station at Bargoed] will not be more than $1\frac{3}{4}$ lb per kilowatt unit.'[93] Bramwell calculated that this represented $2\frac{1}{2}$ percentage of a week's output of coal at the colliery, which he thought was an 'excellent' position.[94]

George Hann then declared Powell Duffryn's commitment to electrical generation, and made a profound admission. The company had ordered for a Bargoed power station, a 5,000 kW turbine operating at 350 lb/in², 750°F, with the guaranteed consumption of 10.2 lb of steam per kW hour on full load, which was a better performance than the best machines then in use. He then recalled he had 'previously expressed the opinion that electric winding was not justified, except where waste power could be utilised; but as a result of this experience there appears to be no reason to doubt that the supply of a number of collieries from a central station is economically sound'.[95]

Hugh Bramwell had foreseen, in January 1905, that sourcing electrical power from a central electricity generator at a suitable price, an economic case for electric winding, and the electrification of other colliery plant and equipment, would be made.[96] In essence, Powell Duffryn's Aberdare Valley collieries electrical scheme was proved that year, and it was later connected to the Rhymney Valley's electricity grid. So, it was probable that within Powell Duffryn thought was given to establishing Bargoed Colliery as a central generator for the purposes that the Great Western Colliery Company's general manager had described. Although the case for the electrification at Britannia was held as being partly due its 'confined' site, Powell Duffryn's George Hann had the humility to admit that Hugh Bramwell's earlier foresight was sound.

In addition to saving energy for winding, the company learnt much about the application of electricity for colliery engineering. Powell Duffryn realised that electricity as a system for transmitting power, compared with energy lost in both mechanical machines and in steam pipes, the low efficiency associated with the use of compressed air, possessed many advantages.[97] The energy loss in transmission of electricity was much less than the alternative systems. Indeed, there are no losses whatever when an electricity system is delivering no power, unless transformers are used. The power transmitted can be used for lighting as well being turned into mechanical work such as winding. In general, electric machines are highly efficient. The serious worry was the dangers posed by electricity when strict precautions were ignored. However, maintained by skilled electricians in a safe way, and with adherence to special regulations, the wider use of electricity stood to reap benefits for the company.

Significantly, though, George Hann's experience of engineering both Penallta and Britannia Collieries was important not only for his development as a manager, but also for Powell Duffryn. The company had in waiting a man prepared ready to be its general manager of collieries when Edmund Mills Hann retired.

NOTES

1   'President's Gold Medal', *SWIE*, Vol. XXVIII, (1912), pp.4-5.
2   David Hann, 'The Hann Family–A Mining Dynasty of South Wales part 3, F. P. Hann (1885-1966', *Glamorgan Family History Society, Journal* No. 40, (Dec., 1995) p.12.
3   W. W. Price, Card Records, Hann 2, National Library of Wales.
4   Research Notes as at March 2007. Raymond Lawrence. Colliery manager information.
5   Edmund L. Hann, 'The Sinking and Equipping of Bedwas Colliery', *SWIE*, Vol. XXIX, (1913), pp.330-345. The description of Bedwas Navigation Colliery is based upon this paper unless otherwise stated. The site of the colliery – OS grid reference ST 202857.
6   *Geological Excursions in South Wales & the Forest of Dean*, Ed. Douglas Basset & Michael Basset, *op. cit.*, p.60.
7   A. Bassett, 'The Port of Newport and the Coal Field', *SWIE*, Vol. V, (1866), p.135.
8   A. Bassett, *op. cit.*, p.146.
9   OS grid reference ST 181869.
10 A. Bassett, *op. cit.*, p.62.
11 Letter, Trevor Boyns to Writer, 25 July 2005.
12 Letter, Trevor Boyns to Writer, 25 July 2005.
13 Edmund L. Hann, *op. cit.*, p.330.
14 Edmund L. Hann also mentioned that the superheat 120⁰ F and steam pressure 160 lb/in² used was considered to be 'rather beyond the limit for the satisfactory operation of the Corliss valve'. See, *op. cit.*, p.330-331.
15 R. W. M. Clouston, 'The Development of the Babcock Boiler in Britain', *Transactions, Newcomen Society*, Vol. 58 (1986-7), p.80. The writer, as Babcock's Power's Assembly Shop superintendent was responsible for the last ever mechanical stokers made and supplied by the company. The stokers were exported to Peru to burn bagasse, a residue of sugar cane.
16 According to the 1942 classification, classed as bituminous III (gas coal) having a volatile content of 29-36% (the highest in the South Wales Coalfield); its carbon ranged from 84-88% (the lowest in the coalfield); hydrogen 5-5.5% (the highest); and had a calorific value 15,050-15,650 Btu/lb. As a rough comparison, except for the amount of volatiles, Bedwas coal was like a Durham coal. Data from the *South Wales Coalfield (Including Pembrokeshire) Regional Survey Report, op. cit.*, pp.20-21. The data used for the comparison taken from *The Efficient Use of Fuel*, (HMSO,1944), table 1, p.7, and 'Group 4', p.8.
17 Comment A. J. Edwards to Writer, 24 Aug 2005, Around 1947, he conducted a study of energy usage at Nine Mile Point Colliery.
18 The compressed air provision was estimated at 8,000 ft³ per min. One 5,000 ft³ per min compressor plus two units each 4,000 ft³ per min.
19 'The Sinking and Equipping of Bedwas Colliery', *SWIE*, Vol. XXIX, (1913), pp.387-398.
20 'The Sinking and Equipping of Bedwas Colliery', *SWIE*, Vol. XXIX, (1913), pp.488-490.
21 *The Powell Duffryn Steam Coal Company 1864-1914, op. cit.*, p.70.
22 *The Merthyr Express*, 4 February 1911, p.10.
23 *The South Wales Argus*, 15 April 1912, p.6.
24 'Special Meeting of the Institute', *SWIE*, Vol. XXVIII, (1912), p.343.
25 'Electric Winding Engines', *SWIE*, Vol. XXVIII, (1912), p.431.
26 Trevor Boyns, 'Contracts Sealed by Company for Electrical Equipment', (Unpublished). The contract price was for £31,114 10s 0d. Associated switchgear cost a further £3,367.
27 'The Sinking and Equipping of Penallta Colliery', *SWIE*, Vol. XXVII, (1910-1911), p.300.
28 'The Sinking and Equipping of Penallta Colliery', *SWIE*, Vol. XXVII, (1910-1911), pp.358-90.
29 George Hann, 'Paper on a Modern Colliery', *SWIE*, Vol. XXXIV, (1918), p.297.
30 'President's Inaugural Address', *SWIE*, Vol. XXVII, (1910-1911), p.23.
31 'The Sinking and Equipping of Penallta Colliery', *SWIE*, Vol. XXVII, (1910-1911), p.300.

32   'The Sinking and Equipping of Penallta Colliery', *SWIE*, Vol. XXVII, (1910-1911), p.298.

33   Hugh Bramwell, 'Re- Sinking and Re-Equipping the Great Western Colliery Company's Maritime Pit', *SWIE*, Vol. XXVI, (1918-1910), pp.147-8. The rope drum was driven by a British Westinghouse's system comprising: three-phase electricity winding motor; electrically controlled by a switchboard on the engineman's platform, oil break reversing switches, water rheostatic resistance, liquid starter for equalising flywheel set, automatic field regulator, transformer (2,200 to 440 V), rotary converted AC-DC, and equaliser flywheel set DC.

34   Hugh Bramwell, 'Re- Sinking and Re-Equipping the Great Western Colliery Company's Maritime Pit', *op. cit.*, p.143.

35   W. H. Patchell, 'The Electrification of the Ferndale Collieries', *SWIE*, Vol. XXVI, (1908-1910), p.902.

36   Gerald Hooghwinkel, 'Electric Winding at the Maritime Pits', *SWIE*, Vol. XXIV, (1908-1910), p.351.

37   Gerald Hooghwinkel, *op. cit.*, p.351.

38   T. Boyns, 'The Electricity Industry in South Wales to 1949', *The Welsh History Review: Cylchgrawn Hanes Cymru*, Vol. 12, No. 1, (1990), table 2, p.85. The Board of Trade Unit was used as the term for a kilowatt hour.

39   T. Boyns, 'The Electricity Industry in South Wales to 1949', *op. cit.*, p.84.

40   T. Boyns, 'The Electricity Industry in South Wales to 1949', *op. cit.*, p.86.

41   T. Boyns, 'The Electricity Industry in South Wales to 1949', *op. cit.*, p.87.

42   *The Powell Duffryn Steam Coal Company 1864-1914*, *op. cit.*, p.62.

43   E. M. Hann, *Brief History of The Powell Duffryn Steam Coal Company Ltd*, pp.36-7.

44   George Hann, 'Paper on a Modern Colliery', *SWIE*, Vol. XXXIV, (1918), pp.217-8.

45   'The Sinking and Equipping of Penallta Colliery', *SWIE*, Vol. XXVII, (1910-1911), p.582.

46   The 1942 classification, ranked the colliery's coal as bituminous I: volatiles; 17-23%, carbon ranged from 90-92%; hydrogen 4.3–5%, and calorific value 15,650 to 15,800 Btu/lb. Data from the *South Wales Coalfield (Including Pembrokeshire) Regional Survey Report*, *op. cit.*, pp.20-21.

47   George Hann, 'Paper on a Modern Colliery', *op. cit.*, Vol. XXXIV, (1918), p.229.

48   Two of the five founding directors of Universal Steam Coal Company were Herbert C. Lewis (Lord Merthyr's son), and Henry William Martin who left Powell Duffryn in 1883 to take charge of Dowlais Iron Company's collieries. John H. Brown, *The Valley of the Shadow*, (Alun, 1981), p.21.

49   *Western Mail*, 15 Oct 1913, pp.7-8.

50   The seam having this depth was the Four Feet, which was 6ft thick. When the Lancaster pit was sunk, bottoming at 650 yards, five workable seams were identified: Two Feet Nine at 493 yards; the Four Feet at 507 yards; the Six Feet at 530 yards (actually just over 4ft thick); the Universal at 535 yards, and the Nine Feet at 558 yards. John H. Brown, *op. cit.*, pp.22-3.

51   *Western Mail*, 'Ray of Hope at Senghenydd', 15 Oct 1913, p.7.

52   *Western Mail*, 15 Oct 1913, pp.7-8.

53   John H. Brown, *op. cit.*, p.82. This can be inferred from the *Western Mail* identifying that the Rhymney Valley team was the first of such rescue bodies to enter the colliery. *Western Mail*, 'First Impressions of a Pit Disaster', 15 Oct 1913, p.8, col.1.

54   E. E. Edwards, *Echoes of Rhymney*, (The Starling Press, 1974), p.54. Kitto's team comprised at least Charles Williams, Thomas Griffiths, Benjamin Rees, F. C. Gregory, Thomas Reynolds, and William Williams; see John H. Brown, *op. cit.*, p.88. Harry Hurcombe, 116 Jubilee Road, New Tredegar was also a team member. *Western Mail*, 16 Oct 1913, p.8, col.7.

55   *Western Mail*, 16 Oct 1913, p.7.

56   *Western Mail*, 16 Oct 1913, p.8, col.5.

57   *Western Mail*, 17 Oct 1913, p.8, col.5.

58   *Western Mail*, 18 Oct 1913, p.7, col.1.

59   A monument, erected in 1991, to the memory of men killed at the 1913 Universal Colliery disaster, can be found at OS Ref ST 114911.

60   *Western Mail*, 'Returns of Relief Committee', 18 Oct 1913, p.8, col.2.

61   *Western Mail*, 'Most Fatal Coal Areas', 15 Oct 1913, p.8, col.4. Between 1857 up until before the Universal Colliery disaster, 2,908 men ('men' includes also boys and youths) were killed due to 60 'serious disasters' in the South Wales Coalfield. In second place was the Lancashire and Cheshire Coalfield where 1,934 men were killed

due to 'serious disasters'. The definition of a 'serious disaster' was not given.

62   *Western Mail*, 15 Oct 1913, p.8, col.4.

63   'The Sinking and Equipping of Penallta Colliery', *SWIE*, Vol. XXVII, (1910-1911), p.100.

64   *Western Mail*, 17 Oct 1913, p.7, col.8. 200,000ft^3 minute was given by John H. Brown, *op. cit.*, p.107, who also quotes 150,000ft^3 on p.23 as per *Western Mail*.

65   *The Powell Duffryn Steam Coal Company 1864-1914*, *op. cit.*, p.28.

66   The pit pillar was an underground zone that lay under the surface buildings of a colliery and was not mined to minimize the risk of ground subsidence affecting surface buildings.

67   George Hann, 'Paper on a Modern Colliery', *op. cit.*, Vol. XXXIV, (1918), p.230.

68   E. M. Hann, *Brief History of The Powell Duffryn Steam Coal Company Ltd*, pp.35-7.

69   George Hann, 'Paper on a Modern Colliery', *op. cit.*, Vol. XXXIV, (1918), p.232.

70   George Hann, 'Paper on a Modern Colliery', *op. cit.*, Vol. XXXIV, (1918), pp.233-5.

71   George Hann, 'Paper on a Modern Colliery', *op. cit.*, Vol. XXXIV, (1918), p.225. Three compressors were installed at the colliery: one supplied 2,500ft^3 per min., another 3,500ft^3 per min., and the third, 6,000ft^3 per min. A variable speed unit with maximum rating of 5,000ft^3 per min. was put in place for fluctuations in demand thereby ensuring 'the maximum efficiency under all conditions'.

72   George Hann, 'Paper on a Modern Colliery', *op. cit.*, Vol. XXXIV, (1918), p.227.

73   The pump capacities were: 1 off Sulzer 800 HP – 75,000 gallon per hour; 1 off Sulzer 1,000 HP – 84,000 gal per hr; 1off Sulzer 300 HP – 40,000 gal per hr; 1 off Sulzer 600 HP – each 40,000 gal per hr; and 2 off Mather & Platt 440 HP – 40,000 gal per hr. *The Powell Duffryn Steam Coal Company 1864-1914*, *op. cit.*, p.64.

74   E. M. Hann, *Brief History of The Powell Duffryn Steam Coal Company Ltd*, p.38.

75   George Hann, 'Paper on a Modern Colliery', *op. cit.*, Vol. XXXIV, (1918), p.215.

76   W. W. Price, Card Records, Hann 2, National Library of Wales.

77   Trevor Boyns, Britannia Colliery-Employment Figures 1909-1938. (Annual List of Mines).

78   Research Notes as at March 2007, Raymond Lawrence. Tonnage information.

79   John Cornwell, *Collieries of South Wales*: 1, *op. cit.*, p.42.

80   E. M. Hann, *Brief History of The Powell Duffryn Steam Coal Company Ltd*, p.29.

81   Research Notes as at March 2007, Raymond Lawrence. Colliery manager information.

82   Roy Church, *The History of the British Coal Industry*, Vol. 3. (Clarendon, 1986), p.161. Messrs Welsh Garden Cities Ltd, formed in 1910, helped inaugurate such a co-partnership scheme.

83   'Underground Conveying', *SWIE*, Vol. XXIX (1913), pp.314-6.

84   'Machine Mining in the South Wales Coalfield', *SWIE*, Vol. XXX (1914), p.31-2.

85   G. D. Budge and W. E. Jayne, 'Machine Mining in the South Wales Coalfield', *SWIE*, Vol. XXIX (1913), pp.350-365.

86   'President's Inaugural Address', *SWIE*, Vol. XXX (1914), p.16.

87   T. Boyns, 'Jigging and Shaking: Technical Choice in the South Wales Coal Industry between the Wars', *The Welsh History Review: Cylchgrawn Hanes Cymru*, Vol.17, No.2, (1994), p.242.

88   E. M. Hann, *Brief History of The Powell Duffryn Steam Coal Company Ltd*, p.36.

89   A. E. Du Pasquier, 'Electric Winding Engines', *SWIE*, Vol. XXVII, (1912), pp.462-3.

90   'Electric Winding Engines', *SWIE*, Vol. XXVIII, (1912), pp.432-3.

91   T. Boyns, 'The Electricity Industry in South Wales to 1949', *op. cit.*, table 3, p.102. Powell Duffryn's costs made no allowance for depreciation charges.

92   George Hann, 'Paper on a Modern Colliery', *op. cit.*, Vol. XXXIV, (1918), p.220.

93   George Hann, 'Paper on a Modern Colliery', *op. cit.*, Vol. XXXIV, (1918), p.223.

94   'A Modern Colliery', *op. cit.*, Vol.XXXIV, (1918), p.287.

95   George Hann, 'Paper on a Modern Colliery', *op. cit.*, Vol. XXXIV, (1918), p.223.

96   Discussion, 'Electric Winding Engines', *SWIE*, Vol. XXIV, (1904-1906), pp.74.

97   G. M. Harvey, *Colliery Electrical Engineering*. (Pitman, 1924), pp.1-4.

The worldwide demand for South Wales Coalfield steam coal was key to Powell Duffryn's commercial success. A coastal chain of company depots, including one at Bordeaux, distributed coal in France. The photograph, circa 1903, shows a fleet of PD barges, outfitted with sail, floating upon the Garonne, Bordeaux, taking coal from a collier. The barges moved coal within the largest fine-wine district in the world by navigating the Garonne and Dordogne rivers.

Chapter Eight
PROGRESSIVE & PROFITABLE

The year 1914 saw Powell Duffryn Steam Coal Company celebrate its fiftieth year as a business. During Sir George Elliot's era of 'practical direction' the Aberdare Valley collieries were at the centre of the company's activity. However, during the period 1864 to 1888, Sir George Elliot courted the wrath of Powell Duffryn's shareholders since their investment in the company yielded less than satisfactory returns. Trevor Boyns's studies of Powell Duffryn found:

'Evidence that some of the shareholders wanted the enterprise to come to an end as early as 1868/69, given the large calls being made on their financial resources – each of the company's 100 shares had a nominal value of £5,000 (a considerable sum of money at the time), and though only £1,000 was called up initially, by 1874 this had risen to £4,800. Evidence from the Board minutes, however, reveals that the dividends paid out on the ordinary shares between 1864 and 1874 amounted to £4,750 virtually covering the amounts called up – however, the shareholders had received little cash, it all being ploughed back into the business in the form of amounts credited as being paid up on their shares! The lack of payment of dividends in poor trade after 1874 meant that the ordinary shareholders received little return, though many held preference shares and debentures, for which they did receive a return, but not always every year as they should have done.'[1]

Yet, the company founder's ground-breaking move occurred in the Rhymney Valley when he instigated Elliot Colliery. His seemingly reckless action to establish the colliery positioned the company for expansion in the Rhymney Valley.

Powell Duffryn was also fortunate in having Edmund Mills Hann as its general manager of collieries at a crucial moment in its evolution. He possessed the character, skill and knowledge needed to engineer productive Rhymney Valley collieries beginning with Elliot Colliery and then Bargoed Colliery. Then, by 1914, in addition to the company opening Penallta and Britannia Collieries, there had been a re-development of a number of other collieries. Due to winning the support of the company's directors, the fruition of Edmund Mills Hann's colliery engineering was a rich statement in terms of technical progress.

By 1914, Powell Duffryn's compound steam winding engine practice differed markedly from that generally used in the British coal industry.[2] In 1927, Major E. Ivor David reflected upon the history of winding engines, and observed that 'the compound engine was the exception while there were hundreds of low-pressure, medium and high-pressure double cylinder engines working'.[3] He also appraised Hann's action regarding Powell Duffryn's use of compound steam winding engine with the 'modified cylindro-conical drum', and acknowledged that Hann had obtained 'highly successful results'.

Although Edmund Mills Hann encouraged technical development, he had to be assured that a proposed development could lead to economic benefits for the company over some term before sanctioning its application. Maybe it was his objective approach to making plant and equipment investment decisions that impressed the company's directors. Perhaps he earned their regard when he salvaged a future for the company from the debacles that hit

Medal issued to mark the company's 50th year.

Courtesy Mark Smith

the early years of Elliot Colliery. Sinking the colliery's east shaft made it a feasible coal mining operation. Engineering a solution to the floods that marred the colliery operation in the 1890s saw the company spare no expense in order that he sourced the best pumping machinery. Arguably as a result of Elliot Colliery's debacles the company's directors recognised that quality colliery engineering was a fulcrum for business success, market conditions allowing.

Certainly a picture emerged between 1890 and 1914, beginning with Elliot Colliery, that Powell Duffryn put great trust in innovative colliery engineering. The coal washery plants at Elliot Colliery, and Middle Duffryn, were pioneering events in the history of the South Wales Coalfield. Underground conveyors were introduced, as were coal-cutting machines, if reluctantly since the first trials of such machines had yielded less than satisfactory results.

Electrical engineering, in a basic form when planning the founding of Bargoed Colliery, took on revolutionary form as the Aberdare Valley scheme. As a measure of this technology's subsequent advance, and as an indication of the growth in importance of the company's Rhymney Valley operation compared with the Aberdare Valley's, the electrical units generated in these respective areas in 1913 were: Middle Duffryn Power Station 18,623,800; and the Rhymney Valley Power Stations 30,348,700.[4] Moreover, by 1916, a nine mile 30,000 volts line was erected to connect the Britannia Colliery to Middle Duffryn Power Station in the Aberdare Valley.[5] So the company's electricity supply schemes in the Valleys of Aberdare and Rhymney were linked together.

For a general manager of collieries who was ready to share knowledge of Powell Duffryn's experiences with competitors, who collaborated with other coal companies, such as Cory Brothers Company via Penrikyber Colliery, and the Bedwas Navigation Colliery Company, he valued autonomy with regard to generating electricity. Powell Duffryn took sole control of electricity generation and distribution so as to safeguard its own interests as a coal company. Moreover, Britannia Colliery became the concrete expression of the value of electricity for the winding of coal. The company's fifty years company history proudly proclaimed that 'the plant at Britannia is all electric, and the Colliery is a model one, there being no stacks or steam seen'.[6] Wasted clouds of steam hanging above a Powell Duffryn colliery looked an unlikely prospect in the future.

Pioneering chemical engineering also featured in the design of the Bargoed Colliery by-products plant at a time when this branch of engineering was relatively new.

By the mid 1910s, Powell Duffryn undoubtedly took great pleasure in being seen as a progressive company as demonstrated by its colliery engineering. In 1913, the peak year for coal output in the history of the South Wales Coalfield, the company's collieries produced nearly four million tons of coal which represented nearly a 7% share of the total coal output of the South Wales Coalfield, which was 56,830,000 tons. Powell Duffryn's history, published by the company in 1914, included a reflection that in 1902 the company's directors were 'pursuing' a 'consistent policy of expansion' by acquiring mineral property at Pengam [Britannia Colliery] and Penallta.[7] Their collieries at Elliot and Bargoed had been model collieries of their kind at the time of their foundation. Penallta Colliery attracted admirers from those attached to steam winding, but Britannia Colliery retained for the company a technical pioneering image that it had earned under the leadership of Edmund Mills Hann. Although the application of innovative

engineering technology, plant and equipment was synonymous with at least colliery developments that Edmund Mills Hann led for Powell Duffryn, what impact did they have upon the fortunes of the company?

The trust that the directors of Powell Duffryn put in Hanns' technical knowledge, and judgment was handsomely rewarded. In 1914, Edmund Hann reflected upon the company's results: '*The continuance of exceptional trade conditions and high prices for Coal and most commodities has enabled the Company to pay the same dividend of 20 per cent each year*'.[8]

He then tabulated the company's performance from 1904 and 1913 which, in a slightly modified form, was:

Year	Output Tons	Average Cost per Ton	Average Selling Price per Ton	Profit
1904	2,890,000	7s 8d	9s 1d	76,155
1905	2,740,000	7s 8d	8s 6d	81,965
1906	2,940,000	7s 6d	8s 6d	140,168
1907	3,170,000	8s 5d	10s 9d	346,358
1908	3,040,000	9s 4d	11s 7d	322,718
1909	3,550,000	8s 6d	9s 6d	198,293
1910	3,220,000	8s 11d	10s 4d	253,349
1911	3,440,000	9s 1d	10s 4d	224,769
1912	3,500,000	9s 4d	11s 0d	248,472
1913	3,870,000	9s 10d	12s 0d	364,421

Moreover, by 1913, the company's Reserve Fund stood at £800,000, and this moved the Board to issue a Bonus Share for each two fully-paid shares held, and one for every four partly-paid shares. This created the issue of 541,407 new shares that resulted in the authorized Capital Account standing at:

	£
6% Preference Non-Cumulative 31,159 shares of £5	155,795
Ordinary Shares, fully paid	1,572,657
Ordinary Shares, partly paid of £1	51,562
Total	1,780,014

Most of Powell Duffryn's shareholders would have been fervent supporters of the company's management by 1913 due to the financial strength of the company. This contrasted with the days when Sir George Elliot gave the company 'practical direction'. Together, Edmund Mills Hann and Bickerton Pratt shared the pain of the unprofitable years that dogged Sir George Elliot's days in charge of running the company. According to Hann, under Bickerton Pratt 'the commercial development [of Powell Duffryn] … kept pace with that of the Colliery section'.[9] Indeed, one key policy of Bickerton Pratt's period in charge of the Commercial Department would have been to achieve a global coverage of coal stations, as stockpiles of company coal at ports, so as to bunker ships.

In 1913, Powell Duffryn's directors approved the thirty-seven years old William Reginald Hann's appointment as Commercial Manager in succession to Bickerton Pratt who had chosen retirement.[10] Bickerton Pratt died shortly afterwards on the 25th April, 1913. The commercial address for the company was 54, Bute Street, Cardiff. One sequel of W. R. Hann's appointment was that members of the Hann family held all Powell Duffryn's highest executive management offices with the exception of the company's post of Secretary of the Company, which in 1914 was held by H. R. Clarke.

Powell Duffryn's Cardiff Office., the three-window section on the left was a later extension to the original.   *Paul Jackson collection*

Bickerton Pratt, Commercial Manager, 1877-1913   William R. Hann, Commercial Manager, 1913-c1944

H. R. Clarke, Company Secretary.

William R. Hann, the eldest son of Edmund Mills, was born at Brotton in 1876, and educated at Aberaman, until fourteen years of age, before attending Haileybury and Imperial Service College. He 'gained good academic grades throughout and excelled at rugby'. In 1896 he joined Powell Duffryn as a member of its accounts department. 'His personality and knowledge of the French language made him an obvious choice in 1896 to work in the Rouen Agency of the company gaining experience of European Markets. He returned in 1908 to become Assistant Manager of the Commercial Department at the Cardiff Docks Office'. The responsibilities of Powell Duffryn's Commercial Manager included finding markets for the company's coal, distributing the coal by road, rail, or ship to customers, controlling the distribution depots, and supervising agencies.

So, what was the market outlook in 1914? On the 29th January, Edmund Mills Hann complemented Henry T. Wales for his presidential address to the South Wales Institute of Engineers. Hann judged that it was 'a very excellent exposition of the present state of things in the coal trade and other trades affecting South Wales'.[11] Henry Wales's address took as a reference the year 1912's coal output figures that showed that the South Wales Coalfield represented one-fifth of the total output of the United Kingdom coalfields, at just over 50 million tons and 260 million ton respectively.[12] He also mentioned the corresponding world's total annual production of oil which was 50 million tons, and recognised that there were moves taking place around the world to increase its output.

The fact that the South Wales Coalfield's output in weight was equal to the world's output of oil went without a remark. However, Henry Wales observed that 'in work done, one ton of oil is equivalent to $1\frac{1}{2}$ tons of steam coal', and predicted, for the South Wales Coalfield, that the 'coming of oil as a source of power [coal] would not feel, in the greatest degree, any competition which might arise from the use of oil for producing power on board ships'. He judged that much had to be done to further develop the Diesel engine for it 'to drive a large war vessel by using oil in an internal combustion

engine'. Moreover, although he was aware that the British Navy had 'many vessels fitted to burn oil and coal together', he thought that it was unlikely 'that many of the large war vessels' would be 'constructed to burn oil only', due to the 'uncertainty of oil supply', and also its expense.

A study of the emergence of oil, considered a rank outsider as a threat to coal in 1914, as a major player in the world's energy market, is a subject beyond the scope of this work. However, between 1911 and 1915, oil began its intrusion into a sector of the market held dear to the coalowners mining Welsh steam coal. This period coincided with the First Lord of the Admiralty being Winston Churchill. He set 'in train the conversion of the whole [British] fleet from coal to oil'. Roy Jenkins wrote that this had the effect of increasing the speed of the battleship, the 'cleanliness of life afloat and the speed of refuelling', and 'had the benefit of leading to an immensely profitable British government controlling investment in the Anglo-Persian Oil Company'.[13] The crews of His Majesty's ships would have been happy to be relieved of the dirty, arduous labour of bunkering a fleet of ships with coal. The Admiralty's action to substitute oil for steam coal, an emblem of the success of the South Wales Coalfield, seemed to be an ominous warning not least for Powell Duffryn.

The South Wales Coalfield's dependence upon export business was then common knowledge. Henry Wales stressed that the 'market' for its coal was 'largely a foreign one, 60 per cent of the output being shipped', and its production was 'liable to the competition of other coal producing countries, particularly of Germany, as well as other coalfields of this kingdom'. Yet, he seemed more worried about 'new collieries', particularly those 'lying in South Yorkshire, within a radius of twelve miles from the town of Doncaster', as the threat to the South Wales Coalfield's collieries. He offered his Welsh audience though some reassurance: *'Fortunately the demand for coal all over the world continues to grow', and that 'we may reasonably look forward to getting a fair share, in the future, provided that we are able to produce at a figure that will make it worth the while of the consumer to send orders to our district'.*

That Edmund Mills Hann did not demur from Henry Wales's analysis suggests that he shared this outlook. Around this time Hann prepared a contribution for a history celebrating Powell Duffryn's fiftieth year. And the subsequent publication was dismissive of oil as a threat to coal:[14]

'The advent of oil as a motive power need not be taken seriously for many years, if ever, and with the natural growth of manufactures in all parts of the world, the extension and development of railways, the expansion of the mercantile marine, and the increase of trade generally, the prosperity which Powell Duffryn now enjoy is bound to continue. Great as the output is, it is small compared to the quantity unworked,' the approximate figures of their reserves being:

RHYMNEY VALLEY:

New Tredegar and Elliot Pits	94,000,000 tons
Bargoed	86,000,000 tons
Penallta	100,000,000 tons
Pengam	90,000,000 tons
Sub total	370,000,000 tons
ABERDARE VALLEY	78,000,000 tons
Grand total	448,000,000 tons

Moreover, it was considered that these reserves were 'sufficient to furnish an annual output of $4\frac{1}{2}$ million tons for 100 years' for the company.

Powell Duffryn's confident outlook might, with hindsight, be ascribed to arrogance. Yet, the facts available for the early part of the twentieth century endorsed the company's view. An International Labour Office study of 1938 estimated that 'in 1913 in the world as a whole coal and lignite accounted for some 75 per cent of all energy; in Britain the figure (for coal, coke, and manufactured fuels) was not less than 94.5 per cent, while gas and electricity (both produced with coal) accounted for almost a further 5 per cent'. However, in 1987, Barry Supple, having referred to the foregoing fact, identified that the year was notable: 'In 1913 the [British] industry employed 1.1 million men and boys, and produced 287 million tons of fuel – a level of output which was never again to be achieved'.[15] Indeed, also in 1913, the South Wales Coalfield reached its zenith with a coal output of 56,830,000 tons.

But, unaware that a peak in the trade cycle had been reached, Powell Duffryn's confidence about the future trade in coal was buoyant. In 1914, the 'most important users of P.D. coal' were the 'Navies of Great Britain and of other great powers in the world'. Moreover, 'all the great lines of passenger steamships' bought its coal, which saw 'large quantities' of PD coal shipped from Welsh ports, or by rail, to Southampton, Birkenhead and the Thames. Also 'dotted' around the world, 'especially' the Mediterranean, South America, and the East, were PD coal stations to supply the steamships. The railways of the world, British, mainland European, Indian, Argentinean, Uruguayan, and Brazilian, were also customers for the company's coal. Powell Duffryn daringly competed against national producers in their own ports. For example, in the Black Sea with the Dönetz collieries of the Ukraine, and, perhaps more significantly, the German, Belgium, and French coalfields products were challenged at Antwerp, Bremen, Calais, Dunkirk, Hamburg, and Rotterdam. Such was the company's

commercial confidence that it boasted, with good reason, that: 'Through nearly a thousand ports in the world Welsh steam coal reaches its markets, and to speak of Welsh coal is to speak of P.D'. Yet, Welsh coal's value as an international fuel was tarnished by the human life incurred winning it. In the year 1913, exclusive of explosions like that at Universal Colliery, Senghenydd, 296 lives perished underground in the South Wales Coalfield.[16]

William Galloway's Contribution Recognised

In 1914, Edmund Mills Hann, as chairman of the Monmouthshire and South Wales Coalowners' Association, led a ceremony to recognise the 'very prominent' contribution which William Galloway had made regarding his investigations into coal-dust and colliery explosions, at a joint meeting of the Association and the South Wales Institute of Engineers. Hann presented a portrait, in oils, of Galloway to its subject.[17] In praising him, Hann said: '*I am inclined to say that, since the invention of the safety lamp a century ago, it is the greatest reform in mining practice which has been introduced – this, recognition, and placing on a scientific basis, of the danger of coal dust in the propagation, if not in the production, of the disastrous colliery explosions which has afflicted the mining areas in this and other countries*'. Adding, '*the coal dust problem is a striking instance of the length of time which it takes for great ideas to permeate the consciousness of the people*'. Although death due to explosions represented just over one-fifth of all deaths underground in the South Wales Coalfield between 1874 and 1914, the 1913 explosion at Universal Colliery, Senghenydd, serves as a poignant reminder of the vast devastation that an explosion can have upon mining communities.[18]

In 1914, the sixty-four year old Edmund Hann had served Powell Duffryn as its general manager of collieries for three decades. He

Bunkering a ship with PD coal. '*Through nearly a thousand ports in the world Welsh coal reaches its markets, and to speak of Welsh coal is to speak of P.D*'.
Pope/Parkhouse Archive

projected a formidable personality, and had the appearance of an affluent businessman. That year he resided at 'The Oaklands', Aberaman. He was established as one of the most important men in that part of the Aberdare Valley.

Cottage Hospital – Aberdare Valley

In June 1914, work at last began in the Aberdare Valley to build a cottage hospital. The project was revived, after a four year lull, on the 16th October, 1912, at a meeting of the community's committee, which Edmund Mills Hann appears to have chaired.[19] He told the meeting that the directors of Powell Duffryn were 'prepared to erect and equip a Cottage Hospital – similar to that erected at Bargoed [Aberbargoed] – at their own expense, on a site which' it 'would provide' on land behind Woodland Terrace, Godreaman, subject to the workmen providing the necessary funds for its maintenance'. The company's proposal was well received since it prompted 'arrangements' that led to deductions from the workmen's wages of one half-penny per week as from 1st March, 1913.

Edmund Mills Hann further arranged that 'several prominent' architects in South Wales were invited to present their plans for a hospital design competition. The entries for the competition were later adjudicated by Colonel Vaughan, of Cardiff, who was an 'acknowledged authority on Hospital construction'. George Kenshole of Bargoed made the winning submission, and his plans were placed on public show in Cwmaman and Aberaman Institutes in December, 1913. According to Edmund Mills Hann, Horace Davies of Bargoed, 'built the Aberbargoed Hospital', and he was awarded the building contract. *The New Tredegar Bargoed and Caerphilly Journal* differs by naming the builder of Aberbargoed Hospital as John Lloyd, of Ystrad Mynach.[20] Work commenced on the cottage hospital in June, 1914, but came to a halt after August 1914 when the First World War began.

First World War

The South Wales Coalfield miner, who volunteered to join the army, journeyed to the Somme expecting a short battle, and a quick return to home. He swapped the hazards of toiling at the coal face for an uncertain life in the fresh air of the fields of the Western Front. His physical fitness and toughness was equal to the task of digging trenches. By the end of the War, there was a continuous line of trenches from the North Sea coastline to Switzerland. Once the miner had dug his fighting butt, he had to endure the horrors of trench warfare.

When a stalemate in the battles between the British and Germany armies arrived, it was possible that bored soldiers, who were previously employed as Powell Duffryn engineers and miners, joined Tunnelling Companies of the Royal Engineers. The work of tunnellers was a branch of warfare that Captain David Ivor Evans MC later 'properly designated' as being the actions of a 'Suicide Club'.[21] He wrote they were formed in early 1915 as a counter-measure to the enemy's tactic of 'driving underground galleries from its front line trenches and extending to points underneath our trenches', so that they could place high explosives. The surprise of such an offensive move by the Germans wrought dreadful consequences, and caused great anxiety among British soldiers. The response of the British tunellers was to 'cut off the enemy galleries', and prevent 'any further encroachment'. 'Listening galleries' were driven so as to detect the advance of an enemy's

gallery. The British Army next copied the enemy's tactic and drove galleries under 'No-man's land'. Some of the British tunnellers were either killed in underground hand-to-hand fighting with German miners, or by booby traps.

Most of the recruits drawn to the Western Front from the South Wales Coalfield, between 1914 and 1918, forgot about the need for steam coal to fuel the battleships of the Royal Navy. Moreover, the importance of coal mining for the wealth of the nation had no practical meaning when fighting to survive warfare. Nonetheless, on the 29th July, 1915, the Government's Minister for Munitions, David Lloyd George, spoke at a National Mining Conference held in London. He said: '*In time of peace coal is the most important element in the industrial life of this country. The blood which courses through the veins of industry is made of distilled coal. In peace and war King Coal is paramount Lord of Industry. It enters into every article of consumption and utility; it is our real international coinage. We buy goods, food, and raw material abroad, we pay not in gold but in coal*'.[22]

The British coal mining industry's trade collapsed at the start to the First World War. Redmayne recorded that several important foreign markets were closed, while others were either temporarily, or partially disorganised.[23] He continued: 'More coal was in consequence available for home consumption than was required, so that for a while many of the collieries were on short time. Whilst the normal consumption in some industries in the country was curtailed, there was an expansion in several others. Transport facilities were considerably impeded by reason of the diversion of rolling stock and tonnage by the Government to other services; freights rose abnormally, and certain trade routes were closed for purposes of defence'. Thousands of tons of coal were initially banked at British collieries.

The manning level of the coal industry also fell. By April, 1915, 1,415 of Powell Duffryn's men had signed up to fight in the Great War, and, by the end of the war, the number reached 6,407. Two hundred and two company employees lost their lives fighting for the nation.[24] The effect of war on the trade in coal meant little for those left to grieve the deaths of men killed in France and Belgium.

In the South Wales Coalfield, in 1915, output fell by 6 per cent, but the Admiralty pressed for more output of Welsh steam coal. Barry Supple found that: 'In South Wales for example, where the Navy had purchased about 1.5 million tons for the predominantly coal-fired Fleet before the War, such demands were running at an annual rate of 15 million tons (almost 25 per cent of the district's output) by the spring of 1915'.[25] So what effect did the Great War have on Powell Duffryn's output figures? The company's annual outputs, and for comparison that of the South Wales Coalfield, were:[26]

	Powell Duffryn Tons	South Wales Coalfield Tons
1913	3,873,780	56,830,000
1914	3,948,404	53,880,000
1915	3,564,186	50,453,000
1916	3,659,016	52,081,000
1917	3,722,873	48,508,000
1918	3,794,635	46,717,000

So Powell Duffryn held 'near to' its 'pre-war output'.

The Admiralty placed orders on the company for coal to power the nation's fleet. Before the War, thirty South Wales Coalfield coals were named on the Admiralty list. During the War, the Admiralty 'practically' sourced coal from fifty-nine named coals.[27] The fifty-nine named coals included a coal termed 'Powell Duffryn', and coals called New Tredegar, Powell Duffryn Aberdare, and Powell Duffryn Bargoed. For the War, it seems, the Admiralty also sorted the fifty-nine coals into two categories, identified as 1st and 2nd. The Aberdare Valley coals mined by Powell Duffryn certainly belonged to the 1st category, which as the superior coal might have been allotted to naval ships where great speed and stealth, and smokeless fuel were seen as vital. The properties of some Rhymney Valley steam coals might have been placed in the 2nd category. The mention of a generic 'Powell Duffryn' suggests that coal won at Penallta and Britannia Collieries was requisitioned for use by the British Navy ahead of merchant shipping bunkered with coals from these collieries.

The demand for coal aside, Edmund Mills Hann considered that the company's programme of 'cottage building', begun in 1912, played a vital role in enabling the company 'to keep as near to our pre-war output'.[28] The build programme of 3,000 houses 'commenced' at Aberaman, and to grow the workforce at Penallta Colliery, Pengam, Tir-y-berth, Cascade, and Hengoed. However, 'the War interfered with and finally stopped these projects, and only 993 houses were actually built'. Nevertheless, the new housing attracted new workers to join the company.

In October 1916, Powell Duffryn's directors elected Edmund Mills Hann to a seat on the Board.[29] A director's vacancy occurred due to the death of Arthur March Tapp who had been a director of the company since 1889 and a member of the Managing Committee from 1899. On the 15th September, 1917, the company's directors crowned this notable achievement in Hann's career by presenting him with a portrait in oils of himself by Solomon J. Solomon RA. A replica of the portrait was hung in the boardroom in London. Moreover, the directors gave him a gift of a silver salver, and Mrs Hann received a diamond brooch. He recorded his gratitude for the 'handsome' manner in which the company had commemorated his 'long connection with the Company'. Although the directors of Powell Duffryn had full confidence in the general management of its collieries, the Government took a contrasting view.

The independence of the coalowners was challenged by the Government as the War's stalemate continued. The Government's first move towards controlling the running of the British coal industry occurred in December, 1916, and it was focused upon the South Wales Coalfield. Labour unrest in the South Wales Coalfield gave rise to anxiety within Whitehall about the prospect of fickle coal supplies from Admiralty listed collieries. By March, 1917, Government control of the coal industry extended throughout the British coal industry.

In addition, the trade and transport of coal for general and domestic use within Great Britain was controlled.[30] A survey had preceded the introduction of Government controls. The survey found that within Great Britain there was an 'export' and 'import' trade taking place between the separate coalfields. A Government Order was introduced to restrict such movements. As a generalisation, output from the South Wales Coalfield was restricted to south Wales, and the south-west counties of England.

The vital exception, of course, was the movement of vast quantities of steam coal hauled by rail to northern Britain so that the ships of His Majesty's Royal Navy could be bunkered. Such transport of coal passed along the railway near Kentchurch,

Herefordshire, where the home of Powell Duffryn's chairman, Joseph Shaw, was located. The rumble of this traffic gave him an idea of the scale of the British war effort, and gave him comfort about earning an income from his stake in Powell Duffryn.

Torpedoes launched from German submarines posed a threat to collier ships, contracted to move coal from Cardiff and Newport docks, and other South Wales ports. Nevertheless, coal shipments were made from South Wales' ports to supply British naval harbours, Belgium, France and other countries.

The rationing of domestic coal was introduced, and coal price controls were established.[31] The company greeted the imposition of Government measures with mixed feelings, and was eager for them to end. The wait for the Government measures to be ended created growing annoyance within the company. 'Formal control lasted until the end of March 1921'.[32] By which time, annoyance seems to have reached a high pitch within the company due to some aspects of its plans being thwarted.

Nevertheless, during the War, according to Redmayne, the objective regarding price controls was to maintain colliery prices as at June 1917 so as 'to stabilize the prices by prevention of fluctuations to preserve regularity in the distribution and export of coal in the differing producing centres'. He further claimed that this meant that 'practically one market price for a given class of coal was maintained and speculation in coal cargoes eliminated'. Maybe it was some consolation to at least Joseph Shaw that steam coal prices were not reduced. But the Controller, at some point in the war, instructed the coalowners not to apply a consequential reduction of wages arising out of a coal price adjustment.[33]

A Better Life for Miners

Miners recruited from the South Wales Coalfield who survived the Great War, were demobbed after November, 1918, following Germany's surrender. They returned to their native valleys wanting a better life simply measured as a rise in their incomes. Such an outlook was further fostered once they heard that, as a general rule, coal companies had accumulated very large profits and reserves during the war.[34]

Some miners, re-employed by Powell Duffryn, may not have been placated by a charitable gesture of the company. During the war, the company paid 7s. per week to wives, and 1s. 6d. each to children of their employees who had joined His Majesty's Forces, which in total cost the company £151,195.[35] The miners' desire for a pay rise, though, was lifted when they found a great demand for their services to win coal since 'the market for British coal remained, and its value [was] greatly inflated'.[36]

The miners' desire for a better life was countered by some concerns about the coal industry's future. As a labour intensive industry, unlike the developing oil industry that would be shaped by vast capital investment, controlling the workers' wage bill was crucial for a coalowner's survival. Miners' quests for better wages risked being at odds with the coalowners' objective: to offer the market competitive coal prices.

The war had accelerated the exploitation of the best seams of coal of the South Wales Coalfield, and contrary to the misgivings of some of its engineers, increased underground mechanisation was a way towards cost efficient mining. The miners' desires, and antipathy towards the coalowners, vied against accommodating an owner's need for change in terms of underground mechanisation.

The period around the Great War also saw some working men

question Britain's class based social order, and the perceived injustices of its economic system. The Bolshevik Revolution, in November, 1917, in Russia, offered for such men a new vision: a world free of class antagonism, company ownership brought under the control of the State, and emancipation for all people. Communism probably gripped the consciousness of only a tiny minority of the miners. Yet, if such men were elected to senior offices in the coal mining trade unions, driven by a quest to found a British Communist state, they could become a potent threat to the likes of Powell Duffryn. David Evans's account of the strife of 1910 at the Aberdare collieries had identified 'younger leaders' among the South Wales Miners' Federation who were 'Socialist imbued with Communistic theories concerning the relations of Capital and Labour'. These 'younger leaders' were, by the end of the Great War, the likely new executive leaders of the SWMF.

Abernant House, the General Hospital

Demobbed Powell Duffryn colliery workers of the Aberdare Valley came home to one pleasant surprise: a new hospital. The project had not turned out as they had expected before they left for the Western Front, or to join the Royal Navy.[37] Foundation work was halted on the Aberaman cottage hospital at the outbreak of war. In July 1915, the agent for the Marquis of Bute Estate made known that it was the Estate's intention to close the Bute Cottage Hospital at Aberdare. This caused the Aberdare Valley and Hirwaun Medical Association to explore other ways for providing hospital care. However, the Association's search proved unsatisfactory, and so the body made an appeal to the Marquis of Bute for help, in July, 1915. The Marquis responded in August, and was prepared to lease Abernant House subject to provisos and conditions. One proviso concerned 'the right to work minerals underneath [the property] without liability for any damage done to the property'.

The attractions of Abernant House, and the commitment of Powell Duffryn to the cottage hospital at Aberaman, evident as excavated footings, then arose as an issue. The Medical Association realised that to further their idea they needed support from the same bodies committed to the Aberaman cottage hospital. Dr. Thomas Finney, secretary of the Medical Association, and a personal friend of Edmund Mills Hann, acted to broker a deal.

Abernant House was claimed to be 'situated in the centre of one of the most delightful spots in the County of Glamorgan', and had 'a commanding view of the whole of the valley'. The Medical Association approached miners' union leaders and Edmund Hann. 'After much persuasion', by Dr, Finney, the Powell Duffryn man visited Abernant House.

Although Hann was 'very much impressed', due to the Aberaman Cottage Hospital scheme, he felt 'unable to support' the alternative scheme 'without the approval of the Cottage Hospital Committee, to whom he was morally bound'. Hann, though, raised the matter with the Aberaman Cottage Hospital Committee, and recommended a visit to the Abernant House, which occurred, and all were 'charmed' by the place. Then, subject to questions of capital charges and maintenance costs', and other administrative matters, the Committee agreed to support what was then seen as a 'General Hospital' scheme. Sometime afterwards, Powell Duffryn acquired the mineral rights underneath Abernant House partly to accept any building repair costs that could arise due to mining subsidence.[38] So an aspect of the risk to the maintenance of the property was covered.

The general hospital scheme gathered momentum. A proposal to raise the weekly levy on local workmen from half-penny to one penny per week for the hospital's maintenance fund was accepted by the Aberaman Cottage Hospital Committee. A public meeting was held in 1915, under the chairmanship of Charles Kenshole, the High Constable of Miskin (Higher), to discuss the scheme. 'A crowded' meeting 'enthusiastically' adopted the scheme. George Kenshole prepared the plans for the conversion of Abernant House into a hospital, and the associated work was carried out by the workers employed by Horace J. Davies, of Bargoed. Powell Duffryn's chairman, Joseph Shaw opened the hospital, which accommodated forty beds, on 17th July, 1917, 'amid scenes of great rejoicing'.

New mining possibilities and marketing initiatives

Powell Duffryn's general manager of collieries was rankled by one effect of the war: the concentrated coal production effort caused a crippling of all engineering operations.[39] Nonetheless, the bullish spirit prevailing within Powell Duffryn, up to the eve of the war, had moved it to secure new mining possibilities. In 1914, in the Aberdare Valley, the company took leases from the Marquis of Bute at Abernant, Gadlys, and Blaengwawr.[40] Although such leases involved drowned workings, the aim was to secure them so as to get coal 'without any loss of life'. Around the same year, the company looked to the Bargoed Rhymney Valley as a location for future mining. A lease 'was entered into with the Marquis of Bute for an area of about 1,000 acres lying west of New Tredegar and Elliot Collieries, with an undertaking to commence sinking upon it within two years of the conclusion of Peace'.[41]

Seeking new mining possibilities was essential not only for sustaining or bettering the company's annual coal output into the future, but also for securing export business. Edmund Mills Hann's son, William Reginald, made his mark not long after he was made Powell Duffryn's Commercial Manager, in 1913. On the 1st January, 1914, the company formed, under French law, Compagnie Française des Mines Powell Duffryn, with its registered office at 24, Quai Gaston-Boulet, Rouen, so as to further develop the company's trade in France. By 1918, the company had offices at: 17, Cours du Chapeau Rouge, Bordeaux; 24, Rue Jules Lecesne, Le Havre; 28, Rue Latour-d'Auvergne, Nantes; and 56, Rue Faubourg St. Honoré, Paris.[42] In essence this involved the reorganisation of its French Agencies,

Powell Duffryn's depot at Nantes.
Powell Duffryn Steam Coal Co. Ltd, 1864-1914, Paul Jackson collection

COMPAGNIE FRANCAISE

DES

MINES POWELL DUFFRYN

Société Anonyme au Capital de 15,000,000 de Francs

Télégr. : "DUFFRYN PARIS."   Tél. : ANJOU 0.26.
                                                0.27.
                                      INTER 0.28.
Siège Social : 56, FAUBOURG ST.-HONORÉ, PARIS.

AGENCES

ROUEN   LE HAVRE   NANTES   BORDEAUX

CHARBONS INDUSTRIELS.   "SYNTHATAR."

CHARBONS DOMESTIQUES.   "SYNTHAPRUFE."

COKES METALLURGIQUES.   "SYNTHACOLD."

BRIQUETTES "P.D."   "PRESOTIM."

BOULETS AMIRAUTE.   "PRESOMET."

Fournisseurs de la MARINE NATIONALE,
des principales COMPAGNIES de NAVIGATION
et des RESEAUX de CHEMINS de FER Français.

Advertising the formation of Compagnie Française des Mines Powell Duffryn.

and shrewdly accommodated a finding that some potential French customers operated plants not designed to burn Welsh coal. So, 'in addition to selling' the company's coal production, Powell Duffryn made commercial arrangements to market coal from other coalfields, such as Yorkshire, Durham, and Scotland.[43]

As the Great War entered its final years the company also took a 'half interest' in the Normandy Shipping Company, 'with seven steamers', in readiness for shipping coal to Continental markets.[44]

Powell Duffryn also linked up with agencies located at British ports so to assist the distribution of coal. The network eventually comprised: E. Lawrence & Co., 5, Fenwick Street, Liverpool; Richard Munro & Co., 160, Hope Street, Glasgow; for coke only, A. McBean & Son, Wolverhampton; and in London, at its own offices, 101, Leadenhall Street.[45]

Powell Duffryn's depot at Rouen, a base for barging coal up the Seine.

Discharging Powell Duffryn coals at Rouen.

Powell Duffryn Steam Coal Co. Ltd, 1864-1914, Paul Jackson collection

During the war, a mining priority for Powell Duffryn was opening out Britannia Colliery so as to exploit its possible coal reserves. The war's need for horses, to haul guns and supplies to the trenches, had a notable effect upon the colliery's underground practices. 'Mechanical haulage had to be resorted to, and the conveyor' lent 'itself to mechanical haulage from the face because the output is concentrated at one point'.[46] Timber was a scarce resource. This forced the coalowners to partly abandon their 'very strong prejudice against the withdrawal of the timber from the gobs in South Wales'. A benefit was less trouble with the roof. George Hann reported that: 'Previously it was quite a common thing to have a conveyor-face stopped with a fall, but it is now a rare occurrence'.[47] However, a shortage of miners at Britannia Colliery held back production. George Hann believed: 'The yield per yard of face would have' been 'greater if more men were available'.[48]

The development of Penallta Colliery appears to have been frozen during the war. Not until 1918 was a decision made to erect there a Baum Washery, having a capacity of 150 ton per hour.[49] The washery came into operation in 1922 in anticipation of a 'demand for cleaner small coal – especially from the Continent'.

After the war, some Aberdare Valley miners might have found new employment opportunities of interest. River Level Colliery had been purchased in March, 1915 by Powell Duffryn from the Bute Estates.[50] By sinking two shafts to the Nine Feet seam, the company re-opened the colliery, which had been closed since December, 1896, due to an inrush of water. The colliery's winding gear, and surface plant and equipment, stood in the middle of the ruins of the Abernant Iron Company's former works.[51] In 1918, the colliery employed 425 persons.[52] By 1932, the numbers employed at the colliery had risen to 934 men.[53]

However, miners of Blaennant Colliery, also known as the Old Balance Pit, felt some uncertainty about their futures due to a change in the colliery's ownership. Before the war they took their wages from the Bute Estates. In 1915, the Bute Estates sold the colliery to Powell Duffryn.[54] The colliery lay near the 1,000 foot contour on Mynydd Aberdar, which separated the Aberdare Valley, to its west, from the Taff Valley, to its east. Maybe the morale of some Blaennant's miners was lifted, when walking home from work to the Aberdare district, on spying Abernant House.

A Family's Tragedy

Edmund Mills Hann became, in April, 1918, the first president of the Court of Governors of Abernant House, the General Hospital.[55] Powell Duffryn also purchased and presented three acres of land to the hospital. The land was located on the southern side of the hospital, and was used to create Abernant Gardens. The

River Level Colliery, Abernant, near Aberdare. Powell Duffryn acquired the colliery from the Bute Estates in 1915. The colliery employed 425 persons in 1918. Set among the ruins of the Abernant Iron Works, opened in 1800 by Messrs. F. & R. Tappington. The works was acquired by Fothergill & Co., in 1812, and traded as the Aberdare Iron Company.
Inset: River Level miner's lamp check.
Courtesy of Rhondda Cynon Taf Libraries
Courtesy of Lyn Gladwyn

Blaennant Colliery (Old Balance Pit). Sunk in the 1840s by the Aberdare Iron Company. The Bute Estate owned the colliery from 1899 until 1915 when it was sold to Powell Duffryn.
Pope/Parkhouse Archive

company's act served also as another tribute paid to their general manager of collieries. Mrs George Hann, of Ysguborwen House, Aberdare, also donated X-Ray Apparatus, together with a Radiant Heat Bath for the Out Patient Department. However, not long afterwards, hospital medical care became crucial for the survival of a Hann.

A plan regarding the future leadership of the management of Powell Duffryn had matured during the Great War. In 1918, at sixty-eight years of age, Edmund Mills Hann anticipated retirement, and his son, George, was his designated successor. In July 1918, news arrived at Aberaman, from London, which shattered such succession planning. George had died aged thirty-nine, following an operation at the Marylebone Hospital, London.[56]

George Hann enjoyed a remarkable, if brief mining career. Nepotism, which was not uncommon in the management of South Wales Coalfield collieries at the time, granted him the privilege of a management development programme within Powell Duffryn, stewarded by his father. He won accelerated promotion, which he did not disabuse. He demonstrated marked similarities to his father's behaviour. He attended to practical details. For example, in seeking improvements to the way that stone-dusting was used to reduce the 'make of coal-dust, he designed an appliance, activated by passing trams, which produced satisfactory results.[57] Compared with its South Wales Coalfield rivals, Powell Duffryn appeared to be superior in such practices.[58]

Within, and beyond, the bounds of Powell Duffryn, George Hann's qualities attracted admiration. John Fox Tallis spoke at a meeting of the South Wales Institute of Engineers, 26th July, 1918, about his 'scrupulous care and accuracy', and 'lamented that one so

eminently useful, and so full of brilliant promise should be cut off in his prime.[59] Dr Henry K. Jordan recalled that 'in his intercourse' with George Hann he 'recognised his exceptional attainments and practical clear-sightedness, and he was confident he would have made a brilliant president of the Institute had his life prolonged'. Joseph Shaw, chairman of Powell Duffryn, added to these epithets:

'His mind was characteristically keen ... and there was nothing to indicate the impending disaster. Mr George Hann's death was a great loss to the Powell Duffryn Company. His father and he (Mr Shaw) had been looking forward to placing him at the top of the whole concern – a position for which his great capacity admirably suited him, because he was a man of cool intellect, who had a metier for the big things in the engineering world. Probably no man in South Wales grasped to the same extent the possibilities of electricity in its application to coal-mining and kindred industries; and it was all very sad that such a man should not have been spared to them for many years to come.'

Colliery Management Changes

A protégé for Edmund Hann was recruited with little delay. Edmund Lawrence Hann was recalled to Powell Duffryn. He resigned from the Lawrence and Hann partnership, which he had formed with Arthur Lawrence, as Mining and Civil Engineers.[60] In addition to acting as consulting engineer to Bedwas Navigation Company, Edmund L. Hann's services had been given to the Chislett Colliery Company, Kent; the Merios Collieries Ltd; the Main Colliery Company, Neath, and several other important companies. His home at the time appears to have been Miskin Manor, Miskin, to the south of Llantrisant.

In 1918, Powell Duffryn also saw it appropriate to celebrate the years of service given to the company by two managers.[61] R. T. Martin, the company's Agent at Newport was given a plate 'as a mark of appreciation for fifty-four years' service to the company. Remarkably, R. T. Martin had earlier worked with the Powell family. A 'similar presentation' was made to the Agent in charge of New Tredegar, Elliot and Bargoed Collieries, Nehemiah Phillips. Phillips 'owing to advancing age' retired from the company after thirty-four years service during which he watched the development of Edmund Mills Hann's sons as colliery managers. Edmund Lawrence Hann's return to Powell Duffryn coincided with the start of Powell Duffryn Steam Coal Company's opposition to proposals presented to Government aimed at revolutionizing the management of the coal industry.

Sankey Commission

The constant strife between coalowner, and the industry's trade unions, was not limited to the South Wales Coalfield. Barry Supple recalled that: 'The end of the War was accompanied by the assertion of trade-union power and a political crisis which persuaded many people (among coalowners as well as less interested sections of society) that nationalization or some drastic measure of public ownership was inevitable.'[62] Such advocacy was made in the publication of a Government Royal Commission into the coal mining industry in 1919. The publication became known as the Sankey report due to the Commission's chairman being Justice Sankey. The Government, led by Prime Minister David Lloyd George, set up the Commission to deal with miners' threats of a strike if they were not granted higher pay, shorter hours and the nationalization of the mining industry. According to the history of the Trade Union Congress, this Commission's membership 'came down as a majority' in favour of "the State ownership of coal mines be accepted."

A member of the Commission was Sidney Webb (1858–1947), a campaigner for social reform. In 1892, he married Beatrice Potter, the daughter of a founding shareholder of Powell Duffryn, Richard Potter. Soon after 1921, she published an account of her 'apprenticeship' as a socialist. Beatrice Webb had not only witness-ed her father's death, in 1892, but had also lost faith in the way he conducted his business affairs. She wrote: 'Even the oppression and frauds of the capitalist profit-maker had their uses in that they drove the proletariat of hired men, which capitalism had made ubiquitous, to combine in Trade Unions and co-operative societies; and thus to develop their instinct of fellowship, and their capacity for representative institutions, alike in politics and in industry.'[63] Her thinking had been partly inspired through her study of the Co-operative Wholesales Societies, and so she 'perceived' that there was 'a possible alternative to modern business enterprise.'[64] Then, from the time she met her future husband, her political views took on 'a more decidedly socialist turn'.[65]

Nationalization, the Sankey Commission's proposal for the future management of the coal industry, was keenly supported by the Webbs. However, it was believed that until nationalization was put into effect, endemic conflict would prevail within the coal industry.

With shareholder support, Powell Duffryn lodged a protest with Government about the 'iniquitous proposals' of the Sankey Report. Edmund Mills Hann later claimed: '*I feel sure that these combined efforts had the effect of establishing the fact that undue

Government interference or control of this vital industry could have nothing but serious detrimental effect'.[66] The Commission's proposals subsequently proved repugnant to Lloyd George's Coalition Government, and it also proceeded to retract its wartime controls over the industry. So, the industry was eventually returned to full private control, in 1921.

Nevertheless, in 1920, Powell Duffryn embarked upon a strategic change regarding the organisation of the distribution of coal by linking up with Stephenson Clarke, a coal shipping business.[67]

Stephenson Clarke

In 1730, two brothers, Ralph and Robert Clarke, founded at North Shields, near Newcastle upon Tyne, Northumberland, a business that later became Stephenson Clarke & Associated Companies. The North Shields company acquired an interest in ships to move coal initially from the Durham and Northumberland Coalfields. In 1776, the company began to trade in London, and afterwards the Clarkes' fortunes grew.

In 1920, Stephenson Clarke and Powell Duffryn joined together to form the Maris Export & Trading Company to deal with the export business of both companies. The new company was funded by Powell Duffryn, Stephenson Clarke, and Compagnie Française des Mines Powell Duffryn each taking a one-third share. In 1922, Stephenson Clarke was converted into a limited company that opened the way for Powell Duffryn to acquire Stephenson Clarke & Company in 1928.[68] The figurehead of Stephenson Clarke during this period was Henry Kent, and his son, (Sir) Stephenson Kent, would later succeed him in this role.

Rhymney Iron Company

The period also saw Powell Duffryn adopt a new strategic course regarding expanding its coal reserves. In 1920, the company acquired 'practically the whole of the share capital in the Rhymney Iron Company'.[69] Trevor Boyns gained an impression that the company appeared 'to have entered the field at the last moment, but its bid was accepted by the directors of the Rhymney concern and resulted in Powell Duffryn, which already had substantial interests in the Rhymney Valley, becoming a virtual monopolist in that valley'.[70]

Powell Duffryn offered a patchwork of share purchase options so as to tempt the shareholders of the Rhymney Iron Company to relinquish ownership. The Rhymney Iron Company's shareholders were offered: two Powell Duffryn Ordinary Shares of £1 each fully paid for every five old and/or new Ordinary Shares of £1 each in the Rhymney Iron Company, plus a payment of 10s. in cash; the price of 21s. per share for each old and/or new Ordinary Share of £1 each in the Rhymney Iron Company; and an exchange for each Preference Share in the Rhymney Iron Company one of six per cent non-cumulative second Preference Share of £1 each fully paid in the Powell Duffryn Company, or alternatively to pay the price of 18s. per share in cash.[71] Edward Mills Hann noted that the offer 'proved so attractive that of the 600,000 Ordinary Shares and 400,000 Preference Shares in the Capital of the Rhymney Company, Powell Duffryn acquired 599,420 and 397,935 shares respectively'. One legacy of the acceptance of such an offer was that the name of the Rhymney Valley's pioneering company of the Industrial Revolution was supposedly erased.

The Rhymney Iron Company was mentioned just over a decade later in the Report of Powell Duffryn to its shareholders in 1932 in terms of an agreement between the two companies. The agreement, reached earlier that March 1932, detailed that Powell Duffryn would manage the collieries and businesses of the Rhymney Company. 'By the terms of the Agreement ... Powell Duffryn Company takes any profits that may result from the working of the Rhymney Company's collieries and investments, but on the other hand, bears all the losses'.[72] Such an Agreement gave Powell Duffryn the incentive to make 'considerable economies' so as to work the Rhymney Company's coal.

In 1920, the Rhymney Iron Company's collieries that came under Powell Duffryn's charge were: Gilfach (near Bargoed); Darran (north-west of Bargoed), which worked the Brithdir seam at a depth of 110 yards; Rhymney Merthyr No. 1 and No. 2 (immediately south of Pontlottyn); Pengam (sited just south of Britannia Colliery), sunk in 1881 to a depth of 312 yards to work the Brithdir seam; Groesfaen (north-west of Bargoed), which was sunk in 1902 and operational 1906-1907, raised steam coal; and Mardy (east of Pontlottyn).[73] The numbers employed at these collieries in 1920 were respectively: 390, 108, 1031, 519, 992, and 261.[74] New Duffryn, west of Rhymney, was also purchased, but closed immediately afterwards.

Powell Duffryn's pleasure at buying the Rhymney Iron Company was offset by having a puzzle to solve: how to manage an acquired brewer, Andrew Buchan Brewery? The beers of this Rhymney brewer quenched the thirst of many miners, colliery mechanics, and officials, in, and around the Rhymney Valley. Nonetheless, Powell Duffryn, as Brian Glover later rather dryly remarked, 'had little taste for the brewing business'. Finding a buyer for Andrew Buchan Brewery became a mission of the company's.

Andrew Buchan's Brewery, Rhymney. In 1920, Powell Duffryn acquired the Rhymney Iron Company, which owned the brewer that began in 1839. Andrew Buchan, a Scot, was appointed as its first manager, and retired from the post in 1869.
From 100 Years of Brewing: Rhymney Beers-Famous over 100 Years

Powell Duffryn chose also to take some responsibility for the health of people living at the northern end of the Rhymney Valley. Years later, possibly after 1927, the company made contributions to help the Rhymney Cottage Hospital survive. This hospital, opened in 1904, was funded by a Rhymney Workmen's Medical Aid Fund.[75] In 1927, financial difficulties hit the hospital. Dr. R. V. De Acton Redwood was the hospital's surgeon for forty-three years, and after he died in 1947, in his memory, his former place of work became the Redwood Memorial Hospital. In 1907, Edmund

Groesfaen Colliery, Bargoed Rhymney Valley. In 1920, Powell Duffryn took over the running of the Rhymney Iron Company's collieries, which included Groesfaen Colliery. Sunk in 1907, the colliery's manpower was 995 in 1918.
Inset: Groesfaen Colliery token.
Pope/Parkhouse Archive
Courtesy of Lyndon Rees

Lawrence Hann married Mary Alice Redwood of Rhymney, the daughter of a doctor, T. Hall Redwood.[76] The nature of the family connection, if any, between the two Redwood medical men is unknown.

Nonetheless, Powell Duffryn's general manager of collieries judged that the acquisition of the Rhymney Iron Company was an 'outstanding feature' of 1920. Indeed, the seventy years old Edmund Mills Hann had emulated the action of the forty-nine years old George Elliot, when, in 1864, Powell's steam coal collieries were purchased to form Powell Duffryn. Although the acquisition of the Rhymney Iron Company caused an increase in Powell Duffryn's Share Capital make-up, the power of the small coterie of shareholders that had exercised control of the company since it had broken Sir George Elliot's control of the company was diluted. The number of shareholders in Powell Duffryn had stood at twenty-five in 1890, but exceeded 5,500 by around 1921.

But the acquisition would have been viewed as a fortunate outcome by those Powell Duffryn shareholders familiar with the company's past. The fates of both Powell Duffryn and the Rhymney Iron Company could have been entirely different. If, after 1882, the Rhymney Iron Company had won coal at what became known as Elliot Colliery, what would have happened to a nearly bankrupt Powell Duffryn? With Powell Duffryn in a dire financial state, faced with limited coal resources in the Aberdare Valley, and denied new reserves of coal in say the Rhymney Valley, extinction beckoned. Sir George Elliot's meddling with the negotiations between the Rhymney Iron Company and Lord Tredegar, regarding mining property south of New Tredegar Colliery, was proved in time to be of benefit to Powell Duffryn.

Following the Rhymney Iron Company acquisition, in July, 1921, Edmund Mills Hann retired from Powell Duffryn Steam Coal Company.[77] He was seventy-one years of age, and his address at Aberaman was then given as 'Ysguborwen House', which he had apparently occupied for a number of years.[78] Geoffrey Evans's research into the various homes of the Hanns in the Aberdare area found many contradictions in occupation dates. He found, for example, that Edmund Mills Hann lived at 'The Oaklands' in only 1908.

After the acquisition of the Rhymney Iron Company, Edmund Mills Hann acknowledged that 'it will be realised how great a strain was placed upon the Directors and Administrative Staff in order to bring the Rhymney Iron Company's collieries and equipment, which has been neglected owing to lack of financial resources, to a standard comparable with that of the Powell Duffryn Company'.[79] The pursuit of colliery engineering excellence by the company was one of his legacies. After thirty-nine years of service to Powell Duffryn as its general manager of collieries, Edmund Mills Hann and his wife removed to the 'The Rise', Llanishen, Cardiff, for retirement. The company retained his services by assigning him a role as 'Supervisory Engineer' and paying him a fee of £5,000 per annum, a generous amount for the time.[80]

Edmund Lawrence Hann succeeded his father as Powell Duffryn's general manager of collieries. Moreover, Douglas Alfred Hann became the company's assistant general manager. One of the projects their father bequeathed to them to deliver concerned an additional, and larger, Engineering Works for the Rhymney Valley. Their father had foreseen the need for such a works so as to 'assist greatly' the 'important feature ... the proper maintenance' of the company's operation.[81] So, around 1921, the company opened

Tredomen Engineering Works, Rhymney Valley. Powell Duffryn opened the works around 1921 to support the maintenance of the Rhymney Valley collieries.

Pope/Parkhouse Archive

Tredomen Engineering Works, near Ystrad Mynach. Although this facility was crucial for running the mining operation, the company had in-hand plans essential to its future survival. The company's plans called for considerable capital investment in ambitious and risky ventures.

Envisaged was a wave of new colliery sinkings. These collieries would become known as Ogilvie, Llanharan, and Llantrisant. Ogilvie Colliery was sited in the Bargoed Rhymney Valley, located north-west of Bargoed, to mine coal west of Elliot Colliery in neighbouring territory. The South Crop was chosen as the location for Llanharan, and Llantrisant collieries.

Any memory of Thomas Powell's South Crop activities, six decades earlier, had little significance for the planning of these two collieries. The scope of Powell Duffryn's colliery engineering plans was considerable. The two new collieries would be powered using electricity generated at Bargoed.

Furthermore, Bargoed was designated as the central site for supplying most of the Rhymney Valley collieries with compressed air. In summary: the company planned to implement two ambitious engineering projects simultaneously. And, regarding electric generation and supply, the coal company took steps to upgrade the connection between the Aberdare and Rhymney schemes.

In 1921, Edmund Mills Hann revealed that just as the Great War began 'the development of the face conveyors and coal cutting machines used up all ... [the company's electrical] power'.[82] One solution progressed by the company's electrical engineers during the war, as mentioned earlier, was to connect the collieries of the two valleys by overhead transmission lines. He considered that

this offered two advantages: first, 'a permanent economy of prime cost by enabling peak loads and breakdowns to be taken on by either Valley'; and last, 'an economy in working cost'. However, he handed over to his son a much more extensive means for the self-determination of electricity supply for the company's current and future collieries.

Bargoed Power Station

In 1921, standing on a plot of ground immediately south of Bargoed Colliery, was the company's new central electricity power station. According to Edmund L. Hann, Bargoed was chosen 'chiefly on account of its convenient geographical position, as there appeared to be no possibility of placing the station in such a position that an ample supply of water could be obtained for condensing purposes without the use of cooling towers '.[83] Charles P. Sparks was credited for the design of Bargoed's new power station.[84]

The power stations' coal fired steam raising boiler plant comprised ten Babcock & Wilcox steel-cased marine type boilers. Each boiler unit featured an integral superheater, and superimposed steel tube economiser. In general, coal was fired using standard stokers. However, for trial purposes, one novel compartment stoker was installed. The company's earlier experiments with stoker furnace design, and due to lessons learnt at Bedwas Colliery, saw the 'Welsh' or middle arch' setting used. However, sometime later, furnace design was modified to the 'front' or 'coking' arch setting 'with a view to obtaining longer life'. The steam raised from the boilers was piped to electric generating plant that set in motion the following turbo-alternators:

Bargoed Power Station commenced generating electricity in 1921, and was recognised as 'one of the largest electrical plants in the country – a great deal bigger than any concern in London'.

Pope/Parkhouse Archive

Bargoed Power Station – Interior.

Proceedings, SWIE, Vol. XXXIV, (1922-23)

- One 6,000 kW, 3,000 rpm (supplied by British Thomson-Houston)
- One 12,000 kW, 1,500 rpm (British Thomson-Houston)
- One 12,000 kW, 3,000 rpm (Escher Wyss [Zoelly type seven impulse stages] turbine, Siemens Schuckert alternator)

Regarding Powell Duffryn's preparations for Bargoed Power Station, Edmund L. Hann expressed irritation with Government policy that affected the specification of these turbo-alternators. The variation in size of the units was due to post-war Government restrictions, which also affected design details of the power station's buildings. The company originally wanted three 12,000 kW sets. His frustration was further aggravated by the company receiving higher than expected price quotations from the initial enquiries made to buy the two 12,000 kW sets. So, 'orders [for the 12,000 kW sets] were delayed until the demand for power made their being put into use imperative'.[85]

The power station featured a range of other electrical equipment. Messrs A. Reyrolle and Company provided 33 kV electrical switchgear, with Metropolitan Vickers Electrical Company supplying 11 kV switchgear. Also installed were three generator panels, seven split conductor panels, four feeder-panels fitted with overload relays, and two bus-bar dividing panels. Erected were four incoming panels: two from the 2,000 kVA transformers, and two from the Bargoed gas engine station. Installed were nine outgoing feeders, with seven of them assigned to the power

house's auxiliaries, and two for outside feeders.[86] Operated from a control desk, the new Bargoed power station commenced regular electricity supply in 1921.

In 1923, Edmund L. Hann's noted his 'indebtedness to Messrs Ivor Williams, E. I. David, and E. K. Regan, all of whom had given him great assistance' for establishing Bargoed Power Station. Ivor Williams was destined to become the company's Chief Engineer.[87] Such recognition by Edmund L. Hann suggested that, unlike his father's hands-on style, he delegated responsibility for colliery engineering work.

According to Hann, the new central electricity power station caused a notable enhancement of the company's previous developments. Provided was 'sufficient electric power for the complete electrification of the shallower pits in the Rhymney Valley and to provide sufficient compressed air to enable all those seams in which the conditions were suitable to be worked by conveyors and coal cutters, and at the same time very largely to replace the use of horses by compressed air haulages'.[88] Moreover, 'the scheme also included the provision of electric power for the new collieries at Llanharan and Llantrisant to be completely equipped, and later the entire electrification of the Rhymney Iron collieries'.

Electrical transmission from Bargoed power station was carried out at 33 kV, 11 kV, and 3.3 kV. The 33 kV line was suspended between terminal poles [pylons], so as to connect with 'the three main areas of the Company's properties, namely Rhymney Valley, Aberdare Valley, and Llantrisant'.[89] Geographically this coverage represented, in terms of direct distances from Bargoed, twelve miles south-west to Llantrisant, and eight and a half miles to Aberaman to the west, and four or so miles north up the Rhymney Valley. The whole project impressed *The Colliery Guardian* since it observed, in 1922, that Powell Duffryn owned 'one of the largest electrical plants in the country – a great deal bigger than any concern in London'.[90]

Compressed Air Transmission Pipeline

The merit of the electrical engineering project did not outshine another major project of the company's: a compressed air distribution system. The system's pipeline network, which served the Rhymney Valley collieries, was made from lap-welded steel pipes, laid to run along the ground, and joined together by acetylene welded joints. Three lines spread out from Bargoed: one pipeline branch went southward down the valley, via Britannia Colliery, to Penallta; the second up the Bargoed Rhymney Valley to Groesfaen (formerly a Rhymney Iron Company colliery) to end at the planned Ogilvie Colliery; and the final, and northern leg, took in Elliot Colliery, New Tredegar Colliery, Pontlottyn, to conclude at Rhymney Sub Station (so serving former Rhymney Iron Co. collieries at Mardy, south of Rhymney, and near Pontlottyn, Rhymney Merthyr Colliery). Hann claimed that the transmission of such large volumes of air was new in 'this country', which suggests the United Kingdom.[91] The Bargoed compressed air station came into operation in 1922.

The heart of the new compressed air system installed at Bargoed was a Messrs Brown, Boveri & Company, of Baden, Switzerland,

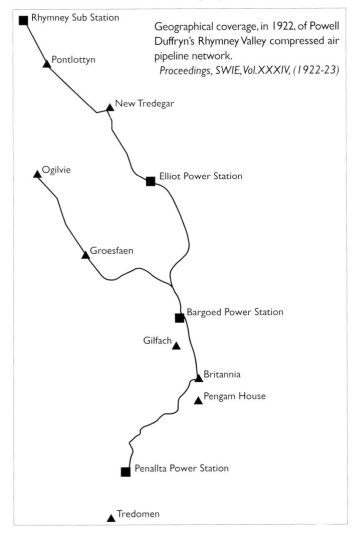

Geographical coverage, in 1922, of Powell Duffryn's Rhymney Valley compressed air pipeline network.
Proceedings, SWIE, Vol.XXXIV, (1922-23)

Rhymney Valley collieries' compressed air pipeline network under construction. Acetylene welded assembly being used.
Proceedings, SWIE, Vol.XXXIV, (1922-23)

turbo-compressing plant, driven by a Messrs Escher Wyss & Company, S. A., steam turbine. Three such units were installed at Bargoed, and each one was capable of compressing 40,000ft^3 of free air per minute at normal atmospheric pressure to 78–85 psi.[92]

The operational results of both the power station and compressed air system fully justified the investment at Bargoed, Hann revealed.[93] He also advised that any further development would see the replacement of existing boiler plant, and the 'utilisation of their exhaust steam in mixed pressure turbines'. Powell Duffryn's investment, which he did divulge, may have been envied by other coal companies. However, he conceded the 'disadvantage' of such an arrangement for 'comparatively small collieries', since 'the units cannot be made of sufficient size to obtain high efficiencies'. To console readers who managed such collieries, he suggested that it 'might be overcome by two or more collieries, even if under a different ownership, combining their plant'.

Edmund L. Hann also fired a salvo of opposition against additional expansion of utility electricity companies in South Wales. He appeared indignant that, with a wider adoption of the company's electrical scheme, 'the necessity for large district super power stations, such has been suggested, might be avoided'. The root of his apparent hostility towards these 'super' powers stations seemed due to him viewing them as a threat to Powell Duffryn's ambitions as a utility supplier of electricity.

As early as 1908, the company sold some of the electricity it generated to external customers. Although other coal companies got involved in the same trade, the company's Bargoed power station contained some extra capacity to supply the utility electrical energy market. Indeed, he hinted at this when he prophesised that 'the supply of electric power for lighting and domestic uses of the mining villages could well be supplied from a colliery for distribution either by the Local Authority or by a supply company, the results being a very large saving in transmission lines'. However, the prophesy did not deceive rival coal companies into believing that Powell Duffryn's future lay as an electrical utility company.

Prior to the First World War, the company had agreed mining leases with the Marquis of Bute so as to work an underground area west of Elliot Colliery from a new colliery sited in the Nant Bargoed Rhymney Valley. The Great War caused the postponement of the plan for the colliery, but in the early 1920s work on it begun.

Ogilvie Colliery

The colliery, Ogilvie Colliery, marked the company's association with the Ogilvie family. Powell Duffryn had been served by a succession of Ogilvies. Alexander Ogilvie was a founding director, and Arthur Graeme Ogilvie had served as chairman, between June 1892 and September 1897. In August 1921, Campbell Patric Ogilvie sat on the company's board with other successor generations of founding company directors, G. B. Heyworth, Lt-Col F. K. McClean, and H. L. C. Brassey MP.[94] The Hanns had also, through matrimony, made links with the Ogilvie family. Mary Anne née Ogilvie of Sizewell, Suffolk, was the widow of George Hann.[95] Nearly four decades had elapsed since the company had previously called a colliery after one of its directors, the privileged one being Sir George Elliot. The naming of the colliery suggests that the company's directors held a high regard for the Ogilvies.

Powell Duffryn completed the sinking of Ogilvie Colliery in 1923.[96] The colliery stood just over two miles north-west from Bargoed, on the east side of the Nant Bargoed Rhymney Valley.[97] Evidence was found during the sinking of the colliery that a landslide had struck the locality some centuries earlier. This discovery was reported by W. E. Jayne in a paper by Professor George Knox about 'Landslides in South Wales Valleys'.[98] 'During the sinking [at Ogilvie Colliery] down to the stone head', it became 'evident' to Jayne and the foreman sinker 'that they were sinking through an old landslide'. 'A farmhouse just above the colliery which was built many years ago, and if one could judge from the state of this building it must have been erected a long time after this landslide had occurred, as the building showed no trace of movement'.

W. E. Jayne, as a Powell Duffryn official, had also had the 'misfortune to witness the landslide' at New Tredegar in 1905 since he had then lived upon 'the slide'. He later read that Professor George Knox had identified that 'two types of slides which occur most frequently [in the South Wales Valleys] are soil creep and mixed soil and rock'.[99] Jayne offered the professor a significant general observation: 'whether it was a mere coincidence or could be scientifically explained. If a line, a mile and a half wide were taken from Ogilvie Colliery to the north-east, it would be found to embrace all the landslides', reported for the heads of the Monmouthshire Valleys. He added: 'In all of the instances mentioned, the landslides occurred in an area in which the coloured beds underneath the No. 2 Rhondda had been exposed, and decomposition provided the lubricating material necessary to produce the instability described'. Jayne's observation endorsed a statement of the professor's: 'These slides occur immediately downhill of the Pennants. The valleys in which they most frequently occur are those having a large gathering of water on the hills above them'.

Interest in the phenomena of South Wales Valleys' landslides was set to prevail. The local civic authorities wondered if a slide could hit a community of homes. Powell Duffryn's engineers pondered whether another landslide could strike New Tredegar Colliery.

As if untroubled by such a fear, Ogilvie Colliery was designed for an annual output of 625,000 tons.[100] The colliery's South Pit, the 20ft diameter upcast shaft, was sunk to the Five Feet/Gellideg seam at 566 yards. The 20ft diameter shaft of the North Pit, the downcast and winding pit, reached the Red Vein seam at a depth of 483 yards. The shafts cut through the No. 2 Rhondda seam, and Nine Feet seam.

Ogilvie Colliery, Bargoed Rhymney Valley. The colliery's name acknowledged the part that the Ogilvie family had played in the growth of the company. Sinking began in 1923, and the colliery's manpower was 1,236 persons in 1938. *Courtesy of Terry McCarthy*

The winding engines, air compressor, and other machinery were all placed in one building. A Walker type fan, 18ft 6in. in diameter and 7ft 6in. wide, ventilated the underground workings. The whole of the machinery was electrically driven from the company's electric generating system. The winding engines were driven by 1,600 hp AC motors.[101] Worked at full winding capacity, the expectation was that an engine would raise approximately 4,000 tons of coal a day.

The main seams worked at the colliery were the Upper Four Feet and Rhas Las (Nine Feet) seams.[102] The smokeless steam, and steam types of coal were raised at the colliery. Coal production began in June 1923, and a year later the colliery's output was reported as 'gradually increasing'.[103] The colliery's operation became relatively trouble free compared with the opening of other company collieries of this period. The identified colliery managers that served there included: in 1923 D. Hughes; A. T. Minhinnick, from around 1927 to at least 1935; W. H. Knibbs held the post in 1938; and T. Carthew in 1943.[104] The colliery employed 1,236 men in 1938, its only known peak since the figures for the Second World War years have not been found.[105]

The colliery's coal was moved southward by railway down the Nant Bargoed Rhymney Valley to Bargoed. The Rhymney Railway owned the railway's stage from Bargoed up the valley to a junction, south of the colliery, where the railway's ownership changed.[106] The Brecon & Merthyr Railway Company ran the railway to the north of this junction, which included access to the colliery, and northwards to both Merthyr Tydfil, and the town of Brecon. The Darran and Deri railway station was sited south of the junction to serve the village of Deri that lay the east of the station. Deri was another community set to grow as a result of the founding of a Powell Duffryn colliery.

The company had also, in 1921, taken measures to secure the growth of a cluster of villages around Penallta Colliery. 'A re-start in a small way' was 'made by building twenty-five houses at Tir-y-berth on a basis of commission, and twenty at Cascade on a contract whereby the Company' provided 'all materials and the contractor supplies the labour only'.[107] The thought behind such a contract strategy, according to Edmund Mills Hann, was to show that 'the prices asked by contractors and seriously entertained by some public bodies are exorbitant'. As an illustration also of its spirit of free enterprise, Powell Duffryn acquired the Wernddu Brickworks, located at Caerphilly, and opened at the old Abernant Ironworks another brick works. The company was commercially engaged in establishing communities in the locations around its new collieries like it had done at New Tredegar to man Elliot Colliery.

The founding of Ogilvie Colliery coincided with the opening of a notable hospital at Caerphilly. Previously, the miners employed by the companies operating at the southern end of the Rhymney Valley used the Cardiff Royal Infirmary, where, during the First World War, wounded soldiers took priority, and miners had to be nursed at home. This caused the East Glamorgan District of the South Wales Miners' Federation to arrange with the coalowners of the Caerphilly district a levy on the wages of colliery workers so as to grow a fund to build a new hospital. During 1919, an organising committee was set up, and subsequently agreed on the 23rd August, to purchase 'The Beeches', Caerphilly. The owner of this large house was Frederick Piggot, the contractor responsible for sinking Bedwas Navigation Colliery. The committee's ambition was to convert 'The Beeches' into a thirty-two bed hospital.

The price that was offered for 'The Beeches' was £5,000. Cardiff Collieries Limited, owners of Llanbradach Colliery, donated £1,000 of this, but the larger balance of the cost was paid from the miners' savings. The Caerphilly District Miners' Hospital took form in January 1923 with two wards. The number of wards at the hospital grew to four, and bore the names of collieries: Bedwas, Penallta, Llanbradach, and Windsor. The inclusion of Penallta suggests that Powell Duffryn made some donation to the hospital as the number of wards grew. The Caerphilly District Miners' Hospital was officially opened on the 30th June 1923, and admitted its first patient on the 2nd July, 1923.[108]

The Caerphilly hospital was the continuation of a trend among the miners of the South Wales Coalfield to create a health service that cared for their medical needs. The British electorate had yet to consider if this model, legislated for by the state, ought to be made universal in the United Kingdom.

In the 1920s, though, the hope of the shareholders of Powell Duffryn was to earn an income from the company's colliery expansion programme. In addition to Ogilvie Colliery, Edmund Mills Hann had made a decision, in 1912, to mine coal at the southern outcrop of the South Wales Coalfield. He possibly knew the locality due to his time with the Loftus Iron Company. He judged that the district around Llanharan and Llantrisant could help the company meet 'improving' customer demands for coal of 'a more bituminous character' that were appropriate to 'gas making, coking, iron and steel manufacturers in this country, and also for Continental markets'.[109] The company acquired mining leases for 4,000 acres, and the plan, in 1921, was to sink two collieries first, and then, 'in ten or twelve years' time', a third colliery.[110]

Llanharan Colliery

Llanharan Colliery became Powell Duffryn's first sinking on the South Crop. The village of Llanharan, located 12 miles west-north-west of Cardiff, stood nearby. The Great Western Railway's line served the locality, and the sinking there of the relatively small Meiros Colliery Deep Mine, in 1880, had helped bring an urban character to a rural area.[111] Powell Duffryn's surveyors reasoned that the rock strata in the vicinity dipped in a northern direction. Moreover, they might have speculated that under the colliery's site lay distortions in the strata, not unlike corrugations, shaped by earth movements over geological time. In 1923, the sinking of the colliery's first shaft began. The North shaft was wisely sited either by the surveyors, or due to luck. A quarter of a mile north of the site was a thrust line, or boundary, around which dwelt geological havoc.[112] The mining history of the location retained a warning. At what became the site of the South Pit, a shaft 144 yards deep, had been abandoned in 1875 due to doubt about the future economic value of the coal seam found.[113]

In March 1924, sinking was reported as having been completed at Llanharan Colliery, and that the development of one of its seams 'was taking place, at what appear to be favourable conditions'.[114] The North Pit was sunk to the Six Feet seam at 376 yards, and the South Pit was sunk 454 yards to the Gellideg seam. However, a geological puzzle lay ready for the miners to find once they had driven through the pit pillar.

Powell Duffryn reported that its total output for 1923, produced by 17,195 workers, was 4,760,591 tons. This set a new high mark regarding the company's annual output.

P.D. COLLIERY   LLANHARAN

Llanharan Colliery. Sinking began in 1923 of the company's first colliery on the 'South Crop' of the South Wales Coalfield. In 1934, the colliery's manpower was 1,054.

Llanharan Colliery was designed to add 350,000 tons output per year to the company's output of coal.[115] Before sinking the colliery, the company's mining engineers expected to find eight coal seams. Yet, once the underground puzzle met beyond the pit pillar of the strata was unravelled, sixteen seams were identified.

A number of years later, in March, 1928, Edmund L. Hann, who by 1927 held the positions of deputy-chairman and managing director, chaired the company's Annual General Meeting due to Shaw's absence. At the meeting, he told shareholders that Llanharan Colliery was producing a house and gas coal of very fine quality. However, the colliery's development gave some shareholders grounds for despair. Alert to such pessimism, Hann remarked: 'In spite of considerable mining difficulties, we have no reason to regret our venture here'.[116] The company's shareholders had to wait at least another five years to value the worth of this prediction. In March, 1933, Hann announced that Llanharan Colliery's 'problems had been largely solved' by 'constantly trying new mining methods for meeting the very serious difficulties we have encountered in this area and our efforts have met with considerable success'.[117] And he repeated his forecast: the colliery would become profitable.

Undoubtedly the ability, grit and determination of the colliery's manager and his officials had had a telling effect upon improving Llanharan Colliery's prospects. The colliery's managers included: William Thomas, from the time of the colliery's sinking; W. Bisp appears to have succeeded William Thomas; and from around 1933, until 1941, Jack Gregor was in charge.[118] Ivor Prosser, the colliery's mechanical engineer, moved from New Tredegar to be party to sinking the colliery, and still held the post in 1945. In terms of employment, the colliery attained its maximum numbers

at 1,054, in 1934.[119] This may suggest that Edmund L. Hann's prediction of success, in general, was proved.

Whilst sinking Llanharan Colliery, and so unaware of the trials and tribulations that lay ahead underground there, the company proceeded to sink its second colliery on the South Crop. This was at Llantrisant, three miles east of Llanharan.

Llantrisant (or Ynysmaerdy) Colliery

A walk along Llantrisant's 'steep winding streets of the old town' can lead to a 'rocky eminence' giving 'magnificent prospect over the plateau of the vale of Glamorgan'. Apparently, Llantrisant's men had already acquired the nickname the 'Black Army' before any of them decided to take work as miners. Their ancestors had served with the Black Prince's army during the French Wars of the 14th century.[120]

In 1924, a platoon of sinkers marshalled at Ynysmaerdy, just north-west of Llantrisant, and adjacent to the River Ely.[121] The main engine with permanent winding machinery had been erected to assist excavation work.[122] Compared with Llanharan Colliery, Powell Duffryn had greater hopes for Llantrisant Colliery. The colliery was designed to raise an annual output of 900,000 tons.[123] Such an outlook may have been founded upon a pinch of vanity among the company's mining engineers. Three shafts were sunk. The deepest shaft was No. 1 Pit at 700 yards with working the Bute seam its objective. Number 2 shaft was sunk to 625 yards so as to access the Two Feet Nine seam. The No. 2 Rhondda seam was the attraction for sinking the No. 3 Pit to 205 yards.[124]

The sinkers struck the lower seams of coal just before March 1926, and found geological disturbances. Headings were then driven to 'prove the extent of the disturbances'.[125] On the 27th March, 1927, at the company's Annual General Meeting,[126] Edmund L. Hann said:

'I have heard that rumours have circulated that the Powell Duffryn Company has expended enormous sums of money in the explorations from the Llantrisant shafts. I take this opportunity of informing you that, although it is quite true that the disturbances which have been met with in this Colliery have been disappointing, yet in spite of the fact that a considerable amount of the work was done at a time when the cost of labour and materials was very high, the total expenditure at this Colliery is no way abnormal. There is no reason to doubt that, given much better times, this well equipped Colliery will form a valuable addition to the profit-earning power of the Company.'[127]

However, in late 1927, a decision was made to 'confine exploration to the No. 3 Rhondda seam'.[128] According to Hann, this was, 'besides being one of the most valuable seams in the neighbourhood' was 'capable of being worked profitably upon a much smaller scale than is possible with the lower seams'.[129]

Although minor in terms of the global economic slump that followed in the wake of the Wall Street Crash of 1929, Llantrisant Colliery's woes continued. Early in 1930, the colliery was dogged by a lack of demand for its gas coal, but the company somehow managed to sell its coal to the steel trade, 'the chief customer for this class of coal'.[130] But, the sales coincided with a period when steelmaking hit serious financial troubles due to poor economic conditions. The steelmakers' troubles persisted. So, regarding Llantrisant Colliery, in 1934, Powell Duffryn decided that 'it was impractical to continue working in its present day conditions of trade'.[131] Nevertheless, the company's wish, it appeared, was to

try and nurture faith in the colliery by also reporting that it was 'maintaining ... improved results'.

Even so, the colliery's manning level pattern later revealed the degree of doubt that existed within Powell Duffryn about establishing Llantrisant as a producer of 900,000 tons of coal a year. The highest number ever employed by the company at the colliery was three hundred men, which occurred in 1931.[132] Employment numbers at the colliery, after 1931, fell to 170. Yet, the company did not abandon the colliery until after June, 1941 when an explosion destroyed the winding facilities, and headgear, of its No. 2 shaft.[133] The explosion also killed the colliery's manager, Jack Gregor, the engineman, Noah Fletcher, the telephone switchboard attendant, David Thomas, and the Banksman, Ernest Evans.[134] The colliery's seams were afterwards worked from Llanharan Colliery, which suggested a company wish, or maybe a legal duty, to hold on to the coal property. Nevertheless, the withdrawal to, and focus upon Llanharan Colliery, was a sign of some curbing in the company's ambitions for mining in the district. Indeed, Powell Duffryn never opened a third colliery at the South Crop as originally planned.

The Colliery Manager

The relatively short life of Llantrisant Colliery, and due to the explosion, the death of its manager, reveals some of the employment risks faced by a colliery manager. Although a colliery manager's career appears to have been as uncertain as that of miners, he shouldered onerous responsibilities. A colliery manager was held responsible for the supervision and discipline of hundreds

Llantrisant (or Ynysmaerdy) Colliery. The company's second sinking on the South Crop began in 1924. Three years later, rumours about geological difficulties met opening the colliery troubled City of London investors. Although the colliery's manpower reached 300, the colliery was closed in 1941. An explosion also occurred at the colliery in 1941, which killed four men.

of men and youths. Accountable for the operation of expensive assets as plant and machinery, he was tasked with the delivery of coal output targets. A salaried employee of the company, he was in fact a junior manager since he reported to a Powell Duffryn agent in the line to the general manager of collieries. Nevertheless, as the highest representative of a coal company in a mining community, he attracted, on the whole, enmity from the colliery workers.

Francis and Howells considered that the 'evils of private enterprise tended, in the minds of the local people, to be personified by this one man'.[135] Indeed, the colliery manager, according to anecdotal information from men who worked in the South Wales Coalfield was blasphemously maligned as either 'God Almighty', or 'Lord Almighty'. The colliery manager, in some locations, though was seen as a patrician figure by miners, and their families. Indeed, if Elliot Colliery's Nehemiah Phillips was considered such an archetype, then they 'ruled in a gracious way'. Although a colliery manager appeared to be a notable man in a mining community, Ina Zweiniger-Bargielowska identified, in 1992, that 'colliery managers' had 'been largely ignored by historians'.[136] Regarding a history of Powell Duffryn, the role of a colliery manger deserves a fuller account than the limited one that follows due to the absence of pertinent archival material.

The colliery manager was unique in British industry. Perhaps only a ship's captain was made accountable at the centre of a legal regime of rights and duties like a colliery manager. The Coal Mines Act of 1911 required that every mine was managed by one manager, and was deemed 'responsible for the control, management, and direction of the mine'.[137] Notably it was the colliery manager who was held 'personally responsible for safety'.[138]

A prescribed course of education and training was demanded by law for the formation of a colliery manager, which was not the case for managers in the British manufacturing industry. Moreover, unlike in British industry in general, the pool of colliery manager candidates was created as a result of a process of examinations. Imperfect as tests maybe for the selection of managers, the process introduced some objectivity into colliery management appointments. Indeed, it is possible that the process produced managers of comparatively superior calibre to their counterparts in manufacturing industry.

Such superiority though did not necessarily work to their advantage concerning the pursuit of industrial relations. Each colliery manager's style of man management was largely shaped by their personal character, and ways of relating to people. However, due to pragmatism, their style of management was also fashioned by a coal company's management culture, an aspect that is difficult to define since it is somewhat intangible. For Powell Duffryn it is tempting to believe that the behaviour of the company's general manager of collieries shaped its management culture. Alas, this cannot be confirmed since no Powell Duffryn colliery managers' memoirs were found to gain an idea of what they saw was the company's culture. Yet, one attribute that the colliery manager, and also the general manager of collieries appeared to have shared, was a temperament to withstand unpopularity.

What rewards then did a colliery manager enjoy so as to be able to tolerate such unpopularity? In general in the South Wales Coalfield, the colliery manager enjoyed rent-free accommodation, free coal and electricity, a gardener, and gifts such as Christmas bonuses.[139] Such perks attracted envy, but they represented in-kind danger money for when the colliery manager walked through a

colliery's strike picket line. Nonetheless, the salary earned by the colliery manager was maybe the true measure of his value to his employer. In 1920, the Monmouthshire & South Wales Coalowners' Association recommended a minimum salary of £400 per annum for managers of colliery's that employed less than 100; and £500 per annum with more than 100 under a manager's charge.[140]

Although no collaborative evidence was found to justify claiming that Powell Duffryn's colliery's managers earned at least 10% per cent more than this recommendation, it is taken for convenience to be the case so as to gauge relative earnings. In 1928, the average weekly earnings of a Powell Duffryn miner for a five shift week was approximately £2 10s, so the annual wage of a miner can be estimated to have been £130. Thus, a Powell Duffryn colliery manager's earnings were just over four times that of a miner.[141] This differential might suggest that a colliery manager was an affluent person.

A review of the permanence of security in employment of a Powell Duffryn colliery manager also merits attention. Viv Lewis, 'who had been employed by Powell Duffryn', reflected in the early 1990s: 'if there were [no] results sooner or later you would lose your job … [for managers] there weren't discontent but a lot of fear. Fear that they'd lose their jobs'.[142] Less than productive colliery workers would have also shared his fear. However, no hire and fire regime is evident in the lineage of the colliery managers employed at Powell Duffryn's Rhymney Valley collieries. In the case of the Rhymney Valley collieries a pattern of manager change can be found that sees individuals moved between the company's collieries.

What then can be inferred from the corresponding lineages at the Aberdare Valley Collieries? Holders of the position at Aberaman Colliery included: in 1878, J. Sanderson; in 1896, D. Bowen Jones; between at least 1908 and 1923; T. L. Davies from 1923 to 1927; in 1927, C. L. Watson; from 1933 until at least 1938, W. Moore; and from 1943 to 1945, T. J. Hughes.[143] Colliery managers appointed at Cwmneol Colliery comprised: in 1878, L. Evans; in 1884, Rees Rees; in 1908, W. E. Jayne; between 1915 and 1919, J. W. Jordan; 1923 to 1930, John Barry, or Barrie; in 1934, C. L. Watson, in 1938, T. J. Hughes; and from 1943 to 1945, J. S. Evans.[144] J. S. Evan's nickname was 'stoneface'.[145] This casts an impression of a stern person, and it might well have been a natural feature of Evans' visage, but it may also been an image he wished to project to command regard. Fforchaman Colliery saw the following men in the post: from at least 1896 to 1908, T. L. Davies; from 1916 to maybe 1918, J. Powell; in 1919, J. Hughes; between 1923 and 1927, H. Rutherford; and from 1930 to 1945, Walter Jones.[146] These names may not be the complete lineages of colliery managers per these Aberdare Valley collieries. Nonetheless, the careers of T. L. Davies and T. J. Hughes suggest a pattern of manager change like that identified as a feature of the Rhymney Valley collieries. Moreover, W. E. Jayne appears to have experienced a variety of managerial roles, including Agent, during his career with Powell Duffryn. Nonetheless, in the Aberdare Valley there is also evidence of longevity of stay by managers at a number of collieries.

Yet, uncertainty of employment troubled some colliery managers. Rhymney Iron Company's colliery managers would have felt uncertainty about continued employment when the collieries they managed came under the control of Powell Duffryn.

The company's colliery managers in the Rhymney Valley experienced, beginning in the mid 1920s, trials and tribulations caused by natural events. At New Year, 1925, severe storms struck the Rhymney Valley. The compressed air main was broken, and saw the 'stoppage' of '4,000 to 5,000 men at New Tredegar and Elliot collieries'.[147] The air main was repaired a number of days later. The efforts of these employees of the company could have consoled worried Powell Duffryn shareholders.

Perhaps Shaw, in his chairman's speech at the company's 1925 Annual General Meeting, was intent on lifting shareholders' spirits by offering two facts. He reported that the company owned outright 8,149 railway wagons and 18 locomotives. The company remained a force in moving coal by railway. Concerning electricity, he stated that 'we generate something like 140,000 kW, and that the constant load factor stands very high, in other words, we run cheaply and economically'. An acquisitive utility electricity company might have noted such a statement.

Nevertheless, Edmund L. Hann's defence of Llantrisant Colliery, covered earlier, served to remind shareholders about the perils of coal mining. For shareholders familiar with the history of the company's search for coal, nothing had changed as regards the risks involved in coal mining. Underground flooding, in the Rhymney Valley, had been succeeded by geological disturbances in the South Crop. Edmund Mills Hann's introduction to the South Wales Coalfield seemed to have been the South Crop, so he might well have anticipated some of the difficulties. Although retired, the members of the South Wales Institute of Engineers had not forgotten his contribution.

Recognition of a 'Great Man'

At a Special General Meeting of the South Wales Institute of Engineers, in May 1925, Edmunds Mills Hann was awarded Honorary Membership.[148] The seventy-four year old Edmund Mills Hann was the subject of much praise. The men who stood to speak at the meeting were, like himself, steadfast members of the Institute, and had an intimate appreciation of both his character, and contribution. T. H. Deakin observed: 'The outstanding characteristic of Mr Hann was his ability and his modesty'. He elaborated: 'Although no man had accomplished more in South Wales, or raised himself to the highest position in the mining profession – for he was at the top of it – yet he remained the same quiet, unassuming gentleman. Had some men accomplished half what Mr Hann had done, their heads would have become so swollen that little of the rest of their bodies would be in evidence'. H. T. Wales asserted that Hann 'was a bold man who attempted to-day to look into the future'.

The Institute's president, H. Spence Thomas, reflected upon Edmund Hann's contribution: an author of papers, a recipient of the Institute's Gold Medal, and having served as its president. Then he rendered an accolade: 'We all know you as a great man'. This he qualified: 'Your outstanding ability, unbounded energy, and tenacity of purpose are things to be admired and honoured, and your contribution to the success of the South Wales Coalfield there is no doubt. Up and down the coalfield your name is a household one, and we are continually being reminded of your accomplishments as the burning light of that huge undertaking, The Powell Duffryn Steam Coal Co., which is ever growing large'.

Edmund Mills Hann acknowledged the importance of the honour by registering his appreciation of having been appraised by his peers. He recalled that when Dr Griffiths spoke at the Institute's meeting to confer the same honour upon Lord Kelvin, some seventeen years earlier, he had said 'that what constitutes

the chief distinction of the honour is that it is the testimonial of those that know and not of the ignorant whose opinions possess no value'. Hann then recalled other distinctions that the Institute had given him, and referred to his entry into the mining industry in 'the great Northern Coalfield' which caused him to relate his impressions of Nicholas Wood, and Sir George Elliot. He also repeated his admiration for Sir William Galloway's work that had reduced the 'appalling catastrophes caused by the explosion of gas and coal dust'.

The retired mining engineer then gave a brief review of 'the numerous improvements and developments that have taken place in the interval [the fifty-nine years of his career] in the art of coal mining, amounting to a revolution in methods'. 'The substitution of high speed for heavy mass in so many classes of machines is of course one of the salient features, and that has been facilitated very much by the introduction of electricity, and instead of a steam piston moving at 400ft per minute maximum, we have rotative speed many thousand of feet per minute'. He was critical of the 'enormous increase in the costs of production of coal'. 'The restrictions of labour and by government regulations', had, he contested, 'entirely obliterated the effect of technical skill and engineering improvements'. In his opinion, the effect had been to lose the British Coalfield advantages it had once held. He closed his speech by expressing his hope that the Institute would have a 'long prosperous future devoted to the benefit of commerce, of the nation, and of mankind'.

Abernant House, the General Hospital, also had reason to thank the former Powell Duffryn general manager of collieries. New entrance gates and railings to the hospital had been previously identified as being necessary.[149] Edmund Mills Hann used his influence to persuade the company to gift money so that such an improvement could be realised. He performed the opening ceremony of the new gates in July, 1925. Arthur Humphreys reported that the event was watched by a 'large gathering of people, and under the happiest of times'.

The company's managing director, on the other hand, squared up to the challenges arising from an 'ever growing' Powell Duffryn. One issue that concerned Edmund L. Hann was building homes to house colliery workers. 'Between the years 1923 and 1928, following the sinking of Ogilvie, Llanharan and Llantrisant Collieries, 655 houses were built, either directly or through wholly-owned subsidiary companies, at an average cost of £526'.[150] As mentioned earlier, a Powell Duffryn miner's annual wage was reckoned to be £130.[151] So, the value of a built house was four-times a miner's annual income. But their employment depended upon trade. The worries of Powell Duffryn shareholders, due to the company's South Crop ventures, may have lessened on learning that the company had been party to finding coal at a new colliery in an appendix of the Taff Valley, Cwm Bargod.

Taff-Merthyr Colliery

The company, and its notable rival, the Ocean Coal Company, had earlier got together to sink Taff-Merthyr Colliery on unexploited coal territory that lay between both companies mining properties.[152] Taff-Merthyr Colliery's site lay north-west of Penallta, and just over a mile north of the Ocean Company's Deep Navigation Colliery, Treharris.[153] Curiously Edmund Mill Hann gave no hint of a plan for such a joint venture in his third and final part of a history about the company, which covered the period

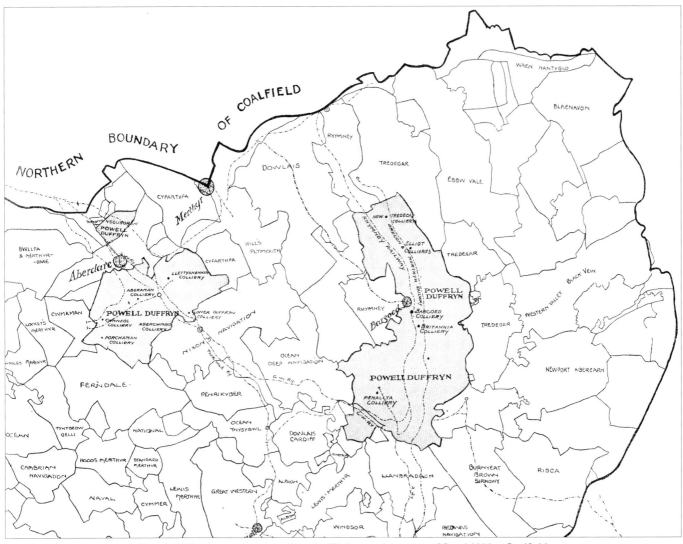

Powell Duffryn's steam coal territory in 1914 – northern part of South Wales Coalfield

1914 to 1921. Discretion, due to business confidentiality, might have been the reason for such an omission. However, it is possible that the joint venture was an initiative of Edmund L. Hann's. His period outside the company opened his mind to other ways for investing in coal mining ventures.

The joint venture was formed as the Taff Merthyr Steam Coal Company Limited. Powell Duffryn's Board Minutes, for 18th July, 1922, confirms such an agreement between the two coal companies. Around that time, Ogilvie, Llanharan and Llantrisant Collieries had extended Powell Duffryn's potential mining capacity by approximately 2.1 million tons. Taff-Merthyr offered the company access to a further 1 million tons.

Sinking four collieries at more or less the same time raised the risk of financially over committing Powell Duffryn, but a joint undertaking at Taff-Merthyr hedged the gamble. Moreover, in jointly owning Taff-Merthyr's coal property, a likely clash of interests at least was avoided. On the 20th March 1923, a Powell Duffryn director observed: 'The Ocean Co. and ourselves had a Naboth's vineyard between us; we both wanted it, but we could not have it, so we came to the conclusion that we had better make a joint concern of it and run it together'.[154] Joint ventures, though, can prove to be less than amenable to run.

The design of Taff-Merthyr Colliery testified that Powell Duffryn took command of its engineering. Preparation for this 'All-Electric'

colliery began in 1922, and, by February 1923, the sinking of its two shafts, together with the erection of winding gear, was underway.[155] Major E. Ivor David, the company's chief electrical engineer, designed the colliery's electric winding system.[156] An AC electric winder was installed at the colliery's North Pit.[157] Major E. Ivor David informed that the colliery's winder had a raising capacity of 525 tons per hour.[158] Built upon a reinforced concrete raft, the engine house was the same size as the one at Penallta Colliery. After fourteen months sinking work, in November, 1925, the colliery's upper productive seams were reached at 680 yards. Feeders of water were encountered. In 1926, the Taff Merthyr Steam Coal Company announced that it proposed to 'work the celebrated 4ft seam only, which was measured as '6ft of clean coal'.[159]

In March, 1927, Edmund Lawrence Hann told Powell Duffryn shareholders that Taff-Merthyr Colliery looked 'likely to turn out, as we had always anticipated, an extremely valuable property'.[160] 'The output is increasing regularly and the quality of the coal produced is certainly equal to the very best that has been worked in the Coalfield. The plant, which is the best practice known, is complete'.

Yet, the effect of the market for coal in the mid 1920s defied the optimism that had led the company to sink Ogilvie, Llanharan, Llantrisant, and Taff-Merthyr Collieries. 'Many companies, especially the single-colliery concerns, were unable to make ends meet and went into liquidation', and so 'their assets were

The Taff-Merthyr Colliery of the Taff Merthyr Steam Coal Company Ltd, was located in a valley east of Merthyr Vale. The colliery was the result of a Powell Duffryn- Ocean Coal Company joint venture. The colliery's winding house was identical to that at Penallta Colliery. Sinking began at this 'all-electric' colliery in 1923. In 1926 the company announced it proposed to work the 'celebrated' Four Feet seam. Around 1934, a notable inter-union dispute occurred at the colliery. In 1945, the colliery's manpower was 1,119 persons.

Courtesy of Amgueddfa Cymru-National Museum of Wales

sold at knock down prices'.[161] However, Powell Duffryn, Trevor Boyns observed, possessed an 'ability to approach the capital markets for funds' to finance the acquisition of troubled single-colliery concerns.

In 1925, the company bought the Windsor Colliery from the receiver of Windsor Steam Coal (1901) Ltd for £250,000. The colliery was situated in the Aber Valley, near the village of Abertridwr. Senghenydd, with its infamous Universal Colliery, was Abertridwr's neighbouring village to the north.

Windsor Colliery

The colliery took its name from the landowner that had granted the Windsor Steam Coal Company a ninety-nine year mining lease, Lord Windsor, the Earl of Plymouth (1857-1923).[162] The Windsor Steam Coal Company was formed in 1896 with its principal shareholders being James Walter Insole, George Frederick Insole, and William Henry Lewis. The Insole's great grandfather, George Insole, had a claim, as a coal trader, to pioneering the London market for south Wales's coal. George Insole prospered, and ventured into coal mining first in the Taff Valley, and then the Rhondda Valley. By 1880, James Insole's interests included Cymmer Colliery Company, and George Insole & Son, a Cardiff coal trading company, which were controlled through some kind of partnership.[163] In general, for the next two decades, the Insole family earned wealth from their business interests, but did not appear to have a desire to grow as a coalowner until the idea of Windsor Colliery arose.

Windsor Colliery provides a Rhymney Valley example where 'speculative venture and high risk' yielded financial loss for its investors.[164] Sinking of the colliery began in 1898, and with the proving of steam coal the Windsor Steam Coal (1901) Ltd was formed.[165] Mining difficulties then followed at the colliery that cumulated as a financial loss. Although in 1920 the Windsor Steam Coal company made a rare profit, the owners dealt with financial calamity by seeking voluntary liquidation.[166] And so, on the 5th June, 1925, the colliery was sold to Powell Duffryn. Richard Wilson noted: 'It had been an expensive venture for the Insoles and the Lewises, they not only lost nearly all their capital invested in the project but the company never paid a dividend on its ordinary shares, the bulk of which they held'.[167]

The shareholders of Powell Duffryn Steam Coal Company, in the 1880s, nearly became as crestfallen as those of the Windsor Steam Coal. Elliot Colliery needed much more finance for its development than was first envisaged by Sir George Elliot. Maybe Powell Duffryn, unlike the Windsor Steam Coal Company, was better placed to pawn more collieries than the Windsor Steam Coal to stave of bankruptcy. Powell Duffryn, though, somehow skimped on expenditures, diverted earnings, and no doubt begged for some financial help to survive.

Investment secured Windsor Colliery's future. By early 1928, Windsor Colliery had been electrified.[168] If Powell Duffryn was intent on defying the logic of the market, by keeping its belief in technical development, and purchasing coal companies, it did so aware of the perils of industrial relations in the South Wales Coalfield.

Windsor Colliery. Purchased by Powell Duffryn in 1925 from Windsor Steam Coal (1901) Ltd, the colliery operated in the Aber Valley, an tributary of the Rhymney Valley. A contemporary of Bargoed Colliery, its sinking began in 1897, but was not completed until 1906.   *Pope/Parkhouse Archive*

NOTES

1 Letter, Trevor Boyns to Writer, 21 July 2005. Attachment: 'Some thoughts re. Powell Duffryn', pp.1-2.

2 The writer speculates that the collieries of the Rhymney Valley represented the most concentrated use of compound steam winding in one coal mining area anywhere in the British coal industry. The use of compound steam winding engines in the Aberdare Valley provided a challenger to this claim. John Boucher commented to the Writer, 21st September 2006, that Edmund Mills Hann's policy regarding compound steam winding engines was 'interesting'. With regard to the use of compound steam winding in coalfields other than South Wales he observed: '*In the last major coalfield in the Doncaster and Nottinghamshire Areas, Bentley (1906) had two cross compounds by Fraser & Chalmers [the maker chosen for Penallta], Askern (1910) had two tandem compounds by Yates & Thom (a third to the same drawings being preserved at Astley Green in Lancashire, Thorne (1909) had one twin tandem compound and one duplex (also Fraser & Chalmers)*'.

3 Major E. Ivor David, 'The History of Winding Engines', *Iron & Coal Trades Review*, Diamond Jubilee Issue, (December, 1927), p.24, col.1.

4 *The Powell Duffryn Steam Coal Company 1864-1914, op. cit.*, p.32.

5 George Hann, 'Paper on a Modern Colliery', *op. cit.*, Vol.XXXIV, (1918), p.216.

6 *The Powell Duffryn Steam Coal Company 1864-1914, op. cit.*, p.62.

7 *The Powell Duffryn Steam Coal Company 1864-1914, op. cit.*, p.25.

8 E. M. Hann, *Brief History of The Powell Duffryn Steam Coal Company Ltd*, p. 34. This page was part of what he described as his history's 'Second Part – The Period from 1910 to 1914', and is suspected as being used as source material for the company's fifty years history.

9 E. M. Hann, *op. cit.*, p.9.

10 David Hann, 'The Hann Family–A Mining Dynasty of South Wales part 2, W. R. Hann (1876-1945)', *op. cit.*, p.4.

11 'President's Inaugural Address', *SWIE*, Vol.XXX, (1914), p.20.

12 'President's Inaugural Address', *SWIE*, Vol.XXX, (1914), pp.4-19.

13 Roy Jenkins, *Churchill*. (Pan Books, 2001), pp 219-220

14 *The Powell Duffryn Steam Coal Company 1864-1914, op. cit.*, p.95.

15 Barry Supple, *The History of the British Coal Industry, Volume 4, 1913-1946: The Political Economy of Decline*, (Clarendon Press, 1987), p.6.

16 F. A. Gibson, *A Comparison of Statistics of the Coal Mining Industry of the United Kingdom …* (Cardiff, 1922), pp. 136-37. In terms of the underground death rate per 1,000 persons employed in the South Wales Coalfield, in 1874 this was 2.57 people versus, in 1914, 1.68 people, which indicated a fall of 35%. However, compared with the underground death rate per 1,000 people employed in the United Kingdom's Coalfields as a whole, in 1874, it was 1.82 people, whereas in 1914 it was 1.15, which was a drop of 37%. So, comparatively, underground deaths in the South Wales Coalfield were worse than the UK average. See, T. Boyns, 'Work and Death in the South Wales Coalfield, 1874-1914', The Welsh History Review: Cylchgrawn Hanes Cymru, Vol.12, No.4, (1985), p.536.

17 'Presentation of Portrait', *SWIE*, Vol.XXX, (1914), pp.548-50.

18 T. Boyns, 'Work and Death in the South Wales Coalfield, 1874-1914', *op. cit.*, p.534.

19 Arthur W. Humphreys, *op. cit.*, p.7.

20 *New Tredegar Bargoed & Caerphilly Journal*, op. cit, 16 Dec 1909, p.3, col.3.

21 Capt. D. Ivor Evans, 'Mining Warfare', *SWIE*, Vol.XXXVI, (1920), pp.385-419. David Ivor Evans served in the 251st Tunnelling Company, Royal Corps of Engineers.

22 Sir R. A. S. Redmayne, *The British Coal-Mining Industry During the War*. (Clarendon, 1923), p.2.

23 Sir R. A. S. Redmayne, *op. cit.*, p. 9.

24 E. M. Hann, *Brief History of The Powell Duffryn Steam Coal Company Ltd*, p.50.

25 Barry Supple, *op. cit.*, p.47.

26 E. M. Hann, *op. cit.*, p.56.

27 Llewellyn J. Davies & D. Owen Davies, *South Wales Coals*. (Cardiff, The Business Statistics), pp6-9. Admiralty 1st coal had a composition of 3 to 5 per cent ash, volatile matter of 14 per cent, while the 2nd category coals had a composition of 4 to 5 per cent ash, volatile matter of 14 to 18 per cent. Regarding the range of calorific values per each category, the source gave details of ranges for 'calories', the respective unit not given but thought to be cals/gm, and for a 'representative analysis' of samples of coals per category in British Thermal Units. Alas the test basis used to determine calorific values was not made clear, and was judged likely to cause confusion with this work's use of such data drawn from the *South Wales Coalfield (Including Pembrokeshire) Regional Survey Report, op. cit.*, pp.20-21. As a guide, in terms of the *South Wales Coalfield (Including Pembrokeshire) Regional Survey Report*, Admiralty 1st coal's corresponded roughly to the 'sub-bituminous' class and Admiralty 2nd coals to the 'semi-bituminous' class.

28 E. M. Hann, *op. cit.*, p.56.

29 E. M. Hann, *op. cit.*, pp.49-50.

30 Sir R. A. S. Redmayne, *op. cit.*, pp.101-108.

31 Sir R. A. S. Redmayne, *op. cit.*, pp.110-113, and pp.120-124.

32 Barry Supple, *op. cit.*, pp.78-116.

33 Sir R. A. S. Redmayne, *op. cit.*, pp.157-8.

34 Barry Supple, *op. cit.*, p.47.

35 E. M. Hann, *op. cit.*, p.50.

36 Barry Supple, *op. cit.*, p.117.

37 Arthur W. Humphreys, *op. cit.*, pp.7-9.

38 The mineral rights were probably associated with the De Winton Colliery. Cynon Valley History Society, *Cynon Coal, op. cit.*, p.212.

39 E. M. Hann, *Brief History of The Powell Duffryn Steam Coal Company Ltd*, p.50.

40 E. M. Hann, *op. cit.*, p.53.

41 E. M. Hann, *op. cit.*, p.53.

42 *The South Wales Coal Annual for 1919*. (Business Statistics Company, 1929), p.xxxix. In 2011, the offices of the French edition of Vogue magazine occupied the Paris address of Compagnie Française des Mines Powell Duffryn.

43 E. M. Hann, *op. cit.*, pp.42-3.

44 E. M. Hann, *op. cit.*, p.57.

45 *The South Wales Coal Annual for 1919, op. cit.*, pp.xxxviii.

46 George Hann, 'Paper on a Modern Colliery', *SWIE*, Vol.XXXIV, (1918), p.230.

47 George Hann, 'Paper on a Modern Colliery', *op. cit.*, p.236.

48 George Hann, 'Paper on a Modern Colliery', *op. cit.*, p.230.

49 E. M. Hann, *op. cit.*, p.55.

50 Cynon Valley History Society, *op. cit.*, p.234.

51 Cynon Valley History Society, *op. cit.*, pp.40-1.

52 *The South Wales Coal Annual for 1919, op. cit.*, p.20.

53 Cynon Valley History Society, *op. cit.*, p.234.

54 Cynon Valley History Society, *op. cit.*, p.204

55 Arthur W. Humphreys, *op. cit.*, p.9.

56 David Hann, 'The Hann Family – A Mining Dynasty of South Wales part 2, G. G. Hann (1879-1918)', *Glamorgan Family History Society, Journal* No.39, (September, 1995) p.6.

57 G. D. Budge, 'Notes on Stone-Dusting', *SWIE*, Vol.XXXII, (1916), pp.215-6.

58 'Notes on Stone-Dusting', *SWIE*, Vol.XXXII, (1916), pp.314-5. Based upon a view of Tredegar Coal Company's A. S. Tallis.

59 'The late Mr George Gilroy Hann', *SWIE*, Vol.XXXIV, (1918), pp.239-240.

60 David Hann, 'The Hann Family – A Mining Dynasty of South Wales part 3, E. L. Hann (1881-1968)', *Glamorgan Family History Society, Journal* No.40, (December, 1995) p.10.

61 E. M. Hann, *op. cit.*, pp.59-58.

62 Barry Supple, *op. cit.*, p.47.

63 Beatrice Webb, *My Apprenticeship*. (Longmans, 1926), p.347.

64 Beatrice Webb, *op. cit.*, p.393.

65 Beatrice Webb, *op. cit.* p.409.

66 E. M. Hann, *Brief History of The Powell Duffryn Steam Coal Company Ltd*, p.60.

67 Alfred Read, in a 'Foreword' to a document whose title was not stated, but it had been reprinted from a Fuel Development Folder, July 1937, p.iv.

68 Stephenson Clarke was acquired with monies raised by Powell Duffryn via 6% Redeemable Notes, which were redeemed in 1933 from the 'proceeds of an issue of Cumulative Shares in Stephenson Clarke & Company. Document, *Powell Duffryn Limited - Short Survey of the Organisation, Growth and Development of Powell Duffryn Limited*,(Powell Duffryn, 1946), p.22.

69 E. M. Hann, *Brief History of The Powell Duffryn Steam Coal Company Ltd*, pp.60-1.

70 Trevor Boyns, 'Rationalisation in the Inter-War period: The Case of the South Wales Coal Industry', *Business History*, Vol.XXIX, No. 3, (July, 1987), p.289.

71 E. M. Hann, *op. cit.*, pp.60-1.

72 Report-Proceedings, AGM of the Company, Powell Duffryn Steam Coal Company (hereafter PDSCC), 22 March 1932, p.10.

73 *A Directory of Colliery Companies in the South Wales Coalfield*, (The

Monmouthshire & South Wales Coal Owners' Association, 1917), p.14, and Raymond Lawrence, *The Coal Workings of the Caerphilly County Area*. (Private Publication, circa 2007), pp.121-122..

74 *The South Wales Coal Annual for 1919*. (Business Statistics Company, 1929).

75 E. E. Edwards, *Echoes of Rhymney*, (The Starling Press, 1974). pp.81-2.

76 David Hann, 'The Hann Family – A Mining Dynasty of South Wales part 3, E. L. Hann (1881-1968)', *Glamorgan Family History Society, Journal* No.40, (December, 1995) p. 10.

77 David Hann, 'The Hann Family – A Mining Dynasty of South Wales part 1, E. M. Hann ', *Glamorgan Family History Society, Journal* No. 38, (June, 1995) p.40.

78 Geoffrey Evans, 'The Hann Family and Aberdare', (Geoffrey Evan's research notes dated 2005).

79 E. M. Hann, *Brief History of The Powell Duffryn Steam Coal Company Ltd*, p.61.

80 Powell Duffryn Board Minutes, 12 July 1921.

81 E. M. Hann, *op. cit.*, p.62.

82 E. M. Hann, *op. cit.*, p.54-5.

83 Edmund L. Hann, 'A Modern Colliery Power Plant', *SWIE*, Vol. XXXIX, (1922-1923), pp.584-6.

84 Edmund L. Hann, 'A Modern Colliery Power Plant', *op. cit.*, pp.588-610.

85 Edmund L. Hann, 'A Modern Colliery Power Plant', *op. cit.*, p.586.

86 Edmund L. Hann, 'A Modern Colliery Power Plant', *op. cit.*, pp.597-599.

87 Form, Transference Graduateship to Associate Membership – Graeme Mentieth Hann (Institution of Mechanical Engineers, April 1945). The application's Seconder was Ivor Williams and his company position and address was given as 'Chief Engineer, Powell Duffryn Ltd, Engineers Department, Ystrad Mynach, Hengoed, Glam.' Ivor Williams had earlier, in 1914 at least, been the engineer responsible for Bargoed Colliery: see E. M. Hann, *op. cit.*, p.45.

88 Edmund L. Hann, 'A Modern Colliery Power Plant', *SWIE*, Vol. XXXIX, (1922-1923), p.584.

89 Edmund L. Hann, 'A Modern Colliery Power Plant', *op. cit.*, pp.611-13.

90 *The Colliery Guardian*, Vol. CXXIII, 17 March 1922, p.681.

91 Edmund L. Hann, 'A Modern Colliery Power Plant', *op. cit.*, pp.614-24.

92 Edmund L. Hann, 'A Modern Colliery Power Plant', *op. cit.*, pp.599-610.

93 Edmund L. Hann, 'A Modern Colliery Power Plant', *op. cit.*, pp.630-1.

94 E. M. Hann, *Brief History of The Powell Duffryn Steam Coal Company Ltd*, p.64.

95 David Hann, 'The Hann Family – A Mining Dynasty of South Wales part 2, G. G. Hann ', *Glamorgan Family History Society, Journal* No. 39, (September, 1995) p. 6.

96 A sketch in the keeping of Bargoed Library identifies Ogilvie Colliery's North Pit as the downcast, and the South Pit the upcast. Concerning the South Pit: the Elled seam was located at a depth of 1,255.9ft below the surface datum which was given as 895ft above sea level datum; this suggests that the seam was 113ft above its equivalent in Elliot East; the landing for the Rhas Las was located at a depth of 1,415.2ft, which suggests that it was 155ft shallower that than its equivalent at Elliot East. A seam identified as the 5ft – the Four Feet, or Old Coal – was sited at a depth of 1,636ft 10in. that suggests that it was 174ft shallower than its possible equivalent at Elliot Colliery. The shaft's sump bottom lay at a depth of 1,897ft 6in. Underground, a pump house served the Elled seam, and another pump house served the Rhas Las. A note written on the sketch, signed D. J. P. and dated 26 Dec 1990, recorded that up to 1990, the South Pit remained open for pumping. The colliery was closed in 1975. The landscaped colliery's site is now a part of the Parc Cwm Darran.

97 OS grid reference SO 121029.

98 George Knox, 'Landslides in South Wales Valleys', *SWIE*, Vol. XLIII (1927-1928), pp.239-240.

99 George Knox, 'Landslides in South Wales Valleys', *op. cit.*, p.229.

100 Document, 'Powell Duffryn – Short Survey of the Organisation, Growth and Development of Powell Duffryn Limited', (Powell Duffryn, 1946), p.2.

101 W. W. Price, Card Index on the Hanns, sheet 6, 'Romance of Coal Industry', an unattributed newspaper item.

102 Research Notes as at March 2007, Raymond Lawrence. The seams worked, and ventilation details.

103 *The Colliery Guardian*, Vol.CXXVII, No. 3298, 14 March 1924, p.694.

104 Research Notes as at March 2007, Raymond Lawrence. The colliery manager details.

105 Trevor Boyns, Ogilvie Colliery-Employment Figures. (Annual List of Mines). 1,011 men worked underground and 225 on the surface.

106 R. W. Kidner, *op. cit.*, p.103.

107 E. M. Hann, *op. cit.*, pp.56-57.

108 The main source was the only surviving page of a 'History of the Caerphilly District Miners' Hospital', and attributed to J. H. L Mabbit, circa 1978, which was once kept at the Post Graduate Library, Caerphilly District Miners' Hospital, Gwent Healthcare NHS Trust. The hospital was closed in 2011.

109 In the 1910s the coal was termed as being a bituminous manufacturing coal. According to the 1942 classification its coal was bituminous III (gas coal) with a volatile content of 29-36% (the highest in the South Wales Coalfield), its carbon ranged from 84-88% (the lowest in the coalfield), hydrogen 5-5.5% (the highest), and a calorific value 15,050-15,650 Btu/lb. The coal, except for volatiles content, matched the properties of Durham coal. Data from the *South Wales Coalfield (Including Pembrokeshire) Regional Survey Report, op. cit.*, pp. 20-21. The data used for comparison taken from *The Efficient Use of Fuel*, *op. cit.*, table 1, p.7, and 'Group 4', p.8.

110 E. M. Hann, *op. cit.*, p. 57.

111 T. J. Witt, *A Time of Tears – Llanharan & Brynna*. (Whitchurch Books, 2000), pp.28-9.

112 T. J. Witt, *op. cit.*, p.93.

113 Research Notes as at March 2007, Raymond Lawrence. Llanharan Colliery information. The depths of the North Pit and the South Pit were 1,128ft 5in. and 1,362ft 7in. respectively.

114 *The Colliery Guardian*, Vol.CXXVII, No. 3298, 14 March 1924, p.694.

115 Short Survey- Powell Duffryn Limited, *op. cit.*, p.2.

116 Report-Proceedings, AGM of the Company, PDSCC, 27 March 1928, p.6.

117 Report-Proceedings, AGM of the Co., PDSCC, 23 March 1933, p.7.

118 Research Notes as at March 2007, Raymond Lawrence. Colliery manager information.

119 Trevor Boyns, Llanharan Colliery-Employment Figures. (Annual List of Mines). 899 men worked underground and 155 on the surface.

120 C. J. O. Evans, *Glamorgan, its History and Topography, op. cit.*, pp.305-9.

121 OS grid reference ST032840.

122 *The Colliery Guardian*, Vol.CXXVII, No. 3298, 14 March 1924, p.694.

123 Short Survey- Powell Duffryn Limited, *op. cit.*, p.2.

124 Research Notes as at March 2007, Raymond Lawrence. Llantrisant Colliery information regarding shaft and coal seam details. The precise depths for Nos. 1, 2, and 3 were 2,100ft, 1,876ft, and 613ft 10in. respectively.

125 *The Colliery Guardian*, Vol.CXXXI, 12 March 1926, p.633.

126 Winchester House, Broad Street, London, E.C.2, was used as a regular venue for the company's AGM for the years around 1927. The company's registered office remained at 101, Leadenhall Street, London, EC 3.

127 Report-Proceedings, AGM of the Co., PDSCC, 27 March 1928, p.6.

128 A later finding suggests that it may have been the No.2 Rhondda seam, and it had a thickness of around 54 inches. Research Notes as at March 2007, Raymond Lawrence. Llantrisant Colliery information.

129 Report-Proceedings, AGM of the Co., PDSCC, 27 March 1928, p.6.

130 Report-Proceedings, AGM of the Co., PDSCC, 27 March 1930, p.7.

131 Report-Proceedings, Adjourned AGM and Extraordinary General Meeting of the Company, PDSCC, 4 July 1934, p.7.

132 Trevor Boyns, Llantrisant Colliery-Employment Figures. (Annual List of Mines). 258 men worked underground, and 42 on the surface.

133 T. J. Witt, *op. cit.*, p.89.

134 T. J. Witt, *op. cit.*, p.89.

135 Hywel Francis and Kim Howells, 'The Politics of Coal in South Wales 1945-48', *Llafur*, Vol. 3. No. 3, (1982), p.75.

136 Ina Zweiniger-Bargielowska, 'Colliery Managers and Nationalisation: The Experience in South Wales'. *Business History*, Vol.34, No.4, (1992), p.59.

137 Coal Mines Act, 1911, 1 & 2 Geo. 5c50, S.2(1).

138 Ina Zweiniger-Bargielowska, *op. cit.*, p.59.

139 Ina Zweiniger-Bargielowska, *op. cit.*, p.64.

140 Ina Zweiniger-Bargielowska, *op. cit.*, p.61.

141 Short Survey- Powell Duffryn Limited, *op. cit.*, p.17. Average earnings per man shift was given as 9s 5$^{1}/_{4}$ d.

142 Ina Zweiniger-Bargielowska, *op. cit.*, p.62.

143 Research Notes as at March 2007, Raymond Lawrence. The colliery manager details.

144 Research Notes as at March 2007, Raymond Lawrence. The colliery manager details.

145 Bryn Cummings, telephone conversation with writer, 16 April 2007. Bryn Cummings, of Aberdare, worked for Powell Duffryn from 1940

to the end of 1946 as clerk to the company's mining engineer in the Aberdare Valley.

146 Research Notes as at March 2007, Raymond Lawrence. The colliery manager details.

147 *The Colliery Guardian*, Vol.CXXIX, No.3340, 2 Jan 1925, p.44.

148 'Special General Meeting-New Honorary Members', *SWIE*, Vol. XXLI (1925), pp.207-227.

149 Arthur W. Humphreys, *op. cit.*, p.10.

150 Short Survey- Powell Duffryn Limited, *op. cit.*, p.11.

151 Short Survey- Powell Duffryn Limited, *op. cit.*, p.17. Average earnings per man shift was given as 9s 5¹/₄ d.

152 Short Survey- Powell Duffryn Limited, *op. cit.*, p.12.

153 OS grid reference ST 104989.

154 21 Kings 21, *The New English Bible,* (Oxford University Press, 1970). Naboth of Jezreel owned a vineyard close to the palace of Ahab king of Samaria. Ahab made a proposal to Naboth so as to acquire the vineyard so that it could be turned into a garden. Ahab declined the offer. A scheme of Ahab's wife, Jezebel, resulted in the death of Naboth. Ahab gained possession of the vineyard.

155 *The Colliery Guardian*, Vol.CXXXI, No.3400, 26 Feb 1926, p.491. Major E. Ivor David was the author of this brief account about the colliery.

156 Major E. Ivor David was the company's chief electrical engineer for eight years, from around 1919. Educated at Lewis School, Pengam, and Liverpool College, apprenticed as a mechanical engineer at the North-Western Steel Works, Workington, in 1903, he won a scholarship to University College, Cardiff and studied mechanical, electrical, and civil engineering. He served in the RAF during the Great War. Major E. Ivor David, 'The History of Winding Engines', *Iron and Coal Trades Review*, Diamond Jubilee Issue, (December, 1927), p.21, col.1.

157 Major E. Ivor David, 'The History of Winding Engines', *Iron and Coal Trades Review,* Diamond Jubilee Issue, (December, 1927), Fig.8, p.24, cols.1 & 2.

158 Major E. Ivor David, 'The History of Winding Engines', *op. cit.*, p.26, col.1.

159 *The Colliery Guardian*, Vol.CXXXI, No.3402, 12 March 1926, p.633.

160 Report-Proceedings, AGM of the Co., PDSCC, 29 March 1927, p.7.

161 Trevor Boyns, 'Rationalisation in the Inter-War period: The Case of the South Wales Coal Industry', Business History, Vol. XXIX, No.3, (July, 1987), pp.289-290

162 Richard Watson, *Rhondda Coal, Cardiff Gold-The Insoles of Llandaff Coal Owners and Shippers.* (Merton Priory Press, 1997), p.141.

163 Richard Watson, *op. cit.*, p.84.

164 Richard Watson, *op. cit.*, p.113.

165 Richard Watson, *op. cit.*, p.138.

166 Richard Watson, *op. cit.*, p.158.

167 Richard Watson, *op. cit.*, p.159.

168 *The Colliery Guardian*, Vol.CXXXVI, No. 3506, 9 March 1928, p.970.

Powell Duffryn advertisements from 1919 (above) and 1924 (right).

Penallta Colliery workers taking a meal break in 1931. The photograph was taken for the Daily Herald newspaper by James Jarché, a notable Fleet Street photographer of the period. The lighting equipment he used involved measures that minimised the risk of being the cause of an underground explosion in the event of an escape of gas from the rock strata.

Courtesy of the Science Museum

Chapter Nine
CONFLICT & COAL COMPANIES

Industrial relations conflict and the South Wales Coalfield were synonymous. 'The reputation of South Wales as a coalfield was determined not merely by its rate of growth. It was also attributable to the intensity of mining operations, the tensions between labour and capital, and the general configuration of the industry, clustered as it was in narrow and deeply etched valleys which gave birth to tightly knit and distinctive communities'.[1] The TUC and the Labour Party also crusaded for the nationalization of coal, under the banner slogan of 'The Mines for the Nation'. Regardless, the latent threat of a major industrial relations confrontation arising in the South Wales Coalfield was ever present.

Trevor Boyns found that 'towards the end of 1923 signs were beginning to emerge that trade was turning downwards and this was accompanied in the Rhymney Valley by complaints that the owners were being more aggressive in their attitude to double shifts'.[2] He featured a dispute at Britannia Colliery as an example. An apparent concession of Britannia Colliery's miners to work double shifts, gave way to confusion, counter claims about non-payments for double shifting, and a reversal to single shift work. Powell Duffryn 'forced the issue up to the Joint Disputes Committee', a conciliation body set up to resolve coalfield disputes. A company spokesman, in summary, said: 'that though the company had not wanted to work double shifts, they had introduced the system to avoid putting men 'on the road' some 'two years earlier when they lost 400 yards of face'. Moreover, other 'South Wales colliery owners attempted on a number of occasions, after the war, to get the men to change working practices and adopt double-shift working, but they were always rebuffed at the coalfield level'.[3]

The growth of trade unionism among Rhondda mineworkers, according to historian Gwyn Williams, began around 1872. '*The men marched into unionism and the Amalgamated Association of Miners (AAM), based in Lancashire, made headway in the early 1870s. The great coal combines were already beginning to form. From 1864 one bought out Powell's mines to create Powell Duffryn (nicknamed PD, Poverty and Death). Between 1872 and 1875, miners' wages were forced down by 25 per cent and the AAM went bankrupt. Out of its ruins emerged a patchwork of intensely local unions under local satraps'.*[4] And so the South Wales Miners' Federation [SWMF] was formed in 1898, which became more familiarly known as 'the Fed'. Gwyn Williams claimed that by the 1920s the Fed had become a 'formative power second to none within South Wales society'.[5]

A 'great fire' at Powell Duffryn's Bargoed By-Product plant, in late May, 1926, was an aside to the advent of a cataclysm in the history of the South Wales Coalfield.[6] The damage to the plant was considerable, but catastrophe was avoided due to the work of firemen. Severely buckled railway lines adjacent to the tar-refining plant illustrated the intensity of the fire's heat. Firemen isolated benzol naphthalene storage tanks, and gasometers, from the risk of ignition. The tar plant was, by 1928, 'entirely rebuilt with all modern improvements'.[7]

GREAT FIRE AT POWELL DUFFRYN COLLIERY, BARGOED: F

Bargoed By-Product Plant – 1926 Fire. The plant was severely damaged by fire, and rebuilt. *Courtesy of both the Western Mail, and Llyfrgell Genedlaethol Cymru – The National Library of Wales*

Soup and Speeches

The year 1926 probably saw the most savage rupture in industrial relations in at least the history of the South Wales Coalfield. Idris Davies later wrote in Gwalia Deserta poem XIII:

'Do you remember 1926? The summer of soup and speeches,
The sunlight on the idle wheels and the deserted crossings.'

These two lines of poetry present a picture of one of the bleakest times experienced by South Wales Coalfield miners and their communities. Such times arose from a failure of a meeting between the Prime Minister of the 1924 to 1929 Conservative Government,

Stanley Baldwin, and representatives of the miners and the coal-owners to discuss the Report of the Samuel Commission. The recommendations of the Report, issued on the 10th March, 1926, included reducing miners' wages, and the Government to halt subsidising miners' wages on the 30th April, 1926, when an earlier agreement ended. Moreover, although the Samuel Commission opposed nationalizing the coal industry, it advocated that rationalisation occur through company amalgamations, and advised the State to buy the owners' royalty rights.[8]

The rigid stance taken by the miners' leaders, particularly those from the Durham, South Wales and Yorkshire Coalfields, especially against the wage cut recommendations of the Samuel Commission Report, put the Government on alert of a nationwide coal strike. The Government involved the TUC but to no avail. On the 30th April, 1926, the Government proclaimed a State of Emergency. An Emergency Powers Act was enforced on the 1st May. A provision in the Act directed that an unauthorised person approaching any public building, mine, shop factory, or even road, 'may be deemed guilty of intent to do injury thereto'. Policemen were instructed to search, or arrest, anyone.[9] Moreover, anticipating civil unrest in the South Wales Coalfield, a battalion of troops from the Southern Command were ordered to occupy barracks in Cardiff.[10] On the 3rd May, a national strike began.

Islwyn Jenkins later recollected: 'The miners began a strike which according to their leader A. J. Cook would concede to the owners not one penny, not one minute'. The British trade union movement's reaction was to call a General Strike, which also began on the 3rd of May. The General Strike lasted for 'nine dramatic days'. But, miners in the South Wales Coalfield did not return to work.

Earlier that year, Rhymney born Islwyn Jenkins left school to work as a miner at Bargoed Colliery. He later sketched his impression of the time:

'For years in the coalfields after the Great War there had been an accumulation of mistrust. The workmen above and below ground felt exploited by their employers who paid low wages which varied from pit to pit. In the spring of 1926 the situation between miners and management became worse. Men who refused to work for lower wages were locked out of the pit.'[11]

The Monmouthshire and South Wales Coalowners' Association imposed a lock-out as a normal course of action when faced with a major dispute. The imposition of a lock-out was a dimension of the coalowners' autocratic behaviour that angered miners.

So the 1926 lock-out helped to further advance the political mission of the South Wales Coalfield's union officials: to challenge the prerogatives of company ownership. By 1917, 'hostility to capitalism had become part of the political creed of the majority of SWMF'.[12] The political dimension was not the only feature that made 'the situation different in the mining valleys of South Wales'. 'The totality of the commitment to the miner's cause,' it was later claimed, 'was a form of class consciousness which translated itself into a community consciousness, so overwhelming were the miners in numbers and influence'. Maybe a manifestation of such an analysis by Francis and Smith was that the strong sense of autonomy prevailing among the miners of the South Wales Coalfield encouraged them to ignore the ending of the General Strike. The outcome, as Powell Duffryn later noted, was a coal miners' strike of seven months duration in the South Wales Coalfield.[13]

Francis and Smith later judged that 'the polarising of class and community forces' during the seven months strike 'was more ennobling than enfeebling'. Regarding 'social class polarisation', they perceived that it deepened. Adding: 'what characterised the South Wales miners was the scale and degree of their resistance and the way in which they confronted the dual problems of relief and 'blacklegging''. The 'relief' came from a mix of sources such as 'sporadic Federation strike pay', and touring choirs and bands. The communal kitchens became the 'cement in holding miners and families together'. Nevertheless, they conceded that 'enormous problems of hunger and demoralisation' occurred.

Such deprivation begat strike breaking. Some miners, distressed by their families being poverty-stricken, risked both personal injury and ostracism by the community, and returned to work. *The South Wales News* reported that in New Tredegar, on the 28th June, 'hostile crowds' harried thirty-three men who had opted to return to work. 'They were confronted at Elliotstown and Phillipstown by women armed with white shirts and a supply of whitewash'.[14]

Strike breaking spread across the South Wales Coalfield. The police forces of Glamorgan, Monmouthshire, Breconshire, and Carmarthenshire became stretched trying to maintain law and order when faced with crowd hostility towards strike breakers. Hampshire, Brighton and Portsmouth policemen were drafted in to reinforce Valley policemen. Baton-charging policemen were deployed to discourage crowds of stone throwing miners, women, and children. The catastrophic confrontation between labour and capital ended in the South Wales Coalfield in November, 1926.

According to Islwyn Jenkins, when it was 'called off the miners felt cheated and deserted, victims of political and commercial incompetence'. He added that 'the miners continued the long losing battle until an agreement was very reluctantly signed in the third week of December'. He claimed that 'Rhymney had the distinction of being the last place in the valley to show a majority against giving the South Wales miners' executive power to negotiate a settlement'.[15] Powell Duffryn's business confidence had suffered to some extent, but their miners were demoralised.

Aberdare's Edwin Greening returned to work as a miner at Blaengwawr Colliery after the 1926 strike ended. 'On his first day back at work, it all seemed so dark, so strange and so hard after nearly eight months from it all. When the shift ended, I dragged myself home, and by 11. 30 p.m., I was in bed'.[16] The event caused him to reflect: 'it was a poverty-stricken, dreary life with eight hours of hard, dangerous work down the pit'. His sufferings at Blaengwawr Colliery did not last long. The colliery was closed.

Unemployed, Edwin Greening traipsed from one colliery to another seeking work. 'At each pit', he joined 'crowds of men all looking for work. It was terribly disheartening as usually there was a board on top on which was written No Men Wanted'. 'I was pale, thin, and poorly dressed,' he later wrote. However, a neighbour tipped him off about a job at Powell's Pit, which he obtained. His 'good luck soon ran out', Powell's Pit was closed in March 1927, causing 'seven hundred workers' to draw 'dole' at twelve-shillings and sixpence a week.

A short period of unemployment ended for Edwin Greening when Aberaman Colliery restarted. He was employed 'working a deep gallery called the Dugout'. He 'did not like working at the pit; it was dangerous and the attitude of the Powel Duffryn Coal Co. Ltd managers and officials was very arrogant and extremely oppressive'. The strike left its mark upon his mind for the rest of his life. The bitterness dwelling among fellow South Wales Coalfield miners was further whetted.

Francis and Smith revealed that 'the Fed was shattered for nearly a decade, lodge officials and activists were victimised, a rival 'scab union' [this insult was directed at the South Wales Miners' Industrial Union-SWMIU] reared its head, the migration of population out of the valleys accelerated'.[17] The coal companies acted against some of the strike's leaders. For instance, at Powell Duffryn's Windsor Colliery all the leading activists were 'put back on the afternoon shift which soon afterwards ended: all were taken back except for about twenty or thirty of the hardcore militants, including the Communist leader, Jack Roberts, known in the Aber Valley as 'Jack Russia'.[18] Such sacked miners were probably seen as scapegoats by their comrades. If the company's authority over its miners was re-established partly through fear, it did not shy away from justifying its actions.

Edmund L. Hann, in 1927, was 'personally involved in the events which led up to the Strike and in the negotiations during the Strike'. He was 'firmly convinced that there were two influences that led to the prolongation of the stoppage'.[19] First, there was an 'inability of politicians to realise that this was not an ordinary industrial dispute and that the extremists who had obtained control of the Workmen's Organisations were not prepared to negotiate on the merits of the case. Last, there was the interference of persons having no knowledge of the Industry, which led the extremists to believe that they could obtain terms which the industry could not afford to bear'. He was forthright in apportioning blame: 'So long as the Workmen's Organisation is in the hands of extremists there is no prospect of a better relationship for the extremists openly avow their desire to destroy the industry'. And he believed that 'there is a feeling on the part of a large section of mining community that the leadership of the last few years is leading to the destruction of the industry'.[20]

Time, though, would test the truth of his belief about the nature of the mood prevailing within communities blighted with poverty as a result of the 1926 strike. Indeed, some of the miners' leaders, which he maligned as extremists, would later stand at general elections, and, like Aneurin Bevan (1897-1960) of Tredegar, be returned as Members of Parliament for South Wales constituencies. The idea that socialism was an alternative to capitalism was set to win the support of many people in the south Wales Valleys.

The strike, and unemployment, also provoked people to leave the Valleys. For example, some New Tredegar people moved away to such places as Slough in Berkshire, Dagenham in Essex, Leicester, Luton in Bedfordshire, and also to Canada, the United States of America, Australia, and New Zealand.[21] Nevertheless, it was Hann's hope, in 1927, that 'we must have an end of the doctrine which has been so prevalent, that any action which injures the employers results in a benefit to the workmen'.[22] The socialist protagonists within the Fed, on the other hand, looked forward to the day when miners owned the industry.

However, those with political ambitions within the executive of the South Wales Miners' Federation were irked by what had taken place at Taff-Merthyr Colliery during the long strike. The colliery became the centre of a 'crucial break with the union, and saw a rival emerge'.[23] Early in 1926, the Taff-Merthyr Colliery Company 'sought and obtained the permission of the SWMF' to commence the opening out of the workings from its South Pit. However, according to James Griffiths, the President of the SWMF between 1934-5, the company took 'advantage' of this to 'induce workmen to go to the pit', and so it 'proceeded to develop a full coal producing pit whilst the stoppage was in progress'.

Alternative ideas about how miners' interests at Taff-Merthyr Colliery could be represented were mooted during the strike. On the 20th November, 1926, a large meeting of some of the colliery's men was held at the Bontnewydd Hotel, Trelewis. W. A. Williams, the secretary of the Nelson Conservative and Unionist Association, was the convenor of the meeting, which ended with the formation of a Taff-Merthyr Works Committee with an aim to work 'harmoniously with management, avoid politics, and be entirely separate from the SWMF'. A week later this 'movement' spawned the South Wales Miners' Industrial Union (SWMIU). W. A. Williams then campaigned in the South Wales Coalfield to grow the SWMIU's membership, 'beginning in the neighbouring Rhymney Valley'. One of his campaign's appeals was: 'Are you in favour of a Trade Union free from all party politics?'

At Britannia Colliery, W. A. Williams's appeal to miners won a 'yes' vote of 2,000 against 251 voting 'no'. The local SWMF miners' agent, Bryn Roberts, 'disclaimed the potential of the SWMIU but also spoke bitterly of the way in which a weakened SWMF was being treated'. Britannia Colliery officials, he claimed, took robust measures that saw Federation officials 'driven off the colliery premises', and the union's notices 'torn down from notice boards'. Bryn Roberts further claimed that the SWMIU was 'their [Powell Duffryn's] child'.

Although, in general, W. A. William's South Wales Coalfield campaign was initially unsuccessful, at Taff-Merthyr Colliery the new trade union established itself. Moreover, the SWMIU's appeal, in at least the Rhymney Valley, was not subverted by the mud-slinging Fed.[24] By early 1927, the SWMIU set up twenty-one branches, principally in the Rhymney Valley.[25] But, according to the submission of Francis and Smith the Fed's 'main concern at this time' was 'momentous national issues', and so 'tended to relax its vigilance at local level'.[26] So, the Fed appeared to shelve a wish to wipe out the SWMIU.

Somehow the distractions of the 1926 strike did not divert Powell Duffryn from pursuing plans it judged were key to its survival in the coal industry. The company's spirit for enterprise remained, and as a result it took advantage of its electrical generating capacity as if it was an electric utility company.

A Switch to Electrical Light

A night shift policeman at New Tredegar Police Station switched on an electric light in his place of work for the first time in 1927. Gas's hold on the lighting market in at least the Rhymney Valley was destined to end. The staff and patients at Aberbargoed's Cottage Hospital had enjoyed night time illumination by electric light for a number of years. But from the year 1927, homes in the communities of the upper reaches of the Rhymney Valley began to be wired up for the age of electricity.

The utility electricity supply was generated by Powell Duffryn. The company's supply of electricity spread beyond the bounds of the Bedwellty Urban District Council, in part, constituted of wards in New Tredegar and Aberbargoed. Communities in the Urban District Councils of Aberdare, Gelligaer, and Rhymney were also later lit at night due to the company's supply of electricity. Other coal companies of the South Wales Coalfield entered the electricity utility market.[27]

The financial benefit to Powell Duffryn of supplying electricity to the community was later subjected to an evaluation, which proposed that it was profitable. Trevor Boyns studied, for the period between the years 1911-38, the company accounts of a selection of South Wales companies active in the electricity market.[28] He reckoned, on a unit cost comparison of electricity generation and sales, that 'large colliery power stations could generate electricity far more cheaply in the 1920s than was possible by the power company or other major statutory undertakings in South Wales'. Indeed, in 1923, 'Powell Duffryn remarked that they could provide the Rhymney Iron Company with supplies at 0.44d. per unit of and 'still make a profit'. So, Edmund L. Hann's worry, around that year, about the threat posed by a 'super power station' generating electricity to that of his company's investment in power generation, was during the 1920s proved groundless. Moreover, the company generated electricity at a price that stood to earn it financial gain. However, if enlightened self-interest had enabled the communities in the reach of the company to enter the age of electricity, the company's mind remained focused upon coal mining.

Amalgamation and Centralisation

In 1928, the company raised £4.2 million of loans to enable it to acquire other coal companies.[29] Considering the problems that beset the coal industry, general anxiety about high national unemployment, it was a notable achievement of Powell Duffryn's to raise finance from the capital market. Although the directors of the company appear to have been of the gentlemen class able to relate to capital lenders in the City of London, the case put by them to raise new capital had to measure up to a lender's yardstick.

Powell Duffryn had also to be confident that it was able to repay lendings by the end of any agreed term. So, it would seem that the company's successful record in operating low-cost, efficient collieries profitably over the previous years was crucial for securing the loans.[30] Powell Duffryn probably argued that by applying its colliery engineering practices, acquired colliery companies would in time yield profitable financial returns.

The raised capital enabled Powell Duffryn to acquire two major concerns: Great Western Colliery Co. Ltd, and the Lewis Merthyr Consolidated Collieries. The company bought the whole of the share capital of Great Western Colliery Co. Ltd, and took ownership of collieries that comprised Hetty, No. 2 & No. 3, Tymawr, Maritime pit, Penrhiw, and Cwm, and coke ovens and by-product plant.[31] In general, all these assets were situated in the vicinity of Pontypridd. The company originated when the Great Western Railway purchased, around 1854, the Gyfeillion Colliery, close to the village of Hopkinstown, Pontypridd, and renamed it Great Western Colliery. John Calvert, the track laying contractor for building the Taff Vale Railway, a less than capable business man, was responsible for sinking in 1854 the Gyfeillion Colliery. The chief mechanical engineer of the Great Western Railway, (Sir) Daniel Gooch, led his company's purchase of the colliery. During the 1890s, the Great Western Colliery was the biggest colliery operating in the Rhondda Valley. The Great Western Colliery Co. Ltd, formed in 1865, for the period of three years 1925 to 1927 had incurred losses aggregating over £250,000.[32]

Great Western Collieries, Pontypridd.

In 1928, Powell Duffryn acquired the collieries of Great Western Colliery Co. Ltd generally located at the mouth of the Rhondda Valley. The Great Western Colliery stood to the west of Hopkinstown, near Pontypridd. The photograph shows, to the left of the most prominent chimney stack, steam rising from the Hetty Pit's winding house. Hetty was sunk in 1905, and its surviving Barker & Cope, Kidsgrove, Staffs., horizontal double steam engine of 1875 may have been purchased second-hand from another colliery. The No. 2 Pit's headgear can be seen on the left of the winding house. The house on the hillside was for many years the home of Hugh Bramwell, an innovative mining engineer.   *Pope/Parkhouse Archive*

Right: Tymawr Colliery, as it was for sometime before 1925, was sunk by Great Western Colliery Co. Ltd in 1891. The colliery used the first compound steam winding engine installed in the South Wales Coalfield. Acquired by Powell Duffryn in 1928.

Below: Penrhiw Colliery was sunk by Great Western Colliery Co, Ltd in 1897. Acquired by Powell Duffryn in 1928.

Below: Maritime Pit before 1908. Originally known as Pontypridd Colliery, was one of a number of Great Western Colliery Co. Ltd collieries acquired by Powell Duffryn in 1928. Sunk in the 1840s, the colliery was the first in the English and South Wales coalfields to use electric winding for raising deep mined coal.

Lewis Merthyr Consolidated Collieries' property comprised the following collieries: Bertie, Hafod Downcast, Hafod Upcast, Coedcae, Trefor, Lady Lewis Pit, Universal Colliery at Senghenydd, and Rhondda Main (Ann Pit). The purchase of Coedcae Colliery, in the 1870s, marked the start of William Thomas Lewis's growth of the colliery company that in part used his surname. Although he might have been a critic of Sir George Elliot's stances regarding the South Wales Coalfield strike of 1875, he respected and trusted him sufficiently to invest in at least one joint coal mining venture, in Nova Scotia. The fortunes of Lewis Merthyr Consolidated Collieries wilted after the death of its founder. Powell Duffryn bought Lewis Merthyr Consolidated Collieries from the Receiver. In the two years 1925 and 1926, Lewis Merthyr Consolidated Collieries incurred losses amounting to more than £350,000.[33]

W. T. Lewis's Lewis Merthyr (Bertie and Trefor) Colliery was the westerly neighbour of the Great Western Colliery.[34] Through acquiring Lewis Merthyr Consolidated Collieries, and the Great Western Colliery Co. Ltd, Powell Duffryn had not only secured ownership of mining property in the Rhondda Valley, but, as a simile, grasped the throat of the world's most famous valley for coal.

Moreover, by taking ownership of Lord Merthyr of Senghenydd's Universal Colliery, the company's control of the Rhymney Valley took on barony-like form. Lord Merthyr died in 1914, which was the year after the colliery's infamous disaster. Powell Duffryn was unmoved by any lingering melancholy at Senghenydd. The company promptly closed Universal Colliery and worked its coal reserves from the adjacent Windsor Colliery.

The company's coal company purchases involved assembling a jigsaw of underground coal mining properties. The significance

then being, as Trevor Boyns later observed, Powell Duffryn had gained 'control of a large area extending from the base of the Rhymney Valley … to Pontypridd and Porth at the base of the Rhondda Valleys'.

In 1928, *The Colliery Guardian* admired the company's acquisitiveness.[35] The journal appraised Powell Duffryn as being 'almost the largest coal-producing concern in the British Isles', and valued the company's acquisitions as 'epoch-making in regard to the history of this enterprising concern and that of the South Wales Coalfield'. *The Colliery Guardian* no doubt aroused some envy, or even fear among Powell Duffryn's rivals, by noting that 'the increased capital requirements had been furnished on comparatively easy terms by a leading firm of private bankers', J. Henry Shröder & Company. Significantly observing, Powell Duffryn's means of raising money was 'almost a novelty of colliery finance'.

Furthermore, Powell Duffryn's growth was, as far as *The Colliery Guardian* was concerned, 'a fact' that 'should help subdue the idle chatter in and out of Parliament, which persists in representing British colliery owners as being obstinately and perversely blind to the advantages of amalgamation'. Adding: it 'should prove most heartening to those who cherish bold and sanguine views as to the future of the mining industry'. The Labour Party's manifesto for the 1929 General Election pledged to nationalize the industry. Maybe having got wind of this Labour Party commitment, or sensing moves to force the private coal companies to amalgamate, the journal also berated what it considered to be uninformed opinion within Parliament.

Nonetheless, in the South Wales Coalfield, Powell Duffryn's future lay in mining new coal reserves. Blessed with immense resources

In 1928, Powell Duffryn acquired the collieries of Lewis Merthyr Consolidated Collieries Ltd. Lord Merthyr of Senghenydd, as William Thomas Lewis, was the moving force behind the formation and growth of this acquired coal company. The photograph shows, left to right, the headgears of the Bertie Pit, sunk in 1881, and Trefor, sunk in 1894, and the Coedcae Pit which was sunk earlier than the Bertie Pit at an unknown date. In 1945, the Bertie and Trefor Pits employed 778 and 655 persons respectively. Today, part of the site has been preserved as the Rhondda Heritage Park at Lewis Merthyr Colliery.

Views of Lady Lewis Colliery, Ynyshir, Rhondda Fach Valley. Sunk in 1901 and operational in 1904 as part of Lord Merthyr's growth of Lewis Merthyr Consolidated Collieries Limited. Although the colliery was acquired by Powell Duffryn in 1928, it seems to have ceased operation in 1925. The colliery was used for ventilation In 1945. *both Pope/Parkhouse Archive*

of quality coal, the Great Western Colliery Company was rated as being a first class acquisition. A further bonus was that the collieries of the Great Western Colliery Company were 'well equipped'.[36] This was partly a legacy of Hugh Bramwell's time in charge of the company. The Lewis Merthyr Collieries had less coal resources than Great Western Colliery, but its coal was of fine quality. However, Lewis Merthyr Colliery was 'not well equipped'.[37] The design and co-ordination for the re-engineering of the acquired collieries was probably done at Ystrad Mynach, not Aberaman.

Around the beginning of 1928, the Rhymney Valley became the home for the company's central Colliery offices.[38] The offices stood north-west of Ystrad Mynach, and overlooked the company's Tredomen Works. The offices' location was a logical choice since it was centrally placed in Powell Duffryn's territory. Edmund L. Hann judged that the Aberaman offices had for 'sometime become more inconvenient', such 'that the efficiency of the management was becoming affected'. After six decades, the Aberdare Valley was robbed of its kudos for being the 'centre of the most important collieries'. However, the new office building was built earlier than the company wished, preferring that it was opened in 'more prosperous times'. Stalwart collieries of the company were suffering a poor time.[39]

In 1928, Powell Duffryn temporarily closed Aberaman, Lower Duffryn, and New Tredegar Collieries. Lower Duffryn Colliery suffered the same fate as Blaennant Colliery, which was closed the year before. The quality of coal being won at Bargoed Colliery caused a rethink about its operation, and so its steam coal pits were temporarily closed so that one of the shafts could be sunk to the Four Foot seam. Some colliers in both the Aberdare and Rhymney Valleys wondered if their employment days were numbered since they read that the company was pursuing growth through amalgamation.

Colliery amalgamation brought its penalties. Immediately, in 1928, Powell Duffryn was put 'under severe financial strain' due in part to the acquisitions of the Lewis Merthyr and Great Western colliery companies.[40]

The company's business situation, around 1928, forced it into contemplating selling its electricity interests. The South Wales Power Company proposed that 'Powell Duffryn should sell its generating stations and distribution network to the power company in return for either cash or debentures in the power company'.[41] However, Powell Duffryn 'was very fearful of what could happen if, having sold its power stations to the power company, that the company should then fold'. Although the company was 'almost induced' to sell its generating stations and distribution network, 'nothing materialized'.

As another indicator of the bleak economic times that had struck the South Wales Coalfield, Trevor Boyns identified that Powell Duffryn 'politely' declined several approaches from companies seeking to sell their coal mining assets. '*If* [colliery properties] *were contiguous to existing undertakings of the company they would be purchased since their working could be rationalised in conjunction with other parts of the Powell Duffryn concern. With the mines all adjoining one another economies could be gained from reorganising underground working, extending the company's electricity and power supply, etc., but such developments would be less feasible with mines situated at any great distance from the rest of the company's pits*'.

Powell Duffryn's Tredomen Works and Offices, Ystrad Mynach. The offices, shown being built beyond the workshops on the right, succeeded Aberaman's offices as the company's central offices for the management of the collieries around the beginning of 1928.   *Pope/Parkhouse Archive*

Llanbradach Colliery

Powell Duffryn, though, decided to build a relationship with Cardiff Collieries Limited that owned Llanbradach Colliery.[42] As Edmund L. Hann stated it was 'obvious that a closer working arrangement between the two Companies must be advantageous'.[43] By 1928, Cardiff Collieries Limited had serious financial problems, which were aggravated when bankers called in overdrafts totalling nearly £200,000.[44] Powell Duffryn took up a Cardiff Collieries issue of £200,000 of Debentures, and as a part of the financing deal, bought a small amount of previously unissued ordinary and preference share capital.

Powell Duffryn's William Reginald Hann and Evan Williams then took places on the board of Cardiff Collieries. Evan Williams, who was later knighted, was elected as a director to the board of Powell Duffryn in circa early 1928 due to a vacancy created by the retirement of Edmund Mills Hann from the board.[45] A majority of Cardiff Collieries board members were unhappy with the arrangement, maybe fearing a future takeover by Powell Duffryn. Subsequently, Powell Duffryn sold its shareholding in Cardiff Collieries when Cardiff Collieries paid off the debentures. However, both Walter Reginald Hann and Evan Williams sat on the Cardiff Collieries' board until at least 1940.[46] A factor that had brought about this attempt at forging some union of company interests was the coal trade, which in 1928 plunged into the doldrums.

Edmund L. Hann told Powell Duffryn shareholders, as the company's deputy-chairman and managing director, that the year of 1928 'will go down to history as the worst experienced in the British coal industry in living memory'.[47] Statistics confirm his mordant comment: 'the volume of trade' had fallen concerning the exports from the United Kingdom 'from 73,400,000 tons in 1913 to 50,000,000 tons in 1928 – a decrease of 23.4 million tons'.

An increase in the price of coal after the Great War had caused every 'nation having coal deposits' to develop them 'to the fullest effect'. However, the pursuit of national coal interests was at odds with market and economic trends identified by Edmund L. Hann. He noted 'a gradual replacement of coal for marine purposes by oil', and, following 'wild fluctuations' of monetary exchanges rates, there was 'a general stagnation of trade'. German Reparations following the Great War also hit coal exports, for example German coal exports took a greater share of the Italian market at the expense of the South Wales Coalfield. Furthermore, there was a 'depression in the [British] iron and steel industry'. Hann also protested about the effect of mounting legislation, and increases in wages.

Notably, regarding the history of Powell Duffryn, the year 1928 saw the resignation of Joseph Shaw as chairman of Powell Duffryn, although he remained as a director. He had served as the company chairman for thirty-one years. He joined the company's

Llanbradach Colliery, Cardiff Collieries Limited. William Galloway engineered the colliery, which was sunk 1885-1894. Earlier experiments by him led to a better understanding of the causes of underground explosions, which Edmund Mills Hann heeded. Galloway was the first professor of mining at University College of South Wales and Monmouthshire, today Cardiff University, and was later knighted. In 1928, and for a period afterwards, Powell Duffryn became a shareholder of Cardiff Collieries Limited. *Pope/Parkhouse Archive*

'Board at a time of great adversity.'[48] Joseph Shaw had overseen a transformation in the company's fortunes. Ill health, suffered for a number of years, caused Shaw to resign as chairman. Edmund Lawrence Hann was elected as the company's Acting Chairman.

Regarding Edmund L. Hann's spell in charge of managing the company, both mining coal, and its marketing became complementary activities. Maybe, by the late 1920s, the type, and quality of coal mined and its marketing had become crucial to success. Trevor Boyns discerned, that an 'influential factor in determining the choice of colliery properties was the need for the company to acquire control over pits producing high grade coals as a prelude to effecting a merger with a major sales agency. The purchase of the Lewis Merthyr and Great Western concerns was thus a major step in obtaining the agreement of Stephenson Clarke to merge with Powell Duffryn'. Moreover, the vital 'necessity' of this merger to Powell Duffryn, according to Boyns, 'was reflected in their willingness to accept readily the high price circa £3 million being asked by Stephenson Clarke'. The acquisition of 'Stephenson Clarke, well known coal factors and distributors' was a notable strategic move of the company. Reorganisation also arose as a result.

A Central Committee was established to co-ordinate and control coal production and marketing. Members of the committee were Sir Stephenson Kent, Sir John Hyndley, Evan Williams, and Hann. Hann claimed that it was 'the first occasion in the history of coal trade in this country in which the functions of production and marketing have been merged on such a scale'.[49] This was true regarding the scale featured in merging the production and marketing functions, but the Ocean Company and Wilson Ltd had taken such a measure earlier.

Nantgarw Colliery

Powell Duffryn continued to buy colliery companies. Windsor Colliery's coal property lay to the east of and adjacent to Taff Rhondda Navigation Steam Company's colliery of the same name. The colliery, more commonly known as Nantgarw Colliery, stood near to the mouth of the valley of the River Taff. Taylor's Navigation Steam Coal Company sank Nantgarw's two shafts in 1915 to 'an unprecedented depth for South Wales' of 856 yards.[50] The Taff Rhondda Navigation Steam Company acquired the colliery in 1924. However, as a failed venture, the company's Liquidator sold it to Powell Duffryn in 1928. Taff Rhondda Navigation's coal property of 1,071 acres, Powell Duffryn judged, had commercial potential for producing coking coal.

The company bought the Nantgarw Colliery when mining troubles plagued Llanharan and Llantrisant Collieries. So the company knew about the risks of mining at Nantgarw Colliery. The workings of the colliery lay very close to the southern edge of the South Wales Coalfield, where geological disturbances dwelt. A convenient event coincided with the purchase of Nantgarw Colliery. There was a modest rise in demand for coal in the south Wales iron and steel industry, and this helped make a claim that the colliery was an 'attractive' prospect' for the company.[51] However, the colliery was to prove troublesome to exploit, and Powell Duffryn procrastinated regarding its development. A decade and a half later the company was reputed to have toyed with introducing a Continental European mining technique called horizon mining at the colliery, but Llanharan Colliery eventually became the venue for the pioneering of this technique in the British coal industry.[52]

Even in the troubled year of 1928 Powell Duffryn did not shy away from being enterprising and continued to pursue innovation. Steel pit props were introduced into the company's collieries with the aim of replacing an old practice, using timber. This development was pioneered by the company at Penallta Colliery.[53] However, the company appeared to have been slow to adopt the practice. Propping up the underground workings with steel sections appears to have begun in the South Wales Coalfield around 1890 due to W. W. Hood installing steel arches, or rings, at the Glamorgan collieries in the Rhondda Valley.[54] This lead seems to have been followed before the Great War by the Tredegar Iron & Coal Co at Oakdale Colliery, sited near the town of Blackwood, in the Sirhowy Valley.

The introduction of steel supports into the South Wales Coalfield faced objections from both colliery officials and miners. Creaking timber supports warned miners of a possible roof collapse whereas steel supports yielded to the forces of geology with little notice of a potential threat to human life. The relatively higher cost of steel props versus timber also discouraged their use. Tradition and safety fears had further encouraged a practice in the South Wales Coalfield of not recovering timber from underground waste. Timber was salvaged, and re-used in other coalfields of Britain. The cost of using steel props was later recognised as offsetting the expenditure involved following the South Wales Coalfield's timbering tradition. A growing awareness that steel props also improved underground safety also encouraged change. Powell Duffryn learnt, by 1928, that underground conditions at each colliery determined a need for bespoke designs of steel props. Education and training were also helpful to furthering the application of steel roof supports.

In the year 1929, an existing building at Britannia Colliery was converted for use as a Mining School.[55] A mining lecturer was appointed to coach young employees with 'a desire' to become company mining officials. The young employees were given practical tuition regarding colliery management, including planning and roof control, with the objective of 'enabling a high standard of mining practice to be maintained'.[56] Moreover, those under instruction were 'encouraged to sit', and 'were prepared for the Colliery Manager's Certificate with a view' that they might be developed to fill positions as under-officials at the company's collieries, and 'later' to become candidates to 'qualify as assistant managers and managers'. The award of a second class, and then a first class Colliery Manager's certificate recognised the personal development stage reached by a potential colliery manager. At sometime later, the company established a similar school at Tymawr Colliery for trainees drawn from its hinterland, the Rhondda Valley. Investment in training was a sign that Powell Duffryn held to a belief of a future for coal.

What was to prove to be just a blip of a lift in the coal trade, the company reported 'the volume of business obtained for the year 1929' was 'altogether better than it was in 1928'. As a result, Cwmneol, and New Tredegar Collieries were re-opened.[57]

The company accepted that marketing, and by-products from coal, were ways for securing a commercial future. A coal product, called 'Penallta Mixture', was sold in 1929 to ship owners, and they filed 'satisfactory reports'.[58] The company kept an eye upon a 'slow' technical development: pulverised coal fuel.[59] Advocates in the coal industry believed that pulverised coal could 'check the rapid rate at which motor driven [oil fuelled] ships' were 'being constructed'. Earlier, in 1927, the Bargoed By-Product Plant processed for the first time a product branded as 'Presotim'.[60] Presotim was a wood preservative for both interior and exterior building use. In 1929, Presotim was used to decorate the interiors of over 400 houses being built at Newport, which as an example, was used for marketing the product.[61] By 1930, with more varieties of colour available, sales growth of Presotim was confirmed.[62] Another new special product, a bituminous black paint, was made at the Bargoed plant, and launched in 1929.[63] Sold as "Presomet", the paint was said to be able to protect steel, and corrugated iron, from corrosion.

The morale of Bargoed Colliery's miners might have lifted on hearing that a new battery of coke ovens were commissioned in 1929.[64] However, the lift in demand from the iron and steel makers for coke, mentioned earlier for 1928, proved to be brief. Moreover, Edmund Lawrence Hann had identified a serious threat to the British steel industry, and was acutely conscious of the business risk the company had taken investing in new coking ovens. He had learnt, during an earlier visit of his to the Westphalian Coalfield, to inspect coking plant, about the apparent stability of Germany's steel industry, which benefitted that nation's collieries. He bewailed an effect: the dumping of Germany's excess steel production in Britain.[65]

Andrew Buchan's Breweries

A flourishing beer trade in 1929 might have given Edmund L. Hann a good news story to share with Powell Duffryn's shareholders in 1930.[66] Although the company did not consider it desirable to operate in the brewing trade due to the general poor state of the economy, the company's attempts to dispose of their brewery interests 'upon satisfactory terms' had been frustrated. However, the coal company did not hinder the development of the brewer. In October, 1929, Andrew Buchan's Breweries, Limited was formed under the chairmanship of Lieutenant-Colonel G. L. Hoare.

The Rhymney brewer proceeded to buy 'additional licensed properties', which also included some breweries. In 1930, Andrew Buchan's Breweries acquired a Crumlin brewer, D. F. Pritchard Ltd, and one prize was the right to use a 'distinctive trade mark': a hobby horse. The trade mark was then used by the brewer,

Andrew Buchan's Breweries Limited's Beer Bottle Labels in 1949. In 1929, Andrew Buchan Breweries Ltd was formed by Powell Duffryn with the aim of selling the brewer. In 1930, the brewer acquired, through merger, the 'hobby horse' brand that was later linked to 'Rhymney Beer', which many South Wales beer drinkers enjoyed up until the 1960s.

From 100 Years of Brewing: Rhymney Beers-Famous over 100 Years

and would later be seen on its many public house signs across a territory 'from Gloucestershire in the east to Pembrokeshire, in the west from the Bristol Channel in the south to mid-Wales and Herefordshire in the north'. Andrew Buchan Breweries' later geographical coverage was due in part to acquisitions like D. Williams & Co (Merthyr) Ltd, in 1936, and also in that year, Crosswells Cardiff Brewery which had a 'modern' brewery at Ely, Cardiff. Alas the brewer's own history, that marked its centenary, does not date when its link with the coal company ended, but it occurred after 1930.[67]

The main concern among New Tredegar people, shared by some of them over pints of beer, was the state of Powell Duffryn as a coal company. The re-opening of New Tredegar Colliery in 1928 would prove to be the start of its final chapter.

Never-Ending Woes

Company shareholders learnt in the spring of 1930 about the effect that 'unprecedented floods' in the Valleys, during November and December of 1929, had had upon the company's collieries. Edmund L. Hann, sitting in the fug of a room in London's Cannon Street Hotel with shareholders, reported that thirty-nine inches of rain had fallen at Valley locations during the last two months of 1929. Concerning Bargoed Colliery: 'On one occasion the Rhymney River rose five feet in one hour and on that occasion and other occasions the water found its way into the regenerators of our coke ovens, and it was only with great difficulty that it was prevented from flowing down the shafts'.[68] Although he praised the 'energetic way' in which the company's employees had worked, so as to avoid 'serious calamities', he noted as 'a matter of regret to the Directors', that the pay reduction imposed upon the employees the previous year would continue. Magnanimously, the company's directors also waived a 'substantial portion of their fees'.

At New Tredegar Colliery, the inclement weather triggered-off a repeat of the 1905 landslide. 'Expert advice' was taken 'to arrest' its movement. Edmund L. Hann further disclosed that 'the greater part of the coal remaining to be worked' could be 'won from other newer collieries of the Company'. He also recognised New Tredegar Colliery's place as 'one of the oldest collieries of the Company'. The manpower of the colliery reached its peak after it was re-engineered in 1905 and 1906: In 1912, the colliery employment numbers reached 1,698, and stood at 1,700 men in 1926. The colliery's manager succession saw, in 1915, J. A. Price, then T. Bailey, with T. Benyon taking the position afterwards in 1923, which made him possibly the last holder of the post.[69]

A fortnight after the company's Cannon Street Hotel meeting, on the 11th April, 1930, another landslide struck New Tredegar Colliery. Vast quantities of rock and earth slipped from Mynydd Bedwellty. A road, and a railway which had carried coal for a century, were ruined overnight. New Tredegar Colliery's surface buildings were wrecked. The company decided to salvage some of the colliery's plant and equipment before abandoning one of Thomas Powell's ventures. Vestiges of the 'Old Pits' survived until the 1970s, after which, they were swallowed by a clay and rock morass known locally as 'The Slip'. Maybe only a New Tredegar historian could use the colliery's disappearance as a metaphor to mark the end of the golden age of mining in the South Wales Coalfield.

In 1930, Powell Duffryn's Registered Office became 1, Great Tower Street, London, which stood a stroll away from the Tower of London with its memory of executions. Although the company reported a profit of £370,294 for 1930, coal output at its collieries was curtailed, and coke ovens were closed.[70] An indignant Edmund L. Hann attacked the Coal Mines Act of 1930, which called for a 'strict observance of and the maintenance of minimum prices'. Concerning this 'incalculable handicap', he remarked that the company was 'under the most severe pains and penalties if to maintain a business that we may have held for years [if] we were to reduce our price to meet this competition, whereas the Foreigner, knowing our price and being perfectly able to estimate the additional costs of delivery' under-cut the company's quotations.[71] Such a situation wrought an inevitable consequence: Powell Duffryn focused upon reducing coal production costs. Concerning Government, he was equally concerned about proposals for compulsory amalgamation of coal companies.

Edmund L. Hann hoped that the Government would 'drop' such 'very harmful proposals'.[72] As an executor of colliery amalgamations, he was at one with an objective to reduce the 'number of coal producing organizations'. However, he 'deplored' any scheme of compulsory amalgamation. Besides the 'great practical difficulties involved', he was of the opinion that it was 'entirely opposed to the British psychology, and to harness compulsorily unwilling partners cannot be to the good of the concerns involved'. Powell Duffryn followed its logic for colliery amalgamation the following year.

The company purchased the Albion Steam Coal Co. Limited's Albion Colliery, Cilfynydd, in the Taff Valley, for £40,000.[73] The colliery's best seams were exhausted, and the owner had accumulated losses of nearly £100,000. Albion Colliery's mining property adjoined those of Lewis Merthyr's and Great Western's. Crucially for Powell Duffryn, the colliery was 'ideally suited' to work 'more easily' some 72 million tons of reserves of these

neighbouring collieries. Consequently the company invested £218,000 to re-model the colliery.[74] Acquired at such a 'modest' price, the colliery offered handsome rewards since access was obtained to 'one of the best Admiralty descriptions', which 'in ordinary circumstances' would command a 'high selling price for both large and small coal'. Indeed, Trevor Boyns later reckoned that the 'phoenix-like resurrection of the colliery' was perhaps for Powell Duffryn its 'most spectacular achievement' during this period of amalgamations. The process engaged in to acquire Albion Colliery though suffered some disruption.

On New Year's Day, 1931, colliery workers of the South Wales Coalfield went on strike due to a dispute about the wages agreement made after the 1926 strike.[75] The strike lasted until the 19th January, when both sides agreed to an independent review, and to accept its recommendations. F. P. Schiller KC was the chairman of the review.

The review's recommendations became 'infamous' among colliery workers according to James Griffiths, then an emerging miners' leader.[76] The minimum percentage paid upon the standard or basic rates was cut from 29 per cent to 20 per cent. The amount of subsistence allowance paid to lower paid men, which was 'scandalously low' according to Griffiths, was lowered further. What seemed to further annoy James Griffiths was that 'Mr Schiller justified his award on the basis of the financial position of the industry in South Wales as revealed in the 'ascertainment' [a system based upon the ascertained results of the finances of the coalfield for each quarter]'. The ascertainment system arose out of the settlement of the 1926 strike. However, both parties to the dispute had agreed to accept the review's recommendations

The coalowners, according to Edmund L. Hann, 'though gravely disappointed at the serious inadequacy of the reductions awarded

Albion Colliery, Cilfynydd, Taff Vale. Around 1931, Powell Duffryn acquired the bankrupt Albion Steam Coal Co. Ltd whose colliery's seams were nearly exhausted. The location of the colliery's coal property enabled Powell Duffryn to exploit its adjoining coal reserves. The colliery was sunk between 1884 and 1887, and the photograph shows it early in the 1900s. In 1945, the colliery's manpower was 991.

by him [Schiller], accepted his judgment without question'. He shared his appraisal of the dispute with company shareholders: 'You will have seen that on the other side the Award has been received with much adverse comment and it is only [due to a] small majority that a motion to strike against it was lost'. However, the miners' temper was one of anger.

The passing of the Coal Mines Act of 1930 had brought about the reduction in a colliery workers' day from to eight to seven and a half hours. The miners' joy that greeted news of this change turned to gloom the moment they picked up lesser wages for working fewer hours. Their mood soured further on hearing about the Award given by Schiller. Hann, aware of this reaction, rationalised: 'To my mind, apart from the incitement of the Communists, the attitude of the workmen to the Award was mainly due to their having been led to expect that they could have shorter hours without reduction in wages, that they could get the same money as before for less work. I firmly believe that if the workmen had been told the truth the majority of them would have preferred to work eight hours as before'

Edmund Lawrence Hann's remark could suggest that Powell Duffryn was impotent when it came to influencing the attitude and outlook of their colliery employees. Or, on the other hand, the company had completely misjudged the state of disaffection and cynicism among the miners, which their union leaders were able to use for furthering their ends. Nonetheless, his outlook, based upon reflection, was possibly a message for the ears of at least the company's miners: 'The constant agitation over the past twenty years which has culminated in the crowning folly of reducing hours of work at the present critical period of our history has reduced a once flourishing industry to a state of penury'.

From James Griffiths's perspective: 'The coalowners had only one solution to offer, lower wages, and longer hours, as the means of winning back the markets coal had lost at home and abroad'. Public ownership of the industry appeared to be Griffiths's alternative solution to this situation.[77] A question was: could a state owned coal industry cope with the market in a fashion that was radically different from the way coalowners dealt with it?

In the year 1931, Powell Duffryn continued its battle in the market. The company tackled a sector of a market seen previously by it as not as important as the marine sector. The company made 'considerable progress in introducing Welsh coal' for use in domestic households' fire grates.[78] The spur for developing such a trade, apparently, was an observation that the atmosphere of Cardiff was both clearer, and less prone to fog, than London's, and the industrial towns of the North of England. The cause: Welsh coal, firing the hearths of the Welsh city, emitted no smoke, and was comparatively low in sulphur. Awake to the possibilities, which branding offered marketing products, the company registered the name of 'PhurnoD' to sell smokeless coal for domestic purposes.

A company shareholder, D. Rupert Davies, contributed a bleak assessment of the coal market at the company's AGM. 'When I think of all the interferences and publicity given our difficulties, I am surprised that we have survived at all. If we only consider the use of other fuels than coal, if we realise that whereas in pre-war days the British Admiralty took 1,700,000 tons of Welsh coal per annum and now only takes about 100,000 tons, if we consider that the liners now burn oil almost exclusively, and yet in spite of all this realise the fact that our exports are still over 80 per cent of what they were in the peak year of 1913, it must be obvious that

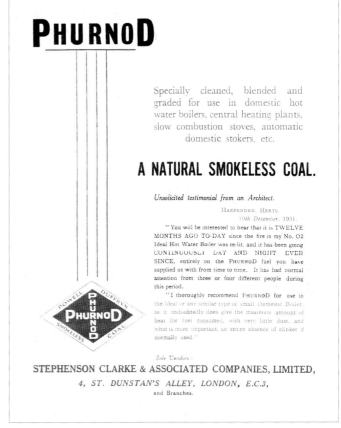

'PhurnoD' advertisement.

there is not much wrong with the administration of our collieries, nor the abilities of our coal exporters'.[79] The shareholders of Powell Duffryn endorsed his views. The year 1931 though saw the never-ending woes of the coal trade continue, and later that year the company's shareholders heard news of the death of Edmund Mills Hann at eighty years of age.

Death of Edmund Mills Hann

Edmund Mill Hann's final years, after retirement from Powell Duffryn, were not easy. He lost his wife in 1926, when she was seventy-seven years of age. He also suffered a stroke, and had to learn to walk and talk again as a consequence.[80]

The South Wales News carried, on the 5th October, the headline 'Death of Mr E. M. Hann; Pioneer of Welsh Coal Trade; A Just Employer'. The obituary declared that what separated him from 'other outstanding personalities' associated with the Welsh coal mining industry was that 'he was both a technical expert and an able business man'. This was appraised as being 'a rare combination', and, which, 'many accounted for the remarkable development of Powell Duffryn'. The obituary noted that he had possessed an 'alert mind' which 'was ever ready to assimilate the most modern ideas and to make full use of the most up-to-date equipment'. In this context his association with Elliot, Bargoed, Penallta, and Britannia Collieries was particularly identified by name, but omitted was mention of their technical merit. An architect's obituary would have highlighted the significant features of buildings that he, or she, had designed. Nevertheless, *The South Wales News* correctly noted his willingness to share his knowledge and experience with his professional colleagues, the mining engineers of the South Wales Coalfield and beyond.

Edmund Mills Hann (1850-1931).
Powell Duffryn's general manager of collieries from 1883 to 1921. His peers ranked him as one the greatest mining engineers in the history of the South Wales Coalfield. The illustration is of a painting in oils by Solomon J. Solomon RA that was given by the company as a gift to Hann in 1917. A replica hung in the company's London board room.

Courtesy of Amgueddfa Cymru - National Museums & Galleries of Wales

The newspaper also noted he was 'accorded' the highest honours of the South Wales Institute of Engineers. Indeed, his Institute contemporaries lauded him as one of its greatest mining engineers, which was considerable praise for he worked in a period when there was a great surge in colliery expansion in the South Wales Coalfield.

The South Wales News recognised that he had given 'unswerving loyalty' to Powell Duffryn. Although he had never shirked from confrontation with the company's miners, when they challenged the company's interests, the newspaper judged '*he was highly esteemed as an employer*'. According to the newspaper it was '*frequently remarked by the men that they could always depend upon Mr Hann's word*'. He was '*acknowledged as being always a just man*'. He had also worked studiously to improve safety standards at the company's collieries. During his time in the company there was not a mining tragedy like the one at New Tredegar Colliery in 1875.

Sir Leonard Brassey was lavish with praise in his eulogy about the former general manager of collieries given at the company's Annual General Meeting, March, 1932.[81] Edmund Mills Hann's 'very great reputation' in the South Wales Coalfield, was due to 'his own great personal ability, his own wonderful industry, and his great force of character'. Brassey recounted that Hann had held the position of general manager of collieries for thirty-eight years, and was elected a member of the Board but, due to ill health, had to resign from it in 1927. He then listed the characteristics he had admired in Hann: '*The first was his intense loyalty to the interests*

of the Powell Duffryn Company. He also possessed great courage to meet the difficulties that occur in the history of every big coal mining concern, and which certainly were not absent from the past history of Powell Duffryn Company. He faced those difficulties with consummate courage. He was a firm man, but to those that knew him he had behind that somewhat grim exterior a very kindly heart. Another characteristic, I always thought, of Mr E. M. Hann, was that he simply radiated good hard common sense, and not least of his services to this company, to which I should allude, is that he has left us a legacy of sons to continue the work that he himself carried on for so many years'.

Some of Edmund Mills Hann's work for the company had taken form as impressive colliery engineering. The easels for the creation of such work were the drawing boards at the company's Aberaman office. During his lifetime engineering technology advanced considerably in terms of its breadth, as represented by the number of its separate technical disciplines, and also in its deepening complexities. His abilities as an enterprising mining engineer, quality of leadership, inspired the company's engineers and draughtsmen to exploit engineering technology for the advantage of a coal business. Partly as a result, his management reign saw Powell Duffryn Steam Coal Company's output grow from one million tons of coal per year to one winding four million tons per annum when he retired. This three hundred per cent increase in output was also due to the energy market for coal being in the company's favour for most of his career.

As general manager of collieries, Hann did eventually sense the threat to Powell Duffryn's business from oil. By 1925, he clearly saw that a coal company's only practical response was to correct the 'enormous increase in the costs of production of coal' so as to compete against oil into the future. Moreover, he censured 'the restrictions of labour and by government regulations'. He believed that these two factors had 'entirely obliterated the effect of technical skill and engineering improvements'. He departed life when the South Wales Coalfield, that had fully used his knowledge, skill, and talents, was struggling in general to remain solvent, rife with disaffection among its miners, and confused by uncertainty. Such symptoms of decline made it harder for management to achieve the aims of a coal business than in his day. With regard to Powell Duffryn Steam Coal Company, it was left to his son to manage the associated difficulties for the satisfaction of its shareholders.

A month after the death of his father, in November, Edmund L. Hann was 'once again considering seriously' a further approach to buy Powell Duffryn's electricity interests.[82] Earlier, in 1929, the Electricity Commissioners, 'in the process of devising the area scheme for south-west England and south Wales', tested if Powell Duffryn 'would agree to the Bargoed power station, which was currently generating about 75 million units of electricity, being included in the scheme'. Powell Duffryn 'would not'. In November 1931, the Shropshire, Worcester & Staffordshire Electric Power Company, which was part of the Edmundsons Electricity Corp-oration, a group controlled by Americans that had taken over the South Wales Power Company, enquired if Powell Duffryn was prepared to sell its electricity assets. The coal company, faced with 'finding satisfactory methods to repay over £4 million of notes and debentures which had been raised in 1928', found the £1.75 million offered by the Shropshire, Worcester & Staffordshire Electric Power Company for its electricity assets 'tempting'. However, for 'unclear' reasons the offer was rejected.

In 1932, Edmund Lawrence Hann appraised the company's shareholders about the 'seriousness of the situation': the annual downward trend apparent in the coal output of the South Wales Coalfield. He tabled the coalfield's output for the years 1913, 1929, 1930, and 1931:

Year	Tons
1913	56,830,000
1929	48,150,000
1930	45,214,000
1931	37,522,000[83]

Up until the late 1920s, in the wake of 1913, the peak year of coal production in the South Wales Coalfield, the fall in production had been relatively modest, but by the start of the 1930s the falling trend reached alarming proportions. Moreover, the growing threat to the coal industry of oil could be seen in South Wales in the physical form of an oil refinery.

The Anglo-Persian Oil Company, later known as British Petroleum, opened an oil refinery at Llandarcy, near Swansea, in 1922. The travel writer H. V. Morton considered the place to be one of the 'sights of South Wales'.[84] He offered this comment after a journey of his around Wales also in 1931. Morton referred to it as the largest refinery in Europe. His tour of the refinery confirmed his 'first impression' that 'the oil refinery requires a minimum of human effort', and departed from it 'rather awed by its silent efficiency'.

'Half a Mile below the Surface'

H. V. Morton's tour of Wales included the Valleys. He discovered a 'chain of mining towns founded a little over a century ago during the Klondike rush to the minerals of South Wales'. Featured in the Valleys were house 'terraces, and villas, chimneys, and chapels, institutes and railway sidings'. He travelled through what he described as a 'black country where pit wheels spin against the sky, where rivers and streams are black, where black men come blinking from the depths of the earth'.[85]

Morton's tour included a visit to Penallta Colliery. On the colliery's surface, he was ushered into a cage with a group of miners. He wrote, the cage 'moved and began to fall!' He stared at 'walls rushing upward. A cold, damp wind blew a gale. Then it was dark! Our safety lamps were like glow worms. The cage fell faster and faster. It roared. It rattled. It banged. It was like being in a drunken Underground train. I felt that my feet had left the bottom of the cage and that my ears were being pulled upward'. Then 'it slowed down a bit; it became comparatively steady, and in a few seconds it dropped us very gently at the bottom of the shaft'. An 'uncanny world of silence' that 'was cold with the chill of a vault', greeted him as he stepped out of the cage. And he felt that 'the weight of a half a mile of rock and earth above me seemed to press on my head'.[86] Due to his visit to the colliery, James Jarché, a Fleet Street press photographer also descended with him in the cage.

Penallta Colliery's hewers at the coal face wielding mandrels in 1931. The photograph was taken by James Jarché and it featured in H.V. Morton's *In Search of Wales* (1932).

A Penallta Colliery miner using a pnuematic drill. He might have been preparing a hole for explosives, or speedily removing rock to enable more productive work to take place at the coal face. The photograph was taken by James Jarché for the *Daily Herald*.
Courtesy of the Science Museum

Penallta Colliery miners sorting coal cut at the face in 1931. Steel channels as pit props are featured, which were pioneered by Powell Duffryn at the colliery in 1928 having been supplied by Tredomen Works. James Jaché took the photograph. *Courtesy of the Science Museum*

'Specially secured pictures', and 'remarkable sights' captured on film by Jarché's camera appeared particularly in the *Weekly Illustrated*.[87] He was a British pioneer of photojournalism, and became 'something of a celebrity'.

James Jarché used some novel procedures for his photographic assignment at Penallta Colliery. He produced, according to Morton, 'the only flashlight' photographs' that had been 'taken in a mine which contains explosive gas'. 'In order to secure' the pictures, 'Mr Jarché used a new safe-light apparatus. Even so, the perfectly safe flash of light made us very nervous!'[88] One photograph featured in Morton's *In Search of Wales*, some in the *Daily Herald* and others were used in a 1934 edition of the *Weekly Illustrated*.[89] Neither publication disclosed the colliery where the photographs were taken. However, many years later a photograph was published that captured Morton and Jarché together on the surface of a 'Powell Duffryn Pit'. Slung on Jarché's left shoulder was a box, which contained his camera equipment.[90]

'Half a Mile below the Surface' was the caption used for a *Weekly Illustrated* photograph by Jarché. Such a depth, below the surface of the earth, points to Penallta Colliery as the colliery visited by Morton, and the location for Jarché's historical photographs. Sound anecdotal information also recalls that afterwards the Government's mines inspectorate investigated the nature of the photographic assignment. As a sequel, the mines inspectorate threatened possible court action against the colliery's manager since it contended that the lives of his miners were put at risk. Some accommodation was reached between the company and the mines inspectorate, and it seems no legal action was taken.

Morton noted after his visit that the 'post-war depression' was apparent in the South Wales mining valleys. He saw the effects of unemployment in a location he called 'Heartbreak Valley'. In his opinion, 'the miner' was 'misunderstood', and 'misrepresented'.[91] The 'Welsh miner', was 'proud and sensitive', and using 'the word with deliberation and in its true sense – [a] gentleman'. '*The miner's wife*', he judged, was '*one of the heroines of Great Britain. For at least ten years, she has been pinching and scraping. Yet you never hear her complain*'. Adding: '*She is obsessed by three thoughts: to pay the rent, to feed and clothe her family, and to have hot water and food ready when her man comes home*'.[92]

The sons of the miners he thought were 'a national problem'.[93] A practice was that boys of fourteen years old age entered the industry as miners. He thought that such employment 'appeals to all that is adventurous in a boy: the darkness, the queer, dangerous life underground, the association of older men, [and] the spice of peril'. Yet, it was the bleak employment prospects he found in the Valleys that provoked him to ask: what was going to happen to the sons of miners? He believed that there was 'no future for them in the coalfield'.

Powell Duffryn's faith in a future for coal

In the year 1931 Powell Duffryn claimed that it 'maintained' its 'relative position in the trade'. Although such a position represented a fall in business performance, deft financial control by the company helped it return a profit of £304,280.[94] The January miners' strike had some affect upon the financial performance of the company. The cost of running the company's collieries also rose to some extent due to heavy rainfall in the winter months of 1931-1932. This wet period, the worst in fifty year, swamped the Valleys and adversely hit colliery operations. The Rhymney River, for example, spilled its banks to flood part of Bargoed's coke ovens.[95]

Edmund L Hann, though, shared some good news with the shareholders. At Aberaman, the company previously installed pilot pulverised fuel plant was judged a success. As a result, in 1932, work was put in hand to convert the boiler plant at Middle Duffryn to pulverised fuel.[96] The company's hope was that the Middle Duffryn plant would 'convince customers that high efficiencies can be obtained with ... low volatile coals and dispel the illusion generally held that it is only high volatile coals which are successful for firing as pulverised fuel'. Around 1931, the company had also introduced a coal marketed as 'Powell Duffryn VIRTICOL Smokeless Coal' for use in vertical boilers, and increasing sales were reported for 'PhunoD' in England.[97]

In the year 1932, Edmund Lawrence Hann also re-emphasized: 'It has always been the policy of this Company to modernise its Plant and keep up-to-date in everything connected with the preparation and marketing of its coal in a manner to satisfy the requirements of the individual customer'.[98] During the 1930s, the company's engineers and draughtsmen were kept busy. The Windsor, Lewis Merthyr, Albion and Great Western Colliery Company collieries saw their underground lay-out and methods of working re-planned and reorganised.[99] Windsor and Albion Collieries were connected to the Powell Duffryn electricity grid, and action was taken to transmit electric power to collieries formerly owned by the Great Western Colliery Company and Lewis Merthyr Collieries.[100] Washeries were built at Albion, Lewis Merthyr and Great Western Collieries. The Great Western Colliery coke ovens were also substantially rebuilt, and a flotation plant installed to prepare for coking the residual coal from the washery, which until then had been regarded as a waste product.

Powell Duffryn held its faith in a future for coal despite the prevailing adverse trading conditions due to a world economic recession between the years 1929 and 1932. In 1932, the company's profit improved to £403,241.[101] In 1932, he announced: 'Never in the history has our company been more efficient, both on the technical and on the commercial side'. 'In every way we are ready to take advantage of the good times when they return, as return they must'.[102] Confounding the generally poor financial state of the industry, the company also returned a profit of £600,000 in 1933, with a qualification that it was for 15 months trading.[103]

Sometime in 1933, Stephenson Clarke & Company (which was owned by Powell Duffryn) and William Cory & Sons Ltd, as equal share holders, created Coal Distributors (South Wales) Ltd. From Powell Duffryn's perspective, Coal Distributors (South Wales) Ltd 'resulted in a close working arrangement with the great firm of William Cory & Sons Ltd'. Perhaps such an arrangement was a remote possibility decades earlier when Joseph Shaw joined Powell Duffryn as a director.

Death of Joseph Shaw

On the 14th December, 1933, Joseph Shaw died at West Southbourne, Hampshire. He was seventy-seven years of age. He served as chairman of the company from 1897 until 1928. He resigned as a director of the company in 1930 due to ill health, and so was the last one able to recall, based upon personal experiences, Sir George Elliot's 'practical direction' of Powell Duffryn. As a

barrister, Joseph Shaw distinguished himself, becoming a KC in 1910. He married twice. In 1885, he married Charlotte the eldest daughter of Sir Phillip Smyly MD, and they had a son and a daughter. In 1926, when he was seventy, he married the fifth daughter of Sir Phillip Smyly, Constance Isabel. After living at Kentchurch Court, in Herefordshire, for a number of years, he removed first to Alderbury House, Banbury, in Oxfordshire, before finally residing at West Southbourne. Unlike Sir George Elliot, he would appear to have been a person that valued his privacy, and was not attracted to take a position in public life for which his wealth, background, and education made him eminently suitable.

Unlike Elliot, he appears not to have meddled in the practical business of running the company. On the other hand, via the managing committee of directors, he steered the company towards survival and progress. Alas Hann's brief account of the history of the company provides few clues for understanding how the crucial relationship between him and Joseph Shaw profoundly affected Powell Duffryn, and no written account was found giving Joseph Shaw's personal appraisal of Edmund Mills Hann.

The lengthy tenure of Edmund Mills Hann's office suggests that Joseph Shaw approved of the way in which the company's general manager of collieries conducted company affairs. That the two men featured as a pair of directors sitting on a board of directors in least two other colliery company ventures suggests that they valued working together. In 1910, in addition to their involvement in founding Bedwas Navigation Colliery Company, they were party to developing Billingsley Colliery Company, which operated one colliery in the Wyre Forest Coalfield, located west of Birmingham.[104]

Edmund Lawrence Hann's statement, 4th July, 1934, at an Adjourned General Meeting of the Company, began with a remark that he was 'in the happy position after a number of years [for the company] to declare a dividend on the Ordinary shares'. He then said: 'Yet our feelings of satisfaction cannot but be tempered by the knowledge that one who in the past did so much to build up the fortunes of the Powell Duffryn Company is no longer with us. Mr Joseph Shaw, who was Chairman of this Company for over thirty years and was largely responsible for its rise in prosperity, passed away in December last after a long illness. To those who were fortunate enough to work under and with him, the late Mr Shaw's qualities will always be a source of inspiration'.[105]

At the same meeting, Sir Leonard Brassey offered his opinion about Powell Duffryn's state of affairs. The company's results were 'remarkable for a number of reasons'.[106] The company's export trade was vulnerable due to 'the adverse exchange rates, the financial instability of many foreign countries, the generally unsettled state of the world, and the artificial measures taken by many foreign countries to foster their own coal industries. Some of that of course, is no doubt the legacy of that disastrous strike of 1926'. Since no reference was made to the 1926 strike by Edmund L. Hann, during his report to the meeting, Brassey's link to the strike suggests a personal release of seething rancour.

Taff-Merthyr Colliery Inter-union Dispute

Some unresolved issues had festered since the 1926 strike, and one concerned both Taff-Merthyr Colliery, and the Fed's grudges against the South Wales Miners' Industrial Union (SWMIU). Moreover, when the miners of the South Wales Coalfield struck in January, 1931, Taff-Merthyr Colliery had operated as normal. The colliery's workforce of 1,400 men produced 2,000 tons daily, whilst the Federation's members at neighbouring Deep Navigation Colliery were idle.[107] Neither did the incomes of Taff-Merthyr men suffer with the implementation of the Schiller Award, which added more ill will to the Fed's store of animosity towards the SWMIU. In part due to association the Fed detested the parties managing the colliery, Powell Duffryn and the Ocean Company.

Bedwas Navigation Colliery, which Edmund L. Hann retained strong ties with, though, became the site first chosen by the Fed to pick a fight with the SWMIU. In February, 1932, the Bedwas colliery company recognised the SWMIU.[108] The SWMF reacted by picketing the colliery, which roused local incidents of rioting. However, by the end of April, 1932, only the SWMIU represented the colliery's miners.

Then, two years later, Taff-Merthyr Colliery was chosen by the Fed for an attack on the SWMIU. The instigator of the attack was its new president, James Griffiths. He later documented his perspective of the Fed's Taff-Merthyr Colliery campaign.[109] On taking office as president, he called a special conference, which decided to pursue two priority tasks: ridding the coalfield of the 'bogus Spencer Union', and to 'mobilize [the Fed's] forces in an endeavour to raise the wages of the men from the scandalously low level to which they had fallen since 1926'. Sometime before 1927, George Spencer founded the Nottinghamshire Non-Political Miners' Trade Union, and he campaigned in defence of the SWMIU through the Welsh press.[110] However, Spencer's interference was resented by the SWMF, and, his surname was seen as prey by the Fed for maligning the SWMIU.

James Griffiths put into action what he thought was a 'bold plan'. He felt much reassurance from knowing that of the 140,000 miners at work in South Wales in 1934, 76,000 were members of the SWMF. The plan's aim was to oust the SWMIU from Taff-Merthyr Colliery by challenging the colliery company's condition of employment, which was perceived to justify the SWMIU acting for the interests of the colliery's miners. The plan began with an attempt to recruit new members for the SWMF at the colliery. In early October, 1934, the 'Federation propagandists claimed that 1,100 out of the 1,650 employed at Taff-Merthyr had accepted federation cards, threatened a stoppage and guaranteed the victimised men the equivalent of 'unemployment pay'.[111] This report contrasted with that of C. B. Tellyn, chairman of Taff-Merthyr branch of the SWMIU: hundreds of the Federation's cards were torn up by the colliery's miners.[112]

Then, on Monday, 8th October, officials of the antagonist unions squared up to each other. The officials of the SWMIU (also referred to as the Industrial Union) stood on one side of an approach road to the colliery. Standing on the opposite side of the road were several members of the Executive Council of the Miners' Federation. 'A strong company of police' kept watch on the two groups of adversaries, and maybe as a result there was 'no hint of disorderly scenes'.[113] However, the evening of the Tuesday saw the window of a Bedlinog shop owned by Edgar Evans smashed. Edgar Evans, a member of Gelligaer Council, was host to two guests, who were members of the Federation's Executive.

On Friday, the 12th October, the SWMF reinforced its contingent at Taff-Merthyr Colliery so that it included James Griffiths, two MPs, Ted Williams, and W. H. Mainwaring, and a future MP for Caerphilly, Ness Edwards. The contingent's intention was to take Federation contributions from its members working at the colliery. The colliery also attracted further attention from 'workmen',

and a 'crowd of unemployed who lined the roadway [and] sang hymns in real Welsh style'.[114] A large force of police watched the throng as bystanders.

Later that day, events 'took a serious turn when some of the night-shift decided to strike'. This was due to the company 'writing out notices for those who had joined the Federation'. The company's action was apparently prompted by the SWMIU having 'intimated' their members not to work with 'Federation men'.[115] These events caused James Griffiths to issue a statement at dawn on Saturday: "Unless we obtain a satisfactory settlement by to-night, the attention of Government will be called to this dispute and the Mines Department will be asked to intervene." Shortly afterwards, with the roads to the colliery patrolled by police, workmen and unemployed singing the "Red Flag", SWMIU members were booed as they made their way to work.[116]

On the Sunday afternoon, the village of Treharris, which lay south-south west of the colliery, became the 'centre of activity'.[117] The crowds of people attracted to a meeting of Federation workmen at the village's Public Hall prompted an over-flow meeting at the village's Co-operative Hall. Welsh Hymns were sung 'with great fervour' by meeting goers. Miners' agent Ness Edwards, the Public Hall meeting's chairman, claimed that 'the day would henceforth be known as "Independence Day" among the Taff-Merthyr workman'. By Monday, 15th October, the 'picketing was in full swing but the colliery worked as usual'.

Sometime afterwards, Oliver Harris, the Fed's general secretary, sent Edmund L. Hann a letter. The letter contained the claim that '90 per cent of the men at the colliery wished to join the Federation, but that Jayne (the colliery agent and General Manager) and Hughes (the local manager) would not discuss the matter'. Moreover, he asserted that the company denied the 'elementary right to join the Organisation which is responsible for the arrangements in this Coalfield, [thus] peace will be impossible'. Hann's letter of reply rejected as false the claims made in Harris's letter.

On the night of Friday, 26th October, C. B. Tellyn, of the SWMIU, was 'violently assaulted by a hostile crowd in Trelewis's High Street' when 'proceeding to his home'. The village of Trelewis was Treharris's eastern neighbour. Tellyn suffered facial injuries but 'was able to resume duty on Saturday morning'.[118]

Francis and Smith narrated the subsequent manoeuvres of the SWMF. 'Relentless picketing' continued at Taff-Merthyr Colliery. Member workers, upon returning to their homes at the neighbouring villages of Bedlinog, Trelewis, and Nelson, received a 'hostile reception'. The Fed attempted to hinder what was called a 'ghost train', that brought workers recruited from the unemployed of the Rhymney Valley to the colliery. There were 'silent demonstrations, in the [adjacent] villages, against [what Federation supporters called] 'scabs', this time women carried wreaths to make the point clear'.

The Taff Merthyr Steam Coal Company Ltd distanced itself from the dispute by representing it as an inter-union matter. The company enacted such stance by declining any call for a meeting from either trade union. The SWMF was annoyed by having their call for a meeting with the company declined. Whether, or not, as a result, one sequel was that the Rhymney Valley 'ghost train' ran, but with no passengers on board.

The crucial moment, perhaps, of the Taff-Merthyr Colliery dispute occurred in November. Miners' delegates of the SWMF followed its Executive's recommendation to tender fourteen day's notice of a strike after a consultation with the [trade union's] lodges. According to the Fed, the threat of a Coalfield strike saw the company 'relent'.

Edmund L. Hann sent a letter, dated 10th November, to Oliver Harris in which he stated his willingness to meet 'the three top Federation officials'. A meeting took place, and he agreed to a secret ballot at the colliery so that its miners could decide which union they desired to join, and to accept its result.[119] The ballot resulted in the recognition of the Federation as the trade union to represent the miners of Taff-Merthyr Colliery. Yet, the matters that arose during the execution of James Griffiths's 'bold plan' left a muddle of opinion about its efficacy. Francis and Smith concluded, for instance, that in 'no sense can the SWMF be credited with an overwhelming success at Taff-Merthyr-in 1934 and 1935'.

So, what could be said about the Taff Merthyr Steam Coal Company's role in the matter? Francis and Smith judged, concerning the prelude to the dispute, that 'direct collusion between the [coal] owner and the SWMIU' was 'not easy to find since both sides were vehement in their denial of such a link'.[120] They, however, presented the views of David Davies, Lord Davies of Llandinham, the Ocean Coal Company's leader essentially Edmund Hann's equal in the joint-venture. Francis and Smith considered Lord Davies to be an enlightened coalowner, the characteristics of which they did not define.[121]

Nonetheless they quoted from an 'important memorandum' that the Ocean man had written, in November 1934.[122] Lord Davies saw the policy pursued at Taff-Merthyr Colliery to be *divide et impera* [divide and rule], which was destined to fail since it was based 'on fundamentally wrong principles'. To him, it violated the 'principle of freedom of choice – but we rightly condemn Federation intimidation'; and 'by granting privileges to one Union which we deny to others; by deducting contributions from wages and handling the proceedings to the Industrial Union we place the individual miner at the mercy of the Union and our managers'. Lord Davies also judged that 'by being a non-associated Colliery we reap all the advantages without any of the responsibilities. But we risk, by our isolation, embroiling the whole coalfield in a stoppage'. He wondered if the outcome would prove to be a 'Pyrrhic victory', and was fearful that 'Taff-Merthyr' would become the battle-cry of every Federationist in South Wales', noting that the Fed was 'not down and out yet'.[123] And he worried over a 'delusion' of a 'régime of coercion' regarding 'our men at Taff-Merthyr'.

Edmund Hann's reflections about the 1934 battle at Taff-Merthyr Colliery apparently will never be known. Powell Duffryn, it is claimed, destroyed all written material to do with the dispute other than 'non-controversial' official Association papers.[124] Lord Davies's memorandum might be used to infer that Powell Duffryn wielded power that adversely affected the course of events. However, no information was found to support such an inference. The anxiety and hurt felt by the colliery's miners during the inter-union battle might have been salved if the blame could have been pinned upon the employer for an end that no one body could crow victory. The stature of the battle's antagonist, James Griffiths, appeared not to suffer. In 1936, he stood as candidate for the Labour Party at a by-election, and was elected Member of Parliament for Llanelli.[125]

Following the end of the battle at Taff-Merthyr Colliery, the Fed made a decision to continue a campaign against both Powell Duffryn, and the Ocean Colliery Company, where these coal companies were judged to be encouraging non-SWMF membership. Moreover, Edmund L. Hann, as a director of the Bedwas Navigation Colliery Company, also became embroiled in negotiations with the Fed that suggested that he was attempting to sustain that company's recognition of the SWMIU.[126] Nonetheless, in early 1938, the two trade unions reached an accommodation and the SWMIU was merged with the Federation. By which time Powell Duffryn had become a much more powerful coal company.

NOTES

1 Barry Supple, *op. cit.*, p.20.
2 Trevor Boyns, 'On Machines and Men', *Llafur*, Vol.5, (1989), p.32.
3 Trevor Boyns, 'Jigging and Shaking: Technical Choices in the South Wales Coal Industry between the Wars', *The Welsh History Review: Cylchgrawn Hanes Cymru*, Vol.17, No.2, (1994), p.244.
4 Gwyn A. Williams, *op. cit.*, pp.217-218.
5 Gwyn A. Williams, *op. cit.*, p.234.
6 *Western Mail*, 'Great fire at Powell Duffryn Colliery, Bargoed: By-Product Plant Burnt Out', 25 May 1926.
7 Report-Proceedings, AGM of the Co., PDSC, 27 March 1928, p.8.
8 A Samuel Commission recommendation, that the State acquire the coal company royalty payments was attractive for especially Powell Duffryn. In 1935, Edmund L. Hann told company shareholders: 'So far as South Wales is concerned, royalties etc. amount to a figure as high as 8¾d. to 9d. on every ton of coal that districts sells, whereas other districts this figure varies from 4d. to 6d. per ton of coal sold'. He then called upon Government to deal with the matter; see Report-Proceedings, AGM of the Company, PDSCC, 11 July 1931, p.11. As an idea of Powell Duffryn's cost burden due to royalties, in 1930, it was £210,000; see Report-Proceedings, AGM of the Co., PDSCC, 26 March 1931, p.21.
9 *South Wales Echo*, 'The Act Explained', 1 May 1926, p.1, col.3.
10 *South Wales Echo*, 'Troops for Cardiff', 1 May 1926, p.1, col.2.
11 Islwyn Jenkins, *Idris Davies of Rhymney*. (Gomer, 1986), p.63.
12 Hywel Francis and David Smith, *The Fed*. (Lawrence and Wishart, 1980), pp.54-6.
13 Short Survey- Powell Duffryn Limited, *op. cit.*, p.3.
14 Hywel Francis and David Smith, *op. cit.*, pp.59-65.

15 Islwyn Jenkins, *op. cit.*, p.66.
16 Edwin Greening, *From Aberdare to Albacete*. (Warren and Pell, 2006), pp.33-35. Edwin Greening (1911-2003) after a period of self-education, qualified to be a school teacher.
17 Hywel Francis and David Smith, *op. cit.*, p.66.
18 Hywel Francis and David Smith, *op. cit.*, p.82. Jack Roberts of Abertridwr was a strong advocate of Communist Russia's trade union's funding support to miners' struggle. The Russian contribution to the British Miners' Relief fund was £1,161,459 2s. 6d. See pp.53-54.
19 Report-Proceedings, AGM of the Co., PDSC, 29 March 1927, p.9.
20 Report-Proceedings, AGM of the Co., PDSC, 29 March 1927, p.10.
21 G. M. Harries, *op. cit.*, p.7.
22 Report-Proceedings, AGM of the Co., PDSC, 29 March 1927, p.11.
23 Hywel Francis and David Smith, *op. cit.*, pp.91-95.
24 Later, in 1930, S. O. Davies, the Fed's agent for the Dowlais District, took responsibility for tackling the issue of Taff-Merthyr Colliery. He berated the SWMIU as the 'Scab Union'. He later became MP for Merthyr Tydfil. Hywel Francis and David Smith, *op. cit.*, p.93.
25 Hywel Francis and David Smith, *op. cit.*, p.114.
26 Hywel Francis and David Smith, *op. cit.*, p.93.
27 For example, the Ebbw Vale Steel, Iron & Coal Company supplied Ebbw Vale, and the Welsh Navigation Steam Coal Company supplied Tonyrefail and Gilfach Goch. Trevor Boyns, 'The Electricity Industry in South Wales to 1949', *The Welsh History Review: Cylchgrawn Hanes Cymru*, Vol.15, No.1, (1990), pp.84-5
28 Trevor Boyns, 'The Electricity Industry in South Wales to 1949', *op. cit.*, pp.101-103.
29 Trevor Boyns, 'Rationalisation in the Inter War Period: The Case of

the South Wales Steam Coal Industry', *Business History*, Vol.XXIX, No.3, (July 1987), p.288. A footnote details that this financial package was based upon an issue of debentures, and use of redeemable notes. J. Henry Schroder & Co. handled the matter with its Norman Holden playing a notable part. Norman Holden became a director of Powell Duffryn in May 1928.

30 Trevor Boyns, 'Strategic Responses to Foreign Competition: The British Coal Industry and the 1930 Mines Act', *Business History*, Vol. 32, No. 3, (July 1990), p.140.

31 *A Directory of Colliery Companies in the South Wales Coalfield*, (The Monmouthshire & South Wales Coal Owners' Association, 1917), p.10. And, Short Survey - Powell Duffryn Limited, *op. cit.*, p.2.

32 Short Survey - Powell Duffryn Limited, *op. cit.*, p.3.

33 Short Survey - Powell Duffryn Limited, *op. cit.*, p.3.

34 *A Directory of Colliery Companies in the South Wales Coalfield*, (The Monmouthshire & South Wales Coal Owners' Association, 1917), p. 11.

35 *The Colliery Guardian*, Vol.CXXXVI, No.3508, 23 March 1928, p.1154.

36 Report-Proceedings, AGM of the Co., PDSC, 27 March 1928, p. 12.

37 Report-Proceedings, AGM of the Co., PDSC, 27 March 1928, p. 12.

38 Report-Proceedings, AGM of the Co., PDSC, 27 March 1928, p. 5. OS grid reference ST 135946.

39 *The Colliery Guardian*, Vol.CXXXVI, No. 3506, 9 March 1928, p.970.

40 Trevor Boyns, 'The Electricity Industry in South Wales to 1949', *op. cit.*, p.95.

41 Trevor Boyns, 'The Electricity Industry in South Wales to 1949', *op. cit.*, p.95.

42 Report-Proceedings, AGM of the Co., PDSC, 27 March 1928, pp.12-13.

43 *The Colliery Guardian* also noted this in its 1928 favourable appraisal of the company. *The Colliery Guardian*, Vol.CXXXVI, No.3508, 23 March 1928, p.1154.

44 Letter, Trevor Boyns to Writer, 4 Jan 2007. Comments regarding the Llanbradach Colliery link with Powell Duffryn. See also Trevor Boyns in Dennis G. Sellwood, *Llanbradach Colliery 1887-1961*. (Dennis G. Sellwood, 2002), pp.18-19.

45 Report-Proceedings, AGM of the Company, PDSCC, 27 March 1928, p.2.

46 Dennis G. Sellwood, Llanbradach Colliery 1887-1961. (Dennis G. Sellwood, 2002), p.20.

47 Report-Proceedings, AGM of the Co., PDSC, 26 March 1929, pp.8-9.

48 Report-Proceedings, AGM of the Co., PDSC, 26 March 1929, p.2.

49 Report-Proceedings, AGM of the Co., PDSC, 26 March 1929, p.10.

50 Dr W. Gerwyn Thomas, *Welsh Coal Mines*. (National Museum of Wales, 1976), p.50.

51 Report-Proceedings, AGM of the Co., PDSC, 26 March 1929, p.4.

52 Horizon mining involved driving underground roadways on a level plane and was used first at Llanharan Colliery 8 October, 1948. T. J. Witts, *A Time of Tears*. (Whitchurch Books, 2000), p.211.

53 Report Proceedings, AGM of the Co., PDSCC, 27 March 1930, p.9. The company's board minutes, 30th July, 1928, noted that Tredomen works made 100 to 200 steel props per week.

54 Trevor Boyns, 'The Use of New Materials', (Unpublished, re. BOOK.08D) pp.1-2. The source used for information about steel roof supports.

55 Report-Proceedings, AGM of the Co., PDSCC, 27 March 1930, p.10.

56 Short Survey- Powell Duffryn Limited, *op. cit.*, p.7.

57 Report-Proceedings, AGM of the Co., PDSC, 27 March 1930, p.9.

58 Report-Proceedings, AGM of the Co., PDSC, 27 March 1930, p.8.

59 Report-Proceedings, AGM of the Co., PDSC, 27 March 1930, pp.10-11.

60 Report-Proceedings, AGM of the Co., PDSCC, 27 March 1930, p.8.

61 Report-Proceedings, AGM of the Co., PDSC, 26 March 1929, p.12.

62 Report-Proceedings, AGM of the Co., PDSC, 27 March 1930, p.10.

63 Report-Proceedings, AGM of the Co., PDSC, 27 March 1930, p.10.

64 Report-Proceedings, AGM of the Co., PDSC, 27 March 1930, p.8.

65 Report-Proceedings, AGM of the Co., PDSC, 27 March 1930, p.8-9.

66 Report-Proceedings, AGM of the Co., PDSC, 27 March 1930, p.9-10.

67 An inference that may be drawn from a read of *100 Years of Brewing*, (1939, Andrew Buchan's Breweries), is that Andrew Buchan's Breweries was still owned by Powell Duffryn in 1939, which seems unlikely. The brewer was not listed as an asset of Powell Duffryn Associated Collieries formed in 1935.

68 Report-Proceedings, AGM of the Co., PDSC, 27 March 1930, pp.6-7.

69 Research Notes as at March 2007. Raymond Lawrence. The source of manager details and employment numbers at the colliery.

70 Report-Proceedings, AGM of the Co., PDSC, 26 March 1931, p.5.

71 Report-Proceedings, AGM of the Co., PDSC, 26 March 1931, p.6.

72 Report-Proceedings, AGM of the Co., PDSC, 27 March 1930, p.12.

73 Report-Proceedings, AGM of the Co., PDSC, 26 March 1931, pp.8-9.

74 Trevor Boyns, 'Strategic Responses to Foreign Competition: The British Coal Industry and the 1930 Coal Mines Act', *Business History*, Vol. 32, No. 3, (July 1990), pp.139-140.

75 Report-Proceedings, AGM of the Co., PDSC, 26 March 1931, pp.10-11.

76 James Griffiths, *Pages from Memory*. (Dent, 1969), pp.38-9.

77 James Griffiths, *op. cit.*, p.33.

78 Report-Proceedings, AGM of the Co., PDSC, 26 March 1931, pp.9-10.

79 Report-Proceedings, AGM of the Co., PDSC, 26 March 1931, p.23.

80 David Hann, 'The Hann Family – A Mining Dynasty of South Wales part 1', *Glamorgan Family History Society, Journal* No. 38, (June, 1995) p.40.

81 Report-Proceedings, AGM of the Co., PDSCC, 22 March 1932, pp.1-12.

82 Trevor Boyns, 'The Electricity Industry in South Wales to 1949', *op. cit.*, pp.95-96.

83 Report-Proceedings, AGM of the Co., PDSCC, 22 March 1932, p.8.

84 H. V. Morton, *In Search of Wales*. (Methuen, 1932), pp.226-267.

85 H. V. Morton, *op. cit.*, p.246.

86 H. V. Morton, *op. cit.*, pp.250-251.

87 Derek Smith, *James Jarché-1891-1965*, (Paul Popper, 1980), p. 9.

88 H. V. Morton, *op. cit.*, p. vii.

89 *Weekly Illustrated*, 4 Oct 1934.

90 Derek Smith, *op. cit.*, p.24.

91 H. V. Morton, *op. cit.*, p.247.

92 H. V. Morton, op. cit, p.259.

93 H. V. Morton, op. cit, p.264.

94 Report-Proceedings, AGM of the Co., PDSC, 22 March 1932, p.7.

95 Report-Proceedings, AGM of the Co., PDSC, 22 March 1932, p.10.

96 Report-Proceedings, AGM of the Co., PDSC, 22 March 1932, p.12.

97 Report-Proceedings, AGM of the Co., PDSC, 22 March 1932, pp.12-13.

98 Report-Proceedings, AGM of the Co., PDSC, 22 March 1932, p.11.

99 Short Survey- Powell Duffryn Limited, *op. cit.*, p.5.

100 Short Survey- Powell Duffryn Limited, *op. cit.*, p.4.

101 Report-Proceedings, AGM of the Co., PDSC, 23 March 1933, p.6.

102 Report-Proceedings, AGM of the Co., PDSC, 22 March 1932, pp.16-17.

103 Report-Proceedings, AGM of the Co., PDSC, 4 July 1934, p.6.

104 David Poyner & Robert Evans, *The Wyre Forest Coalfield*. (Tempus, 2000), pp.89-95. A Thornewill & Wareham winding engine was used at Billingsley Colliery. New miners' homes were provided by the Woodhill Garden Village Company Ltd.

105 Report-Proceedings, AGM of the Co., PDSC, 4 July 1934, p.1-2.

106 Report-Proceedings, AGM of the Co., PDSC, 4 July 1934, p.11.

107 Hywel Francis and David Smith, *op. cit.*, p.215

108 Hywel Francis and David Smith, *op. cit.*, p.318.

109 James Griffiths, *op. cit.*, p.35-38.

110 Hywel Francis and David Smith, *op. cit.*, p.224.

111 Hywel Francis and David Smith, *op. cit.*, pp.218-236. The source of most of the following description unless otherwise noted.

112 *The Express*, 'Rival Unions in Conflict', 13 Oct 1934, p.12, col.2.

113 *The Express*, *op. cit.*, 13 Oct 1934, p.12, col.1.

114 *The Express*, 'Taff-Merthyr Colliery Strike', 20 Oct 1934, p.8, col.3.

115 *The Express*, *op. cit.*, 20 Oct 1934, p.8, col.3.

116 *The Express*, *op. cit.*, 20 Oct 1934, p.8, col.3.

117 *The Express*, *op. cit.*, 20 Oct 1934, p.8, col.4.

118 *The Express*, 'Taff-Merthyr Strike', 27 Oct 1934, p.7, col.1.

119 W. W. Price, Card Records, Hann 5, card 3. National Library of Wales.

120 Hywel Francis and David Smith, *op. cit.*, p.118.

121 Hywel Francis and David Smith, *op. cit.*, p.40.

122 Hywel Francis and David Smith, *op. cit.*, pp.228-230.

123 Hywel Francis and David Smith, *op. cit.*, p.236.

124 Hywel Francis and David Smith, *op. cit.*, p.241, footnote no.67.

125 In October 1964, the Labour Government's Prime Minister, Harold Wilson appointed him to a new Government post, Secretary of State for Wales.

126 Hywel Francis and David Smith, *op. cit.*, p.379.

4068. CAMBRIAN COLLIERIES

Cambrian Collieries, Clydach Vale, Rhondda Fawr Valley, in 1905. In 1935, Powell Duffryn acquired these collieries due to its merger with Welsh Associated Collieries (WAC). Samuel Thomas, D. A. Thomas's father, in a partnership known as Thomas, Riches & Co., sunk Cambrian No. 1, in 1871. Between 1874 and 1911, Numbers 2, 3, and 4 were sunk. D. A. Thomas, with his brother, J. H. Thomas, took over the running of these collieries after their father's death in 1879. In 1918, the collieries employed a total 3,500 persons. In 1945, the collieries employed in total 1,366 persons.

Courtesy of Rhondda Cynon Taf Libraries

Chapter Ten
PEERLESS & DISPOSSESSED

On April Fool's Day, 1935, Powell Duffryn Associated Collieries Ltd was formed due to the merging of Powell Duffryn Steam Coal Company and Welsh Associated Collieries (WAC). The merger was a major event in the history of both Welsh industry, and the British coal industry. Welsh Associated Collieries, the flotsam of three decades of mergers and acquisitions, had its origins in the 'Cambrian Combine'. Unless otherwise acknowledged, the following sketch of the development of WAC is based upon a paper by Trevor Boyns.[1]

The Cambrian Combine

The architect of the Cambrian Combine was David Alfred Thomas, hereinafter D. A. Thomas. He was born in 1856 at 'Ysguborwen House', Aberdare. Edmund Mill Hann may have occupied Ysguborwen House at the time of his retirement from Powell Duffryn. Edmund Mills Hann and D. A. Thomas were contemporaries, and their interests coincided on at least one occasion as detailed previously. In 1910, Hann and Thomas called upon General Macready for government action to quell civil unrest caused by miners on strike due to separate disputes with their respective coal companies.

D. A. Thomas's father, Samuel Thomas, born in 1800, began his working life as a shopkeeper in Merthyr Tydfil. He ventured into coal mining in the Aberdare Valley during the late 1840s before sinking collieries in the Rhondda Valley in partnership with his brother-in-law, Thomas Joseph. Samuel Thomas was around seventy years of age when he entered into another partnership, Thomas, Riches and Co., to sink, in 1871, Cambrian No. 1 Colliery in Clydach Vale.[2] Cambrian No. 2 Colliery was sunk four years later. A part of the wealth he earned was spent upon educating his son, David Alfred, the fifteenth child of a family of seventeen children, at Dr Hudson's School, Clifton, in Bristol. D. A. Thomas proceeded to Gonville and Caius College, Cambridge University.

After graduating from Cambridge University, D. A. Thomas joined Cambrian Collieries maybe two years before the year of his father's death, in 1879. With his brother, J. H. Thomas, he then became a managing partner in Thomas, Riches & Co. The formation of D. A. Thomas as a coalowner was rapid, but the pull of a career in national politics deflected some of his interest away from coal mining. In 1888, at thirty-two years of age, he was returned, unopposed, as Liberal MP for Merthyr Tydfil.

D. A. Thomas retained an ambition to increase his wealth as a coalowner. In the early 1890s, he 'attempted' to 'interest his fellow coalowners in south Wales in a scheme to regulate the coal trade

1st Viscount Rhondda
David Alfred Thomas (1856-1918)
Thomas led the growth of Consolidated Cambrian Limited also known as the 'Cambrian Combine'. After his death, Cambrian Combine collieries became part of Welsh Associated Collieries Company (WAC), a GKN subsidiary. He served as a government minister during the First World War, and was responsible for the introduction of food rationing.
Courtesy of Rhondda Cynon Taf Libraries

in order to provide a more regular stream of profits for investors', but 'the plan never got off the ground' due to 'personal differences', 'particularly with his distant cousin Sir W. T. Lewis'. In 1895, he instigated the formation of Cambrian Collieries Limited to take over the running of the Cambrian Navigation Collieries Ltd from the partnership of Thomas, Riches & Company.

As a Member of Parliament, D. A. Thomas does not appear to have gained notices as a parliamentarian of ability. Although he was to hold his seat as MP of Merthyr Tydfil until 1910, and afterwards become a MP for a Cardiff constituency, his fixation became the growth of what became known as the Cambrian Combine. The use of the term 'Combine' placed after Powell Duffryn can be found in some histories of the South Wales Coalfield. However, the term as the exclusive suffix of 'Cambrian' was more commonly used in the vernacular of the South Wales Coalfield after 1906.

In 1906, D. A. Thomas, as chairman of Cambrian Collieries Ltd, acquired Glamorgan Coal Co. Ltd. The coal property worked by the Glamorgan Coal Company lay to the east of Cambrian Collieries' property. The Glamorgan Coal Company's assets comprised Llwynypia Colliery (Nos. 1, 2 & 6), and probably both Sherwood Level, and Gilfach Level.[3]

During the next four years, D. A. Thomas acquired two further colliery companies, and so a Cambrian portfolio of coal companies took form. The period saw him take control of the Naval Colliery Co. (1897) Ltd, whose coal property was contiguous with and south-east of Cambrian's property. Naval Colliery Co. (1897) Limited's mining activities involved Anthony & Pandy Pits, Ely Pits, Nantgwyn Pit, and Adare Level.[4] The second company acquired by D. A. Thomas during this period was the Britannic Merthyr Coal Co. Ltd, whose coal property lay contiguous with, to the south, of Cambrian's. Britannic Merthyr Coal Co. Ltd raised coal at Britannic Merthyr, Trane, and Dinas Main (No. 2 Level).[5] The 'shares acquired in these subsidiary companies were held' by a 'Cambrian Trust Ltd, formed in 1907'. In 1913, Cambrian Trust Ltd became a holding company, Consolidated Cambrian Limited.

'Having formed the nucleus of the Combine with the completion of the purchase of the Brittanic Merthyr Company in April 1910, D. A. Thomas turned his attention further afield'. Fernhill Collieries Ltd was acquired in 1910, whose coal operation was based at Treherbert, near the head of the Rhondda Fawr Valley. The collieries added were: Fernhill Nos. 1, 2, 3 and 4 Pits, and North Dunraven Levels.[6] In 1911, both the Cynon Colliery Co. Ltd and Duffryn Rhondda Colliery Co. Ltd came under the Combine's control. Cynon Colliery

Glamorgan Collieries (Llwynypia Colliery), Rhondda Fawr Valley, in 1910. In 1935, Powell Duffryn acquired the Glamorgan Coal Co. Ltd due to merger with WAC. The colliery was sunk in 1865-1869. In 1906, D. A. Thomas purchased the Glamorgan Coal Co. Ltd, and the action initiated the creation of the Cambrian Combine. *Pope/Parkhouse Archive*

In 1935, Powell Duffryn acquired Naval Colliery Co. (1897) Ltd due to its merger with WAC. Ely Colliery was sunk in 1892 with Nantgwyn Colliery. Circa 1908, Naval Colliery Company became part of the Cambrian Combine. In 1910, a dispute at Ely Colliery caused a Rhondda Valley miners' strike that not only hit the operation of Cambrian Collieries, but featured a riot at Tonypandy. *Paul Jackson collection*

Anthony & Pandy Pits, Naval Colliery Co. (1897) Ltd, Rhondda Fawr Valley. These collieries were acquired by Powell Duffryn in 1935 due to merger with WAC. Upper and Lower Pandy Pits were sunk 1875-1879, and the Anthony Pit in 1910. D.A. Thomas purchased the colliery company to grow the Cambrian Combine. The pits' manpower was 2,300 and 806 in 1918 and 1945 respectively. *Pope/Parkhouse Archive*

Britannic Merthyr Colliery, Britannic Merthyr Coal Co. Ltd, Cwm Ogwr Fach Valley. In 1935, Powell Duffryn acquired Britannic Merthyr Coal Co. Ltd due to its merger with WAC. The colliery was sunk by Christmas Evans, between 1894-1896, as Dinas Main New Pits, and later owned by Brittanic Merthyr Coal Co. Ltd and around 1908 bought by D.A. Thomas. The colliery's manpower was 820 and 522 in 1918 and 1945 respectively *Pope/Parkhouse Archive*

Duffryn Rhondda Colliery, Avan Valley. The colliery was sunk by Duffryn Rhondda Colliery Company in 1903. In 1917, it was owned by Imperial Navigation Company, which in 1930 became part of WAC. In 1935, the colliery became an asset of Powell Duffryn Associated Collieries Ltd (PDAC) formed due to the merger between Powell Duffryn and WAC. In 1935, the colliery's manpower was 1,415 people.   *Pope/Parkhouse Archive*

Co. Ltd, with its head office located in Port Talbot, had its Cynon Colliery situated nearby at Ponrhydyfen.[7] Duffryn Rhondda Colliery Co. Ltd operated Duffryn Rhondda Colliery near Cymmer, located north-east of Port Talbot, in the Avan Valley.

The year 1916 saw D. A. Thomas, partnered by Henry Seymour Berry, who was 'essentially a financier', purchase several more colliery companies. D. Davis & Sons Ltd of Ferndale, Rhondda Fach, and North's Navigation Collieries (1889) centred on Maesteg, in the Llynfi Valley, were purchased to expand the Combine. Ferndale No's 1, 2, 4, 5, 6, 7, 8, and 9 Pits were operated by D. Davis & Sons Ltd.[8] The Combine also acquired Gwaun-cae-Gurwen Colliery Co. Ltd that mined anthracite coal to the south of the Black Mountains of Carmarthenshire. The Gwaun-cae-Gurwen business would become one of many acquisitions situated remote from what can be considered to be Cambrian Combine's heartland, the Rhondda Valleys. Significantly, ownership of the Gwaun-cae-Gurwen Colliery Co. Ltd brought H. Seymour Berry into contact with David Richard Llewellyn, a trained mining engineer, for the first time.

D. R. Llewellyn's father was Rees Llewellyn (1851-1919), chairman of Bwllfa Merthyr Dare Steam Collieries (1891) Limited based west of Aberdare. In 1919, D. R. Llewellyn succeeded his father as chairman of the company. Years earlier, in buying coal levels in the Aberdare area, he began his own colliery acquisition activity. In 1915, he took an interest in the anthracite coal area of the South Wales Coalfield by buying Sylen Colliery, Llanelli. In 1916, he was appointed chairman of the Gwaun-cae-Gurwen Colliery Company.

In December 1916, D. A. Thomas, earlier made Baron Rhondda of Llanwern, relinquished 'control of this empire when he entered Lloyd George's Ministry', during the First World War.[9] He 'handed over the reins [of the Cambrian Combine] to his financial associate, H. Seymour Berry'. In recognition of David Alfred Thomas's

contribution to Government, in 1918, the year of his death, he became 1st Viscount Rhondda.

D. A. Thomas left a puzzle about the logic he used for his acquisitions. The acquisitions were scattered throughout the South Wales Coalfield. Trevor Boyns wondered if D. A. Thomas's activities were 'an attempt to achieve on his own through the acquisition of as many companies as possible what he had been unable to achieve by agreement in the 1890s, although he must have been aware that to obtain control of the bulk of the coalfield's output would have involved far more capital than that to which even he had access'. D. A. Thomas's 'explanation' for the purchases was apparently much 'more simple': to obtain 'a certain number of economies of management'. Yet, the dispersed geographical locations of the acquisitions made it impractical 'to follow the system of collective production in operation at the pits of the original four companies and it seems little was done by pooling profits or centralising purchases of materials'. A postulated 'real link' was that D. A. Thomas 'either held a controlling financial interest or directed their several policies in his capacity as chairman of the respective companies'. D. A. Thomas's acquisitiveness suggests that frustrated by an unsuccessful search for power as a parliamentarian, he found solace exercising corporate strength.

Berry-Llewellyn's Acquisitions

Lord Rhondda's death was followed by H. Seymour Berry and David. R. Llewellyn uniting to acquire: more colliery companies; John Lysaght Ltd, a steel company; and Sankey, a component supplier to the fledgling car industry. In 1920, the 'swashbuckling duo' then tried to takeover Guest Keen & Nettlefolds (GKN), a large industrial conglomerate.[10] Their 'aggressive takeover bid' was 'resisted'. However, two of their companies, John Lysaght Ltd and

Ferndale Collieries, D. Davis & Sons Ltd, Rhondda Fach Valley. In 1935, D. Davis & Sons Ltd became part of PDAC formed due to the merger between Powell Duffryn and WAC. The Cambrian Combine purchased them in 1916 from D. Davis & Son Ltd who sunk them as follows: No. 1 1857-1862; No 2 in 1870 (later considered as No.5); No.4 in 1874; No. 6 and No. 7 sinking dates unknown; No. 8 in 1892; and No. 9 in 1907. The manpower at the Ferndale collieries was 1,388 men in 1945.

Pope/Parkhouse Archive and Paul Jackson collection

Dowlais-Cardiff Colliery, Abercynon, Taff Vale. In 1935, the colliery became part of PDAC formed due to the merger between Powell Duffryn and WAC. The formation of WAC, in 1930, saw GKN collieries included, of which Dowlais-Cardiff Colliery was one. The Dowlais Iron Company opened the colliery, which was sunk in 1890 to 740 yards. The colliery's manpower was 1,001 in 1945. *Pope/Parkhouse Archive*

Sankey, merged into 'GKN, with Berry becoming joint deputy chairman'. A foundation company of GKN was the Dowlais Iron Company, which operated collieries in the South Wales Coalfield. In 1917, GKN owned, generally in the vicinity of Merthyr Tydfil, unless otherwise stated, the following collieries: Cwmbran, north of Newport, Fochriw Nos. 1 & 2, Longwork, South Tunnel, Bedlinog Nos. 1 & 2, Nantwen, and Dowlais-Cardiff at Abercynon.[11]

GKN's 'boarders', Berry and Llewellyn, also became the 'twin driving forces of the new GKN'.[12] However, the conglomerate's business suffered badly during the economic slump of 1921-1922. The company's steel plants, for example, were closed for a period.

However, an 'upturn started in early 1923', and Berry and Sir David Llewellyn, he was made a baronet in 1922, reacted by launching 'what proved to be the final thrust' of their acquisitions' spree that saw them 'gobbling up Welsh colliery companies'.[13] In November 1923, Berry and Llewellyn persuaded GKN to buy D. Davis & Sons and Consolidated Cambrian Ltd. Maybe of interest to Powell Duffryn, North's Navigation Collieries was not sold to GKN. Nonetheless, Berry and Llewellyn's acquisition 'strategy paid-off handsomely' between 1922 and 1924 due in part to a strike of American miners, and a halt in coal production in the Ruhr imposed as a result of the end of the First World War. Trevor Boyns further observed that although some of these purchases appeared to have been logical, 'many others appear to have been made solely for acquisition's sake. The widespread geographical nature of many of the purchases once again meant that technical or production economies were unlikely to result on any scale'.

In 1924, due to a marked decline in the British economy, the demand for coal fell. Berry and Llewellyn 'closed pits and let mining leases lapse. The Dowlais group of collieries, once a mainstay of GKN, was 'effectively wound up'.[14] However, in 1927, two notable developments occurred. 'L. Gueret Ltd and Llewellyn, Merrett and Price [the coal group's sales agencies] were merged to form Gueret, Llewellyn and Merrett Ltd, and in March of that year the new company also absorbed Lysbergs Ltd'.

In 1927, H. Seymour Berry, then Lord Buckland, became chairman of GKN. It emerged after his death, a year later, due to a horse-riding accident, that he held secret talks with Powell Duffryn about selling GKN's coal interests. Lord Buckland was disenchanted with Sir David Llewellyn's handling of the collieries.

Welsh Associated Collieries Ltd

Sir John Field Beale succeeded Lord Buckland as chairman of GKN. Powell Duffryn Steam Coal Company might have been amazed to receive Lord Buckland's approach about buying GKN's coal interests. The company responded with a bid offer to GKN. Beale and Llewellyn, maybe due to a show of bravura, rejected the offer. The industrial conglomerate proceeded to merge its mining interests with those of the Cambrian Combine to form Welsh Associated Collieries Ltd (WAC).[15]

On 23rd January, 1930, WAC was registered with 'a capital of £8½ million, all issued fully-paid to GKN and the various interests within the former Cambrian Combine'. GKN became the largest shareholder in WAC. Sir David Llewellyn and members of the Llewellyn family, as a group, held the next largest shareholding in WAC. WAC owned 60 pits, levels and drifts, employed 32,000 men that mined ten million tons of coal a year, which represented in 1930 a 23% share of the total output of the South Wales Coalfield. Of relevance to the later development of Powell Duffryn, the patent fuel interests of GKN were vested in British Briquettes Ltd.

For comparison, Powell Duffryn Steam Coal Company raised in 1929 just over five million tons that represented around 10% of the coalfield's total output. Moreover, according to Evan William's reckoning, in 1930 the company raised coal 'from 30 pits', operated '250 miles of underground railways and 115 miles of surface railways', and employed 28,000 men. He also noted that Powell Duffryn 'owned 5,000 houses' and paid 'in wages 3¼ million pounds in the year'.[16]

Trevor Boyns evaluated that 'despite its greater size, WAC's financial position was inferior to that of Powell Duffryn'. WAC was further adversely affected, in the early 1930s, by the poor state of the coal trade, and its inability to raise capital. Indeed, 'the company finding it impossible to place a £2 million debenture issue on the stock market in the early 1930s, probably tipped the balance in favour of [GKN's] acceptance of the Powell Duffryn bid in late 1934'. Trevor Boyns recognised that 'the sounder economic and financial strength of the latter was reflected in the terms of the merger agreement, which were far less favourable than those which had been offered to Beale and Llewellyn and rejected by them in 1929'.

Powell Duffryn Associated Collieries Ltd

The trophy: Powell Duffryn created Great Britain's 'biggest colliery enterprise', Powell Duffryn Associated Collieries Ltd (PDAC). This was the considered claim of Barry Supple. He reported that 'by 1938 [PDAC] controlled 50 pits, employed 37,507 men,

and produced almost 12 million tons of coal, or roughly one third of the South Wales steam-coal output'.[17]

Prior to the merger, WAC owned, according to the Powell Duffryn Limited's Short Survey document of 1946, the following coal companies:[18]

Cambrian Collieries Ltd
Glamorgan Coal Co. Ltd
Britannic Merthyr Coal Co. Ltd
Duffryn Aberdare Colliery Co. Ltd
The Dowlais-Cardiff Colliery, property of GKN
And the share capital of:
Aberdare Graig Coal Co. Ltd
Blaenclydach Colliery Co. Ltd
Bwllfa & Cwmaman Collieries Ltd
The Cynon Colliery Co. Ltd
D. Davis & Sons Ltd
The Duffryn Rhondda (1929) Ltd
D. R. Llewellyn & Sons Ltd
Llewellyn (Cyfarthfa) Ltd
Llewellyn (Nixon) Ltd
Llewellyn (Plymouth) Ltd
Troedyrhiw Coal Co. Ltd
Naval Collieries (1897) Ltd

The Mardy Colliery of Locket's Merthyr Collieries (1894) Ltd was also noted as being part of WAC in the company's 1946 Short Survey document. Locket's Merthyr Collieries (1894) Ltd was bankrupted by the 1926 strike. In 1932, Mardy Colliery was acquired by the Bwllfa and Cwmaman Collieries Ltd, which was formed

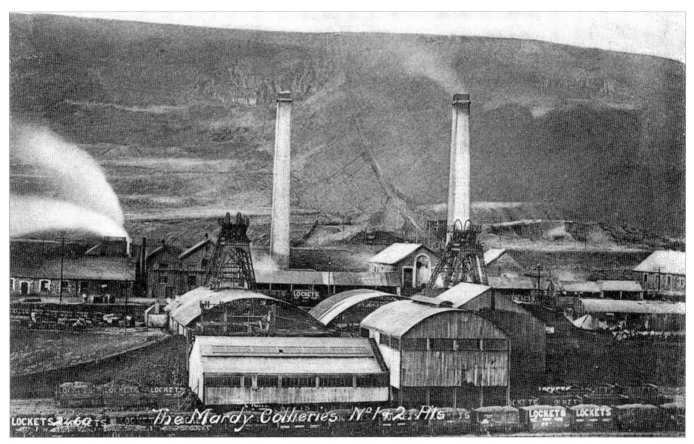

Mardy Colliery's No.1 & 2 was sunk 1875-1877 by M. Jones & W. Cobb, whilst Locket's Merthyr Collieries sunk No.3 & No.4 in 1891-93 and 1914 respectively.
Pope/Parkhouse Archive

in circa 1928. David R. Llewellyn appears to have steered the formation of Bwllfa and Cwmaman Collieries Ltd as chairman of Bwllfa Merthyr Dare Steam Collieries (1891) Limited. However, since Bwllfa & Cwmaman Collieries Ltd was a part of WAC from its conception, the separate identification of Mardy Colliery in Powell Duffryn Limited's 1946 Short Survey, in the absence of an explanation, appears pointless.

Unfortunately the Powell Duffryn Limited's 1946 Short Survey did not name the WAC collieries added to those of Powell Duffryn Steam Coal Company's due to the merger. However, some WAC collieries are identified earlier as a feature of Viscount Rhondda's expansion of the Cambrian Combine. Berry and Llewellyn's acquisitiveness led to PDAC taking ownership of at least the following additional collieries: Abergorki; Deep Duffryn and Navigation, located at Mountain Ash, in 1919 owned by Nixon Navigation Coal Co., and from 1928 by Llewellyn (Nixon) Ltd; Merthyr Vale Nos. 1 & 2, in the Taff Valley, in 1917 owned by Nixon Navigation Coal Co., and from 1928 by Llewellyn (Nixon) Ltd; and Tower Colliery, owned in 1919 by D. R. Llewellyn & Sons Ltd.

As a reflection, Powell Duffryn Steam Coal Company's colliery companies' acquisition activity before 1935 had proceeded at a pedestrian pace compared with WAC's. Powell Duffryn had purchased, beginning in 1920, Rhymney Iron Company followed by the Great Western Colliery Company; and the Lewis Merthyr Consolidated Collieries. In addition, the company bought three one colliery companies: Windsor Steam Coal (1901), Albion Steam

Coal Company, and Taff Rhondda Navigation Steam Company. In summary: for the period between 1920 and just before the merger, Powell Duffryn Steam Coal Company completed six acquisitions versus nearly twenty that ultimately shaped WAC.

Significantly, the merged Powell Duffryn Steam Coal Company-WAC was called Powell Duffryn Associated Collieries Ltd. Such a company name indicated the merger's superior party. Powell Duffryn Steam Coal Company's business strategy had coped with the Great Depression whereas Welsh Associated Collieries' had not. Trevor Boyns further offered an analysis to explain how this occurred.[19]

In summary: the two companies had taken a 'fundamentally different approach to the coal industry'. The business evidence indicates that 'the Cambrian Combine grew largely as the result of the determination of Thomas, Berry, and Llewellyn to achieve financial control over a large part of the [South Wales] industry and this proved successful as long as the coal trade remained buoyant'. However, 'the somewhat haphazard method of colliery acquisition militated against the achievement of major scale economies, which would have been possible if the collieries acquired had been in close proximity to one another which they were not'. Moreover, there was 'much evidence' of a 'lack of investment in many of the Combine's collieries during the 1920s'. Regarding Powell Duffryn, 'its past reliance on developing new pits on previously unexploited territory and incorporating the most up-to-date technology held it in good stead when coal prices began to tumble following the post-war boom'. Trevor Boyns perceived that Powell Duffryn's:

Deep Duffryn Colliery, Mountain Ash, was sunk between 1850 and 1855 by David Williams. In 1870, it was owned as a partnership company, Nixon, Taylor, & Cory. In 1945, Deep Duffryn Colliery's manpower was 592.

Pope/Parkhouse Archive

Merthyr Vale Colliery was opened by Nixon, Taylor & Cory between 1869 and 1875. The colliery's coal property was contiguous with that of Deep Duffryn Colliery's to the west. The view of the colliery is taken from the eastern side of the Taff Valley. Wire ropes were used to stay the headgears of this colliery, and can be seen in the case of the headgear on the right. In 1945, the manpower of Merthyr Vale Colliery was 1,179 persons. The Aberfan disaster of 1967, in which 144 lives were lost, was caused by an avalanche of coal waste falling from the colliery's tip. *Pope/Parkhouse Archive*

'Long-term outlook with its view to ensuring new low-cost production capacity coming on stream to replace high-cost and/or exhausted pits enabled the company to ensure profitable working throughout most of the inter-war period. Of perhaps greatest importance, however, was that the company had concentrated its resources on a geographically compact area of the coalfield, enabling the company to take advantage of major economies of production.'[20] Powell Duffryn's operation in the Rhymney Valley was such an exemplar, but the company needed to add 'an efficient sales and shipping agency to its already efficient production activities' in order to survive market changes. Trevor Boyns reasoned: 'the success of Powell Duffryn was based then on its production activities, but it is clear that without the link with Stephenson Clarke the company may well have suffered problems selling its coal in the 1920s'. He concluded that Powell Duffryn's strategy, based 'upon judicious amalgamation' [this description was attributed by Trevor Boyns to Emlyn Jones, a Cardiff shipowner, and former MP] with 'economic motives to the fore, proved superior to that of the Cambrian Combine' and enabled it to enter the merger of 1935 as the senior partner with the remnants of the Combine'.[21]

The decision made by the directors of Powell Duffryn Steam Coal Company to propose to the company's shareholders a merger with WAC to form Powell Duffryn Associated Collieries Ltd, once enacted, set a new coal industry standard. The company achieved horizontal amalgamation on a scale not seen before in the British coal industry. The directors of Powell Duffryn Steam Coal Company that made the decision were: Edmund Lawrence Hann (chairman), Sir Leonard Brassey, Charles Bridger Orme Clarke,

William Reginald Hann, Norman Edward Holden, Lord Hyndley, Sir Stephenson Hamilton Kent, Sir Francis Kennedy McLean and (later Sir) Evan Williams. Powell Duffryn's company secretary was Alfred Read. Seventy-one years earlier a Brassey and a McLean had been among the company's first shareholders, and directors. The Hanns also had advanced, in the intervening decades, to take director positions in the company's boardroom. Probably more than any of the other directors, Brassey, the Hanns, and McLean, appreciated that the merger put in jeopardy the legacy of their forefathers.

However, in 1935, it was Powell Duffryn's shareholders that approved the merger knowing that their power of ownership would be further diluted. A series of financial actions then enabled the merger to progress. One of the early actions saw 4½% Debentures of both companies (Powell Duffryn £2,500,000 and WAC £1,500,000) repaid, which led to Powell Duffryn issuing 4% Debenture Stock, with no fixed charges, valued at £1,500,000; and 4¾% Cumulative Preference Shares valued at £3,500,000.[22] The merger process further involved 'the voluntary liquidation of the separate companies' in order that the direct ownership of the separate companies, party to the merger, were handed over to Powell Duffryn Associated Collieries Ltd.[23]

The transition to one board responsible for the governance of PDAC appears to have followed a planned course so as to avoid amalgamation difficulties. Edmund L. Hann, at least, was alert to the problems and issues that beset the amalgamation of companies. In 1930, he remarked to Powell Duffryn Steam Coal Company's shareholders that colliery company amalgamations involved 'great practical difficulties', and were 'entirely opposed to the British psychology'. The first step in the merger plan saw the boards of Powell Duffryn Steam Coal Company and WAC survive for a period as discrete bodies, but with an exchange of directors between Powell Duffryn Steam Coal Company and WAC. Sir David R. Llewellyn and J. H. Jolly became directors of Powell Duffryn Steam Coal Company while Sir Leonard Brassey, Sir Francis Kennedy McLean and Sir Evan Williams became directors of WAC.[24]

What might be called Powell Duffryn Steam Coal Company's board of directors immediately after the merger comprised: Edmund Lawrence Hann (chairman), Sir Leonard Brassey, William Reginald Hann, Sir Francis Kennedy McLean, J. P. S. Clarke, Norman Holden, Lord Hyndley, Sir Stephenson Hamilton Kent, Sir Evan Williams, Sir David R. Llewellyn, and J. H. Jolly.

The corresponding WAC's board of directors comprised: Sir David R. Llewellyn (chairman), Sir J. F. Beale, J. H. Jolly, W. M. Llewellyn, H. H. Merrett, Sir Francis Kennedy McLean and Sir Evan Williams. The two separate boards of directors represented a first stage in the transference of corporate power to one board of directors for PDAC.

By 1937, the directors of Powell Duffryn Associated Collieries sat as a discrete board.[25] E. L. Hann (chairman), E. W. Ganderton, Lt Col. C. H. C. Guest, D. A. Hann, Lord Hyndley, J. H. Jolly, Sir Stephenson H. Kent, Sir David R. Llewellyn,[26] W. M. Llewellyn, William McGilvray, H. H. Merrett, and Sir Evan Williams sat on the board. Powell Duffryn Steam Coal Company and WAC had ceased to operate as separate companies.

A business aim of Powell Duffryn Associated Collieries Limited was to earn beneficial gains from large scale and centrally planned operations and specialised services. An early task involved organising the company to achieve such an aim.

The commercial side of Powell Duffryn Associated Collieries took on a robust character from the outset of the merger. Coal sales and distribution was 'broadly … concentrated through three subsidiary companies': Stephenson Clarke Ltd; Gueret, Llewellyn & Merrett Ltd, and Cory Brothers & Co. Limited. Stephenson

Clarke was assigned to 'inland' supply, while export was dealt with by Gueret, Llewellyn & Merrett and Cory Brothers.[27] Two years before its absorption into WAC, Guerets had also acquired a Southampton based company formed in 1859, Bradbury, Son & Co. Ltd. PDAC had world-wide ambitions for both the distribution of coals from the principal coalfields in Great Britain as well as the sale and distribution of the company's coal.[28] In 1937, PDAC distributed 25 million tons of coal of which the company's collieries supplied 12 million tons.

PDAC's sales-distribution representatives were assigned to ports and locations around the world to give the company an extensive market intelligence network. The company also responded to export opportunities. For example, knowledge of the European market identified that coal, in briquette form, was shovelled into at least the fireboxes of French steam locomotives. Powell Duffryn Steam Coal Company had earlier taken an interest in patent fuel briquettes during the First World War. In 1919, the company took a small shareholding in Star Patent Fuel Co. Ltd. However, PDAC purchased share capital in British Briquettes Ltd in 1936, as a prelude to taking full control of the company, in 1939.[29] PDAC also took ownership of Patent Fuel Works that had plants at Cardiff, Newport, and Swansea.

Coal and pitch were used as the raw constituents of patent fuel made at a Patent Fuel Works. PDAC experienced periodical gluts of small coal. The Patent Fuel Works patent fuel making process was modified to use small coal, and the three plants became capable of producing 1,400,000 tons of patent fuel a year. During the three years of such plant operation, prior to 30th September, 1939, one-and-three quarter million tons of small coal was used in the process. The company considered it was following its 'principle of co-ordinating production and sales' by acquiring Patent Fuel Works Ltd.

Concerning 'inland' supply, it appeared logical that Stephenson Clarke Limited oversaw Cambrian Wagon Company Ltd, formerly a WAC wagon making company. In 1937, PDAC operated more than 40,000 railway wagons, which over a period of a year were estimated to travel a total distance of about 100,000,000 miles.[30]

SECOND-HAND WAGONS, ALL TYPES, FOR HIRE OR SALE.

A 20-ton all-steel wagon made by the Cambrian Wagon Company wagon in 1925 at its East Moor Works, Cardiff.

John Alsop collection

Powell Duffryn Associated Collieries Company's wagon works, Maindy, Cardiff. The works was sited between the River Taff, featured meandering to the left of the works, and on its right, the main railway line between Cardiff and the Merthyr, Rhondda, and Cynon Valleys.   *Powell Duffryn*

Cambrian Wagon Company Ltd built and repaired colliery trams, railway and tank wagons. Founded in 1877, as the Cardiff & South Wales Wagon Co. Ltd, it had workshops at East Moors, Cardiff. In 1926, the Cambrian Combine purchased Cardiff & South Wales Wagon Co. Ltd. When the wagon company became a PDAC subsidiary it had workshops at Aberaman, Port Talbot, Llanelli, and in Cardiff at both East Moors, and Maindy. In 1937, the 'Combined works' had a 'potential output of fifty 20-ton all-steel wagons and one hundred and fifty 12-ton wooden wagons a week.[31] The wagon repair service comprised a 'network of out-station depots at the principal railway junctions'. Maindy, Cardiff, eventually became the centre of PDAC's wagon operation.

Another outcome of the merger saw PDAC own 1,000 miles of surface railway lines and underground tram lines. Regarding surface railway lines, the linking up in the Aberdare Valley of Powell Duffryn Steam Coal Company's railway system with Nixon's Navigation Coal Company's presented opportunities for running cost savings. The two railway systems complemented each other due to geography.

A major organisational issue concerned organising the PDAC's collieries into groups of collieries, which took some time to arrange and is dealt with later, but at the outset turning around the generally poor state of the WAC collieries became a priority. The scale of the challenge was described by the company in 1947:

'The addition in 1935 of [WAC's] thirty-four collieries [which suggests that twenty-six collieries had been closed by WAC after 1930] to the Powell Duffryn properties had required the immediate concentration by the management on the many problems of individual collieries. Much of the plant was obsolete; there were batteries of boilers, hand fired, at many separate points, using valuable coal and using much labour force; mechanical methods of coal cutting and conveyance underground had not been brought into use to any great extent, and much time and thought had to be given to the day-to-day mining requirements of ventilation, haulage, compressed air supplies and electrification. Short-term planning naturally took precedence over schemes of greater magnitude, but the long-term reorganisation of the Company's combined properties was continuously under review, and where practicable was put into immediate operation.[32]

The company set overall objectives for achieving 'big' reductions in the cost of its colliery operations.[33] The company aimed to increase the proportion of labour engaged in underground coal production by reducing both the numbers of men employed on the surface and non-productive work underground. The consumption of coal at the colliery was to be lowered by taking out of use boiler plant, and by making other surface cost savings. Underground compressed air systems were to be substituted with comparatively more efficient electrically powered systems. Savings were sought in the time that miners took to travel from the pit bottom to the coal face. Investment in new coal face machinery was identified as one way to increase the company's miners' coal output.

However, the company recognised that 'to convert a colliery from a losing to a profitable undertaking is generally an expensive and protracted business'. The Powell Duffryn Steam Coal Company had a record of successfully making such conversions at Windsor, Lewis Merthyr and Great Western properties.[34] Regarding the WAC collieries selected for redevelopment, the range of engineering tasks included reorganising underground roadways, improving ventilation, revising lay-outs, and introducing new methods of mining.

Many members of the Executive of the SWMF were averse to change due to a fear that the wages and employment conditions of their members would worsen. The political ideology of some Executive members of the SWMF also shaped attitudes to change. Some of them saw it as their life's mission to persuade 'the proletariat' to 'use its political supremacy to wrest, by degrees, all capital from the bourgeoisie, to centralize all instruments of production in the hands of the State'.[35] Moreover, they found it repugnant that: 'Within the process of production, capital acquired the command over labour, that is to say command over the worker. Capital personified, the capitalist, sees to it that the worker shall work properly, and with the required intensity'.[36] Such Executive members of the SWMF were prejudiced against any PDAC scheme aimed at raising the coal output per miner.

In January 1938, the SWMF commissioned an enquiry into the conditions of work and of organisation in the company's collieries.[37] The event that instigated the enquiry was a successfully resolved dispute at PDAC's Merthyr Vale Colliery.[38] However, another reason for the enquiry, according to Francis and Smith, 'lay in the vast size of the group, the consequent difficulty in organising an effective Combine Committee, and the kind of management that had full rein there'. They observed: 'The massively powerful Powell Duffryn Company' resisted the notion of negotiating with such a trade union body that united union delegates from across the company. An opinion within the Monmouthshire & South Wales Coalowners' Association during 1936 was that there was a considerable variation in custom and practices operating in individual collieries, and pooling knowledge about them would enable a union Combine committee to choose, and so pursue, the most advantageous ones.

The SWMF enquiry found that with PDAC collieries 'there was a full tilt move towards intensive methods of working supervised by 'Efficiency Experts'. 'Efficiency Experts' represented practitioners of the principles of scientific management that had advanced in the United States of America, after 1910, due to pioneering work by Taylor and Gilbreth. Following the merger, PDAC implemented the Bedaux system.[39] The Bedaux system was 'firmly based on Taylorist principles', which its advocates claimed 'improved upon [them] in one important respect': it had discovered 'the precise scientific relationship between work and fatigue'.[40] So, the job of the collier became the object of study for 'efficiency experts'. According to Francis and Smith, the enquiry's findings were received by the Fed as a 'depressing result'. Proof, maybe, that the company's quest to improve the efficiency of underground working was alien to the values of the SWMF.

Yet, underground working in the South Wales Coalfield was undergoing rapid change due to the advance of coal-cutting machine use. As a result, the collier's job, historically the hewers of coal at the face, became 'increasingly … one of filling coal, their rate of working had to be adjusted to that of the machine, and they no longer necessarily worked the same "stent", "strut", or "stall" from one shift to the next'.[41] The stress of such change was compounded, as far as the colliers were concerned, when they became the target of 'greater supervision', and their work a field of study for practitioners of the Bedaux system. The colliers felt that their livelihoods were under threat due to the scrutiny of 'efficiency experts', and 'great strains on traditional working relationships' arose. Former WAC miners were possibly unaccustomed to an operational culture set on improving coal output performance whereas former Powell Duffryn Steam Coal miners were familiar with such a culture. All PDAC's miners, though, may have been startled by the introduction of panel mining in the late 1930s.

Panel mining was 'particularly suited to development along Taylorist lines'.[42] This production planning system was imposed on PDAC's colliery managers by the company's upper management. The monitoring of panel mining work was 'entrusted' to "process" men and boys who were 'generally youngsters of between 14 and 21 years of age'. 'The "process" men and boys, and also the "efficiency experts"', were trained in the associated methods at PDAC's own mining schools at Britannia and Tymawr.[43] The training prepared them to 'time and schedule every phase of work' and to propose changes that could improve work efficiency by identifying time lost in operating the machines. The SWMF's enquiry report mentioned 'the employment of boys to do men's work', and 'alleged intimidation by officials'. Such intimidation gave a hint of further tension between colliery management and miners' trade union officials. The growing tension in a colliery became 'stretched to the limit'.

Trevor Boyns found that 'most of the problems that arose were related, in one way or another, to methods of payment'.[44] Anachronistic Price List schemes, in which rates of payments were related in someway to hand-cutting price per ton of large coal, and adjusted to accommodate different seams in a colliery, were 'vigorously defended' by local miners' lodges. 'Negotiations over changes to Price Lists became the focus of the men's resistance to change'. With the introduction, in the late 1930s, of panel mining at former WAC pits 'there was a general open hostility to the Tonnage-Yardage system and towards task work and quota work in general'.

Powell Duffryn's colliery management adopted a 'confrontational approach to the workforce rather than one based on conciliation'. Trevor Boyns concluded: 'In regard to the industrial relations aspects of both mechanisation and the use of production planning techniques, however, the company either failed to see, or was not prepared to admit, that there was any existing or potential problem in respect of management-worker relationships'. As far as PDAC was concerned they exercised their 'right to manage'. The miners, on the other hand, felt they were being subjected to coercion. After the enquiry, the SWMF, according to Francis and Smith, feared that 'the future of the SWMF at PD collieries will be one of gravest difficulty'.

The SWMF had also to deal with a serious issue concerning the health of their members: coalface workers' lungs collected coal dust not least due to the work of the iron-collier. The spread of pneumoconiosis among miners caused acute distress within mining communities. The general reluctance among coal companies to introduce coal-cutting machinery into the South

Wales Coalfield had unwittingly extended some of the lives of its miners. Moreover, the humane motives of Galloway and Edmund Mills Hann, and others, to spread inert dust made from crushed stone, as a means for deterring underground explosions, was not meant to put the health of the miner at risk. The stone which the inert dust came from contained silica, and the effect of silicon oxide on a miner's lung was to make some of them victims of another disease, silicosis. In 1929, after a prolonged campaign by the Miners' Federation of Great Britain sufferers of silicosis began to get financial compensation, although 1934 Silicosis Orders were needed to expedite the procedure.[45] The coalowners acted to stall compensation by maintaining 'legalistic resistance'.

The extent of pneumoconiosis and silicosis among Powell Duffryn underground workers by the end of the 1930s is unknown. However, Powell Duffryn had been to the fore as regards mechanization, and spreading inert dust underground. The company had also operated underground ventilation systems with large air moving capacities that helped remove some of the airborne dust. Nevertheless, if its inaction, and frustration of lung disease claims brought itself further ill will, at the same time it did little to impress its miners with regard to providing a notable symbol of personal health and welfare: pit-head baths.

Sometime before 1936, representatives of Penallta Colliery's Miners' Welfare Committee negotiated with PDAC for land adjacent to the colliery to build a pit-head baths.[46] A benefit of the Mining Industry Act was finance for a pithead Miners' Welfare Fund. The Miners' Welfare Committee managed the building project.[47] Penallta Colliery's pit-head baths was opened on 1st October, 1938, and were considered by the *Western Mail & The South Wales News* to be, in terms of its design and construction, the 'finest and biggest in the country'.[48] Company officials, local industrialists, and politicians were present at Penallta for the opening of the pit-head baths.

Twenty-two years earlier, Ocean Company's Deep Navigation Colliery, Treharris, Penallta Colliery's neighbour to the west, saw the first pit-head baths in the South Wales Coalfield.[49] Perhaps Powell Duffryn believed that pit-head baths were unnecessary due to the good standard of housing built to accommodate its workers. A tin bath and abundant kettle-heated water supply for bathing at home may have been seen as sufficient facilities for washing. If so, this showed that Powell Duffryn had not perceived that pit-head baths were good for the health of its colliery workers and officials.

Douglas Alfred Hann, the joint general manager of Powell Duffryn Associated Collieries Ltd led the opening ceremony. His announcement, that the company would provide the building's canteen with a wireless, was received by the 'assembled crowd' with 'loud cheers'.[50] The wireless, that cost a tiny fraction of the £42,000 expended on the building, enabled its listeners to hear news of war in Europe. The United Kingdom declared war on Nazi Germany on 3rd September, 1939.

Second World War

Before the outbreak of the Second World War, PDAC's coal export business saw a decline in spite of Gueret, Llewellyn & Merrett Ltd, and William Cory & Sons Ltd having been united to act as an export force. Nonetheless, in 1938, the French trade took one-third share of that year's total PDAC coal output of 11,830,050 tons.

The news of the fall of France to Nazi Germany, in 1940, in addition to creating greater anxiety among the British people, brought further turmoil in trade, both at home and abroad. Powell Duffryn later noted: 'From the outbreak of war, most of the coal available for export had gone to France, and almost overnight the export markets for South Wales coals disappeared. There was no inland demand to absorb the coal which had been exported to France, and which amounted to 4,000,000 tons per annum'.[51] Faced with this slump in business, PDAC closed collieries. Such actions

Penallta Colliery – Pithead Baths, the first pithead baths built on former company property. The building's costs were covered by a Miners Welfare Fund, and was opened in 1938 by Douglas Alfred Hann.
Courtesy of Amgueddfa Cymru - National Museums & Galleries of Wales

by the company were also coupled to 'an exodus from the industry; more men were called to the Forces, government armament and munitions factories located in the area drew many more, so that by December 1940, over 5,500 men, or about 15% of those employed, had left Powell Duffryn collieries'. However, the company's home trade for coal recovered to some extent during the period of the war to meet the energy needs of the nation's 'war effort'. So, Powell Duffryn's ability to mine and supply coal was tested partly due to operational handicaps like a lack of man-power.

However, Gueret, Llewellyn and Merrett possessed 'an important feature' of value to the defence of the nation.[52] 'For some years its staff learnt the language and requirements of its foreign customers. Staff were 'sent abroad to obtain first-hand knowledge of customers and their requirements, and, in the case of most of the Export Departments of the firm, all members of the staff speak and write the language of the country which they serve'. The war caused a demand for linguists and translators to support the defence of the nation, and many of Gueret, Llewellyn and Merrett's staff with language skills were recruited for such work.

Perhaps Powell Duffryn's entry into the manufacture of armaments and munitions was viewed by the company as some reparation. The company furthered its experience as an industrial manufacturer. For example, in 1941, surviving workshop buildings at Rhymney, a legacy of the Rhymney Iron Company, were equipped to make shells and aircraft bomb doors.[53]

The supply of chemical engineered products was also vital for the war effort. Fortuitously, due to a chemical engineering venture, PDAC was positioned to act as a supplier. At Caerphilly, a Central Tar Distillation Plant was completed in 1939.[54] The stench from the plant fumes was instantly smelt by Cardiff bound Rhymney Valley railway passengers as they passed en route to enter Caerphilly tunnel.[55] The plant was designed to produce 50,000 tons of crude tar per annum from feedstock supplied by the company's coke ovens, and south Wales steel companies. Moreover, the plant's 'up-to-date' distillation process, designed in 'close collaboration with the Powell Duffryn research department' also yielded a wide range of chemical products.

In 1942, the company also commissioned a 'Phurnacite' plant in the Cynon Valley, at Abercwmboi, situated south-east of Aberaman. [56] Passers-by came to see only a vague silhouette of the plant since it was usually shrouded by dense fumes. The French Disticoke Company designed the plant's process.[57] The product of the process was a substitute for the 'best anthracite' coal. Using a flotation facility, unmarketable steam coal slurries and fines were turned into high grade carbonised ovoids. By 1945, the company's ambition was to double the plant's annual output of 100,000 ton. A casualty of the plant's eventual expansion was the demolition of the Middle Duffryn Power Station.[58] The Phurnacite plant's neighbourhood came to fear the effects of pollution. The people of the Cynon Valley, on the whole, were much more favourably disposed to another legacy of the Hanns'.

In March 1941, the Hann family performed a notable duty at the Aberdare General Hospital.[59] Edmund L. Hann, with other members of the family, attended the re-naming of B, the Male Ward, as the "E. M. Hann Ward". The opening of the ward saw a memorial tablet unveiled by Edmund Stonelake who acknowledged that it 'primarily owed its existence to the efforts of the late Mr Hann, and in justice to his great services and munificence, could have been named the E. M. Hann Hospital'.

Phurnacite Plant –Cynon Valley. Commissioned in 1942, the plant produced an equivalent of 'best anthracite' coal from slurries and fines from steam coal. Public protests about pollution from the plant preceded its closure in 1990. *Photographer: Glyn Davies. Courtesy of Rhondda Cynon Taf Libraries.*

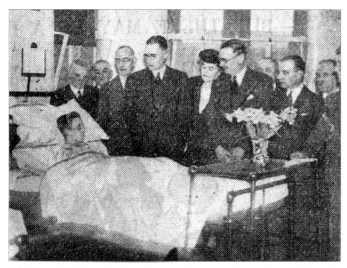

E. M. Hann Ward – Aberdare General Hospital. Opened in 1941 in the presence of the people shown in the photograph: Edmund L. Hann, Frank P. Hann, Mr David Lawrence, Mrs Gregor, E. Stonelake JP, Arthur Humphreys, Harold Hann, and T. Lucas.
Courtesy of both the South Wales Echo, and Llyfrgell Genedlaethol Cymru – The National Library of Wales.

Although, during the war, PDAC halted colliery development schemes, like Edmund Mills Hann had done during the First World War, the company proceeded with colliery acquisitions.[60] Cymmer Colliery, the Insoles' surviving and only mining interest was bought by PDAC, maybe in 1940. The company then 'partially sealed the shafts to a depth of the Rhondda No. 3 seam and used the pit to minimise the water flows and thus assist the Lewis Merthyr Colliery at Trehafod' situated to the east.[61]

In 1940, Powell Duffryn purchased the share capital of Ciley Collieries Ltd that owned Ciley Colliery, Tonyrefail, situated northwest of Llantrisant, just south of the entrance to the Rhondda Valleys and at the head of the Coed Ely Valley.[62]

In 1942, the coal mining activities of Cory Brothers & Co. Ltd became a target of the company's for acquisition.[63] The associated negotiations saw Hann pitched versus Hann. Edmund Lawrence Hann led the PDSC party. Frank Percival Hann, as the general manager of Cory Brothers & Co., was tasked by his company's shareholders to counter PDSC's offers so as to obtain terms that satisfied their wishes. Frank Percival Hann would have been a tough bargainer since he was as seasoned an executive manager as his brother. After he had resigned as Penallta Colliery's manager in 1913, he became the agent for the Penrikyber Navigation Colliery. Some years later he became general manager, and later managing director, of Ebbw Vale Steel, Iron & Coal Company. In 1927, he was gassed taking part in a rescue at one of its collieries, Cwm Colliery, where fifty-eight miners died. His courage was praised by Prime Minister Stanley Baldwin, who visited him in hospital after the incident. The St. Johns Ambulance Association awarded him a bronze medal. He rejoined the company as PDAC, in 1935, to become general manager of the company's Northern Area, and also a director of PDAC. However, in December 1938, he resigned due to differences with the company.[64] He then became managing director of Penrikyber Navigation Colliery, and general manager of Cory Brothers & Company.

The negotiations between Hann and Hann ended with PDAC acquiring Cory Brothers & Co. Ltd and Penrikyber Navigation Colliery Co. Ltd.[65] The Cory Brothers collieries purchased comprised: Braichycymmer & Ffaldau Pits, situated at Pontycymmer, Cwm Garw,

Penrikyber Navigation Colliery. In 1942, PDAC took ownership of the colliery from Penrikyber Navigation Colliery Ltd, seemingly a Cory Bros. & Co. Ltd subsidiary. Cory, Yeo & Company had sunk the colliery 1872-78. From 1907 to 1911, Edmund L. Hann was the colliery's agent, and he was succeeded by his brother, F. P. Hann. At the time of PDAC's acquisition, F. P. Hann was the managing director of Penrikyber Navigation Colliery, and general manager of Cory Bros. & Co. Ltd.

FFALDAU COLLIERY,

R.
5688.
PONTYCYMMER.

In 1942, PDAC took ownership of Cory Bros. & Co. Ltd collieries that included Ffaldau (*above*) and Wyndham (*below*). Ffaldau Colliery, Cwm Garw, was sunk in 1876-78. Wyndham Colliery, Garw Valley, was sunk in 1865 by J. Brogden & Sons.   *both Pope/Parkhouse Archive*

Wyndham Colliery, Nantymoel.

that converges on Bridgend from the north; Ffaldyre Level and Glyncastle Pit, near Resolven, in the Vale of Neath; Penllwyngwent Slant and Wyndham Nos.1 & 2, both at Ogmore Vale in the Ogmore Valley, which also converges on Bridgend from the north. The Penrikyber Navigation Colliery Co. Limited's colliery stood, as mentioned previously, near Mountain Ash.

As the 1940s advanced, the company's manner of engagement in industrial relations irritated the SWMF. The miners of the coalfield believed that Powell Duffryn was 'quietly and stubbornly' maintaining 'an attitude of antagonism towards the Federation'.[66] A particularly stormy event occurred as a result of the company's desire to improve the working of coal in and around Penrikyber Colliery's property. Penrikyber Navigation Colliery's mining properties were contiguous with those owned by PDAC. The company decided to close its adjacent Cwmcynon Colliery so that its coal reserves were worked from Penrikyber Colliery.[67] Negotiations were entered into with the SWMF to prepare the way for this change. They floundered. A strike took place on 20th August, 1942, at Penrikyber Colliery, and men at Cwmcynon, Abercynon, and Albion Collieries came out in sympathy.[68] A conciliation process helped bring an end to the dispute.

At a stage in the conciliation process, Edmund L. Hann, with his brothers Douglas and Frank, met representatives of the SWMF's Executive Council. During the meeting, held in March 1943, Edmund L. Hann was the target for a stinging attack from Arthur L. Horner, the Fed's president between 1936 and 1946. Arthur Horner accused the company of pursuing a 'consistent policy of high-handedness'. Edmund L. Hann complained about Horner's attack.

Horner countered by giving a list of matters that he alleged showed a complete lack of consultation by the company, in addition to that concerned with Penrikyber Colliery. He was described as delivering the list 'with some feeling'. His onslaught of 'accumulated gripes' also included an accusation that the Hanns were fascists.[69]

The company's style of management was autocratic, but the Hanns were certainly not commissars of the totalitarian dictatorship that governed industry in Stalin's Communist Russia. One of the Hanns' duties as managers, of a public limited company, was to make it commercially viable in order that it survived in a market economy. PDAC's future challenges promised to be immense. The South Wales Coalfield no longer attracted a homily that recognised it, as it did for the years 1917-18, as 'the most important and richest coal area of the kingdom'.[70]

Between 1913 and 1946, there was a 'violent decline in importance of the South Wales Coalfield (from some 20 to just under 12 per cent of Britain's output)' whilst there was a 'growth of the national importance of South Yorkshire and the East Midlands'. Over the corresponding time scale the annual output of coal in South Wales fell from 56.8 million tons in 1913, its zenith, to 21 million tons by 1946, accompanied by a marked decline in employment from 232,800 men to 107,600.[71] Such a trend was one that Powell Duffryn could not ignore if it planned to remain a coal company with its mining operation focused upon the South Wales Coalfield.

Predicting the future though had possibly become more difficult for the company and its south Wales rivals than when their predecessors had looked ahead in 1914. The South Wales coalowners had then foreseen correctly the English threat, but oil, contrary to their expectations, became a major contender for a share of the energy market. However, the First World War's effect upon the Coalfield served initially to postpone signs of likely decline.

International economic factors, following in the wake of the war, pitched Edmund L. Hann into a crisis of survival in the 1920s. The depression of the 1930s worsened this crisis. Guided by astute financial management, Powell Duffryn weathered the depression rather better than its rivals, and so was able to enact its amalgamation policy. This was a feat considering, as a coal exporter, it had to cope with adverse money exchange rates, the political instability of Western Europe, and foreign governments subsidizing their coal industries. Powell Duffryn's coal had also to compete on price against the product of American, British and European oil companies using the economics of scale that attracted vast capital investment. Powell Duffryn had somehow managed to retain the interest of investors. Maybe an explanation for this was that the company was viewed as taking concrete measures in terms of capital investment so as to adapt to a changing world. Indeed, the need for change in the mining operation had been inculcated into them by the example of their father, Edmund Mills Hann. Some members of the Fed's executive, on the other hand, were set upon subverting a company like Powell Duffryn in order that some speculative design they may have had for state ownership of the coal industry was substituted.

From the Hanns' point of view, consultation with the SWMF meant seemingly endless negotiation that postponed change. Negotiation in commercial affairs tended to be relatively quicker. Possible profitable returns from investment in colliery development were placed in jeopardy when change lagged behind the consequences of less lucrative commercial agreements obtained in adverse market conditions, and poor economic times. In regard to PDAC's coal mining, difficulties were compounded by 'increasing shortages in the supplies of equipment'. The Second World War was certainly an additional calamity that Powell Duffryn, and their employees, could have done without.

This was equally true for the Federation. Indeed, Francis and Smith appeared to consider that this was a contributory cause of Horner's charge against Edmund L. Hann. The SWMF Executive Council was niggled by a view, expressed by Sir Evan Williams, a director of the company and a leading member of the Monmouthshire and South Wales Coalowners' Association, which 'dismissed coalfield grumbling and stoppages' as the "anarchy" of "the forces of revolt". This was later to be judged a 'simplistic view' by Francis and Smith, who contested that Horner was worried that the support of his members 'had worn very thin in places', and he wanted to avoid strikes at a time of war. The SWMF's Executive Council considered that they were taking 'an unpopular line' whilst being 'conscious of a lack of sympathy' from the company. Nevertheless, the SWMF delegation left the meeting feeling that the Hanns had 'eaten humble pie'. Notably though, the meeting had featured the enmity that existed in the South Wales Coalfield against the company.

Could labour and capital ever be reconciled? By 1945, some of the leaders of South Wales Miners' Federation were convinced that communist USSR had found a solution to the way in which industry could be run for the good of its workers. Indeed, Arthur Horner was a member of the Communist Party, and had made many visits to the USSR.[72] His philosophy, as a trade union leader, included the principle that he acted to 'sell a commodity', labour, and he saw the function of an employer, 'whether' it be 'the

State, private owner or co-operative organization', was to 'buy that commodity'.[73] He acknowledged, though, that there was a need to develop the 'administrative capacity', within the working class, as being 'necessary for economic planning'.[74] His political philosophy was 'based on the power of organized workers at the point of production'.[75] And for him: 'The final victory' would come 'when the miners and all other sections of the working people take into their hands the resources of the nation and plan them in the interest, not of profit for a few, but of ever-expanding well-being for the many'. And he prefaced this by stating that this would 'replace the hated coalowner'.[76] He was not alone, among at least the Executive of the South Wales Miners' Federation, seeking such revolutionary change.

Edmund L. Hann's mission, on the other hand, was to make Powell Duffryn Associated Collieries' South Wales Coalfield business a success.

Managing Powell Duffryn Associated Collieries

After the 1935 merger, the management of Powell Duffryn Associated Collieries evolved in what can be identified as three planned stages. The first stage, that followed the merger, saw a Central Committee set up to deal with the day-to-day business of Powell Duffryn Associated Collieries Ltd.[77] The Central Committee was modelled upon Powell Duffryn Steam Coal Company's management committee mustered in 1888 to replace the form of 'practical direction' that the company obtained from Sir George Elliot. Although the positions held accountable for coal production and sales were respectively the general manager of collieries [Edmund Mills Hann] and the commercial manager [Bickerton Pratt], the management committee acted to monitor operational activities. Boyns and Wale considered that the management committee 'acted as a financial control device to ensure the viability of the company'.[78] Adding that, with respect to PDAC, 'that this role continued largely unmodified, until the late 1930s, though over time the minutes of the committee reveal a gradual shift from concern merely with payments and authorisation of large items of expenditure to a more strategic role in planning and controlling everyday operations'.

The second stage took form in 1939. 'Several changes occurred in PDAC organisational structure consequent upon the outbreak of war. For reasons of safety, many of the staff at the company's London organisation moved to Cardiff owing to the difficulty of holding monthly board meetings in London'. Also, 'to provide more effective control of operations in 1942 …. existing committees were dissolved, and replaced by a streamlined system comprising a central committee and a South Wales production and sales committee'. This central committee was afterwards known as the Cardiff Committee.

The Cardiff Committee was convened in 1944, and was viewed as being an outcome of stage three in the liquidation of the original Powell Duffryn Steam Coal Company–WAC merger.[79] A management committee, previously called the central managing committee, dealt with major policy issues whereas the Cardiff Committee managed day-to-day production and sales matters. Regarding production, the company's coal properties covered over 163 square miles of the South Wales Coalfield. However, it had 'for many years been the practice 'of Powell Duffryn 'to divide [their] undertakings for the purposes of colliery management into areas'. In March 1946, Powell Duffryn noted that 'each area

was placed under the control of a General Manager, who was 'a member of the Cardiff Committee or is co-opted at all meetings of that committee when any problems or decisions affecting his area under discussion'.[80] Each general manager was accountable for running their respective Area.

By the end of 1945 there were four defined areas.[81] First, there was one designated as the Northern Area with its Head Office at Aberdare. Covering 65 square miles and involving fourteen working collieries, the Northern Area's potential gross output of coal was 5.8 million tons per annum. This area's reserves of workable coal were estimated at being 663 million tons. Second, there was the Rhymney Valley Area of 50 square miles, which operated fourteen working collieries capable of producing an annual gross output of coal of 7.2 million tons. The Rhymney Valley Area was estimated to have 550 million tons of reserves, and its Head Office was at Tredomen, Ystrad Mynach. Third, there was a Rhondda Valley Area of 31 square miles that comprised seventeen working collieries with a gross potential output of 3.8 million tons per annum. The estimated reserves of the Rhondda Valley Area were put at 495 million tons, and its Head Office was at Porth, where the Rhondda Fach Valley joined the Rhondda Fawr Valley. And last, there was the Western Area of 17 square miles that had six working collieries with a potential gross output of 2.5 million tons, and reserves estimated at 478 million tons. Tondu, three miles north of Bridgend, near where the Llynfi and Ogmore Valleys are united, was chosen as the site for the Western Area's Head Office. The immediately foregoing sketches how PDAC was organised ready for the days when peace in Europe and the Pacific arrived. However, PDAC was faced with the prospect of there being a revolutionary change in the way in which the British coal industry was run.

Nationalization

The name of Cardiff had for many decades before 1945 become synonymous with steam coal in the conversations of seafarers around the world. Before the First World War, Cardiff was ranked in the United Kingdom as the third greatest port in terms of tonnage shipped. Only the ports of London and Liverpool took precedence. The port of Cardiff's distinction was as the largest exporter of coal in the world.

Maybe, the citizens of Cardiff in the 1940s can be forgiven for any indifference they had towards the Valleys. The constant thunder-like noise of the rumble of railway traffic hauling coal through Cardiff to its dock system was an intrusion into their lives. Moreover, the Valleys seemed to be a foreign province as far as most citizens were concerned. News from the Valleys painted a horrid picture of miners' accidents and deaths, strikes, and riots. Nonetheless, with justification, some coalowners took to reminding Cardiff about how it had become important. In 1937, Alfred Read, PDAC's company secretary, wrote:

'It is an interesting commentary upon conditions in South Wales that a hundred years ago the population of Cardiff was about 6,000. But, in 1840, the first cargo of South Wales coal was shipped from that port, and its smoke-less qualities and excellence for steam generation have since then made its sale and export the chief industry of the district. To-day the population of Cardiff has reached a figure of 225,000. Its municipal income, which now exceeds £1,000,000 annually, was only £1,000 a hundred years ago. The growth of this city with its magnificent buildings and extensive docks is due almost entirely to the development of the coal trade of South Wales.'[82]

Such a message could have been directed equally at Newport, but Cardiff had assumed its place as the capital of Wales though it had yet to gain such official recognition.

In 1937, Cardiff people may have been amused with an idea that they, with the rest of the population of the United Kingdom, could become owners of the British coal industry. The daughter of a founding director of Powell Duffryn Steam Coal Company, Beatrice Webb, née Potter, would though have been delighted if an aspect of her Socialist aspirations, the nationalization of the coal industry, became a reality. However, she died in 1943.

After the Second World War, in 1945, the Labour Party was elected into Government, and so the coal industry was nationalized. 'The measures would have been far more strongly opposed had not relations between the owners and men been so poor for many years'.[83] The Coal Industry Nationalization Act was passed in July, 1946, and as from 1st January, 1947, ownership and operation of the mines was vested in the state. So, Powell Duffryn Associated Collieries ceased as a coal mining business.

Edmund L. Hann must have contemplated this as being a possibility by at least September 1944, when he was appointed by the Minister of Fuel and Power to a committee.[84] The terms of reference for this committee were: 'To consider the present position and future prospects of the [South Wales Coalfield (including Pembrokeshire)] and to report:

> What measures (apart from questions of ownership, form of control or financial structure of the industry), should be taken to enable the fullest use to be made of existing and potential resources in the coalfield; and in this connection, what provisions of housing and other services will be required for the welfare of the mining community'.[85]

As chairman of PDAC, he represented the coalowners with: G. D. Budge, managing director, Cardiff Collieries; R. W. Burgess, general manager, Amalgamated Anthracite Collieries, Limited; D. M. Evans-Bevan, chairman, Evans & Bevan Limited; H. J. Smith, managing director, Partridge Jones & John Paton Limited; Iestyn R. Williams, secretary, the Monmouthshire & South Wales Coalowners' Association; L. D. Williams, chairman, Ocean & United Collieries Limited; and W. D. Woolley, deputy chairman and managing director, Tredegar Iron & Coal Co., Ltd.

The committee also included some civil servants, academics, and four miners' trade union leaders, one of which was Arthur Horner, in September 1944, the President, of the South Wales Area National Union of Mineworkers. Although the subject of the change of ownership of the industry had been excluded from the committee's terms of the reference, the possibility of nationalization had some influence upon its work.

Edmund L. Hann was in a position to foresee both the consequences of the committee's recommendations, and to take advantage of knowledge gained from the committee's work to plan further colliery company acquisitions. Perhaps as a result, in 1945, PDAC acquired North's Navigation Collieries (1889). For some reason, when Berry and Llewellyn sold D. Davis & Sons and Consolidated Cambrian Ltd to GKN, North's Navigation Collieries was not part of the deal. This coal company's operation was generally located in the Lynfi Valley, north of the Vale of Glamorgan town of Bridgend. The collieries purchased were: Caerau Pit at Caerau, Coegnant North and South Pits at Caerau, Maesteg Deep Slant near Maesteg, St John's North and South Pits at Cwmdu.

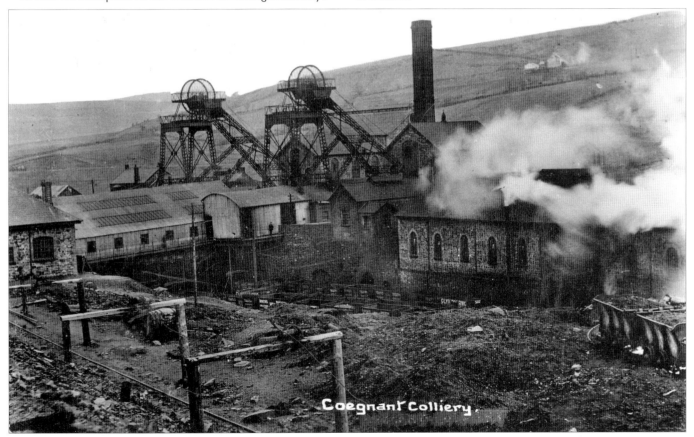

Coegnant Colliery, Caerau, Llynfi Valley. In 1945, PDAC took ownership of the colliery following its acquisition of North's Navigation Collieries (1889) Ltd The colliery was acquired by Powell Duffryn from the Llynfi and Tondu Co. Ltd who sunk the colliery in the same year as Elliot West Colliery, 1883. In 1945, the colliery's manpower was 695.

Pope/Parkhouse Archive

Maybe much more significantly, Powell Duffryn's decision to acquire North's Navigation Collieries (1889), in 1945, seems to suggest that Edmund L. Hann believed that the nationalization of the British coal industry was unlikely to occur in the future. Indeed, also in 1945, the company sank Rhigos Colliery, which decades later appears to have become part of Tower Colliery that closed on the 25th January, 2008.[86] Would Rhigos Colliery's sinking have been authorised if the coal company had doubts about its form of future ownership? Hindsight would suggest that it was an unnecessary venture, but it was to prove notable in that it was the company's last sinking.

The committee's report may have been seen by Powell Duffryn as a gift of information useful for planning its long-term future. The report, for example, contained rival coal companies' disclosures, which enabled PDAC to spot other possible acquisitions.

After all the purpose of the committee work, and its report, was to secure 'the future prosperity of the South Wales Coalfield'. However, the work of the committee had an aspiration: it was 'essential that there must be the greatest possible measure of goodwill and co-operation between all interested in the industry'.[87] The gulf in attitudes between PDAC and SWMF suggested that this aim was a pipe dream. Nevertheless, a hope that 'the differences of every kind', that had arisen 'between the respective parties' of the industry being 'disposed of amicably' was never put to the test. With nationalization, Edmund L. Hann's main task was to recover remuneration from the Government for sequestrated Powell Duffryn assets.

In 1945, from a table later prepared by Supple, that compared average market values of public colliery companies, Powell Duffryn was ranked as the richest coal mining company in the British coalfield.[88] Using average market values (January-June 1945), Powell Duffryn was valued at £15,785,600. For 1945, the company was reported to own fifty-nine collieries.[89] The output of these collieries, in 1938, was 14,671,519 tons, which represented 38.42% share of the total output of the South Wales Coalfield.[90] PDAC's output was just over three times that of its South Wales rivals, Partridge, Jones & John Paton Ltd, that correspondingly produced 4,345,589 tons from twenty-two collieries, and Ocean & United National Collieries Ltd, that owned eighteen collieries that yielded 3,784,464 tons. However, 'the sorry history of South Wales colliery companies continued right down to the act of nationalization: each of the large companies listed (Ocean & United National Collieries; Partridge, Jones & John Paton; and Powell Duffryn) secured compensations much below their market value (Powell Duffryn suffered less, although still receiving only about 80 per cent of its stock market value)', according to Barry Supple.[91] The total 'direct compensation for expropriation' that the Government paid to Powell Duffryn was £12,171,800.

In addition, the company received from the Government just over £2.6 million for its electricity supply network included in a Government measure to nationalize the generation and supply electricity for the nation.[92] Moreover, assets like the Phurnacite works, coke ovens and by-product plants, patent fuel works, Tredomen Engineering Works, houses, farms and lands were not part of the valuation.

The company also topped the list of coal companies owning homes in the South Wales Coalfield. PDAC owned 6,171 houses, which was nearly five thousand more than the company listed in second place, Partridge Jones & John Paton Ltd.[93]

Protracted negotiations took place, until May 1956, between Powell Duffryn and the Government to resolve the value of assets identified for compensation. The aggregate compensation that the company was reputed to have received from the Government has been put at £15,964,712.

Concerning coal mining, the company handed over, like other coal companies, generally neglected collieries to the National Coal Board (NCB), the government body set up to manage the British coal industry.[94] The state of the collieries was partly due to the way collieries were operated during the war. Coal production, not maintenance work, had taken priority. Moreover, a shortage of skilled mechanics and electricians, due to the need for their skills in at least the armed forces, made the neglect of plant and equipment inevitable.[95] Powell Duffryn also had an outstanding load of re-engineering work concerning the WAC collieries to complete. Some later employees of the NCB moaned that the poor state of their collieries was due to Powel Duffryn having anticipated nationalization. Nevertheless, the company, once held up as a paragon by its rivals in its industry, had been dispossessed of its heritage. The NCB took over the management of its coal reserves. Concerning this study the last day of 1946 marks its end. PDAC, founded as the Powell Duffryn Steam Coal Company, could no longer plan to hollow out the mountains of South Wales.

The state denied PDAC the chance of mining for coal in the South Wales Coalfield, which in 1946 was forecasted, in a report by the Government's Ministry of Fuel and Power, as lasting until at least 2044. 'According to the colliery companies' estimates the output from the existing collieries and those projected for development for the next ten years will have fallen to 13.8 million tons in 2044. It is not possible to indicate to what extent this possible fall in output can be made good from new collieries in the virgin area, or from thinner seams as yet undeveloped, but it can be confidently expected that the 1939 level of output [38,498,200 ton] can be maintained for at least a hundred years from the coalfield as a whole'.[96]

Thomas Powell's principle 'to drive out and sell as much coal as possible', remained valid. However, an even greater challenge faced the marketing and selling coal from the South Wales Coalfield. In January 1944, although unrepresentative of a peace-time economy, the main markets for South Wales's saleable steam and bituminous coal, as a proportion of the 21.8 Mton output it raised, were: electricity generation 14.7%; general industries 13.6%; railways 12.5%; coke oven 12.4%; domestic consumers 9.9%; colliery consumption 7.7%; and the iron and steel industry of South Wales 6.9%.[97] Remarkably, possibly related to the Allies' War Effort, 10.9% of the South Wales Coalfield's output was exported.

However, Welsh steam coal's hold upon powering at least the merchant ships of the world had considerably weakened. In 1914, the share of the world's merchant marine propelled by steam, raised in coal fired boilers, was 96.6%. By 1944, this share of the marine power market had slumped to 21.3%. Moreover, the future for coal as a fuel for marine propulsion was bleak since virtually all new ships being built in Britain and beyond featured propulsion systems powered by oil or diesel.[98]

So, what was the future for coal in markets such as electricity generation, railways, and domestic consumers if oil and its products became more plentiful, and competitively priced in Britain? With nationalization, Powell Duffryn was relieved of the business risk in running a coal mining business. The state had taken upon itself the responsibility of finding an answer to the question. Powell

Duffryn's shareholders had borne the business risk for eighty-two years. The nation owned collieries as a 'means of production' perhaps unaware of the associated business risks. The significance of the Powell Duffryn Steam Coal Company, and its collieries, for the subsequent development of PDAC, was one that people in at least the Aberdare and Rhymney Valleys could opt to forget.

For the curious, some remains of the company's coal operation survive. Most of the sites of the collieries and coal tips have been landscaped, or redeveloped. Aberaman House still exists, but the general public will find it inaccessible. Some remains of George Pit, closed in 1905, linger on Mynydd Merthyr. Powell Duffryn Steam Coal Company's invasion of the Rhymney Valley is represented by: the engine house and headframes of Penallta Colliery, which also commemorates, due to its closure on the 1st November, 1991, the last deep mine of the Rhymney Valley; the Elliot Colliery Thornewill & Warham steam winding engine is preserved at the Winding House Museum; a door of steel plate marks an entry into the White Rose Level; and the company's Tredomen offices are occupied by the Caerphilly County Borough Council. The vaulted explosives store house for Ogilvie Colliery can be seen in the Darran Valley Country Park.[99] Remains of the company's operations exist on the South Crop at Llantrisant (or Ynysmaerdy Colliery), and for Llanharan Colliery an obelisk marks the site of its North Pit.

The Lewis Merthyr (Bertie & Trefor) Colliery, the centrepiece of the Rhondda Heritage Park, with to its east the Great Western Hetty Colliery, provide a reminder of some of Powell Duffryn's colliery company acquisitions. Token examples of the company's merger with Welsh Associated Collieries include the Llwynypia Colliery's brick built engine house.[100] Seen as a whole, these monuments provide just a hint of Powell Duffryn's achievements in the South Wales Coalfield.

Conclusion

Powell Duffryn Steam Coal Company's policy for technical innovation, inspired by Edmund Mills Hann, ensured that its colliery plant and equipment was up-to-date, and amongst the best available. Perceptive engineers and investors recognised that this gave the company a competitive edge over its rivals. In their particular ways the company's collieries in the Rhymney valley were 'modern' models for the British coal industry to learn from. They represented the development of steam winding, and also the transition to electrical winding.

In 1928, *The Colliery Guardian* judged that the company had 'long stood as an exemplar in South Wales'.[101] *The Colliery Guardian* further recognised that 'the interlocking processes of the company' constituted what was 'probably the best of its class in the world'. Powell Duffryn's 1905 electrical scheme in the Aberdare Valley was an important technical step towards such an appreciation. It was, though, the Bargoed Power station electricity supply grid that served all Powell Duffryn's collieries in the Rhymney Valley as well as those on the South Crop and the Aberdare Valley that impressed

Penallta Colliery. British Coal closed the Powell Duffryn founded colliery on the 1st November, 1991 and so it became the last deep coal mine in the Rhymney Valley. Both the winding house and headgear currently survive.

Courtesy of Amgueddfa Cymru – National Museums & Galleries of Wales.

The Colliery Guardian. Moreover, the company's compressed air grid was judged by this journal as making the company 'more pre-eminent' in this respect. The company also used the best ventilating and pumping equipment so as to safeguard underground workings from explosions and floods. And the company became a pioneer, in the South Wales Coalfield, in both the use of mechanised conveyors, and coal-cutting machines. Powell Duffryn also led the way by introducing coal washery plant into the South Wales Coalfield. Bargoed by-products plant placed the company among the pioneers of chemical engineering in Britain, and so was enabled to develop new commercial opportunities from by-products of coal. The skill and abilities of the company's technical staff, initially at Aberaman and then Tredomen, was appreciated beyond the boundary of the South Wales Coalfield.

Powell Duffryn's colliery workers had no contact with its commercial side so had little appreciation of its value. Maybe their only view of the market was that its fluctuations were due to a conspiracy between the coalowners and their customers. Yet, the company became adept at marketing. The company's name, Powell Duffryn Steam Coal Company, clearly announced what it did. The company's badge, the Prince of Wales's feathers, declared that it was proud of being a Welsh company. Sir George Elliot's role, regarding establishing the infrastructure for its coal's distribution, proved to be as farsighted as his schemes were imaginative. Examples of his schemes in South Wales include: the Pontypridd, Caerphilly, & Newport Railway, and the Alexandra Dock, Newport. These railway and dock facilities allowed the company to barter for competitive prices for transporting, and shipping its coal. Just two white painted letters, PD, on the sides of thousands of railway wagons was an advertisement. These two letters had a profound effect upon the memory of railway watchers for a long time after the company's wagons ceased to shuttle along Valley lines.

Edmund L. Hann's decision, made before 1929, led to the company joining up with Stephenson and Clarke, so ensuring that it gained a coal factor and distribution channel. This may not have been the first arrangement of its kind in the British coal trade, but probably enabled the company to survive commercially.

The company profited from the reign of 'King Coal' due to being gifted with rich seams of steam coal to mine, and survived changes in the market for both coal and its by-products. In 1945, PDAC offered for sale large coal, nuts and peas. The company had earlier rebranded house coal as PhunoD, and offered Virticol smokeless coal so as to encourage sales. Coke was supplied to the steel industry. Briquettes were made to fuel at least locomotives. Paint as Presotim and Presomet was marketed by the company. Chemical engineered products such as pitch, naphtha, and refined tar were made. The company acted as a utility electricity generating company.

Estranged from the Valley mining communities were the company's directors and shareholders. In 1945, the directors of Powell Duffryn Ltd, as it entered its final days as a coal company, comprised: E. L. Hann (chairman), J. P. S. Clarke, Lord Hyndley, H. H. Merrett, Lord Brassey, E. W. Ganderton, Lt.-Col. C. H. C. Guest, D. A. Hann, F. P. Hann, Norman Holden, J. H. Jolly, Griffiths Llewellyn, William McGilvray, Sir F. K. McLean, and Sir E. Williams.[102] Among these men were the descendants of the original shareholders.

In 1945, Lord Brassey, and Sir F. K. McLean, might have reflected upon the fortunes of the company in terms of four phases. The first phase yielded only a rise in the capital value of their ancestors' investments mainly due to colliery acquisitions in the Aberdare Valley, and the founding of Elliot Colliery. Their families earned little income from company dividends during the period that Sir George Elliot gave 'practical direction' to the company. Fortunately colliery acquisitions due to Elliot like Aberaman and Fforchaman Collieries, for example, bequeathed financial benefits to enable Elliot Colliery to be founded, and so begin the company's Rhymney Valley colliery invasion. The reward for the invasion brought the company's directors as shareholders, after four decades or more of waiting, income returns as dividend payments. The third phase, expansion on the South Crop, was beset by geological set backs. Nevertheless, during the Great Depression, Powell Duffryn shareholders had the confidence and courage to support an amalgamation strategy, the fourth phase.

That the capital market backed, during a dire economic period, Powell Duffryn Steam Coal Company, to grow through amalgamation, was a feat. Coal industry observers appreciated that the feat was a novel one for a British coal company. Consequently, in 1935, with the support of both shareholders and financial institutions, Powell Duffryn swallowed its larger rival, WAC. The merger still stands as probably the greatest business coup in Welsh industrial industry, and the greatest one in the history of private sector coal companies of Britain. Nevertheless, in 1946, the company wisely professed: 'No organisation increases in efficiency merely through its growth; in fact if it is not planned with imagination and with a view to expansion, an increase in its size may destroy the whole fabric'.[103]

The apparent soundness of Powell Duffryn's strategic management was also complemented by powerful control of the colliery operation. The company's colliery managers and engineers acquired a reputation for their demanding manner and, maybe grudgingly, respected by their peers employed in rival companies of the South Wales Coalfield. Powell Duffryn, alert to changes in the world energy market, was relentless in the pursuit of its business. Such behaviour, when the facts of a market economy are disregarded, helps sustain the human habit of classifying a company as being either good or bad.

Indeed, within mining communities where the company operated, its name was defamed. This had much to do with a common hatred among colliery workers, and their families, of the companies belonging to the Monmouthshire & South Wales Coalowners' Association. They were all labelled as tyrants. As the largest one, Powell Duffryn qualified as the greatest demon.

Endemic confrontation nurtured bitterness towards both the company and its rivals. The major strikes, which affected colliery workers, and the company, occurred between 1871 and 1875, and in the years: 1893, 1898, 1910, 1912, 1926, and 1931. Possibly the 1926 strike had a more profound social and political impact upon the people of the South Wales Coalfield and gave an impetus for wanting change in terms of the ownership of the coal industry. However, the 1934 Taff-Merthyr Colliery dispute, which might be seen merely as a parochial issue, was a sign that some working men did not want to belong to a union having political aims. Nonetheless, it was the majority of the workforce and their families that suffered the ignominy of defeat after strikes. The misery, due to hardship and deprivation that arose in the wake of long strikes, fed deep-seated hatred against coalowners.

The decades of enforcement of wages rates on miners, by the coalowners, also poisoned minds against the operation of a market

Edmund L. Hann, chairman of Powell Duffryn Ltd, presents Cpl Edward Chapman VC with a gold watch and chain, 28th July, 1945. Cpl Chapman had served with the Monmouthshire Regiment during the Second World War having previously worked as a miner at Ogilvie Colliery.
Courtesy of Western Mail & South Wales News, and Llyfrgell Genedlaethol Cymru – The National Library of Wales.

economy. Although Powell Duffryn's workers in the Rhymney Valley appeared to earn more than other valley coal companies, their wages were judged to be a poor reward for a tough and dangerous livelihood.[104] Yet, many thousands of men chose to depend upon the company for employment, and their incomes enabled families to enjoy an adequate standard of life. In 1870, the company employed 3,643 men and boys in the Aberdare Valley, and roughly a further 600 at New Tredegar Colliery. In 1928, the company employed 52,079 men at its South Wales collieries.

Notably though, there were miners and colliery workers on the payroll of Powell Duffryn who had joined after their forefathers, some of whom had come to the Valleys in search of work in the nineteenth century. Maybe the men had a stronger allegiance to a colliery than its company, due maybe, to its social dimension rather than a place to earn an income. However, they did not see a colliery as a talisman. Underground there were dangers to life and limb like lose trams, roof falls, a 'fiery' atmosphere, squeezes, and floods. An encounter with the dangers of working underground could have been a spur for men to seek employment in other industries, and districts beyond the boundary of the South Wales Coalfield, since, like their forefathers, they were free to search for

alternative work. Yet, each working day for decades men, many of whom followed in the trail of their ancestors, gathered in a colliery's cage, to be lowered underground, so that their physical fitness, and character, were tested at the coal face.

The company's concern for safety has been disputed down the years due to regular occurrences of deaths and injuries at its collieries due to happenings such as roof falls, and loose trams. Such happenings illustrate that coal mining was a dangerous occupation, and it is suggested that the company's record in terms of deaths, other than due to explosions, was similar to other South Wales Coalfield coal company collieries. Nevertheless, some of the personal grief and suffering that arose as a result of the deaths of miners was vented as insults against the company's name. The company was cursed for not looking after the health and welfare of its workforce.

Yet, this work has presented examples of the company acting in a humane way. In 1878, Edmund Mills Hann was greatly affected by the ideas of Sir William Galloway regarding coal dust and underground explosions. Due to his leadership, Powell Duffryn colliery engineering was to the fore in the South Wales Coalfield in seeking practical solutions to Galloway's ideas aimed at explosion prevention. The ventilation of Powell Duffryn collieries from the

1890s onwards featured large volumes of air circulated underground. Water was sprinkled in underground workings, and stone dust scattered with the aim of suppressing the coal dust hazard. Tragically an unexpected consequence of scattering dust underground was that miners were exposed to silicosis. The company subjected the selection of miners' lamps to rigorous appraisal, and purchased the safest lighting for underground working. That the company experienced a spell of nearly sixty-six years without a mining disaster occurring between the one at New Tredegar Colliery, in 1875, and one at Llantrisant Colliery, in 1941, provides grounds for praising the company for its attention to colliery safety.

The company also sponsored humanitarian services. Powell Duffryn pioneered, supported by other coal companies, rescue stations at Aberaman, and in the Rhymney Valley, which were milestones in the history of the South Wales Coalfield. Although the company did not lead the provision of pit-head baths, the standard of house built for the company, in not least the Rhymney Valley, for its employees, was excellent for the time. The company generously supported the establishment of hospitals at Aberbargoed, and Aberdare. The funding arrangement, the company investing in hospital building and equipment, and the miners paying the maintenance and running costs, led to communities growing a sense of ownership of these hospitals.

Paradoxically, in creating vibrant, close-knit communities, in the Aberdare and Rhymney Valleys, and to a lesser degree on the South Crop, criticisms of Powell Duffryn's behaviour became a common view, repeatedly affirmed. Such critics might have shared Beatrice Webb's dream that there was 'an alternative to modern business enterprise'. If nationalization of the coal industry was the alternative: were the industry's industrial relations ills subsequently cured? Regardless of the hopes for state ownership, the world energy market largely determined the economic course for the British coal industry.

Using compensation received from the Government, Powell Duffryn Ltd became an engineering and trading conglomerate. Sir George Elliot's entrepreneurial inclination, imagination, energy, and mobility in pursuit of opportunities, would have made him an ideal candidate to lead this organisation into world markets, and, more than likely, to form new companies, some abroad. At least the company's name that Elliot adopted in 1864 survived nationalization of the coal industry.

From Powell Duffryn Steam Coal Company directors' point of view, the work of Edmund Mills Hann was more highly regarded. In March, 1922, Sir Leonard Brassey said:

'The history of Mr E. M. Hann's life is largely the history of the Powell Duffryn Company. He was with it through all the difficult early years, he was with it through very troublous and hard times, and he saw the Company rise to the top crest of the wave of prosperity, which it was our good fortune to enjoy for a considerable number of years. When he saw us rise to the height of that wave of prosperity he could well have thought himself, as possibly he did, that it was largely owing to his own work for the Company, his foresight, and the advice that he gave to the Directors from time to time before the prosperous period, that we were able to get the benefits we did. That was a happy time.'[105]

In 1929, J. J. Stewart, a director of Powell Duffryn Steam Coal Company, observed: 'I know that the name of "Hann" is a household name for wise and capable colliery management. I think that the shareholders are fortunate in having in succeeding generations what we may call the hereditary capacity at their service in this great Company'. Edmund Lawrence Hann achieved the distinction of rising above his father's position to become the chairman of Powell Duffryn Steam Coal Company.[106] He led the creation of Powell Duffryn Associated Collieries Ltd, Britain's peerless private coal company. In 1937, Powell Duffryn confidently boasted that it was 'the greatest coal-producing and coal-distribution unit in Europe'.[107]

NOTES

1   Trevor Boyns, 'Rationalisation in the Inter War Period: The Case of the South Wales Steam Coal Industry', op. cit., p.283-288.
2   R. H. Walters, op. cit., p.27.
3   A Directory of Colliery Companies in the South Wales Coalfield (Associated and Non-Associated) [hereafter DCCinSWC]. (The Monmouthshire & South Wales Coal Owners' Association, October 1917), p.9.
4   DCCinSWC, op. cit., p.12.
5   DCCinSWC, op. cit., p.6.
6   DCCinSWC, op. cit., p.6.
7   DCCinSWC, op. cit., p.8.
8   DCCinSWC, op. cit., p.8.
9   Llanwern linked him with his Monmouthshire estate. During the First World War, David Alfred Thomas served as Minister of Food. He is buried in the churchyard at Llanwern.
10 Andrew Lorenz, GKN-The making of a Business 1759-2009. (Wiley, 2009), p.68.
11 A Directory of Colliery Companies in the South Wales Coalfield (Associated and Non-Associated), op. cit., p. 10. The Cwmbran Colliery was acquired in 1872 by Arthur Keen when he was growing the Patent Nut and Bolt Company. See Edgar Jones, op. cit., pp.174-181
12 Andrew Lorenz, GKN-The making of a Business 1759-2009, op. cit., p.68.
13 Andrew Lorenz, GKN-The making of a Business 1759-2009, op. cit., pp.68-69.
14 Andrew Lorenz, GKN-The making of a Business 1759-2009, op. cit., p.69.
15 Another aspect of GKN's restructuring concerned merging its iron and steel interests as British (Guest, Keen, Baldwin) Iron & Steel Co. Ltd.
16 Report-Proceedings, AGM of the Company, PDSCC, 27 March 1930, p.13.
17 Barry Supple, op. cit., p.308. He had sourced his information from

POWE 28/239/17. In 1938 the South Wales Coalfield produced a total of 38,185,000 tons of coal.
18 Short Survey- Powell Duffryn Limited, op. cit., p.5.
19 Trevor Boyns, 'Rationalisation in the Inter War Period: The Case of the South Wales Steam Coal Industry' [hereafter RIWP:CSWSCI], op. cit., pp.292-3.
20 Trevor Boyns, RIWP:CSWSCI, op. cit., p.293.
21 Trevor Boyns, RIWP:CSWSCI, op. cit., p.295.
22 Short Survey- Powell Duffryn Limited, op. cit., p.23.
23 Short Survey- Powell Duffryn Limited, op. cit., p.6.
24 PDAC Management Committee minutes, 25 June 1935.
25 Stock Exchange Year Book (1937).
26 Sir David R. Llewellyn died 15th December, 1940, at sixty-one years of age. W. M. Llewellyn was his brother. Sir Rhys Llewellyn succeeded his father, Sir David Llewellyn, as baronet. Sir Rhys Llewellyn died in 1980, and the title passed to his brother, Sir Lt Col. Harry Llewellyn, who at the 1952 Helsinki Olympics, as the rider of Britain's most famous showjumping horse, Foxhunter, completed the clear round that won the gold medal for the British team. Between 1958 and 1978, Sir Lt Col. Harry Llewellyn was chairman of Andrew Buchan Breweries Ltd that brewed the Rhymney Beer brand.
27 Powell Duffryn Short Survey, op. cit., p.12.
28 Alfred Read, 'Foreword', op. cit., p.ii.
29 Trevor Boyns, RIWP: CSWSCI, op. cit., p.292.
30 Alfred Read, 'Foreword', op. cit., p.i.
31 Alfred Read, 'Foreword', op. cit., p.v.
32 Powell Duffryn Short Survey Document, op. cit., p.18.
33 Powell Duffryn Short Survey Document, op. cit., p.21.
34 Powell Duffryn Short Survey Document, op. cit., p.5.
35 Karl Marx & Friedrich Engels, The Communist Manifesto. (Penguin,

1967), p.104.

36 Karl Marx, *Capital*. (Dent, 1957), p.320.

37 Hywel Francis and David Smith, *op. cit*., pp.389-392.

38 Trevor Boyns, 'Powell Duffryn: The Use of Machinery and Production Planning Techniques' [hereafter PD:UMPPT], in *Towards a Social History of Mining in the 19th and 20th Century*, ed. Klaus Tenfelde, (Verlag C H Beck Munchen, 1989), p.374.

39 Trevor Boyns, PD:UMPPT, *op. cit*, p.375.

40 Trevor Boyns, PD:UMPPT, *op. cit*, p.374.

41 Trevor Boyns, PD:UMPPT, *op. cit*, p.375.

42 Trevor Boyns, PD:UMPPT, *op. cit*, pp.376-377. Panel mining operated after defining a 'panel', an underground area of a colliery. Once the size of the panel was settled upon, a prescribed number of conveyors and men were assigned to work the panel. These resources of men and machines were expected to deliver a fixed rate of advance and meet a set daily output. The associated plan also gave start and end dates for working the panel.

43 Trevor Boyns, PD:UMPPT, *op. cit*, p.377.

44 Trevor Boyns, PD:UMPPT, *op. cit*, pp.378-382.

45 Hywel Francis and David Smith, *op. cit*., p.439.

46 Gareth Salway, *The Architecture of Cleanliness: Miners Welfare and the Pithead Baths at Penallta*. (Gareth Salway & Groundwork Caerphilly, 1993), p.15.

47 Gareth Salway, *op. cit*., pp.7-8.

48 Gareth Salway, *op. cit*., p.12.

49 Gareth Salway, *op. cit*., p.1.

50 Gareth Salway, *op. cit*., pp.13-4.

51 Powell Duffryn Short Survey Document, *op. cit*., p.19.

52 Alfred Read, 'Foreword', *op. cit*., p.v.

53 This workshop became Rhymney Engineering Company Limited, and in the 1960s changed its name to Hy-Mac Limited. Hy-Mac was the brand name of a range of pioneering hydraulic excavators designed, developed, and manufactured at this Rhymney site.

54 Powell Duffryn Short Survey Document, *op. cit*., p.19.

55 OS grid reference ST 165864.

56 Powell Duffryn Short Survey Document, *op. cit*., p.16.

57 Cynon Valley History Society, *Cynon Coal*, *op. cit*., p.178.

58 Cynon Valley History Society, *op. cit*., p.188.

59 Arthur W. Humphreys, *op. cit*., pp.13-14.

60 Powell Duffryn Short Survey Document, *op. cit*., p.19.

61 Richard Watson, *op. cit*., p.165.

62 Short Survey- Powell Duffryn Limited, *op. cit*., p.2.

63 The company was a 'distantly-related Cory family business' of John Cory & Sons, a prominent south Wales shipping company. The chairman of John Cory & Sons, between 1965 and 1991, was Raymond Cory. Raymond Cory was a trainee with Powell Duffryn for a period after the Second World War before joining John Cory & Sons in 1947 as a director. *The Daily Telegraph*, obit, 26 March 2007, p.25, col.5.

64 David Hann, 'The Hann Family–A Mining Dynasty of South Wales part 3', *Glamorgan Family History Society, Journal* No. 40, (Dec., 1995), pp.12-13. F. P. Hann's career details.

65 Powell Duffryn Short Survey Document, *op. cit*., p.13.

66 Hywel Francis and David Smith, *op. cit*., p.392. Originally from an article published in the *Miners' Weekly*, June 1939.

67 Powell Duffryn Short Survey Document, *op. cit*., p.15.

68 Hywel Francis and David Smith, *op. cit*., p.406-8.

69 Hywel Francis and David Smith, *op. cit*., footnote no.97, p.423.

70 Sir R. A. S. Redmayne, *The British Coal-Mining Industry During the War*, *op. cit*., p.105.

71 Barry Supple, *op. cit*., Table 1.5, p.21.

72 Arthur Horner, *Incorrigible Rebel*. (Macgibbon & Kee, 1960), p. 50. The 1926 strike confirmed his faith in the Communist Party, p.93. Born in 1894, he died in 1968.

73 Arthur Horner, *op. cit*., p.148.

74 Arthur Horner, *op. cit*., p.225.

75 Arthur Horner, *op. cit*., p.43.

76 Arthur Horner, *op. cit*., p.10.

77 Trevor Boyns and Judith Wale, 'The Development of Management Information Systems in the British Coal Industry, c. 1880-1947', *Business History*, Vol.XXXVIII, No.2, (Frank Cass, 1995), p.66.

78 Trevor Boyns and Judith Wale, 'The Development of Management Information Systems in the British Coal Industry, c. 1880-1947', *op. cit*., p.66.

79 Trevor Boyns and Judith Wale, 'The Development of Management Information Systems in the British Coal Industry, c. 1880-1947', *op. cit*., pp.66-67.

80 Powell Duffryn Short Survey Document, op. cit., p.12.

81 Powell Duffryn Short Survey Document, *op. cit*., pp.11-12.

82 Alfred Read, 'Foreword', *op. cit*., p.ii.

83 Neville Penry Thomas, *A History of British Politics, From the Year 1900*. (Herbert Jenkins, 1956), p.164.

84 *South Wales Coalfield (Including Pembrokeshire) Regional Survey Report*, *op. cit*, p.1.

85 The company owned 6,171 houses in 1945 of which only 2,731 were occupied by miners employed by the company. This was the highest number of homes owned by any company in the South Wales Coalfield. The next two were Partridge Jones & John Paton, owning 1,530 and Tredegar Iron & Coal Co. Ltd, 1,244. *South Wales Coalfield (Including Pembrokeshire) Regional Survey Report*, *op. cit*., p.217.

86 Bryn Cummings, telephone conversation with Writer, 16 April 2007. He relayed the information concerning progress of the sinking work directly to Frank P. Hann by bicycle as part of his job as clerk to the company's Aberdare Valley mining engineer.

87 *South Wales Coalfield (Including Pembrokeshire) Regional Survey Report*, *op. cit*., p.170.

88 Barry Supple, *op. cit*., pp.662-663, Table 14.3.

89 *South Wales Coalfield (Including Pembrokeshire) Regional Survey Report*, *op. cit*., table LXIII, p.144. The writer's research found only 55 collieries owned by the company. The difference may be partly explained due to whatever was used in 1946 as the definition of a colliery. A number of the collieries the writer identified were assigned support activities e.g. pumping, or ventilation.

90 *South Wales Coalfield (Including Pembrokeshire) Regional Survey Report*, *op. cit*., p.144.

91 Barry Supple, *op. cit*., p.665.

92 Trevor Boyns, 'The Electricity Industry in South Wales to 1949', *op. cit*., p.101.

93 *South Wales Coalfield (Including Pembrokeshire) Regional Survey Report*, *op. cit*, Appendix VII, pp.216-217.

94 Emmanuel Shinwell was the Government minister responsible for setting up the NCB in 1945, and he appointed Arthur Horner as National Coal Production Officer. The first chairman of the NCB was Lord Hyndley who had 15 years' of association with Powell Duffryn through being a partner in Stephenson Clarke & Company. See Arthur Horner, *op. cit*., p.176 and p.195.

95 For example, the father of the writer, William Iorwerth Shore, a mechanic at Elliot Colliery, had enlisted with the Corp of Royal Engineers on the 30 April, 1939 when he was twenty-two years of age. He served in Norway, North Africa, and Italy, and was demobbed in April 1946.

96 *South Wales Coalfield (Including Pembrokeshire) Regional Survey Report*, *op. cit*., para. 290, p.108. This prediction was derived from the 1945 estimate of the South Wales Coalfield's coal reserves made by the Regional Survey Committee. The Report also tabled comparisons of its estimate against the 1942 Fuel Research Coal Survey, which was slightly higher than the Regional Survey Committee's, and also that of Sir William Thomas Lewis's 1905 estimate, which was four times as high as that the Regional Survey Committee's. See *op. cit*., par. 254, p.96

97 *South Wales Coalfield (Including Pembrokeshire) Regional Survey Report*, *op. cit*., p.36-37.

98 *South Wales Coalfield (Including Pembrokeshire) Regional Survey Report*, *op. cit*., p.48.

99 OS grid reference SO 119032. See also Stephen Hughes *et al*., *Collieries of Wales: Engineering & Architecture*, (Royal Commission on the Ancient and Historical Monuments of Wales, undated), p.170. The 'Gazetteer of Protected Colliery Sites' in Collieries of Wales was dated as being 'complete as of September 1994'.

100 OS grid reference SS 993928. See also Stephen Hughes *et al*., *Collieries of Wales: Engineering & Architecture*, *op. cit*., p.169.

101 *The Colliery Guardian*, Vol.CXXXVI, No.3508, 23 March 1928, p.1154.

102 *Stock Exchange Year Book* 1946.

103 Powell Duffryn Short Survey Document, *op. cit*., p.7.

104 This was based upon a qualitative statement made regarding the pay and conditions at Powell Duffryn's Mardy Colliery, acquired from the Rhymney Iron Company, and men employed at the nearby Tredegar Iron & Coal Company's McLaren Colliery. Islwyn Jenkins, *Idris Davies of Rhymney*. (Gomer, 1986), p.43.

105 Report-Proceedings, AGM of the Company, PDSCC, 22 March 1932, pp.1-2.

106 Edmund L. Hann ceased as managing director of Powell Duffryn in August 1948. He retired 'officially' in 1951. His home was then Tregarth, Creigiau, Cardiff. He died in 1968 aged 87. David Hann, 'The Hann Family–A Mining Dynasty of South Wales part 3', *Glamorgan Family History Society, Journal* No. 40, (Dec. 1995), p.12.

107 Alfred Read, 'Foreword', *op. cit*., p.i.

Appendix One
A SELECT BIBLIOGRAPHY

Wide use was made of: the papers of Professor Trevor Boyns; *Proceedings of the South Wales Institute of Engineers*; the *Transactions*, North England Institute of Mining Engineers; *Transactions*, Newcomen Society and *Proceedings* of the Institution of Mechanical Engineers. References also involved: *The Colliery Guardian*, *The Engineer*, *Engineering*, *The Times*, *The Monmouthshire Merlin & South Wales Advertiser*, *Western Mail*, and unpublished research notes of Raymond Lawrence.

T. C. Cantrill, *Coal Mining*. (Cambridge University Press., 1914).

Roy Church, *The History of the British Coal Industry, Vol. 1*. (Clarendon, 1986).

Cynon Valley History Society, *Cynon Coal*. (Cynon Valley History Society, 2001).

Alexander Dalziel, *The Colliers' Strike in South Wales*. (1872).

Dr W. Gerwyn Thomas, *Welsh Coal Mines*. (National Museum of Wales, 1976).

T. H. Davies, *Telford Clarence Batchelor (1857-1947); A Memoir describing the Invention and Development of Locked-Coil and Flattened-Strand Wire Ropes*. (Courier Press, 1951).

David Evans, *Labour Strife in the South Wales Coalfield 1910-1911*, (Educational Publishing, Cardiff, 1911).

Hilda M. Evans, *New Tredegar in Focus*. (Starling Press, 1977).

Hilda M. Evans, *New Tredegar Again*. (Starling Press, 1979).

Hywel Francis and David Smith, *The Fed*. (Lawrence and Wishart, 1980).

James Griffiths, *Pages from Memory*. (Dent, 1969).

David Hann, 'The Hann Family – A Mining Dynasty of South Wales part 1', *Glamorgan Family History Society, Journal* No.38, (June, 1995); part 2, No.39 (September 1995); and No.40, (Dec., 1995).

E. M. Hann, *Brief History of The Powell Duffryn Steam Coal Company Limited 1864-1921*.

Arthur Horner, *Incorrigible Rebel*. (Macgibbon & Kee, 1960).

John Hutton, *The Newport Docks & Railway Company*. (Silver Link Publishing, 1996).

Geological Excursions in South Wales & The Forest of Dean, ed. Douglas A. Bassett & Michael G. Bassett. (Geological Association of South Wales Group, 1971).

J. H. Morris and L. J. Williams, *The South Wales Coal Industry 1841-1875*. (University of Wales Press, 1958).

The Powell Duffryn Steam Coal Company 1864-1914. (Powell Duffryn, 1914).

Sir R. A. S. Redmayne, *The British Coal-Mining Industry During the War*. (Clarendon, 1923)

Gareth Salway, *The Architecture of Cleanliness: Miners Welfare and the Pithead Baths at Penallta*. (Gareth Salway & Groundwork Caerphilly, 1993).

The South Wales Institute of Engineers-Sesquicentenary Brochure 1857-2007, (SWIE, 2007).

South Wales Coalfield (Including Pembrokeshire) Regional Survey Report, (HMSO, 1946).

Barry Supple, *The History of the British Coal Industry, Volume 4, 1913-1946: The Political Economy of Decline*, (Clarendon Press, 1987).

R. H. Walters, 'Capital Formation in the South Wales Coal Industry, 1840-1914', *Welsh History Review X*, (1980).

George Watkins, *Stationary Steam Engines of Great Britain, The National Photographic Collection, Volume 4: Wales, Cheshire & Shropshire*. (Landmark, 1993).

Richard Watson, *Rhondda Coal, Cardiff Gold-The Insoles of Llandaff Coal Owners and Shippers*. (Merton Priory Press, 1997).

Beatrice Webb, *My Apprenticeship*. (Longmans, 1926).

Charles Wilkins, *The South Wales Coalfield Coal Trade and its Allied Industries*. (Daniel Owen, 1888).

Appendix Two
POWELL DUFFRYN'S FOUNDATION COLLIERIES

The list excludes some minor collieries and those acquired due to the company's amalgamation policy followed from 1920. Underlined are the collieries that Powell Duffryn Steam Coal Company owned at its formation in 1864.

Aberaman	Sunk in 1843-47; PDSC took ownership due to purchasing Aberaman Estate in 1867; the location of the first headquarters for the management of the collieries; the first colliery rescue station in the South Wales Coalfield was sited nearby; closed 1967-68.
Abercwmboi	Sunk in 1851; in 1881, PDSC acquired from Messrs D. Davis and Sons; closed 1923.
Abergwawr	Also known as Plough Pit; sunk circa 1855; closed 1875.
Abernant-y-Groes	Sunk in 1837; acquired by Thomas Powell in 1863; closed 1896.
Bargoed	North & South Pits sunk 1896-1901, and closed 3 June 1977; Brithdir Pit sunk circa 1900, its first coal was raised in 1904, and closed in 1949; the site of both a pioneering coal by-products plant, and an electricity generating station.
Blaennant	Opened in 1840s by Abernant Iron Works. PDSCC bought the colliery in 1915 from the Bute Estates. Closed 1927.
Britannia	Sunk 1911-13; the first British colliery 'to be entirely worked by electricity'; closed 8 December 1983; then used for pumping until 1989.
Coed-y-Moeth	Sunk in 1893; closed 1909.

Cwmdare — Sunk 1852-1854; abandoned 1891.

Cwmneol — Sunk 1848; PDSC acquired in 1868 from United Merthyr Collieries; closed 25 November 1948.

Elliot — West shaft sunk 1883-85; East shaft sunk 1886-89; the colliery operated a pioneering coal washery of the South Wales Coalfield; Rhymney Valley Rescue Station stood adjacent, which was the third in the coalfield; closed 28 April 1967; Elliot East winding house preserved as part of Winding House, the Caerphilly County Borough's museum.

Fforchaman — Sunk 1851; PDSC acquired in 1868 from United Merthyr Collieries; closed 25 September 1965.

George Pit — Sunk 1877-1881; closed 1905.

Llanharan — North & South shafts sunk 1923-24; closed 25 August 1962.

Llantrisant — Also known as Ynysmaerdy; sinking of North, South, & House Coal shafts began in 1924; closed May 1941, and then worked from Llanharan. In June 1941, an explosion killed 4 men including the colliery manager.

Llety Shenkin — Sunk 1843; PDSC bought the colliery from Messrs Burnyeat Brown & Company in 1900; closed 1922.

Lower Duffryn — Sunk 1850-1854; closed 1927, but used for pumping until 1970s.

Middle Duffryn — Sunk 1873; became the site of a central washery and electricity power station.

New Tredegar — First sinking 1853; underground explosion killed 23 miners in 1875; struck by landslides in 1905 and 1929; closed 1930; in 1945, used for pumping.

Ogilvie — Sinking completed 1923; used as a location by the BBC to film 'Above us the Earth', and an episode of 'Doctor Who'; closed 1975.

Penallta — Sunk 1906-1909; the deepest shafts sunk by PDSCC; the first winding house in the British coalfield to include two winding engines; closed 1 November 1991; the last deep mine operated in the Rhymney Valley.

River Level — Sunk by Aberdare Iron Company in 1840. PDSCC bought the colliery in 1915 from the Bute Estates. Closed 1939.

Taff-Merthyr — Sunk 1924-25; a joint venture with Ocean Coal Company; closed 1993.

Tir-Ffounder — Acquired the name 'Old Duffryn'. Sunk 1840-1842; closed 1901.

Treaman Colliery — Nicknamed the 'Nici-Naci' Pit; sunk 1846-50; bought by PDSCC in 1867; closed 1912.

Upper Duffryn — Sunk in 1844 by Thomas Powel. Puzzlingly excluded from PDSCC's main histories about its founding.

White Rose — Opening date of the coal level unknown, but before 1863; closed 1908.

Ynyscynon — Also known as High Duffryn; sunk 1843; purchased by PDSCC in 1867; closed 1875.

Ysguborwen — An 'old' nearly 'exhausted' colliery; sunk in 1849; bought by PDSCC in 1909 to make use of its drainage level to prevent flooding of other company workings.

INDEX